EXPLORING CREATION WITH

GENERAL SCIENCE

3rd EDITION

Sherri Seligson

Technical Editorial Contributions:
Tom Burbey
Robert Carter
Bob Davis
Marci-Anne Hanks
Damian Ludwiczak
Paul Madtes
Lucee Price
Chad Snyder
Rachael Yunis

Exploring Creation with General Science
3rd Edition

Published by
Apologia Educational Ministries, Inc.
1106 Meridian Street, Suite 340
Anderson, IN 46016
www.apologia.com

Exploring Creation with General Science, 3rd Edition, is revised and updated from a previous edition authored by Jay Wile.

Printed by Asia Printing Co., Ltd.

Manufactured in Seoul, Korea

First Printing: March 2019

ISBN: 978-1-946506-27-6

Cover: Doug Powell
Book Design: Doug Powell and Andrea Martin

INSTRUCTIONAL SUPPORT

Did you know that in addition to publishing award-winning curriculum, Apologia also offers instructional support? We believe in helping students achieve their full potential, whatever their learning style. When you choose an Apologia curriculum, you are not just selecting a textbook. Every course has been designed with the student's needs in mind.

INDEPENDENT LEARNERS

Apologia textbooks and notebooks are written to students in a conversational tone so that young people can easily navigate through the curriculum on their own. Apologia curriculum helps students methodically learn, self-check, and master difficult concepts before moving on.

AUDITORY LEARNERS

Sometimes students learn best when they can see and hear what they're studying. **Apologia Audio Books** are the complete text of each course read aloud. Students can follow along with the audio while reading.

VISUAL LEARNERS

Sometimes subject matter is easier to comprehend when the topic is animated and presented by a knowledgeable instructor. When available, **Apologia Video Instructional Courses** enhance the student's education with more than 20 hours of instruction, including on-location video footage, PowerPoint lectures, animated diagrams of difficult concepts, and video presentations of all experiments.

SOCIAL LEARNERS

Some students learn best when they are able to interact with others in an online setting and ask questions of a live instructor. With **Apologia Online Academy**, students can interact in real time with their classmates and a professional instructor in a structured virtual classroom. Also, we offer recordings of all our live classes on the Apologia Online Academy Video-On-Demand Channel.

At Apologia, we believe in homeschooling. We are here not only to support your endeavors but also to help you and your student thrive! Find out more at apologia.com.

STUDENT NOTES

EXPLORING CREATION WITH GENERAL SCIENCE

3rd EDITION

Science is a fascinating subject! Some people are afraid to study science because they think it might be difficult. But in reality, everyone is a scientist. After all, science is a study of the world around us. You are being a scientist when you watch soap bubbles float along in the air and wonder how long it will be until they pop. You are studying the world when you blow dandelion seeds into the sky. You learn about science when you figure out how hard and at what angle you need to throw a basketball in order to make a basket.

Science is a systematic way to more deeply explore those observations so we can better understand why and how things work. As you discover the process of science and all the branches of study in this amazing field, you will begin to see God's hand and His order in creation. Together we will discover some of the fundamental laws He set in place when He created the universe and everything in it, and you will be fascinated at His handiwork!

ABOUT THIS BOOK

Course Overview

This text contains 14 chapter-modules. Each module should take you about 2–2½ weeks to complete, working 4 days per school week for about 45 minutes to an hour. At this pace, you will complete the course in 33 weeks. Since most people have school years that are longer than 33 weeks, there is some built-in "flex time." You should not rush through a module just to make sure that you complete it in 2 weeks. Set that as a goal, but be flexible. Some of the modules might come harder to you than others. On those modules, take more time on the subject matter.

To help you guide your study, there are 2 sets of student exercises that you should complete:

- The "On Your Own" questions should be answered as you read the text. The act of answering these questions will help you know if you have mastered the concepts you are trying to learn. Answers to these questions are at the end of each module. Once you have answered an "On Your Own" question, turn to the end of the module and check your work. If you did not get the correct answer, study the answer to learn why.
- You should answer the questions in the study guide at the end of the module after you have completed the module. This will allow you to review the important concepts from the module and help you prepare for the test. The separate *Solutions and Tests Manual* includes answers to the study guide, as well as tests and test solutions.

Words that appear in BLUE, boldface type are centered in the text. You should memorize the definitions or be able to define them in your own words so you know what they mean. Words that appear in black, boldface type are important terms that you should understand. You don't have to memorize them, but make sure you are able to understand what they mean if you see them mentioned later.

In this course, you will learn to read and create tables, graphs, and even infographics. Sometimes, these forms of information will be used in the "On Your Own," study guide, or test questions. Although you do not have to memorize the information in them, you do need to understand the information they present to you.

Instruction Icons

During the first few modules, you will come across this What to Do instructional icon:

It contains information that will take you in a step-by-step manner through how to complete lab reports, your study guide, your tests, and more. For this course, you will be instructed to take the Module 1 and Module 2 tests as open book tests. This way you will better understand how this course and the rest of Apologia's upper-level courses work.

ACTIVITIES

Experiments

This course contains 2 types of activities: experiments and Explore More boxes. The experiments in this course are designed to be done as you are reading the text. Apologia recommends that you complete all the experiments. You do not necessarily have to do all the Explore More activities, but each one helps you to better understand a new concept or take an idea further.

I recommend that you perform the experiments in the following way:

- When you get to the experiment, read completely through it. This will allow you to gain a quick understanding of what you are to do.
- The *Student Notebook* has specific pages for each experiment. You will write down all of the data taken during the experiment on those pages. What do I mean by "data"? Any observations or measurements you make during the experiment are considered data. Thus, if you measure the length of an object, you need to write that measurement down. It is often helpful to make an illustration of the experiment setup so you can better remember what you did. If you collect a large amount of data, you might want to organize it into a table. You will learn how to do that in Module 3. The *Student Notebook* will help guide you in this process.
- For this General Science course, when you have finished the experiments for a module, choose only one of them and write a short report in your notebook. It should be a brief discussion of what was done and what was learned. You should not write a step-by-step procedure. Instead, write a brief summary that will allow someone who has never read the text to understand what you did and what you learned. I will walk you through the process of writing a lab report right after the first experiment in Module 1.
- For the rest of the experiments in a module, make sure you at least write 1 or 2 sentences to explain the major concept learned.
- **PLEASE OBSERVE COMMON SENSE AND FOLLOW SAFETY PRECAUTIONS!** The experiments in this course are no more dangerous than most normal, household activities. Remember, however, that the vast majority of accidents do happen in the home. Chemicals used in the experiments should never be ingested, and hot containers and flames should be regarded with care; and all experiments should be performed while wearing eye protection such as safety glasses or goggles.

Explore More

The Explore More exercises provide a hands-on way to further explore a concept introduced in the module. They utilize simple household materials so you can quickly and easily complete them. If you do them, make a few notes in your notebook, telling what you did and what you learned.

LABORATORY EQUIPMENT

All of the experiments for *Exploring Creation with General Science* utilize household equipment. Any materials you might need to purchase should readily be available from a grocery, hardware store, or pharmacy.

LEARNING AIDS

Student Notebook

The *Student Notebook* is required. This notebook contains a daily student schedule and space for your personal notes. It has the questions and space for your answers to the "On Your Own" and study guide questions. It also has additional exercises for you to do to help you dig deeper into a subject. The notebook also has lab report pages for each experiment found in the text.

Book Extras

Extra material is available to help you in your studies. There is a special website for this course that you can visit. The website contains links to web-based materials related to the course. These links are arranged by module, so if you are having trouble with a particular subject in the course, you can go to the website and look at the links for that module. Most likely, you will find help there. Also, if you are enjoying a particular module in the course and would like to learn more about it, there are links that will lead you to advanced material related to that module.

To visit the website, go to the following address:

apologia.com/bookextras

Once there, create an account or use an existing Book Extras account. Once you log in, use the Add Course button to add the following password to your account:

Godscreativehand

Be sure that you do not put spaces between any of the letters and that the capitalization is correct. When you click on the button labeled "Submit," you will be sent to the course website.

Back Matter

There is information at the end of the book that you will find useful in your studies. An index will tell you where topics can be found in the course. In addition, we have included a complete list of all the supplies you need to perform the experiments and each Explore More activity in this course.

Instruction

An Apologia Video Instruction Course is available for this title. You can learn more about this at our website apologia.com.

The Apologia Online Academy offers live and recorded classes for this title. You can learn more about this at our website apologia.com.

TABLE OF CONTENTS

ACKNOWLEDGMENTS

This book could not have been written without so many who helped. First and foremost, I am grateful for my Lord Jesus, the One in whom I have my hope, and the One from whom any good thing in me comes.

I want to thank my husband, Dave, who has always supported and encouraged me as a wife, mother, grandmother, and even a scientist! His physics/engineering mind was a valuable encouragement as I wrote many of these modules. And even though he thinks physics is better than biology, I still love him!

My children who have always been my "science guinea pigs" are now grown and in their careers, but their loving support has also given me strength to move through this writing process. I am also grateful to them for needing to be taught grammar and vocabulary as homeschool students because as I taught them, I had to learn it myself. I now know not to end a sentence in a preposition!

I also want to thank Sophie and Emma Bastian for their tireless and cheerful work to test all of the experiments for this course. Their feedback was so helpful. I also am grateful for their mother, Cheryl Bastian, for being willing to take time out of her schedule so I could work with them.

I appreciate the reviews and comments offered by the Apologia Customer Service Team. They know firsthand what the customers want and need.

Of course, I am also grateful for the input and careful technical editing by so many fabulous scientists:

Dr. Tom Burbey, Professor of Hydrogeology at Virginia Tech
Dr. Robert Carter, Staff Scientist and Researcher at Creation Ministries International
Dr. Bob Davis, Professor of Physics at Taylor University
Dr. Marci-Anne Hanks Ed.D., Apologia Online Academy Instructor
Damian Ludwiczak, Chief—Mechanisms and Tribology Branch at NASA
Dr. Paul Madtes Jr., Professor of Biology at Mount Vernon Nazarene University
Lucee Price, Limnologist and Apologia Online Academy Instructor
Dr. Chad Snyder, Department of Science and Mathematics Chair and Professor of Chemistry at Grace College and Theological Seminary
Rachael Yunis, Director of Apologia Science

WELCOME

O LORD, how manifold are your works! In wisdom
have you made them all; the earth is full of your creatures.
—Psalm 104:24

You may have used the term "science" before. Maybe you've done lots of science experiments in elementary school, too. But have you ever wondered what science is? Is there a purpose in studying the world around us? Why should we try to understand how things behave the way they do?

He set the earth on its foundations, so that it should never be moved.
—Psalm 104:5

The Bible clearly states that God created everything in our world. He created the Earth, He created the universe, and He created everything that fills it.

The heavens declare the glory of God, and the sky above proclaims his handiwork.
—Psalm 19:1

When looking at a classic painting, experts can determine who painted it by studying the unique brush strokes and specific use of colors and subject matter. Those are the signature "fingerprints" of the painter. In the same way, we can see the fingerprints of the One who made the universe and everything in it. His creation is filled by the works of His unique, artistic hand!

For his invisible attributes, namely, his eternal power and divine nature,
have been clearly perceived, ever since the creation of the world,
in the things that have been made. So they are without excuse.
—Romans 1:20

This is why we should study science. It gives us glimpses of God's creative hand. We learn more about the Creator of all things by understanding more about His creation.

Great are the works of the Lord, studied by all who delight in them.
—Psalm 111:2

Additionally, by discovering universal laws that uphold the universe and keep matter in its place, we can see that God did not just create but He is actively knitting and holding together every part of His creation.

And he is before all things, and in him all things hold together.
—Colossians 1:17

So we will begin a journey across the subject of science. It will take you through specific methods of study as well as how to apply those methods to all the unique scientific branches. In doing this, we at Apologia desire to give you the amazing opportunity to learn more about God's creative hand and see how creation, indeed, brings Him glory!

But ask the beasts, and they will teach you;
the birds of the heavens, and they will tell you;
or the bushes of the earth, and they will teach you;
and the fish of the sea will declare to you.
Who among all these does not know
that the hand of the Lord has done this?
In his hand is the life of every living thing
and the breath of all mankind.
—Job 12:7-10

Dear Student,

I want to talk to you personally before we get into our fascinating year of exploration about the world of science. Actually, as you will soon learn, science is fascinating because it is a way to learn about the God who created the universe. By studying our world around us, we gain clues to His character and His power to create. Trust me. It will be an adventure that I pray will greatly bless you!

Perhaps this is your first formal science course. Maybe you've taken science for years and have read books on dinosaurs, dolphins, and outer space. You might be dreading the idea of taking science, or you may even be afraid of this subject. All of these feelings and experiences are okay to have. God has brought you to this place and time according to His vast and perfect plan. And He has great plans for you!

> For I know the plans I have for you, declares the Lord, plans for welfare and not for evil, to give you a future and a hope.
>
> —Jeremiah 29:11

If you feel afraid or unprepared for this course, let me encourage you. We will be on this journey together this year. I will take you step-by-step through how to navigate each module (a science-y word for chapter), and I hope to spark your interest and awe as we systematically progress through all types of science. It is likely that you will enjoy some modules better than others. That's normal. You see, there are many branches of science, just like there are many types of people. *You* are uniquely created with different strengths and interests, and it will be fun to discover which subjects fascinate you!

But let me encourage you with my story. When I was a young girl, I loved swimming in the ocean. I remember spending weekends on my family's boat, snorkeling in the water, and watching colorful fish swim below me. I was fascinated with the creatures there and wanted to learn more. But school and eventually work required my time. Entering college, I remembered my interest in the world of the ocean, but I felt like I needed to study something "more important." So I majored in pre-medicine. I kept taking classes about marine life, too, and by the time I graduated from college, I realized I wanted a career in a marine field. I got a job working as a marine biologist for Walt Disney World in EPCOT Center. I was responsible for collecting and working with the predators (including the sharks!) and I loved every minute of it... even the part where I had to pick fish scales out of my hair each night.

Then I was married and we had our first child. I left aquarium work to be a stay-at-home mom, eventually homeschooling all my children through high school. Today I write science curriculum for students, and I get to speak to families about how we can see God's creative fingerprints in His creation!

As a little girl swimming in that water, I had no idea what God had planned for my future. I just continued to do the next thing He placed before me. It turns out that as I studied pre-medicine subjects, I was more convinced everything around us could *not* have formed by itself; it was evidence of a Creator! That was further confirmed as I worked with ocean organisms. God even used me leaving my marine career to build more skills in me. I learned to teach my own children and others through co-ops. I even learned proper grammar by teaching it to my kids! All these skills God built in me are useful for my work today.

I tell you this so that you will be open-minded when you begin this journey with me. I pray that God will use our time together to speak specifically to you. Know that He will be building in you skills and experiences to prepare you for something amazing He has for your future...whether it is in science or another area.

Let's enjoy the adventure together this year!

Sherri Seligson

THE HISTORY OF SCIENCE—SEARCH FOR THE TRUTH

Get ready for an exciting year! You might wonder why I know it will be exciting. Well, it is because we are beginning a study of the fascinating world of science. Before I go any further, let's discuss what science is. The word comes from Latin and simply means "knowledge." But today, the word *science* actually means much more. We can begin with a basic definition.

Science—The systematic study of the natural world through observation and experimentation in order to formulate general laws

FIGURE 1.1
Helium Balloons

Let me break that definition down for you. The end goal of science is found in the second part of the definition. *We use science to come up with general laws that help to explain what is going on in the world around us. Why, for example, do most things fall to the ground when you drop them, yet a helium balloon floats upward? Is there a general law to explain that?* Now, the beginning part of the definition

Quaestio

Why is a Latin word heading this section? Well, this course will be taking you through an overview of all of science, including its development and diversity. A major part of science involves asking questions and doing research. Look closer at those words: QUESTion and reSEARCH. Both words have elements of exploration, don't they? That is a large part of science: exploring the world around us to come up with general laws that God set in place to govern our world since the beginning of time. You will therefore be on a QUEST this year, SEARCHing through all facets of science. *Quaestio* is Latin for "question." Every module will start by reminding you that you are on a quest, searching the world for God's fingerprints. So basically, we'll be explorers together, on an amazing adventure!

explains how we come up with those laws. Scientists look at the world around them and collect facts about it. *Balloons filled with air will fall to the ground.* They also develop experiments to gather more facts. *What happens to balloons filled with other gases when they are released? How are air and those other gases different from helium?* That information is gathered in an ordered way to study and better understand our world. *When the weight of a helium-filled balloon is lighter than the amount of air it takes up, the balloon will float upward in the air.*

Now here is the really exciting part. Believe it or not, you have been a scientist from the day you were born. You have watched and listened to things around you. You learned how things felt, tasted, and behaved. As a baby, when you tossed items off a high chair, you were really exploring what we call gravity (even though that was a messy way to do it!). Then as a toddler, you went outside and examined grass, leaves, ants, and caterpillars. You watched it rain outside and studied the trickling of water as it ran down the window pane. And you were fascinated. That is what we are going to continue to do in this course. We are going to keep observing and experimenting to gather more knowledge with the purpose of better understanding the remarkable world that God created!

FIGURE 1.2
Young Scientist

THE EARLIEST SCIENCE: Ancient Times–600 BC

The best way to study how science works today is to learn about how it has developed throughout history. That's because the history of science will reveal how science should and should not be practiced. We will also learn where it is heading in modern times. So we will use this module to travel through time and observe the history of human scientific inquiry. That will allow you to better understand what science is and what it is not. First, let's travel way, way back to some of the earliest historical records.

Egypt

The first science records we have come from 3,000 years before Christ. Ancient Egypt is where we first see the dawn of what we would call medical care. Many Egyptian medical practices could cure illnesses. However, most of these methods came from trial and error. They would keep trying different things until something helped. If a method didn't work, the patient would have to suffer or even die, but the doctors would know not to use that method on the next patient. If the remedy *did* work, then they knew what to do the next time they saw that illness.

One of the physicians of that time, **Imhotep** (eem' oh tep) [c 2650 BC], was well known for his medical knowledge and ability to heal. People would travel hundreds of miles in the hope that he would be able to cure their illnesses.

Although the trial-and-error method of medicine sounds primitive, Egyptian doctors came up with some pretty successful treatments. For example, they learned that a good way to treat an open wound would be to cover it with moldy bread. That would make the wound heal quickly. Because it worked so well, doctors automatically would apply moldy bread to their patients' wounds. Can you imagine walking through an Egyptian doctor's office and seeing people covered with slices and strips of green, moldy bread? But, believe it or not, they were on to something. Today, we know that some bread molds produce penicillin, which is a chemical that kills the germs that infect wounds! So even though the Egyptian doctors knew *nothing* about germs, they still were able to treat open wounds by preventing them from getting infected.

FIGURE 1.3
Moldy Bread

Some people might see these slices of bread and think they should be thrown away, but Egyptian doctors saw their medical value!

The doctors also discovered a way to manage pain. If a patient was hurting, they would feed the patient seeds from the flowering poppy plant. Eating the poppy seeds seemed to bring pain relief. Again, the doctors didn't know *why* it worked. But modern science has shown us why. It turns out that poppy seeds have both morphine and codeine, which are pain-relieving drugs. In fact, they work so well, those drugs are used in medicine today.

One of the major reasons Egyptian medicine progressed so well as compared to the medicine of other ancient nations is that they invented **papyrus** (puh pye' rus).

Papyrus—An ancient form of paper, made from a plant of the same name

As early as 5,000 years ago, Egyptians took the pliable stems of the papyrus plant, sliced them into thin strips, laid them in a crosswise manner on top of each other, wet them, and then allowed them to dry. That resulted in a type of paper that they could write on and store.

Well, that enabled them to document information and send it from person to person. Up to that point in history, Egyptians, Sumerians, and other people groups wrote on clay tablets or on rocks. You can imagine that writing on rocks and clay and toting them around or storing them would be much more difficult. When Egyptians began writing on papyrus, that all changed. It could be readily rolled up into scrolls for easy transport or storage. That meant the knowledge of one scholar could be easily sent to other scholars. Their gained knowledge could accumulate and more easily be passed down to future generations. That helped to make Egyptian medicine the

FIGURE 1.4
Live Papyrus Plants

most respected form of medicine in the known world.

Other Cultures

But let's not leave out other cultures. They had some great inventions, too. At the same time papyrus was first used in Egypt, the Mesopotamians were employing the first known potter's wheel to make pottery. Horse-drawn chariots were being used as well. And as early as 1,000 years before Christ, the Chinese were using compasses to help them navigate. So we can say the ancient world was filled with inventions that transformed life during those times. These inventions are history's first beginnings of science.

FIGURE 1.5
Egyptian Pyramids at Giza

WHAT TO DO

Notetaking: One of the goals of this course is to help you learn to identify main points as you read information in order to get it "into your brain." Reading is only one way to do that. By writing down the important facts and definitions, you are giving your brain another way to review them and, therefore, you will better remember them. Plus, notetaking provides you with an easy way to review the module when it comes time for a test. Don't worry. I'll walk you through that step, too. The *Student Notebook* that accompanies this textbook is designed specifically to help you become comfortable with notetaking. Now, notice that there are 2 definitions in the previous section (science and papyrus). Words and their definitions (in bold and blue font) should be written in your notebook. You will need to memorize them. Your notebook is also designed to give you notetaking prompts. These will help you remember important information. Taking notes while you read your text will become easier with practice, and you will better recall what you have read.

"On Your Own" Questions: As we come to the end of this first section in the module, you might notice the rest of the module is divided up into other titled sections. At the end of each section will be one or more "On Your Own" questions. You should answer these questions (spaces for answers are in your *Student Notebook*) as soon as you come to them in your reading. You can look back at the module as well as your notes to find the information in order to answer the questions. These questions will help you to think about what you just read in the previous section to make sure you understand it. You will check your answer against the solution located at the end of each module in your textbook. If you got the answer correct, you are ready to move on. If you didn't get the answer correct, don't panic. Go back and reread the section of your textbook to try to understand the answer. You can also find additional materials on the textbook's Book Extra page. Make sure you understand the information before you continue your studies. Science builds on itself, so it is important to have a strong foundation.

Timeline: Finally, for this particular module only, we will be time-traveling through the history of science and meeting several notable scientists. Though you will not be required to memorize everything about all of them, you *will* be instructed to learn a bit more about a few. An important activity for this module will be to create a timeline, beginning at 3000 BC to AD 2000. This activity is found in your notebook. As you study each scientist, write his name under the date they lived and include one or more important facts you learned. For example, you learned about Imhotep in this section, so go ahead and add him to your timeline beneath the date 2650 BC. For this module, when I introduce a scientist from history, there will be a bracketed date after the name so you can place the scientist on your timeline.

ON YOUR OWN

1.1 Although the ancient Egyptians had reasonably advanced medical practices for their times, and although there were many inventions that revolutionized life in the ancient world, most historians of science do not think of Egyptian doctors as scientists. Why? (Hint: Look at the entire definition of science.)

TRUE SCIENCE BEGINS TO EMERGE: 600 BC—AD 500

The ancient Greeks are believed to be the first true scientists. Remember our definition of science. It is when observations and facts are gathered and are then used to come up with general laws about our world. So although the ancient Egyptians and Chinese had collected lots of observations and had recorded facts, they didn't go the next step to use those facts to develop explanations of the natural world. In fact, historians believe that didn't happen until the sixth century BC with the Greeks.

FIGURE 1.6
Solar Eclipse

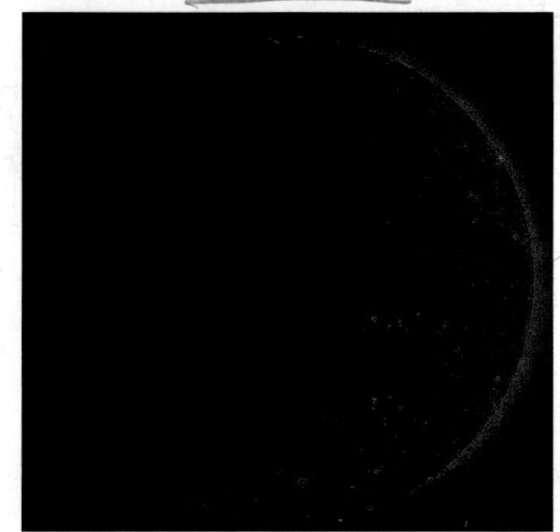

A solar eclipse occurs when the Moon passes between Earth and the sun. The Moon either fully blocks or partially blocks the sun from view.

Three Greek Scientists

Three Greek scientists, Thales (thay leez) [640s–540s BC], Anaximander (an axe' uh man der) [c 500 BC], and Anaximenes (an axe' uh me' neez) [c 546 BC] are believed to be the world's first real scientists.

Thales studied the sky and tried to come up with a unifying theme to explain how the planets and stars moved. He was successful in predicting certain planetary events. In fact, he received notable recognition in his day for correctly predicting what he called the "short-term disappearance of the sun." This was a solar eclipse, which is when the Moon moves between Earth and the sun, blocking most of the sun from our view.

Historians believe Anaximander was one of Thales' students. He studied living organisms and is believed to be the first scientist to try to explain the origin of the human race without reference to a Creator. He suggested that all life began in the sea and at one time in history, humans were a type of fish. This idea was revived much later in history by some other scientists, including Charles Darwin (whom I will introduce in just a bit), and today is known as evolution. We'll discuss evolution later in the course and see what scientific data exist.

Anaximenes was probably an associate of Anaximander. He believed air was the most basic material in nature. He also believed that everything was made of air. So when air is thinned, he thought it would warm and turn to fire. When air is thickened, it would become liquid or solid material. Today, we know that those ideas are incorrect, but Anaximenes did try to explain all things in nature as being made of a single substance. That eventually led to one of the most important scientific ideas introduced by the Greeks: the concept of atoms.

Two More Greek Scientists

Another Greek scientist, Leucippus (loo sip' us) [early 400s BC], built on Anaximenes' thinking, and historians believe he proposed that all matter is composed of little units called atoms. Leucippus had a student, Democritus (duh mah' crit us) [460–c 370 BC]. Democritus' works are well preserved. He came up with a great analogy to help explain his ideas about atoms. Think about walking toward a sandy beach. When you are a long way from the beach, the sand looks like a smooth, yellow blanket. As you get closer to the beach, you might notice that there are bumps and valleys in the sand, but the sand still looks solid. When you reach the beach and actually kneel down to examine the sand, you see it is not solid at all. It is made up of tiny particles called sand grains.

FIGURE 1.7
Sand

Democritus noticed that from a distance the sand on a beach appeared to be connected like a smooth, solid blanket. But as the sand was more closely observed, it was evident that it was made up of small grains. This idea helped him to suggest that all matter was like sand, made up of small particles even though it appeared solid.

Well, Democritus thought that all matter was like sand. Even though it might appear smooth and solid, it is made up of very tiny particles called atoms. **It turns out that some materials in nature have atoms that are more tightly packed together than others.** That makes them behave differently from each other. Explore this idea more in Experiment 1.1.

WHAT TO DO

Before you begin any experiment, you should read **all** of the instructions to make sure you have the materials needed and understand what you will be doing.

EXPERIMENT 1.1
DENSITY IN NATURE

PURPOSE: To understand how atoms could explain things we see in nature

MATERIALS:

- A tall, clear canister or jar with a lid
- A ping-pong ball
- A 3-oz. lead sinker (the kind used for fishing)
- A bag of unpopped popcorn (small dried beans will also work)

QUESTION: What happens to 2 objects of different densities when they are in the same container?

HYPOTHESIS: Make sure you know what you think will happen to the less dense ball before you complete step 4 of this experiment.

PROCEDURE:

1. Fill the canister with popcorn so that it is about ¾ full.
2. Bury the ping-pong ball into the center of the popcorn so that it is just below the popcorn's surface. You should not be able to see the ping-pong ball; it should be completely covered.
3. Set the lead sinker on top of the popcorn and seal the canister.
4. Vigorously swirl the canister around and around in a circular motion from side to side and watch what happens to the balls. **Use common sense when shaking so that your container does not crack.**
5. Record in the lab notebook section of your *Student Notebook* what you saw.
6. Clean up and return everything to the proper place.

CONCLUSION: What happened to the ping-pong ball and the lead sinker when you swirled the canister?

Hypothesis

In the experiments for this course, you will be asked to come up with a hypothesis. A hypothesis is a statement describing what you think will happen in an experiment. You create a testable answer to a scientific question. One of the best ways to state a hypothesis is to write it as an "If-then" statement. It doesn't necessarily have be in this format, but it is a good way to help you plan your question and answer to a situation. For Experiment 1.1, for example, you might state, "IF 2 objects of different densities are in the same container and the container is swirled, THEN the less dense object will not sink as deep as the denser one." Or "IF the canister of popcorn is swirled, THEN both objects will sink to the bottom of the container." That way you can test your hypothesis to see if it is correct. An incorrect hypothesis does not mean the experiment was a bad experiment. Either way, you come out of the experiment learning something. The experiment tests your statement to see if your hypothesis is right. And that is good science!

What did you discover in the experiment? You should have noticed that the lead sinker disappeared and the ping-pong ball took its place. **Actually, the lead sinker sank down into the popcorn kernels and the ping-pong ball floated to the top.**

How is this experiment evidence for the existence of atoms? Well, Democritus suggested that **all things, including both objects, are made up of individual particles called atoms. The way those atoms are packed together will determine each object's characteristics.**

If you hold both objects in your hands, you should notice that one is heavier than the other. The 3-oz. lead sinker and ping-pong ball are not the same size. That means one object—the lead sinker—has atoms packed together more closely than the other. They are more densely packed, or in other words, that item has greater density. **Lower-density substances will always float on top of higher-density substances.** So the lead sinker sank down in the popcorn and the ping-pong ball floated to the top.

All substances, even liquids and gases, are made up of atoms. Some have tightly packed atoms while others have loosely packed atoms. If you imagine every substance to be made up of little grains (like sand), then the more tightly packed those grains are, the more massive the substance will be. Therefore, if you assume that atoms exist, then results of experiments like the one you just did are easy to understand.

Democritus was well ahead of his time. Today we know that all matter is made up of atoms. Scientists even know how distinct types of atoms are arranged in any given substance. That helps us to un-

FIGURE 1.8
Mountain Lake

Everything you see in this figure is made up of atoms, including the solid sand, trees and mountains, the liquid water, and even the gaseous clouds and air!

derstand the concept of density. Democritus didn't get everything right, but he did believe that atoms were in constant motion, even in a solid substance.

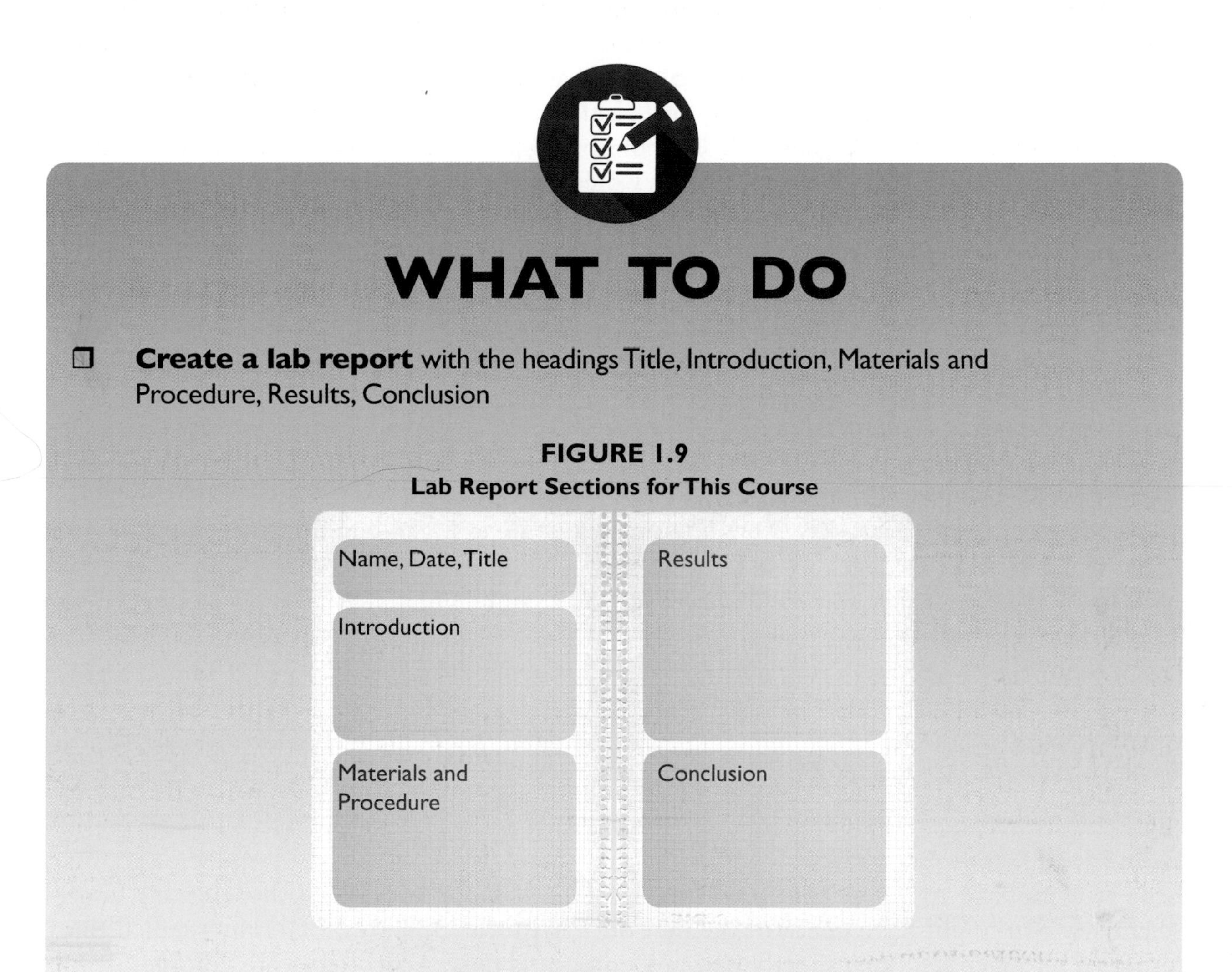

WHAT TO DO

- [ ] **Create a lab report** with the headings Title, Introduction, Materials and Procedure, Results, Conclusion

FIGURE 1.9
Lab Report Sections for This Course

Now that you have completed this experiment, it is time to document what you have done. You will do this by **creating a lab report**. I will walk you through the process of a lab report during the first few modules so it will become very familiar to you (and very easy!).

Basically, a report shows what you did in the experiment and what you learned so that someone who has never done this experiment would understand what happened and why. It is always written in the third person. That means you do not use personal pronouns, such as "I," "we," or "you."

For this experiment, you need to write your name, date, and experiment **Title** on the top of the page. The next section will be the **Introduction**. In it you will write a short sentence or 2 explaining why this experiment is being performed, along with your hypothesis, or what you think will happen before you swirl the canister and why.

Next, write about your **Materials and Procedure**. In this section, you will list the materials you used in sentence form, if possible. Then you will explain in a few simple sentences what you did. You might also want to make an illustration showing the setup.

The next section will be your **Results**, or what happened when you did the experiment. Here, you can also add a sentence or 2 to discuss why you think you got the results you did.

The last section is your **Conclusion**, or what you learned.

To help you figure out what to write, I highlighted key sentences in orange before and after the experiment to give you clues for your hypothesis, results, and conclusion. You should be able to explain what you thought would happen (for the Introduction) and what you did (for the Materials and Procedure). But *please* be sure to write your sentences using *your own* words. Copying someone else's words is plagiarism, and that is not allowed. If you're having a hard time doing that, try to tell your parents or a sibling what you did. Then write down what you said to them.

A sample lab report for this experiment is at the end of this module. For each module, I recommend you choose one of the experiments and do a lab report. Writing one per module will be good practice for the scope of this course. Your *Student Notebook* has a space to write your report.

EXPLORE MORE

Fill one glass with very hot water and another glass with very cold water. Then add a single drop of food coloring to each glass. Watch how the color gets distributed in the water. In which glass does the color spread out faster? It turns out that atoms move faster when a substance is hot, so the glass filled with hot water will distribute the food coloring much more quickly. The cold water will eventually distribute the color as well. Both have atoms moving around, but some move more rapidly than others.

Even More Greek Scientists

Let's now go back to our science time travel and look at the lives of 3 other notable Greek scientists. You might have heard of the first one: **Aristotle** [384–322 BC]. He is called the father of life sciences. Born shortly before Democritus died, Aristotle wrote volumes of works on philosophy, mathematics, logic, and physics. However, Aristotle's greatest work was the study of living things. In fact, he was the first to come up with a system to classify animals and plants, placing them into groups based on their similarities.

Although Aristotle was a respected scientist, he also was responsible for some incorrect ideas that hampered science for many, many years. An example of that is his belief that certain living organisms spontaneously formed from nonliving substances. This idea is called spontaneous generation.

Spontaneous generation—The idea that living organisms can be spontaneously formed from nonliving substances

Spontaneous generation is how some scientists thought maggots (young flies) spontaneously formed from rotting meat. They believed that rotting meat left out for a few days would actually *transform* into maggots.

FIGURE 1.10
Dead Fish

Scientists who accepted spontaneous generation believed that rotting meat, such as this fish, would transform into living maggots. Yet today we know that flies lay their eggs into rotting meat, and the young larvae (maggots) hatch there.

Today, of course, we know that spontaneous generation is impossible. In fact, in all our observed experiences, life can only be formed by the reproduction of other living things. We will go into greater detail about this topic in a later module, but the lesson for us right now is an example of how science should *not* be done. Though Aristotle made great advances in the study of living things, he mistakenly believed in spontaneous generation. And because he was so well respected (rightly) as one of the greatest scientists of his time, spontaneous generation was believed to be true for over 2,000 years after he came up with it!

think about this

Wrong reasoning can lead to wrong science. There are many possibilities for wrong reasoning, sometimes called fallacy, in science. Sometimes a person makes a general conclusion about a subject, but only has a few cases on which to make that conclusion. An example of this hasty generalization is if, after cutting your foot on a shell at the beach and observing that the same thing happened to your friend, you might generalize that "This beach is full of sharp shells that will always cut a person's feet." This is why scientists need large sample sizes to make conclusions about what they observe. Another type of wrong reasoning is when a person assumes something causes an event just because it happened before the event. For example, a baseball pitcher might be chewing a new brand of gum while he pitches his first no-hitter. He might be tempted to say that the new brand of gum was the cause of his perfectly pitched game.

Archimedes (ark uh me' deez) [c 287–c 212 BC] is the next Greek scientist I will talk about. He lived about 100 years after Aristotle and did great work in mathematics, using much of that work to forward science. In fact, he applied mathematical formulas to explain why certain things happened the way they did. The Fields Medal is awarded every 4 years to recognize outstanding mathematical achievement. The medal's image is of Archimedes, and the inscription translates as "Rise above oneself and grasp the world."

FIGURE 1.11
The Fields Medal

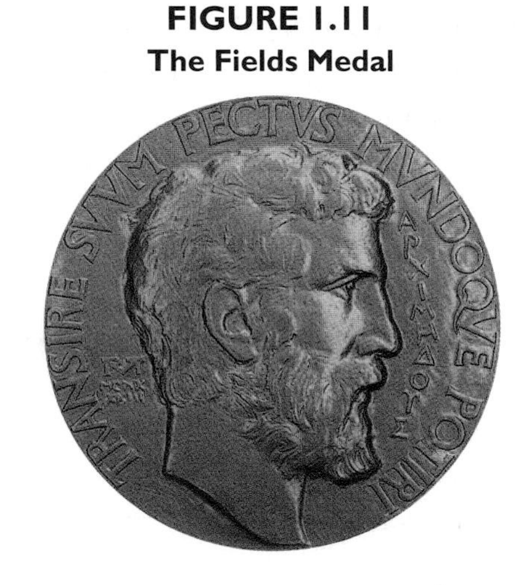

The last Greek scientist I want to talk about lived about 100 years after Christ's birth. Ptolemy (tahl' uh mee) [c AD 100–170] studied the heavens and was one of the first to attempt a complete description of the planets and stars. He assumed that Earth was at the center of the universe, and that the planets and stars orbited about Earth in a series of circles.

In his day, there was lots of evidence to support Ptolemy's hypothesis, so his idea became very popular. This view of the stars and planets is called the Ptolemaic system, or the geocentric system. It was accepted by scientists until about the 1600s. This incorrect idea was accepted for so long because even as more and more data were collected that contradicted the geocentric system, many scientists ignored the data out of great reverence to Ptolemy because he was a great scientist. It also fit many scientists' preconceived notions of how things *ought to be*. They liked the idea of Earth being the center of the solar system, so the geocentric system made sense to them, even though there was more and more data to disagree with it.

FIGURE 1.12
Illustration of the Geocentric System

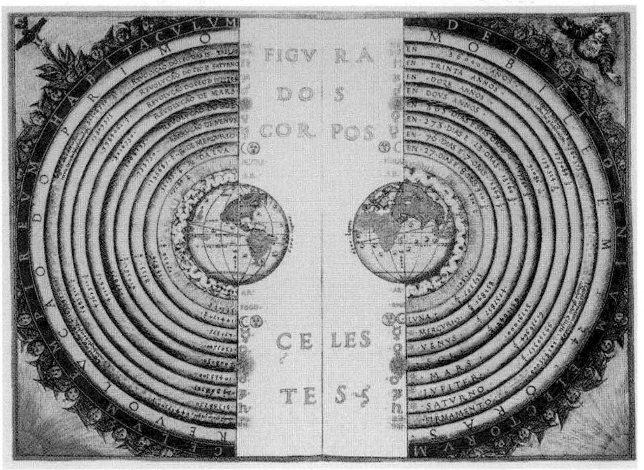

This illuminated illustration shows Earth in the center of the solar system with the Moon and planets orbiting it, as Ptolemy suggested. It was illustrated by Portuguese cosmographer and cartographer Bartolomeu Velho.

Aristotle and Ptolemy's stories can teach us something. A scientist shouldn't hold onto an idea just because it fits some preconceived notions. And a scientific idea should not be accepted just because a brilliant scientist believes it. Science is built on data that are tested time and time again, not on a person's beliefs.

ON YOUR OWN

1.2 Based on your results in Experiment 1.1, what do you think about the density of popcorn kernels? Are they more or less dense than the lead sinker and the ping-pong ball?

1.3 Albert Einstein is one of the most well-known scientists in recent history. (We'll talk more about him later in this module.) Though he received the 1921 Nobel Prize for his contributions to theoretical physics, he also had some ideas that were incorrect. Einstein believed that nuclear power could never be a good source of usable energy. Yet his own groundbreaking equation, $E = mc^2$, is at the heart of over 400 nuclear power stations today, providing a major source of worldwide non-carbon-based energy. Imagine what would have happened if scientists decided not to explore nuclear energy because Einstein, a brilliant scientist, said it wasn't worth exploring. Name one more example of a brilliant scientist who advanced an incorrect idea. What do these examples teach us about how to make scientific decisions?

SCIENCE PROGRESS STALLS AND THEN GETS MOVING AGAIN: AD 500–1500

After the time of the highlighted Greek scientists, science continued to progress steadily. Scientists were exploring ways to study and explain the natural world. Scientific communities formed, referencing and utilizing the works of previous scientists like Aristotle.

But something happened. After the first few centuries AD, scientific progress drastically slowed. This was at the same time the Roman Empire reached its height and was beginning to decline. You see, although the Romans embraced inventions, particularly those that improved the processes of work, there was little desire for *explaining* the world around them. So real experimental science was discouraged throughout the known world. This era is known as the Dark Ages.

Alchemy

Alchemy, on the other hand, grew during the Dark Ages. The main goal of alchemists was to find a way to transform lead (or other inexpensive metals) into gold (or other precious substances). They were doing this because by that time in history, many people observed that when you exposed some substances to each other, they changed into other substances.

EXPERIMENT 1.2
A CHEMICAL REACTION

PURPOSE: To determine what can happen when you mix specific substances together

MATERIALS:
- A fresh lemon
- A small knife
- 3 tarnished pennies (The more tarnished, the better your results will be. Pennies minted between 1962 and 1982 work well for this experiment, as they contain 95% copper and have been in circulation long enough to build up a good coating of copper oxide.)
- A paper towel
- A paper plate
- A teaspoon of salt
- An eyedropper
- Some water

QUESTION: What happens when copper pennies are exposed to lemon juice?

HYPOTHESIS: (A hypothesis is what you think will happen and why.) Write what you think will happen to a penny when it is exposed to lemon juice.

PROCEDURE:
1. Using the knife, carefully cut a few small slits through the lemon peel. You want to cut all the way through the peel.
2. Insert a penny into each slit so that half of the penny is exposed to the juicy inside, not just the peel.
3. Allow the pennies to sit for at least 10 minutes.
4. Remove the pennies, dry them with the paper towel, and note their appearance.
5. Rinse the pennies and place them on a paper plate.
6. Sprinkle a small pile of salt on top of each penny. With the eyedropper, add a few drops of water to cover each penny.
7. Allow the pennies to sit for a few minutes and then blot them with a paper towel so the pennies are exposed to air. Let the pennies sit overnight.
8. Observe the colors of the pennies and write what happened in your notebook.
9. Clean up and return everything to the proper place.

CONCLUSION: What did you observe? What happened to the part of the penny that was exposed to lemon juice?

In the first part of the experiment, you should have noticed that the halves of the pennies exposed to the inside of the lemon turned a bright copper color. That is because the original copper in the tarnished pennies had combined with the oxygen in the air to make a chemical compound called copper oxide. The acid of the lemon juice caused a chemical reaction, causing the copper oxide to break the copper atoms and the oxygen atoms apart, so you could see the shiny copper color.

In the second part of the experiment, you exposed the pennies to salt and water. This caused another chemical reaction to occur by helping the copper in the pennies to react again with the oxygen in the air. So the next day, you should have noticed that the pennies were starting to tarnish again.

Alchemists saw changes like the changes you observed in the previous experiment and thought that if they could find just the right combination of substances, they could mix a metal such as lead with several other substances so it would change to gold. Today, we know this is impossible because there are severe limitations to how much a substance can actually change within a chemical reaction. However, the alchemists didn't know this, so they used trial and error to see if they could stumble upon the perfect mixture to make precious gold out of commonplace lead.

FIGURE 1.13
Medieval Gold Coins

However, they *did* keep records of their work, and as a result, many interesting observations were recorded. Sometimes, one of the mixtures would actually form a useful substance, too. But they never tried to use their observations to draw conclusions about how the natural world works. They just kept trying to make new substances out of existing ones.

The events during this time period can teach us 2 things about science. A stalling of science happened during the time of the Roman Empire's decline. With hampered trade and communication, scientific progress slowed. So, lesson 1 is that **scientific progress depends not only on scientists, but it also depends on government and culture.** And lesson 2 is that **science progresses by building on the work of previous scientists.**

Other Medieval Cultures

Now, other cultures were also exploring the world during this time period. The Arabs and Chinese were making careful observations of the heavens and logging their observations, but (like the Roman scientists) not trying to explain what those data meant. The Chinese noted in AD 1054 the sudden appearance of a bright star. Because their data were written down, future scientists *could* use it to compare to what they saw in the skies and make conclusions. In fact, modern scientists believe the Chinese were observing a supernova, which is essentially the explosion of a star. That is because in the same part of the sky today, there is a large cloud of dust and gas, called a nebula. So scientists used recorded evidence along with modern evidence to suggest that a supernova results in a nebula. These scientists built on the work of scientists who came before them.

FIGURE 1.14
The Crab Nebula

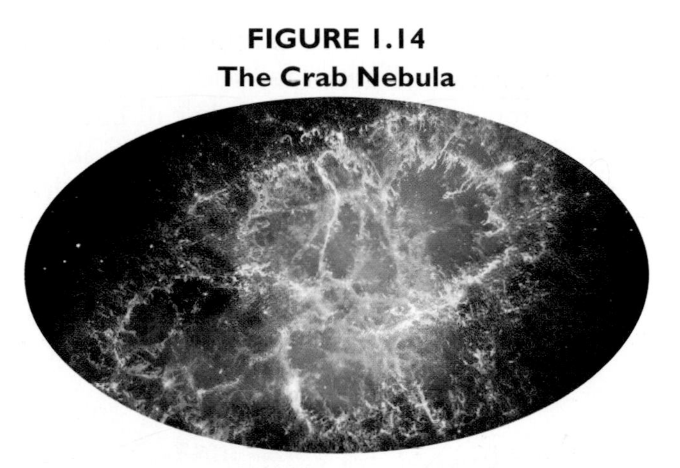

Based on very detailed Chinese records from AD 1054, the Crab Nebula is thought to be the remains of a star that exploded.

EXPLORE MORE

How many dimes does it take to have a mass of 2 oz? Well, you could grab a kitchen scale and a handful of dimes and place them one by one onto the scale until it read 2 oz. But what if you had access to some previous observations made by a scientist? What if you read his documentation that said he determined it takes 12 dimes to have a mass of 1 ounce? You could use that information to further your experiment. If it takes 12 dimes to have a mass of 1 oz, you could start with 12 already on the scale and go from there. Or you could realize that if you doubled that amount to 24 dimes, you would also have double the mass, or 2 oz. Can you see how science can progress by building on the work done by previous scientists? Try measuring dimes to explore this.

End of the Dark Ages

By about AD 1000 Christian scholars began to realize that their belief in a single God who created the universe would have set up specific universal laws to govern it. They believed God's laws never changed, so therefore the natural laws God set into motion should also never change. As a result, the way the natural world worked could be explained if they could discover the natural laws God set in place. Therefore, science began to progress toward the end of the Dark Ages because the Christian worldview began to replace the Roman worldview.

This thinking caused real science to emerge again. Some of the notable scientists of this era include **Robert Grosseteste** (groh' suh test' ee) [c AD 1175–1253]. He taught that the purpose of inquiry was not to come up with random experiments and the observation of their results, but to learn the *reasons* behind those observations, instead. That is really what science is: explaining why things happen the way they do. So Grosseteste is known for coming up with the first ideas behind the scientific method and is often called the father of the scientific method. He believed a scientist should make observations, and then come up with a tentative explanation for why those events happened. Then he should make more observations to test that explanation. If the new observation didn't agree with the original explanation, then the new explanation was probably wrong.

One of Grosseteste's followers, **Roger Bacon,** is even more well known [c AD 1219–c 1292]. Bacon was known for strongly encouraging scientists to use Grosseteste's method, so sometimes people wrongly call Bacon the father of the scientific method. He was known to use science to break superstitions. One example was the conventional belief that diamonds could be broken by goat's blood. He came up with experiments to prove that idea to be wrong. Bacon was a visionary, believing that science could eventually bring about flying machines, explosives, submarines, and the ability to travel around the world!

FIGURE 1.15
World Map with Modes of Transportation

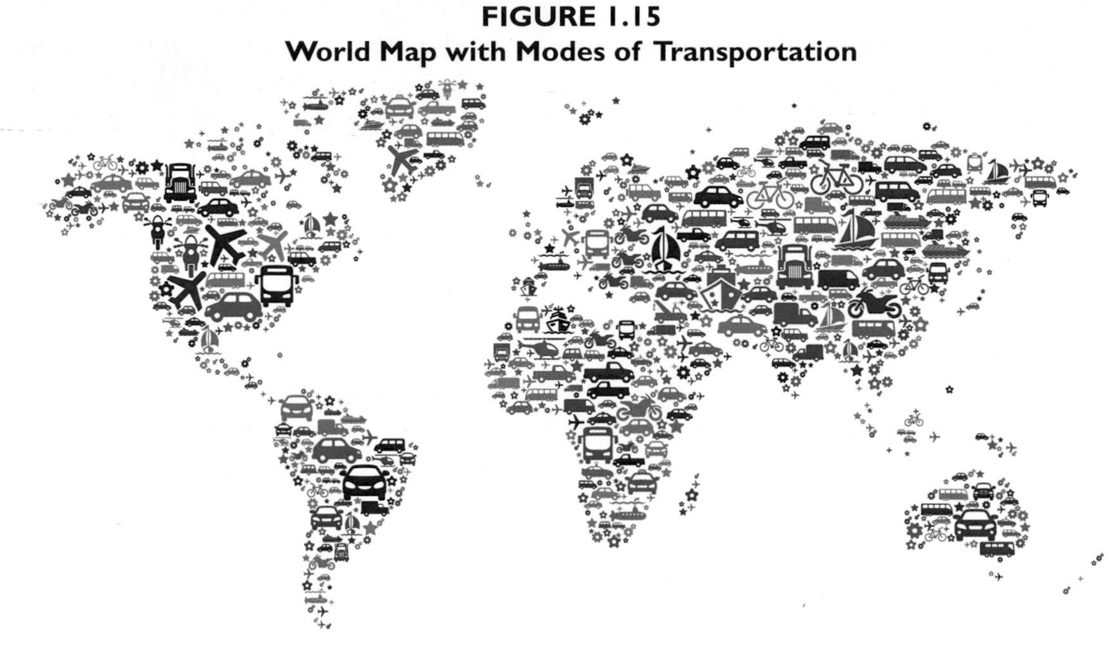

Roger Bacon's ideas of world travel were hundreds of years ahead of his time. It wasn't until the 1600s that a working submarine was built, and the airplane wasn't invented until 1903.

In the early 1300s, Thomas Bradwardine (brad war' deen) [c AD 1290–1349] began work on 2 levels. Bradwardine was a theologian and emphasized salvation by faith alone, through the grace of God. But he also is important in the development of modern science. He was one of the first to critically examine many of Aristotle's ideas and found most of them lacking. Focusing on motion, he came up with equations to try to describe the details of speed, distance traveled, and more. Using mathematics and experiments, he showed that most of Aristotle's ideas about motion were wrong.

Nicholas of Cusa [AD 1401–1464] was interested in the idea that God was infinite. In trying to learn more about God's infinite nature, he studied the planets and stars because he thought they were the largest and most infinite things he could study. He was one of the first scientists to break from Ptolemy's geocentric view and believe that the Earth spins on its axis while it travels around the sun.

ON YOUR OWN

1.4 Explain why it is important to document scientific data.

1.5 Some people believe that science and Christianity are at odds with one another. That idea has developed because in recent years, many scientists are not Christian. Explain how a Christian worldview is, in fact, one of the reasons science got out of the Dark Ages.

Have you noticed that many of the great scientists since the 1000s were devout Christians? In fact, as we go through the rest of this module, you will see that many of the great scientists from the Dark Ages to modern time were devoted Christians. That is because the Christian worldview is a perfect fit with science!

THE RENAISSANCE—THE "GOLDEN AGE" OF SCIENCE: AD 1500–1660

As we enter this time period, we will discover that it is a time when science blossomed. Though lots of amazing discoveries were made about the world by many, many scientists, we will highlight 5 in this section. It begins in 1543 when 2 important works were published. The first was by **Nicolaus Copernicus** [AD 1473–1543]. In it, he laid out his idea about Earth, the sun, planets, and stars. Just like Nicholas of Cusa, Copernicus believed that Ptolemy's view of the universe was incorrect. He instead believed the data he had were better explained if the sun was in the center of our planetary system and all the planets, including Earth, orbited around it. This is known today as the heliocentric (he' lee oh sen' trik) system or the **Copernican system** in his honor.

The other important work published in 1543 was written by a doctor named **Andreas Vesalius** (vuh sal' ee us) [AD 1514–1564]. It contained the most detailed and amazingly accurate illustrations of the human body. In fact, this was the first book to illustrate all of the insides of the body, including the organs, muscles, and skeleton.

FIGURE 1.16
Contributions by Vesalius and Copernicus

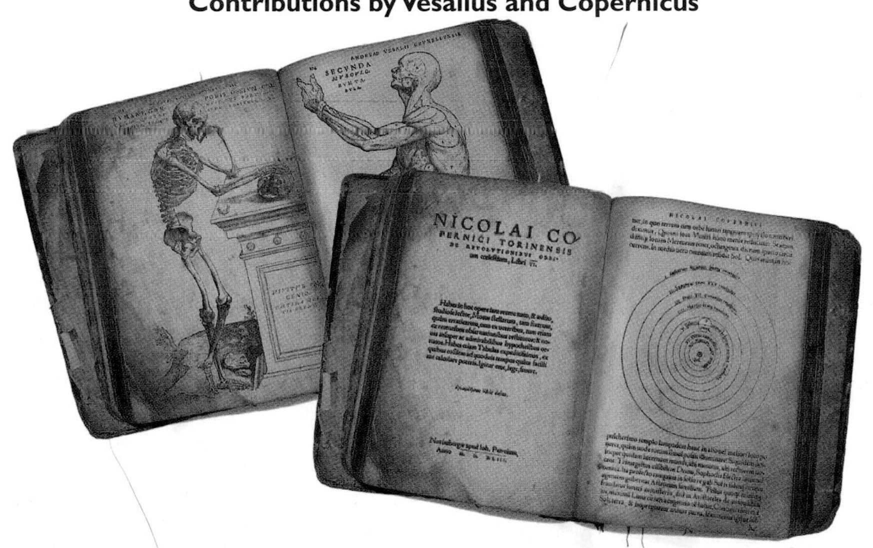

In 1543, both Vesalius and Copernicus published works to help "map" things within their respective fields. Vesalius illustrated the arrangement of the organ systems within the human body, and Copernicus used scientific data to explain how the solar system was arranged. Both systems showed God's perfect order in His design.

Vesalius' book was recognized right away as revolutionary to medicine, but Copernicus' book was not so well received. That's because the church of that time believed the idea of Earth being at the center of everything made more sense. They did have a point in that Copernicus did not have lots of data to support his ideas. He promoted the heliocentric system because he knew there was lots of evidence *against* Ptolemy's geocentric system. Copernicus also thought that God fashioned the heavens using the heliocentric system because it was the more orderly and pleasing of the 2.

As more evidence was compiled, Copernicus' heliocentric view became more readily accepted. One of the most important compilers of that evidence was **Johannes Kepler** [AD 1571–1630]. He wanted to bring glory to God as he studied the heavens. Kepler's detailed observations of the planets helped him to deduce the basic orbits that the planets use to travel around the sun. He could even describe the orbits mathematically.

In fact, his mathematical equations were known as Kepler's laws and became one of the most powerful arguments for the heliocentric system. He could even deduce that planetary orbits were more elliptical, not circular.

A fourth notable scientist who lived in this era is **Galileo** (gal uh lay' oh) **Galilei** (gal uh lay') [AD 1564–1642]. Galileo performed detailed experiments about motion, supporting Bradwardine, and identifying the flaws of Aristotle's thinking. Using designs for a military device, Galileo built a telescope made from a tube with 2 lenses that could greatly magnify distant objects. Though he is not the inventor of the telescope, Galileo greatly improved its design. He was able to compile details about the planets and stars, showing that the planets shone in the sky not because they generated their own light, but by reflecting the light of the sun. This and other facts made it clear that the heliocentric view was superior to the geocentric view.

Blaise (blayz) **Pascal** (pas kal') [AD 1623–1662] was a philosopher, mathematician, and scientist. He is known for making great advances in the study of geometry and algebra. You can thank Pascal for your high school math classes! Additionally, Pascal studied how fluids behave and also demonstrated that the air we breathe exerts pressure on everything, an effect called atmospheric pressure.

FIGURE 1.17
The Golden Spiral

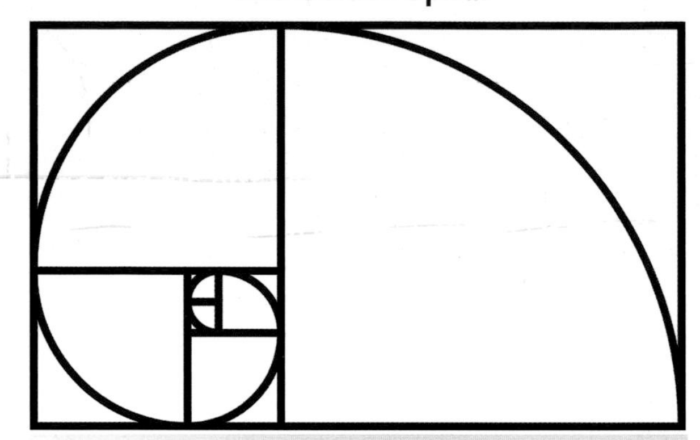

Mathematics play a key role in understanding many scientific phenomena. In geometry, a golden spiral is a spiral whose growth factor increases by a specific amount for every quarter turn it takes. This mathematical principle can be seen in several living organisms, both plant and animal.

EXPLORE MORE

Pascal explained that air is constantly pushing against everything, exerting pressure. Try this quick activity to explore air pressure. Take a drinking glass and fill it one-fourth to one-third full with water. Cover the mouth of the glass with a piece of card stock, making sure the card completely covers the glass. Hold the card in place with your hand flat on it as you turn the glass upside-down *over a sink*. Some water might leak out, but hold the card in place making sure it makes complete contact with the entire rim of the glass. Remove your hand from the card. What happened? The card should stay in place. That's because the pressure of the air pushing up on the card is stronger than the weight of the water and the resulting lack of air pressure pushing down on it from inside the glass (called a vacuum). The card experiences about 15 lb of force pushing upward by the air, but only 1 lb of force pushing downward from the water. Air pressure can be a powerful force!

ON YOUR OWN

1.6 Galileo is often incorrectly credited with the invention of the telescope. Look back in this section to see *exactly* what his contribution to the telescope was. Explain how this is an example of the importance of documenting scientific data and sharing that documentation with other scientists.

THE ERA OF NEWTON: AD 1660–1735

This era of time continues in the footsteps of the golden age of science, but even though there were many scientific discoveries by several great scientists, we are going to focus on only 3. And one of those 3 took center stage. That is because science experienced the greatest advancement during the time of **Sir Isaac Newton** [AD 1643–1727]. Newton was a devout Christian, like many of the great scientists you have already studied. He studied science specifically as a means of learning more about God, and he also believed that the best way to learn about God was by studying the Bible. Newton wrote most of his revolutionary scientific works in a 3-volume set called *Principia* (prin sip' ee uh). The first volume explained Newton's 3 laws of motion. In it he made a direct link between mathematics and science, saying that a scientific law was useless if it did not have a supporting mathematical equation to describe some aspect of nature. That was a major breakthrough for the science of the physical world, transforming it into a rigorous field of study.

The second volume of *Principia* built on the work of Pascal and focused on the motion of fluids. The third volume included Newton's universal law of gravitation. He showed, using detailed experiments, that gravity was responsible for attracting objects to Earth (making them fall) as well as keeping planets in orbit around the sun. Because of his mathematical equations that supported these ideas, his third volume was the last blow to the geocentric view of the heavens.

Robert Boyle [AD 1627–1691] is known as the founder of modern chemistry. He lived at the same time as Newton, performing experiments on gases and formulating laws that are used today in the study of chemistry. He was a dedicated Christian, often writing sermons using nature to give glory to God.

Another notable scientist from this period was **Antoni** (an' ton ee) **van Leeuwenhoek** (loo' en hook) [AD 1632–1723]. Though he was not educated as a scientist, he revolutionized the study of living things by building the first high-powered single lens microscope. That opened science up to a previously unseen world of tiny life forms, including bacteria. And like Boyle, Leeuwenhoek tried to glorify God in all his scientific work. The microscopic world was testimony to him that God made all creatures, great and small.

FIGURE 1.18
Replica of a Microscope Design by Leeuwenhoek

ON YOUR OWN

1.7 Some students think learning mathematics is difficult. In order to teach science to such students, there are many science textbooks written today that do not use mathematics at all. What do you think Newton would say about such textbooks?

THE "ENLIGHTENMENT" AND THE INDUSTRIAL REVOLUTION: AD 1735–1820

Why is the word *enlightenment* given quotation marks in this section title? Well, during this period in history, a change in the underlying assumptions of science and how to look at the world occurred. A philosopher who lived during this time, Immanuel Kant, came up with the term *enlightenment* to describe the change because the word means "to gain knowledge." However, the title word is in quotation marks because that change was only *partly* beneficial to the progress of science.

FIGURE 1.19
Medieval Cross

What is this notable change? For many people, there was a rejection of things from the past, such as religion and monarchies, and there was an emphasis on reason, liberty, and the scientific method. So some of the change in thinking had to do with how people believed the universe came to be. Up to this point in history, God was at the center of virtually all science. In most of the previous sections, the great scientists I have been highlighting were devout Christians. That means that until now, science had a very Christian flavor, with the scientists endeavoring to see God's creative fingerprints in creation and mentioning God reverently in their scientific papers.

Since the Dark Ages, advances in science were the result of scientists questioning the teachings of Ptolemy, Aristotle, and other scientists whose works had dominated science for so long. That meant the scientific community was learning that scientists shouldn't just blindly accept the teachings of former scientists. They realized, rightly so, that all scientists make mistakes, and therefore everyone's work should be critically examined. To sum up, **science stopped relying on the authority of past scientists and began relying on experiments and data.**

Well, that is actually a good change that happened during the Enlightenment. All scientific works *should* be carefully examined. Unfortunately, though, **as science began to ignore the authority of past scientists, it also began to ignore the authority of the Bible.** And that is a bad result of the Enlightenment. So even though a biblical worldview fueled the science of the past, some scientists in this era started to question the truth of the Bible.

There were still some scientists who were devout Christians during this time, but as time went on, fewer and fewer references to God and the Bible could be found in scientific works.

One of the notable Christian scientists during this time is **Carolus** (kair' uh lus) **Linnaeus** (lih nay' us) [AD 1707–1778]. In 1735, Linnaeus published a book in which he created a classification scheme that categorized all living creatures that had been studied. The basic classification he came up with is still in use today. Now, Linnaeus was deeply committed to performing science as a way to glorify God. He believed that God is very organized, so His creation should also be organized.

FIGURE 1.20
Rothschild Giraffe

The Rothschild giraffe is found mainly in Uganda and Kenya. According to today's modern classification system, based on Linnaeus' major scheme, it would be classified in kingdom Animalia, phylum Chordata, class Mammalia, order Artiodactyla, family Giraffidae, genus *Giraffa* and species *camelopardalis*. The Rothschild giraffe would then be placed into a smaller category: subspecies *rothschildi*.

Antoine-Laurent (an twon' law rent') **Lavoisier** (luh vwah' see ay) [AD 1743–1794] was a chemist who analyzed chemical reactions in a systematic way. His most important contribution to science was the law of mass conservation, which stated that matter cannot be created or destroyed—it can only change forms.

John Dalton [AD 1766–1844] also lived during this time period. A devout Quaker, he did many experiments with gases and came up with many new ideas that propelled science forward. One of his most important works was his atomic theory. He built on the works of Democritus and others, proposing a detailed theory of atoms. He is known as the father of modern atomic theory.

This period is also known as the Industrial Revolution because it was a time when the growing scientific knowledge gave rise to a rapid increase in inventions that made work faster and more productive.

EXPLORE MORE

During the Industrial Revolution, many devices were invented that turned hours of manual labor into just a few minutes of work. Even today, robotic machines do in minutes what used to take days. You can make a simple robotic hand using materials in your home.

You will need 4 drinking straws, scissors, a stapler, a ruler, masking or cellophane tape, and about 5 feet of string. If your straws have bending ridges, do the instructed work on the opposite end. Bend the straw at about one inch from the end and carefully cut off one corner of the bend. That should give you a diamond-shaped hole. Do the same thing at 2 inches and 3 inches from the straw's end so that the holes are lined up. Repeat with the other 3 straws. Cut your string into 4 equal lengths. Thread one length of string through a straw so that about 1–2 inches are sticking out of the end closest to the holes. Staple over the string and straw and tie a double knot in the string so it won't slip through the staple. Do the same thing for the other 3 straws. Now lay the straws beside each other so that the diamond-shaped holes are facing upward. Tape the straws together. Gently bend the straws upward at each hole to form a crease on the straw. This will form a finger joint. Now pull on all 4 ends of the string so that the "fingers" bend. Can you grab anything with your mechanical hand?

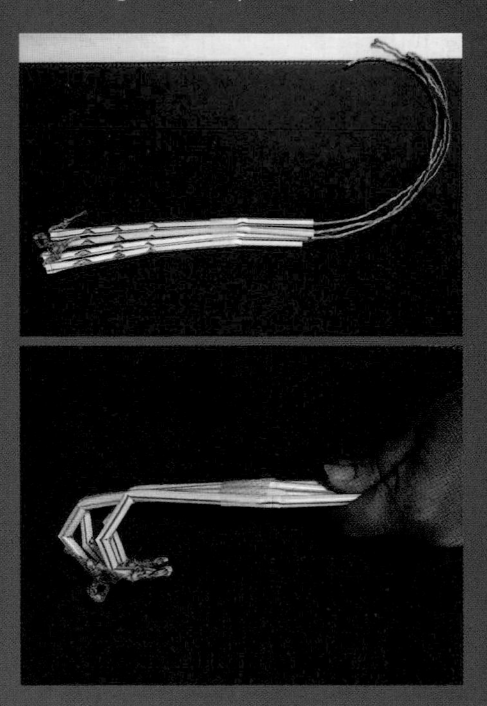

THE REST OF THE 19TH CENTURY: AD 1820–1900

The rest of the 19th century was filled with advances in science, partly due to the fact that people began to appreciate science more than ever before. They could tangibly see how inventions could make their lives better, and that translated to more financial support for science.

One of the most notable scientists during this period is Charles Darwin [AD 1809–1882]. He published a book in 1859 titled *On the Origin of Species by Means of Natural Selection or the Preservation of Favoured Races in the Struggle for Life*, which is often shortened to *The Origin of Species*. This book caused an upheaval within the scientific community. In it, Darwin proposed a theory that tried to explain the diversity of life on Earth and how it came to be without a Creator. He proposed that the same kinds of processes we see occurring today are responsible for all the species on the planet. This is commonly known as the theory of evolution.

You will learn a lot more about Darwin and his theory later in this course and even more in-depth when you study biology. But for now, you need to understand the impact of his work on the progress of science. First, Darwin's ideas were the final development of the Enlightenment. So those who wanted to ignore the authority of Scripture were empowered. They reasoned, if science can explain how we got here without ever referring to a Creator, why should science continue assuming that the Creator exists?

The second impact of Darwin's work was to improve the study of living things dramatically. Now, let me stop here to say that I, as well as many, many other scientists today, think that Darwin's idea of evolution is fundamentally incorrect. Yet, even wrong ideas can help advance science. You see, before the time Darwin published his writings, scientists thought that every type of creature that exists today had existed throughout history. Consider dogs, for example. Up to this time, scientists thought that Great Danes, chihuahuas, and boxers always existed, unchanged through history. That idea is called the **immutability of the species.** But Darwin showed it wasn't true. He had evidence of how living organisms can adapt to changes in their surroundings through a process he called **natural selection.** So over time, an organism would change in its coloring, beak size, body size, and other physical characteristics. That resulted in new versions of old creatures. In our dog example, the original dog breed spread out to different areas of the world and was exposed to various environments. Those in colder climates, for example, would have longer fur because puppies born with short fur wouldn't survive long enough to reproduce. Nature "selected" which features were beneficial. In the same way, breeders would choose the best puppies in a litter that had the features they were looking for, whether it was physical features or even temperaments, and then only allow those to breed. Breeders "selected" which features were beneficial. Over generations, those processes produced the breeds we see today.

FIGURE 1.21
Various Dog Breeds

The first created dog was likely a mutt in its design. As individuals spread to different parts of the world and were exposed to different living conditions, those with physical features that helped them better survive were able to live longer and pass those features on to their puppies. The same thing happened as man selected specific desirable features in domesticated dogs, only allowing individuals with those features to breed.

Another scientist who produced revolutionary work is **Louis Pasteur** [AD 1822–1895]. He came up with experiments that finally destroyed the idea of spontaneous generation once and for all. In a sense, his contemporary—Darwin—was trying to suggest that life came from nonlife, without God. That is technically a type of spontaneous generation, isn't it? But Pasteur demonstrated that life could only originate from other living things.

FIGURE 1.22
Pasteurization Equipment

Pasteur also came up with the process called **pasteurization,** a method to prevent bacteria from spoiling liquids. He used it to keep wine from souring, but today this process is widely used to sterilize milk. Additionally, Pasteur laid the foundation of vaccines.

Gregor Mendel [AD 1822–1884] lived during this time period. An Augustinian monk, he was a devout Christian who devoted much of his life studying reproduction in plants. In fact, the entire field of genetics, which studies how traits are passed on from parent to offspring, is based on his work. He is considered the father of modern genetics.

Science also experienced development in the understanding of electricity and mag-

FIGURE 1.23
Electric Light Bulb

netism. **Michael Faraday** [AD 1791–1867] performed many experiments about electricity, and his ideas are still used today. A devout Christian, Faraday was not ashamed of his faith and would argue with any scientist who tried to refute a belief in God. His faith actually led him to lay the foundations of the work of the next scientist we will highlight, **James Clerk Maxwell** [AD 1831–1879].

Maxwell is considered the founder of modern physics. He worked with Faraday and was interested in Faraday's belief that nature was interconnected at a fundamental level, because he believed nature derived its characteristics from God. So Faraday thought electricity and magnetism were the result of a single process, though he couldn't find evidence for it. Maxwell was able to develop mathematical equations to show Faraday was indeed correct. Electricity and magnetism are both different aspects of the same phenomenon called electromagnetism. This is a great example of what can be accomplished when you allow your science to be guided by a biblical worldview.

The last scientist we'll highlight in this time period is **James Joule** [AD 1818–1889]. He built on Lavoisier's ideas and determined that, like matter, energy cannot be created or destroyed but just changes forms. This is known today as the First Law of Thermodynamics.

ON YOUR OWN

1.8 In this section, you learned about Louis Pasteur, whose experiments dealt a final blow to the idea of spontaneous generation. Today, all scientists agree that spontaneous generation cannot occur. Explain how that fact is a problem for Darwin's idea that life came to be on Earth without God creating it.

MODERN SCIENCE: AD 1900–PRESENT

At the turn of the century from the 1800s to the 1900s, there were scientists who believed that science had discovered almost all there was to discover about nature. By this time, they could chart the planets in their courses, and they knew a lot about stars and visible space. Volumes were written about the microscopic world, and the classification of all known organisms was finally being completed. Thanks to Mendel and others, scientists were understanding the complex process of reproduction, too. Maxwell led the way for electromagnetism to be described. Newton's laws of motion seemed to explain almost every type of motion that could be studied. What else could there possibly be to learn?

Well, in 1900, **Max Planck** [AD 1858–1947] came up with a revolutionary idea. He suggested that in the same way that matter exists in small packets called atoms, energy exists in tiny packets, too. He called these packets quanta. Up to this point, scientists believed that you could give any amount of energy to an object. But Planck proposed that if energy came in packets, you could give 1 packet of energy to an object or 2 packets of energy to an object. But you could not give an object any amount of energy between one and 2 packets. The same way you could not have 1½ atoms, you could not have 1½ packets of energy. Now, Planck had lots of evidence for his idea, and after a long time, it became accepted by the scientific community. The study of this field of science, in fact, is called quantum mechanics.

One of the most famous scientists in the field of quantum mechanics is likely someone you have heard of. **Albert Einstein** [AD 1879–1955] used Planck's idea of little quanta of energy to explain a problem that scientists couldn't figure out. The photoelectric effect couldn't be explained up to this point if he used Newton's laws of motion, but if he used Planck's energy quanta, it could. The photoelectric effect has to do with the release of small parts of the atoms in a substance when light is shone onto it.

FIGURE 1.24
A Young Albert Einstein

To add more evidence to support this effect, **Neils Bohr** [AD 1885–1962] developed a picture of what an atom looks like. It was based on solid mathematics, and it required the assumption that energy comes in small packets. The Bohr Model of the atom revealed many mysteries of what atoms looked like and were made of.

FIGURE 1.25
Bohr Model of a Carbon Atom

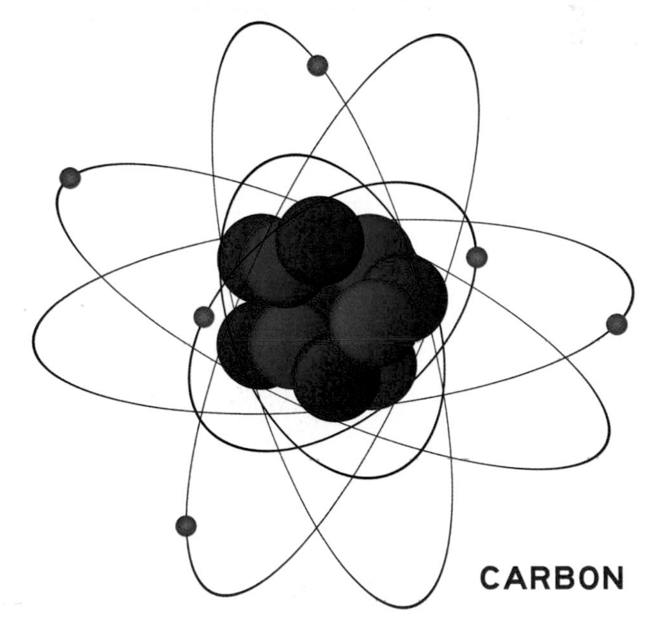

Now, let's jump back to Einstein before we end this module. He is an important figure in many other areas of science. He developed a new way of looking at light, matter, and gravity. His special theory of relativity explained how matter is just another form of energy. Using his now famous equation, $E = mc^2$, he showed how matter could indeed be converted to energy. His general theory of relativity explained how gravity works.

The knowledge gained from quantum mechanics and relativity has led to numerous advances in medicine, technology, and industry. In many ways, they have made life easier for everyone. People live longer today; there are fewer diseases, and there is more food per person today than ever before. Also, we have a clearer picture of how creation works. But don't be like the people at the turn of the century before the 1900s and think we have "figured it all out." Science is constantly uncovering new ideas and new ways of looking at things. That's what makes science so fascinating!

SUMMING UP

Well, we've come to the end of the module. Is your head spinning a little? Well, I wouldn't be surprised. After all, we have traveled through 5,000 years of science history. Why did we do this? You see, when we look at how science has progressed over the centuries, we can learn some lessons, particularly the mistakes that were made. Two major points we learned were written in bold about halfway through the module:

1. **Scientific progress depends not only on scientists, but it also depends on government and culture.**

2. **Science progresses by building on the work of previous scientists.**

I would like to add a third lesson here. We discussed throughout this module how the philosophy of the scientist often affected the work he did. This philosophy has to do with how a person views the natural world or their worldview. It is important to understand the worldview of any scientist, particularly when he takes the data he collects and then makes conclusions from it. We saw that with Darwin. He identified how organisms can change features over time from one generation to another, depending on their living conditions. (A lighter-colored bear cub might live longer than a darker one in a snow-covered environment. Then he would pass those "lighter-colored" features on to his bear cubs when he grows up.) And those observations have been identified as true. But Darwin took those ideas and went a step further to say that those changes could explain how life came to be on Earth without a Creator. There was no evidence for that. It had to do with his worldview and interpretation of the data. So we can say that

3. **The interpretation of scientific data is often dependent on the individual scientist's worldview.**

This is a point you need to understand as you go through any science course in the future. Even this course is taught from a specific worldview.

WHAT TO DO

- ❒ **Answer** study guide questions
- ❒ **Prepare for the exam**
  (review "On Your Own" questions, Student Notebook notes, and completed study guide)
- ❒ **Take exam**

Now it is time to prepare for the exam for this module. On the page following the answers to the "On Your Own" questions, you will find a study guide. This is like a practice test, highlighting all the information that I consider important material from the module. Work through it and try to answer questions (without peeking) about information discussed in the module. Then go back through the module to find the answers for the ones you don't remember. You can check your answers in the *Solutions and Tests Manual*. Once you complete it, you can use the study guide to be just that: a guide for study!

For this module and the next one, you will be instructed to take your exams as open-book exams. That means you will be able to refer to the information in your text for the exam, too. But that is to help you learn how this course works. This is a good way to get you prepared for higher-level work. Test-taking is a skill, and the best way to improve that skill is to work through the process of taking tests, figuring out the best ways you are able to study and learn the material. You are not doing this for a grade so much as you do this to learn the information in the book. And you will be equipping yourself with awesome tools to better your ability to study the world around you and give God glory! After all, the study of the world and its processes is as Johann Kepler says: "Thinking God's thoughts after Him."

ANSWERS TO THE "ON YOUR OWN" QUESTIONS

The blue text is the answer and the black text is further explanation.

1.1 If you look at the definition of science, it contains 2 parts. Science consists of collecting facts, but it also consists of using those facts to explain the world around us. **The Egyptian doctors and the inventors of the ancient world collected lots of facts, but they did not use them to explain the world around them.**

1.2 In the experiment, the lead sinker sank down in the popcorn, and the ping-pong ball floated up. So **the popcorn kernels are more dense than the ping-pong ball and less dense than the lead sinker.**

1.3 Despite the fact that Albert Einstein is brilliant, he can be wrong, just like many other brilliant scientists. There are several examples you could use to show an example of a brilliant scientist who had incorrect ideas **(like the story of Aristotle and his incorrect belief in spontaneous generation). We should therefore not make scientific decisions based on what people believe. Instead, we should make them based on data.**

1.4 There are several reasons scientists should document their work. **Writing it down enables scientists to refer to it later. They are able to share their findings with other scientists in other parts of the world. Their data will be available for future scientists to help them further their understanding of how things work in the world.**

1.5 During this time in history, Christian scholars realized their belief that God created the universe meant He would have set up universal laws for the heavens to follow. God had unchanging laws, so the natural laws should also not change. That meant **the way the natural world worked could be explained if they could discover the natural laws God set in place.**

1.6 Galileo had access to a device that was designed for the military by Hans Lippershey. This tube with 2 lenses magnified distant objects. From that description, Galileo was able to determine how this invention worked, and he made one for himself with the intention of observing the heavens. So **Galileo took another individual's ideas and then improved on them for a different purpose. He might not have come up with his telescope idea if he hadn't had the information from Lippershey. Therefore, science progresses when scientists document their findings and make them available to each other.**

1.7 **Newton would not like such textbooks.** He believed that science had to be linked to math. There was an order to creation, and math helped to explain that order.

1.8 The fact that spontaneous generation has been demonstrated as a nonviable process causes a problem for evolutionary theory. **Evolution relies on the fact that everything in our universe arose without God. So without a Creator, evolutionists have to assume that life comes from nonlife. Yet that is spontaneous generation!**

Sample Lab Write-up for Experiment 1.1:

Experiment 1.1
Density in Nature

Sherri Seligson
1/06/2018

INTRODUCTION

The purpose of this lab is to explore density and how it works in nature. Some materials are denser than others. In this lab, if the 2 objects have different densities and are swirled together in the same container of popcorn, then the less-dense object will not sink as deep as the denser one.

MATERIALS AND PROCEDURE

The canister was filled with popcorn kernels and then the ping-pong ball was buried in the popcorn so that it was just below the popcorn's surface (See Figure 1). Next, the lead sinker was set on top of the popcorn. The canister was vigorously swirled around and around in a circular motion.

FIGURE 1: EXPERIMENT 1.1 SETUP

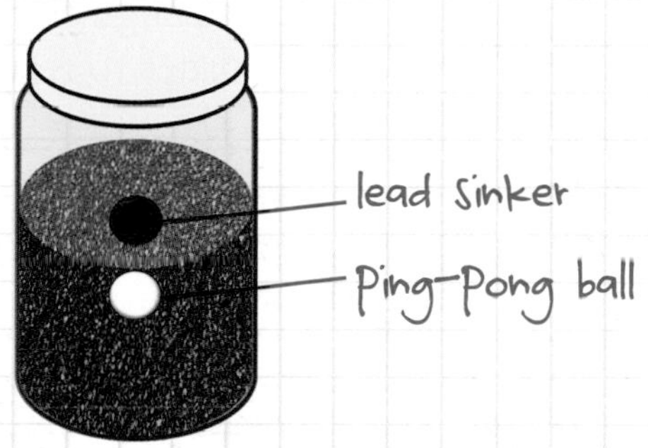

lead sinker
ping-pong ball

RESULTS

When the canister was swirled, the lead sinker started to sink down into the popcorn kernels. The ping-pong ball floated on top. This is because both objects are made up of atoms, and the way the atoms are packed together will determine the characteristics of each object. The lead sinker is denser than the ping-pong ball.

CONCLUSION

When the canister was swirled, the lower-density ping-pong ball floated to the top of the popcorn and the higher-density lead sinker sank into the popcorn. This demonstrates how lower-density materials will always float on top of higher-density materials.

STUDY GUIDE FOR MODULE 1

This guide will help you better understand the key information addressed in the module. It is also exactly what it is titled: a *guide* to help you *study*. Don't worry...it is not graded, but it IS a great way to see how much you remember and review more challenging information. To complete this study guide, first go through the questions and answer them as best you can. You can even make an educated guess. Then, go back through the module to find the answers to any questions you didn't remember. Once it is completed, check your answers with the answer key in the *Solutions and Tests Manual*. Now you have a great source from which to study!

1. Match the following words with their definitions.

   a. Science
   b. Papyrus
   c. Spontaneous generation

   An ancient form of paper, made from a plant of the same name

   The idea that living organisms can be spontaneously formed from nonliving substances

   The systematic study of the natural world through observation and experimentation in order to formulate general laws

2. The Egyptians were not considered scientists, even though they had incredibly advanced medical practices for their time. That is because they used the trial and error method of science. Which of these healing methods did they NOT use on patients?

   a. Egyptian doctors treated open wounds with moldy bread so the wounds would heal quickly (Penicillin created by the mold killed bacteria.)
   b. Patients were painted with mud to heal them from the common cold. (Mud kills bacteria).
   c. Patients who were experiencing pain would be given poppy seeds to eat. (Poppy seeds have morphine and codeine, which are pain-relieving drugs.)

3. What invention helped Egyptian doctors easily document information, transport it to other scholars, and store it for future generations?

   a. horse and carriage
   b. clay tablets
   c. papyrus

4. Scientists often build on one another's ideas. Anaximenes tried to explain all things in nature as being made of a single substance. Leucippus built on that idea and his student, Democritus, took that idea even further. What idea did Leucippus and Democritus propose? (Hint: Think of Democritus on the beach!)
   a. The beach is a relaxing place to do science.
   b. All matter is composed of atoms.
   c. Sand has a higher density than water.

5. True or False: Isaac Newton championed the idea of spontaneous generation and is responsible for it being believed for so long.

For questions 6–9, complete the sentence in your own words:

6. The accounts of Aristotle and Ptolemy teach us that a scientist shouldn't hold onto an idea just because ________________________________ or just because a brilliant scientist believes it.

7. The main goal of the alchemists was to turn lead into ________________.

8. Science began to progress toward the end of the Dark Ages mainly because the ______________ worldview began to replace the Roman worldview.

9. During the Enlightenment, a major change in scientific approach took place. A good change was that science began to stop relying on the authority of ____________________. A bad change was that science began to move away from the authority of ____________________.

Short Answer:

10. Galileo built an instrument out of a tube with 2 lenses, based on descriptions he had heard of a military device. This allowed him to collect a lot more data about the heavens. What did he build? Was he the inventor of this device?

11. Charles Darwin had 2 major impacts on the progress of science when he published his ideas about the origin of species: one negative and one positive. What are they?

12. Louis Pasteur conducted experiments that dealt a final blow to the idea of spontaneous generation, the supposed production of living organisms from nonliving matter. Today, all scientists agree that spontaneous generation cannot

occur. Explain how that fact is a problem for Darwin's idea that life came to be on Earth without God creating it.

13. Yes or no: Does a scientist's beliefs affect the way he interprets data?

SCIENTIFIC INQUIRY AND THE SCIENTIFIC METHOD

Last module, you learned the definition of science. Well, in this module, we'll go further and discuss how science is done. Remember, science is a systematic study. That means when we experiment, we do it in an ordered manner. This study involves observing substances, materials, or processes with keen eyes and then asking questions about what we observe. To answer those questions, we need to design experiments and carefully examine the results so that we can come to reasonable answers.

Quaestio

After some historical context in which we covered the human endeavor of science, we can now start to talk about what science is all about. And a good way to do that is to learn what science is, what it is not, what science can tell us, and what it can't. That way you will have a good foundation of how to approach the study of our world.

FIGURE 2.1
A Scientist Measuring a Very Small Quantity with a Pipette

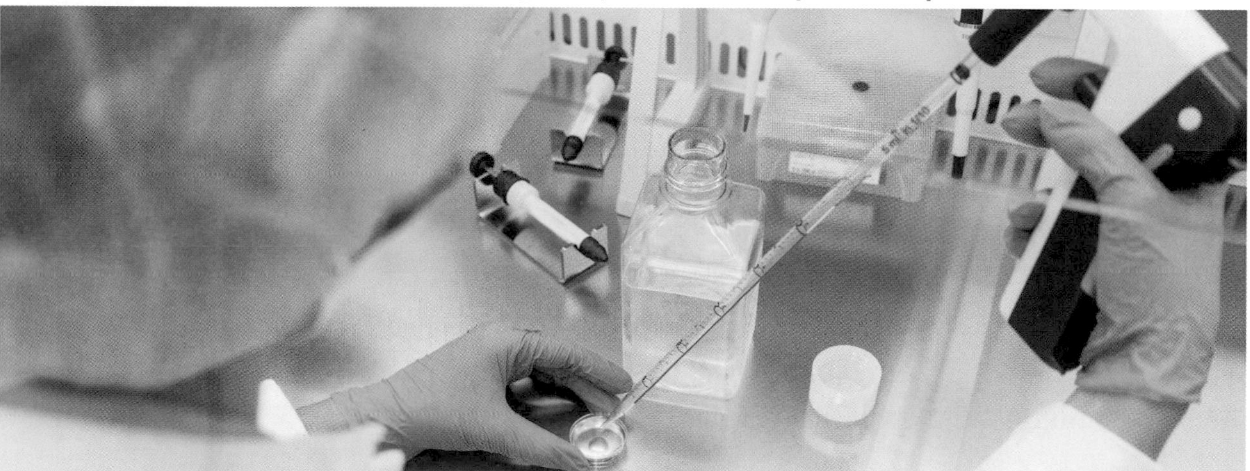

WRONG SCIENCE

It is difficult to quickly explain what science *is*, so I want to start by explaining wrong science. A good way to do that is to do a couple experiments. First, perform Experiment 2.1.

EXPERIMENT 2.1

HOW WEIGHT AFFECTS THE SPEED AT WHICH OBJECTS FALL

PURPOSE: To *prove* that heavy objects fall faster than light objects

MATERIALS:

- A reasonably heavy book
- A sheet of cardboard about the same size as the book (The cardboard that comes on the back of a pad of paper works well. You can also cut a piece out of an old cardboard box.)
- A sheet of heavy paper (like construction paper or card stock) about the same size as the book
- A sheet of regular paper about the same size as the book

QUESTION: What happens when you drop objects that are approximately the same size, but different weights?

HYPOTHESIS: Write what you think will happen when a heavier and lighter object are dropped at the same time.

PROCEDURE:

1. Hold the book in one hand and the cardboard in another. Hold them both at the same height and parallel to the floor.
2. Drop both at the same time.
3. Note in your laboratory notebook which item hits the ground first.
4. Hold the cardboard in one hand and the heavy paper in another. Hold them just as you held the book and cardboard in step 1.
5. Drop both at the same time.
6. Note in your laboratory notebook which item hits the ground first.
7. Do the same thing once again, this time with the heavy paper and the regular paper.
8. Note in your laboratory notebook which item hits the ground first.
9. Keep the materials. You will use them again soon.

CONCLUSION: What can you say about the speed of heavier objects falling as compared to the speed of lighter objects falling?

What happened in the experiment? When you dropped the book and the cardboard, the book should have hit the ground before the cardboard did. When you dropped the cardboard and the heavy paper, the cardboard should have hit the ground first. And when you dropped the heavy paper and the regular paper, the heavy paper should have hit the ground first. What conclusion can be made from those 3 observations? Well, you might say that heavier objects fall faster than lighter objects. That's because the book is the heaviest, then the cardboard, then the heavy paper, and then the regular paper. So when you dropped 2 objects, the heavier one always hit the ground before the lighter one. Does this prove that heavy objects fall faster than light objects? That is what the conclusion might be for this experiment. But don't do a lab write-up for this one, and don't make a final conclusion either. Instead, I want you to do Experiment 2.2.

EXPERIMENT 2.2

MORE ABOUT HOW WEIGHT AFFECTS THE SPEED AT WHICH OBJECTS FALL

PURPOSE: To explore more about the speed at which heavy and light objects fall

MATERIALS:

- All the materials from Experiment 2.1
- A metal paper clip

QUESTION: What happens when you drop objects that are approximately the same size but different weights?

HYPOTHESIS: Write what you think will happen when a heavier and lighter object are dropped at the same time. (You might write the same thing you wrote in Experiment 2.1, but you might also be wondering if there is some extra information you'll be exploring after reading the title of this experiment!)

PROCEDURE:

1. Hold the book in one hand and the paper clip in the other as you did in the previous experiment. Hold them at the same height and drop them simultaneously. Note which hits the ground first.
2. Repeat step 1, this time with the cardboard and the paper clip. Record what happened.
3. Repeat step 1, this time with the heavy paper and the paper clip. Record what happened.
4. Repeat step 1, this time with the regular paper and the paper clip. Record what happened.
5. Wad up the regular paper into a tight, little ball.
6. Repeat step 1, this time using the book and the wadded-up ball of paper. Record what happened.
7. Repeat step 1, this time using the cardboard and the wadded-up ball of paper. Record what happened.
8. Repeat step 1, this time using the heavy paper and the wadded-up ball of paper. Record what happened.

CONCLUSION: What can you say about the speed of heavier objects falling as compared to the speed of lighter objects falling?

WHAT TO DO

You will not have to do a lab write-up for these first 2 experiments, but you should do one lab write-up per module. You still need to *perform* all the experiments in this course, and complete the lab report forms in the lab section of your notebook. On the lab report form you will need to record the data you collect. Additionally, it is a good idea to include a few sentences in the conclusion section of the lab report form in order to sum up what you learned.

Let's discuss what happened in Experiment 2.2. You should have observed that the book and the paper clip hit the ground at about the same time. In other trials using the paper clip, the paper clip probably hit the ground first. However, in steps 6–8, the same paper that hit the ground last in every trial of this and the previous experiment probably hit the ground first, with the exception of step 6, when it was dropped with the book. In that step, the wadded-up ball of paper might have hit the ground at the same time as or just slightly later than the book.

So what does all this mean? Well, the new data from Experiment 2.2 reveal that what we might have believed after Experiment 2.1 was incorrect. Without this new information, we would have come up with a wrong conclusion that heavier things fall faster than lighter things. Think about the new trials with the paper clip. The paper clip was lighter than the cardboard and the heavy paper, but it fell faster than both of those objects. In the trials with the wadded-up ball of paper, notice that the same paper that took the longest time to fall in Experiment 2.1 suddenly fell faster than the cardboard and the heavy paper when it was wadded up into a ball. So heavy objects do not necessarily fall faster than light objects.

You might also realize that the shape of an object affects how it falls. The regular paper fell more slowly when it was a flat sheet as compared to how it fell when it was wadded up, didn't it?

SYSTEMATIC EXPERIMENTS

Systematic experiments like Experiments 2.1 and 2.2 help us to better understand how our world works. Galileo was the first to perform these kinds of experiments, and based on his work and the work of others, we know that there is something called **air resistance**. Air resistance is something that affects falling objects, and it pretty much is what its name tells you. It is a result of air slowing down, or resisting, the movement of objects as they move through it. There are many factors that affect how strongly air resistance slows an object down, but the shape of an object is one of them. Think about the shape of airplanes moving through the sky. They are streamlined with a smooth surface so they minimize air resistance. Imagine how an airplane would fly through the air if it was shaped like a box!

Scientists actually have determined that if you eliminate air resistance, all objects fall at the same rate, regardless of weight, shape, or any other characteristic. This is an important statement, and whenever I want you to really remember something, it will be written in bold blue type.

In the absence of air, ALL objects, regardless of weight or shape, fall at the same rate.

We were not able to exhaust all the experimental trials to come up with this statement, but you just need to know that many other experiments have been performed to come to this conclusion.

For Experiments 2.1 and 2.2, you really cannot use the bold sentence above as a conclusion. Remember, *you* cannot say ALL objects behave this way because you didn't test all objects, and you didn't study the process with enough materials to come up with a generalized statement like that. (After all, think of what a helium balloon would do if you dropped it!) So what you *can* say is that **the shape of an object has an effect on how it falls through the air**.

FIGURE 2.2
Skydivers

Skydivers will fall with their arms and legs spread out in order to increase how much of their body is exposed to the air they are falling through. That increases their air resistance, and they will fall more slowly.

FIGURE 2.3
Archer with a Compound Bow

Archers use arrows that are streamlined and pointed to reduce air resistance.

WHAT SCIENCE CANNOT DO

So what does this have to do with wrong science? Well, after Experiment 2.1, we might have thought we had *proved* that heavy objects fall faster than light objects. Several trials created data that seemed to support that statement. And it kind of made sense to think that heavier objects would fall faster, didn't it?

We had an experiment to back up our conclusion, but even though the conclusion made sense, it was shown to be wrong in the second experiment. This brings us to a very important point:

Science is NOT a means by which something can be proved.

That might surprise you. But no matter what you might hear or read, true science cannot ever prove anything. People (and even some scientists) may make statements that start with "Science has proved…," but it is completely wrong. One of the reasons we are beginning this course with the history of science and scientific inquiry is because we all need to understand that scientific conclusions are *continually* being changed based on new information.

Think of what you learned about Ptolemy. He had a very good explanation for the arrangement of the planets and stars in the sky. Other scientists even had observations and experiments to back up his view. But it turned out that Ptolemy was wrong. This happens in science all the time. Even ideas that scientists thought were true just 20 years ago are being changed or discarded due to new data.

EXPLORE MORE

The idea of science not being able to prove anything is something that may be difficult to believe. But try this activity. Collect a basketful of small items in your house. (Make sure they are unbreakable and are items you are allowed to use.) You can include things like a pencil, bottle cap, stuffed animal, hairbrush, socks, a small toy, and a tennis ball. Get a helium balloon, too, and store it out of sight. Now ask someone who is not taking this course to help you. You want your helper to watch you drop those collected items one at a time in front of you (preferably on a carpeted floor or outside), but don't let the helper see the helium balloon yet. Then ask your helper if this activity you just did proves that all things will fall to the ground if you drop them. If your helper agrees, then pull out the balloon and ask what will happen if you let go of it. Talk about how this additional information might alter your helper's previous conclusion.

Scientific Conclusions

What all this really means is that all conclusions that scientists draw are not permanently settled. It only takes one experiment to destroy a conclusion based on years and years of careful scientific investigation. Read through the previous Explore More if you haven't yet. You could continue the first part of that exercise and continue to drop more and more items to the ground. You could ask other students around the globe to do the same thing at their houses and send you their data. But even with all these data, one little helium

FIGURE 2.4
Helium Balloon

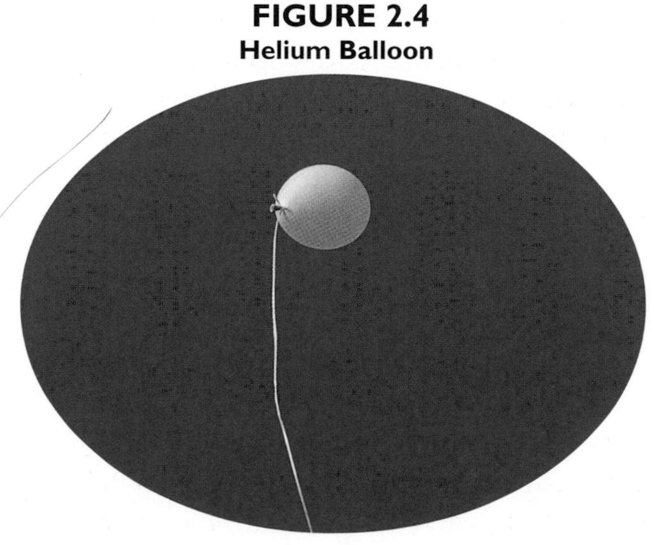

balloon can change everything. In science, that helium balloon is called a **counter example.**

Counter example—An example that contradicts a conclusion

A single counter example can destroy a conclusion built on thousands of years of scientific work!

Counter examples played a part in the recent debate over whether large carnivorous dinosaurs, such as *Tyrannosaurus* and *Gigantosaurus*, were pack hunters. It was long assumed that these large carnivores hunted their food alone and lived isolated lives. But the discovery of these dinosaur fossils and others in Argentina suggested that these carnivores only had very large animals on which to prey. So hunting in packs was a likelihood. How else could large prey be hunted?

Another discovery in the badlands of western Canada added support to this new idea. Twelve individual *Tyrannosaurus* fossils from juveniles to adults were discovered together in a way that suggested they lived as a pack. These 2 counter examples lead scientists today to believe that large carnivorous dinosaurs were more likely pack hunters than isolated hunters.

If you are now thinking that science is not very useful, then let me encourage you to think a bit deeper. When the correct method of science is followed, science can be used to draw conclusions that are reasonably reliable. And those conclusions will hopefully help us better understand the way creation works. Then we can use those conclusions to better our world, like developing new medical procedures or building hospital equipment that can save people's lives. We just need to remember that no matter how reliable we think the conclusions of science are, *they are never permanently settled.*

FIGURE 2.5
***Tyrannosaurus* Skeleton**

This toothy grin with the pointed teeth gives scientists clues to suggest this dinosaur was carnivorous.

ON YOUR OWN

2.1 Explain one way a scientific theory developed by an intelligent scientist might be shown to be fundamentally incorrect.

THE SCIENTIFIC METHOD

I ended the previous section by summarizing that with the correct method, science can draw conclusions that are reasonably reliable. To scientifically investigate the wonders of creation, we need to not only carefully observe matter, but also ask probing questions about it. Then, with detailed precision, we need to conduct experiments and examine the results, looking for sensible answers to our questions. The **scientific method** provides a framework in which scientists can analyze situations, explain certain phenomena, and answer specific questions in an ordered way. You will not be able to be completely certain of the conclusions you draw from this method, but your conclusions will be more reliable than most other conclusions. Therefore, even though science cannot *prove* something, it does give us the best way to draw conclusions about creation.

FIGURE 2.6
Students Performing an Experiment

The scientific method is a systematic way to collect and pursue scientific knowledge. It is a problem-solving approach that begins by making an **observation** and asking a question. Say, for example, you come home with your parents one night and turn on the light switch, but the living room light does not work. You have made an observation. The question you might ask is "Why didn't the light switch cause the living room light to work?" Next, **background research** needs to be done to gather information about the question. So you look outside and see the neighbor's house lights working. You also go to the kitchen, turn on that light switch, and notice that the kitchen light turns on. Now you can form a **hypothesis.**

Hypothesis—An educated guess that attempts to explain an observation or answer a question

Now, a hypothesis is a *testable* explanation. It has to be something you can further explore via experimentation. For example, an explanation such as—*The living room lamp is not working because it wants me to stub my toe*—is not a testable statement. (It is not a rational one, either!) However, you might hypothesize that the light bulb in the living room lamp is broken. Often, a hypothesis is written in an If/Then format. You might hypothesize, then: "*If* I change the light bulb, *then* the lamp will work."

The next step in the scientific method is testing your hypothesis with **experimentation.** Experimentation is methodically testing hypotheses (the plural of hypothesis). So you might go to the cupboard, get a new light bulb, and replace the one in the lamp.

Let's say when you replace the bulb, the lamp works when you turn on the switch. The working lamp would be the **result** of your test. You can then draw a **conclusion** that your hypothesis was correct and report that information to your parents, and they will know they need to purchase a new light bulb to replace the one you used from the cupboard.

However, what if the light bulb did *not* work when you replaced it? That means your result did not agree with your hypothesis, right? If your hypothesis is false, then you need to go back to the "construct hypothesis" step and come up with a new hypothesis. You know that the neighborhood is receiving electricity because of your background research revealing that the neighbor's house has working lights. You also know your kitchen light works. Perhaps the living room lamp is not getting electricity…maybe the cord is not plugged in to an outlet. Your new hypothesis would be: "If I plug the lamp into the wall, then the light will work." You can test that new hypothesis by checking the lamp cord and plugging it in, thus going through the whole scientific method procedure again. This process of the scientific method is summed up in Figure 2.7.

FIGURE 2.7
The Scientific Method

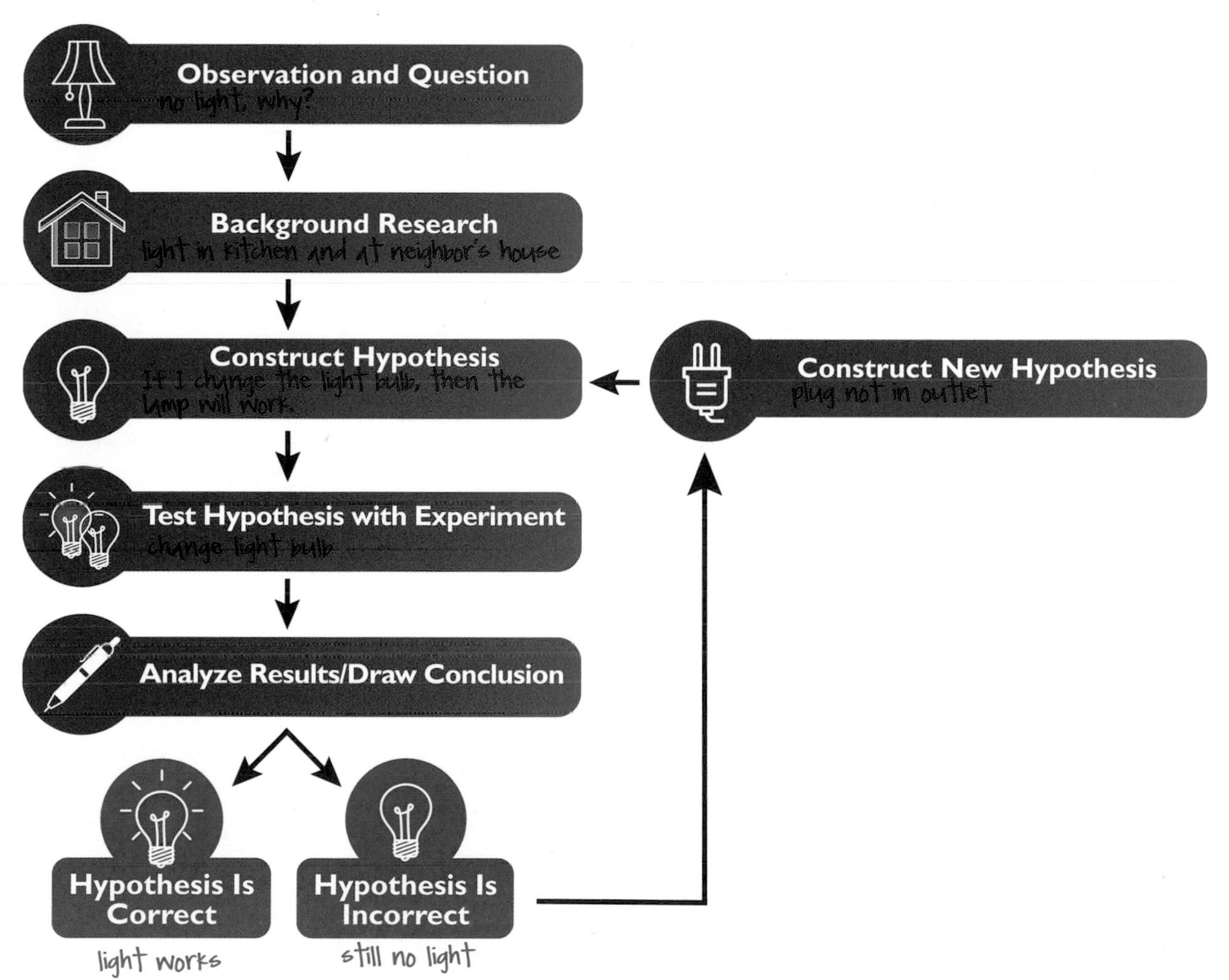

The scientific method gives us an ordered way to go through the process of observation and creation of a question, gathering information about that observation, creating a hypothesis, and testing it. That way, we can discover if our hypothesis is true or not. If it is not true, then a new hypothesis can be formed and tested in hopes of finding an answer to the original question.

Get some practice using the scientific method by performing Experiment 2.3.

EXPERIMENT 2.3
SURFACE TENSION OF WATER

PURPOSE: To explore how soap affects the surface tension of water

MATERIALS:
- A drinking glass
- A small glass
- Water
- An eyedropper
- Some paper towels
- A penny
- Liquid soap

QUESTION: What happens when you add drops of water to a dry penny as compared to a soapy penny?

HYPOTHESIS: Write what you think will happen if you add drops of water on top of a soapy penny.

PROCEDURE:
1. Wash the penny with water and dry it using the paper towel.
2. Fill the drinking glass with water.
3. Place the penny on the kitchen counter or a water-safe surface.
4. Using the eyedropper, add one drop of water at a time to the surface of the penny, making sure to keep track of the number of drops you are adding.
5. Continue adding drops of water and counting them until any amount of water spills onto the counter. Record in your notebook the number of drops you added at that point.
6. Dry the penny and repeat steps 4 and 5 two more times. Record the total number of drops you added each time.
7. Place some liquid soap in the small glass and add enough water to make it a thinner consistency. You may want to gently stir it so it is well mixed.
8. Dip the penny in the soapy water and place it back on the counter. Do not dry it.
9. Now repeat steps 4 and 5 three times, recording the total number of drops you added to the penny each time. Dip the penny into the soapy water before each trial.

CONCLUSION: Write in your notebook if your hypothesis is correct.

What happened in the experiment? If everything worked well, you should have noticed that **the dry penny was able to hold many more drops of water as compared to the soapy penny.** Water has a unique property called **surface tension.** Surface tension has to do with the tendency of individual water molecules to stay together. That **made the water form a large mound on top of the dry penny as you added more and more drops.** Eventually the weight of the water became greater than the force holding the water molecules together, and the water spilled off of the penny.

FIGURE 2.8
Water Strider

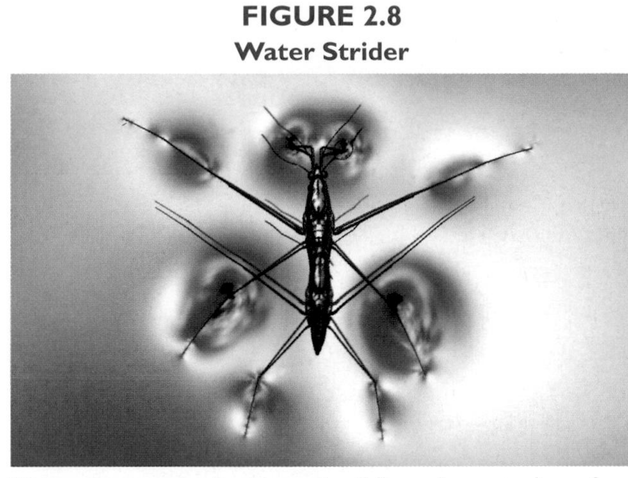

This water strider is able to "walk" on the water's surface because of surface tension.

When you added drops of water to the soapy penny, you should have noticed that it could not hold as many drops before spilling off. That is because **soap has an effect on the surface tension of water, breaking the individual water molecules apart.**

Don't worry if your hypothesis was incorrect. That doesn't mean you will get a poor grade on your experiment. It also doesn't mean you are a bad scientist. Incorrect hypotheses direct scientists in the proper direction as they explore a question or a phenomenon. It lets us know what doesn't work and helps us to look in the right direction for an answer to our question.

WHAT TO DO

❒ **Create a lab report**

Go ahead and do a lab report for this experiment, following the instructions I gave you in Module 1 and using the information highlighted in orange in the experiment and the paragraphs following it (but use your own words!). Remember, there will be 4 sections: Introduction (which includes your hypothesis), Materials/Procedure, Results, and Conclusion. If your hypothesis was incorrect, add a sentence to explain why in your conclusion paragraph. One more thing. This experiment required you to do 3 trials on the dry penny and 3 on the soapy penny. Why do you think you did that? Well, one reason is that each drop of water does not contain exactly the same amount of material. By doing the same activity 3 times, you are able to get a better idea of what is going on, and you minimize any mistakes you might make (like adding smaller drops one time versus larger drops another time). In your lab report, place the data you recorded in a table for the results section. Your table might look something like this:

Drops of Water on Dry and Soapy Pennies

	Dry Penny	Soapy Penny
Trial 1	15 drops	9 drops
Trial 2	18 drops	8 drops
Trial 3	21 drops	10 drops

In the next module, we will go over more detailed ways to record *data* for a lab write-up, but for now, this format will work.

A RECAP OF THE SCIENTIFIC METHOD

Let me now sum up the scientific method. First, a scientist makes an observation and from that will ask a question (refer to Figure 2.7 again). The next step is to gather information about that observation. The scientist then will develop a hypothesis, stating what he or she thinks will happen in a given situation (often in an If/Then format). A scientist will devise a series of experiments to test that hypothesis and collect data to analyze in order to determine if the hypothesis is correct. If the data do not support the hypothesis, the question is asked again, more information is gathered, and a different hypothesis is tested. If the hypothesis *is* correct, a conclusion can be made from the data.

But it doesn't stop there. If a hypothesis is supported by data, then more experiments must be performed in several labs by several scientists, producing a *large* amount of supporting data. At that point, the hypothesis becomes a **scientific theory.**

Scientific theory—An explanation of the natural world that has been thoroughly tested and is supported by a significant amount of evidence

The greater amount of supporting data from both observation and experimentation means that a theory is much more reliable than a hypothesis. And it involves an explanation of why the phenomenon occurs. But we can go even further. As more and more data relevant to the theory get collected, the theory can be tested again and again. If new observations or interpretations come up that cannot be explained by the theory, it can be altered or rejected.

Now, unlike a scientific theory, a **scientific law** describes a natural phenomenon but doesn't *explain* what causes it or why it exists.

Scientific law—A description of a natural phenomenon or principle that is supported by a significant amount of evidence and often includes mathematical terms

A scientific theory and a scientific law are both supported by a vast amount of evidence, often from years and years of observations and experimentation. Some think that a scientific theory can become a scientific law, but that is not the case. Remember laws do not explain why a phenomenon exists or what causes it. As a matter of fact, laws often come *before* theories in science because it is often easier to describe a phenomenon instead of explaining how it happens.

Wrapping up, then, you have learned that the scientific method gives us a methodical way to examine a situation or answer a question. Yet you still need to remember that the conclusions of science are tentative. It only takes a single counter example to destroy a scientific law or theory, and the history of science is filled with such occurrences.

ON YOUR OWN

In the mid-1800s, a Hungarian doctor named Ignaz Semmelweis used the scientific method to determine that there was something unseen but deadly that could be carried from one person in the hospital to another. He noticed that in his hospital ward, patients were dying at a rate exceeding that of many other wards, even wards that had sicker patients. He observed the hospital around him for a while and realized that the only noticeable difference was that his ward was the first one the doctors visited after they performed autopsies on the dead. From his observations, Semmelweis suggested that the doctors were carrying something deadly from the corpses to the patients in his ward. To test this suggestion, he instituted a rule that all doctors had to thoroughly wash their hands after they finished their autopsies and before they examined the patients in his ward.

Up to that time, doctors never washed their hands at all during their work! But after the doctors began obeying Semmelweis' orders, the death rate in his ward decreased to the point that it became the lowest in the hospital! At one point, the doctors complained about having to wash their hands, and when they stopped, the death rate rose again. So handwashing was re-instituted.

FIGURE 2.9
Surgeon Washing Hands

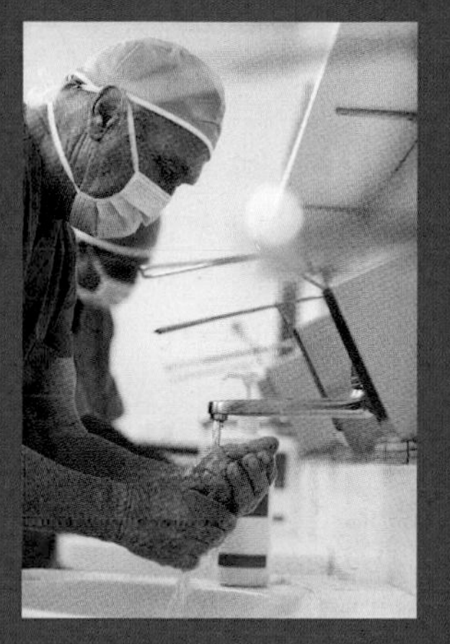

Today, all doctors are very careful to wash their hands before seeing patients so as not to spread germs and disease.

2.2 In this account, what was the observation that led to a hypothesis? What background research was collected?

2.3 What was the hypothesis (write it in an If/Then format)?

2.4 What was the experiment to confirm the hypothesis?

2.5 At the end of the account above, was the presence of something unseen but deadly that could be carried from one person to another considered to be a scientific law?

creation connection

In this section's "On Your Own" account, you learned from Semmelweis' hypothesis that there was something unseen but deadly that was being passed among hospital patients. After other scientists learned of his experiments, they began doing tests on their own and collected much more data to support his hypothesis. Once Antoni van Leeuwenhoek's microscope became a common tool in medical science, doctors were finally able to see that it was deadly germs which were being transmitted from person to person. They performed experiments showing germs infecting and harming healthy tissue, and after years of further experimentation by Semmelweis and others, Semmelweis' theory became a scientific law. But it is fascinating to note that the Old Testament already addressed this issue. It contains meticulous instructions concerning how a priest is to cleanse himself after touching a dead body. These cleansing rituals are some of the most effective means of sterilization before modern practices. Yet the people living during the time the Old Testament was written did not know anything about germs. Well, this shouldn't be a surprise. After all, God knows about germs. So it makes sense that He would lay down instructions as to how His people should protect themselves against them.

DOES THE SCIENTIFIC METHOD ALWAYS PROVE TRUE?

Although the scientific method allows us to draw reasonably accurate conclusions about the world around us, those conclusions are not ironclad. In fact, there have been many examples of how the scientific method has been used to reach conclusions that are completely wrong.

FIGURE 2.10
Valles Marineris Canyon on Mars

The large Valles Marineris Canyon on Mars is almost 4 times the length and 200 times the width of the Grand Canyon on Earth. Scientists are not sure what caused it, but it is definitely not the result of water distribution by living beings on the planet.

The Story of Lowell

One such example occurred in the late 1800s when Italian scientist Giovanni Schiaparelli used a powerful (for its time) telescope to observe the surface of the planet Mars. He noticed several faint lines that seemed to crisscross about the planet. When he published his observations, he said that those lines might be natural or they might be the work of intelligent beings, but he wasn't sure which one was true. Upon seeing Schiaparelli's drawings, American scientist Percival Lowell hypothesized that the lines were actually canals that had been dug by the inhabitants of Mars. He believed that the purpose of the canals was for water distribution. Lowell built an observatory in Arizona to make detailed observations of Mars in order to confirm his hypothesis.

In the early 1900s, Lowell published the results of his observations, providing what he thought was clear and convincing evidence that those lines first observed by Schiaparelli were, indeed, canals built by intelligent beings. The canals changed positions occasionally, and he believed this to be evidence that the canals were for water distribution. He even had what he thought was extra support for this idea.

He noticed that there were blue-green areas on the planet, and their shapes and locations would change from time to time. He assumed these areas were patches of vegetation and that the changing water distribution of the canals (as well as perhaps the changing seasons on Mars) changed where the vegetation flourished and died out.

FIGURE 2.11
Percival Lowell in His Observatory

What Other Scientists Thought

Lowell's work was enthusiastically received by many in the scientific community, and other scientists made observations of Mars that seemed to support Lowell's idea that there were canals, vegetation, and intelligent life on Mars. Some even speculated that the inhabitants of Mars must be incredibly advanced to make a planet-wide network of canals that could be opened and closed based on need. Using that assumption, some actually proposed that the 2 moons orbiting Mars were, in fact, not natural. Instead, these scientists believed that the moons were constructed by the inhabitants of Mars. A few even believed that they were some sort of attack vessels and that the inhabitants of Mars would invade Earth one day!

EXPLORE MORE

Lowell built an observatory in Arizona to make his observations of Mars. Telescopes are devices that help scientists see distant objects much more closely. Build your own refracting telescope by gathering these materials: a desk lamp, red construction paper, marker, scissors, tape, and 2 magnifying glasses. Trace the area of your lamp (where the light comes out) on to the red paper and cut out the shape. Next, carefully cut a triangle shape from the middle of the red paper cutout. Affix the red paper cutout with the triangle in the center to the lamp opening, using tape so it blocks the light. (You may need 2 circles of red paper to make it stiff enough to block the light.) Now turn on the lamp and set it up so it shines onto a nearby wall. Place one magnifying glass between the lamp and the wall so the light passes through it. Observe the image on the wall. Now, get a helper to hold the second magnifying glass behind the first and move it slowly along the length of the beam of light until the triangle image appears on the wall. What is happening is that a telescope makes distant objects appear larger by bending the light before it enters our eyes. The light rays coming from a distant object change direction as they move through the lens and again as they leave the lens. The second moving magnifying glass behaves as an eyepiece to bring the magnified image into focus.

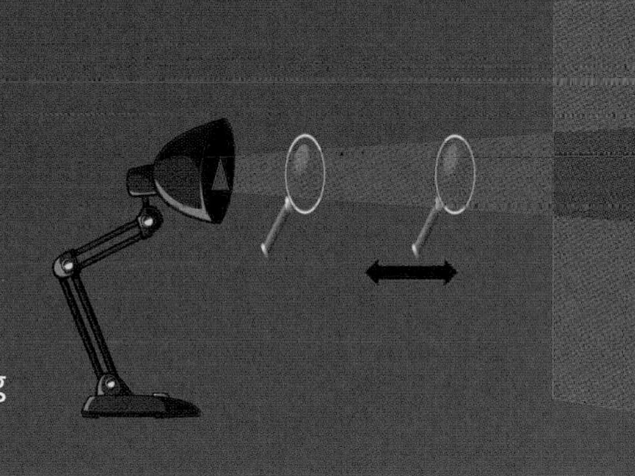

At this point in the scientific method, Lowell's original hypothesis could be considered a theory. Lowell had formed a hypothesis, based on Schiaparelli's observation (canals exist on Mars). He then designed experiments to test his hypothesis (build an observatory and observe Mars in detail). The results of his experiments confirmed his hypothesis. In addition, other scientists had made observations that seemed to support his hypothesis. Thus, the hypothesis could be designated as a theory.

What New Information Revealed

However…as time went on and more powerful telescopes were built, the theory of canals on Mars began to disintegrate. Scientists found that many of the "canals" Lowell and other scientists observed with their telescopes could not be consistently observed by others. Eventually, it was determined that many of them were really optical illusions caused by the poor optics of the telescopes that Lowell and others had used, along with eye fatigue from long hours of observation through a telescope. In fact, even the changing blue-green areas that Lowell and others saw were simply collections of dust that were blown about by regularly occurring windstorms on the planet.

Many robotic spacecraft have since been sent to Mars, and at the time of the writing of this course, the NASA Curiosity rover is moving around the planet, collecting valuable data about the conditions on that planet. The rover carries 3 specialized cameras, spectrometers to analyze sample materials, radiation detectors, and environmental sensors. So far, there has not been any evidence collected to indicate that there was once life on Mars. No dug-out canals have been found, either. In fact, we could say that Mars is the only planet that is completely and exclusively populated by robots (human-made robots, of course)!

FIGURE 2.12
Radiation Assessment Device Deployed on Mars by the NASA Curiosity Rover

You can see that following the scientific method does not guarantee that the conclusions drawn are accurate. Lowell and those who believed as he did followed the scientific method exactly. Yet, their conclusions were wrong. And this can happen in modern science as well.

Now, Lowell was not a bad scientist. In fact, he made many positive contributions to the pursuit of science, including postulating the existence of the dwarf planet, Pluto.

In the end you need to realize that science is not a worthless effort. It is a *valuable* way to learn an enormous amount about the world around us. The use of the scientific method has resulted in longer life spans for people, more productivity for industries, and new inventions like automobiles and airplanes.

So, although the conclusions of science are not always settled, science is a *very* worthwhile endeavor!

ON YOUR OWN

2.6 Lowell's observations of Mars were used to support a theory that has been demonstrated to be false. Are those observations therefore worthless?

THE LIMITATIONS AND MISUSES OF SCIENCE

Science is an interesting and useful pursuit! The process of science has helped us **understand an enormous amount about the world around us.** It also has led to the **development of incredibly useful inventions.** So, even though it has its limits, science has done a lot to make our lives better. As a result, it is important to understand what science can do.

Limitations of Science

However, now that you have seen some instances in which the scientific method failed to produce reliable conclusions, it seems only natural to discuss the limitations of science and misuses of it. First, we need to revisit the statement I made earlier that **science cannot *prove* anything.** It can provide evidence that a certain idea is true, but it *cannot* prove the idea. **Science is also not 100% settled.** Remember from Module 1 that the history of science showed us that scientific theories and laws can be overthrown as the result of new information and ideas. Even a single counter example can demonstrate a theory to be incorrect. And, finally, **science must conform to the scientific method.** That keeps scientists from adding their prejudices to an idea.

You see, scientific knowledge is not a collection of **subjective** opinions—it is not based on an individual's personal evaluation. Rather, it is an **objective** collection of explanations about our world based on observed or predicted phenomena. "Objective" means that a scientist tries to make explanations while trying not to be swayed by personal ideas. And those explanations must be repeatedly verified in order to confirm that it correctly models what we see in the world. With advances in technology, such as improved telescope design, we are able to increase the quality of our observations. That improved data will challenge our explanations, sometimes causing us to alter them so that the newly observed facts are taken into consideration. Then new theories can be formed and further tested.

FIGURE 2.13
NASA's James Webb Space Telescope

The James Webb Space Telescope is the most powerful space telescope ever built and is in the process of going through extreme conditions to test that it is ready to operate when it is sent out into space. This device will help scientists to collect more accurate, objective data.

We can say that while our scientific knowledge changes regularly with more observations and new data, the absolute reality that is being modeled (such as what exactly is on Mars) has not changed. **Scientific method helps us to discover the truth.** No matter what we believed *was* on Mars, what really was there did not change. And eventually, scientists were able to learn what was truly there.

The scientific method can be applied to questions based on what is happening in the world today and even what has happened to the world in the past. For example, we will spend some time in a future module discussing fossils and rocks. We'll cover the different ways they form and, by studying fossils and rocks that are here now, you can learn a lot about what happened in Earth's past. With proper application of the scientific method, we can use science to attempt to answer virtually any question.

Misuse of Science

A misuse of science involves **extending claims into fields that have not been experimentally tested.** In other words, some principles that have been explained are then incorrectly applied to *all* areas of science even though they have not been tested in those areas. What does that mean? Well, it means there is a danger that scientists will start to lay down principles as being universally true, even if the evidence has been tested for only one scientific area.

Further, as you learned in Module 1, **just because a very intelligent and esteemed scientist suggests an idea, it is not automatically truth.**

People need to be humble about what is known and stop **assuming that science knows more than it actually does.** As scientists, we need to make sure we don't make generalizations farther than the facts we are observing. This tendency happens because of pride. We need to have a position of humility and awe at the created universe as we explore its complexities.

A good example of this is when theoretical physicist Dr. Lawrence Krauss and others claimed as a scientific fact that the universe originated from a quantum fluctuation in nothingness. They explained that a quantum fluctuation is the temporary appearance of energetic particles out of empty space. However, no one has ever observed a fluctuation like that. How can a quantum fluctuation be verified or falsified, then? This idea has to be considered **speculation** because it cannot be tested and has never been observed. Therefore, it cannot be asserted as scientific fact.[1]

EXPLORE MORE

There *are* ways to test phenomena we cannot see. Take a balloon and blow it up to a size that still can be held in your hand. Tie it off. With a hole punch, punch a bunch of holes in a sheet of paper, collecting the small bits of paper into a pile. Now, rapidly rub the balloon back and forth over your hair (this works better if your hair is recently washed). Now hold the balloon up to the paper pieces and watch them move around. They may even jump to the balloon and stick to it! What is happening is that you are taking electrons from your hair and moving them to the balloon. Electrons are negatively charged pieces of atoms (the building blocks of all material). We can't see them, *but we can see how they behave.* By creating an electrical charge with all those extra electrons, the balloon attracts some of the paper pieces to itself.

Weather predictions are a way we test phenomena we cannot see. As you will learn in a future module, much of our daily weather is affected by pressure changes. We can't see changes in pressure, but we can measure them with equipment. This allows scientists to predict the upcoming weather. You may have noticed that the predictions are not always accurate, but they are improving as our technology improves.

ON YOUR OWN

2.7 This section was titled The Limitations and Misuses of Science. For this "On Your Own" question, you will be summarizing what you learned. Make a list with 3 columns: What Science Can Do, The Limitations of Science, and The Misuses of Science. The sentences written in orange are key points that were reviewed or introduced. Place them in the appropriate columns. That way you will be better able to study from the information in this section.

SCIENCE AND CHRISTIANITY

Today, science is held in high regard. To emphasize a statement, reporters and writers will often quote scientists in order to add credibility. However, even though people are interested in what scientists have to say about things, many scientists are also stating that religion has no place in science. In fact, many people think it is impossible to be both a Christian and a true scientist.

However, we as Christians *should* seek explanations for the things we see in the world today in naturalistic terms because this agrees with the biblical revelation of God as a God of order. The scripture 1 Corinthians 14:33 says, "For God is not a God of confusion but of peace." In the previous module, you learned about several scientists who held a Christian worldview. They pursued science in order to learn more about the One who created all things. It is because God exists that science is possible. The reason the universe is orderly and logical is because a logical God has imposed order on His creation.

FIGURE 2.14
The Bible

In fact, we can approach science in 2 ways. **Operational science** uses observable, repeatable experiments to try to discover truth. **Historical science** relies on relics from the past and historical records to try to discover truth. These 2 types of scientific research enable us to apply science to things we can observe as well as things that happened long ago, such as the age of Earth or how life originated on Earth.

think about this

A good way to think about the 2 ways we can approach science is to imagine that you are visiting a city with a friend. You point to a statue and ask your friend to tell you about it. The friend starts to describe the statue by considering its physical information. He climbs to the top of the statue to measure its height using a long tape measure and reports the statue is 305 ft high. He then places the statue on a scale and tells you it weighs 450,000 lb. Next, he observes it inside and out and tells you it is made of copper on the outside but supported by an internal structure of cast iron and stainless steel on the inside.

But you want to know more. You ask how old the statue is and who made it. Well, your friend cannot tell you that by taking measurements, so he turns to recorded history. He goes to the local library and comes back to report about the entire history of this famous 130-year-old statue—designed by Frederic Bartholdi and built by Gustave Eiffel—known as the Statue of Liberty.

Gathering Information for Science

In the imaginary scenario of Think About This, notice how some information about a subject can be gathered by examining things with your senses, like the height and weight of a structure. These things can be measured by many people so that the data are repeatable and confirmable. This is operational science.

FIGURE 2.15
The Grand Canyon

The Grand Canyon allows scientists to observe the results of what happened in the past. That helps them to make educated assumptions about how it formed.

However, some information needs to be gathered by examining historical data, which are a primary source of information. Scientists can also make educated assumptions about the past by examining evidence we can see today. This is historical science. We must be careful when we use historical science. That is because assumptions are only educated guesses. In the Think About This example, if your friend did not have access to any records for the Statue of Liberty, he could do some extra research on the composition of the sculpture, study its style, and then make an educated guess as to the date it might have been created, based on when other similar art styles and construction methods were popular. So, indeed, we can use science to study things we do not observe happening today.

Analyzing Information for Science

No matter how the data are gathered, dependable scientific research involves analyzing the data scientists collect. The challenge here is *how* the data are analyzed. You see, to evaluate information, a person approaches that information from a specific worldview. If the scientific method is followed correctly, all scientists study and analyze collected data. Different conclusions come from interpreting data through the lens of what they believe about the world.

Christians believe that the God of the Bible upholds the universe in a particular way so that we can study it by observational and repeatable experimentation. He created universal laws which the universe must obey. A secular worldview comes from the idea that all matter originated by chance from nothing, and there is no cause or reason for anything that happens.

So the confusion caused by different data interpretation is not science versus religion.

It is really worldview versus worldview. And science is the battleground. Some scientists even go so far as to assert that evolutionary humanism, or the idea that all matter originated by chance via the process of evolution (something we'll discuss in a later module), is true science and science cannot be performed unless it is done from the vantage point of this worldview.

A belief in Christianity and the Bible as well as a belief in all matter originating by chance from nothing are both *beliefs*. They are both worldviews. It would seem that the secular scientist would believe that nothing but chance directs the energy that drives the universe. And that would lead to a belief that all processes are natural processes that can be understood by a mathematical equation. The Christian who is a scientist ultimately believes that God's power keeps the laws of nature consistent.

You have seen how many of the greatest scientists were Bible-believing Christians whose worldview motivated their pursuit of science. That shows that a secular view is not necessary for performing science, right? Indeed, science can (and should) be done through a biblical framework.

FIGURE 2.16
Data Analysis

ON YOUR OWN

2.8 What is the difference between operational science and historical science?

2.9 Can scientific study be applied only to things we observe happening today?

2.10 When scientists analyze the same data differently from one another, what might be affecting their thinking?

SUMMING UP

After performing the experiments and activities in this module, I hope you have a better understanding of why we need to carefully design experiments to systematically study things. Additionally, we need to try to interpret our results in a way that removes as much personal bias as we can. Think about the handwashing requirements that Semmelweis instituted in his hospital ward. The doctors didn't like having to take time out of their day to thoroughly wash their hands. After all, they didn't know that there were germs that could harm patients they were getting ready to see. If they were responsible for setting up an experiment, can you imagine that they would want to try to collect only data that showed that handwashing made no difference in saving lives? You see, they might have had a bias. The scientific method and the interpretation of collected data are designed in a way to help scientists remove as much bias as they can. All scientists have a worldview, and the interpretation of scientific data is often dependent on the individual scientist's worldview. Proper scientific method helps us to remove as much bias as possible in order to systematically and objectively study creation.

[1] *Krauss, L. M. 2012.* A Universe from Nothing. *New York: Free Press, 164-165.*

ANSWERS TO THE "ON YOUR OWN" QUESTIONS

2.1 The scientist might collect plenty of data to support his hypothesis. Additional scientists might collect even more supporting data. Yet **it only takes a single counter example** for the theory to be shown to be incorrect.

2.2 **Patients in Semmelweis' ward were dying at a rate that exceeded that of other wards,** even those that had sicker patients. He noticed that **the major difference between other wards and his ward was that doctors visited his ward first after performing autopsies on the dead.**

2.3 Semmelweis hypothesized that the doctors were carrying something deadly from the corpses to the patients in his ward. In an If/Then format, you would write, **"If the doctors are carrying something deadly from the corpses, then the patients in Semmelweis' ward will be more likely to die."**

2.4 Semmelweis instructed the doctors **to remove the unseen material by thoroughly washing their hands before entering his hospital ward.**

2.5 **No.** Even though the experiment results agreed with Semmelweis' hypothesis, there were not enough data to call his hypothesis a scientific law.

2.6 **Those observations are far from worthless!** They can still be used to gain information regarding the surface of Mars. They just don't support the existence of canals on Mars.

2.7 **What Science Can Do: Understand an enormous amount about the world around us, develop incredibly useful inventions, and the scientific method can be applied to questions based on what is happening in the world today and what has happened to the world in the past. The Limitations of Science: Science cannot prove anything; science is not 100% settled, and science must conform to the scientific method. The Misuses of Science: Extending claims into fields that have not been experimentally tested, considering an idea to be truth just because a very intelligent scientist suggests it, and assuming science knows more than it actually does.**

2.8 **Operational science uses observable, repeatable experiments to try to discover truth. Historical science relies on relics from the past and historical records to try to discover truth.**

2.9 **No.** Historical science involves studying historical data and evidence we see today and making educated assumptions about the past.

2.10 **All scientists have a worldview. There is always a risk of their worldview affecting their analysis.**

STUDY GUIDE FOR MODULE 2

1. Match the following words with their definitions.

   a. Counter example
   b. Hypothesis
   c. Scientific theory
   d. Scientific law

   An explanation of the natural world that has been thoroughly tested and is supported by a significant amount of evidence

   A description of a natural phenomenon or principle that is supported by a significant amount of evidence and often includes mathematical terms

   An example that contradicts a conclusion

   An educated guess that attempts to explain an observation or answer a question

2. Fill in the blank. Science is NOT a means by which something can be ___________.

3. The scientific method gives us an ordered way to go through the process of observation and creation of a question, gathering information about that observation, creating a hypothesis, and testing it. That way, we can discover if our hypothesis is true or not. Fill in the blank spaces using the "living room light" example in the text. As you do, think through the scientific method so you better understand and remember it.

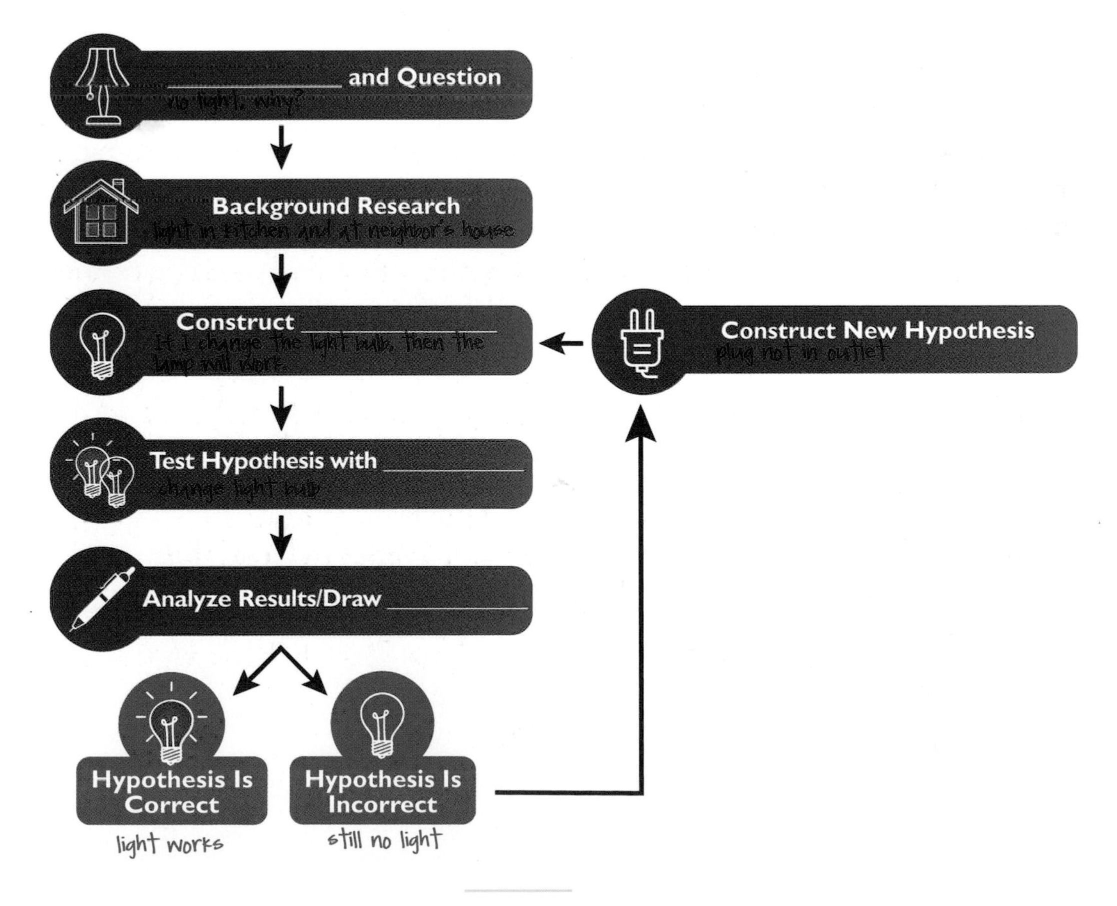

4. Fill in the blank, summarizing the account of Lowell and his hypothesized Martian canals: Although the conclusions of science are not always _________, science is a very worthwhile endeavor!

5. Which one of the following statements about science is NOT true?

   a. Science cannot prove anything.

   b. Science is not 100% settled.

   c. A scientific law can never be overthrown.

   d. Science must conform to the scientific method.

6. Explain why you think humility is important in performing scientific experimentation and making conclusions.

7. Match operational science and historical science with the following definitions: One relies on relics from the past and historical records to try to discover truth, and the other uses observable, repeatable experiments to try to discover truth.

8. Explain this statement in your own words: The confusion caused by different data interpretation is not science versus religion—it is really worldview versus worldview.

DOCUMENTING AND INTERPRETING EXPERIMENTAL RESULTS

As we move systematically through the history and process of science, I hope you are beginning to see that the *way* you apply the scientific method is extremely important. In fact, the application of the scientific method affects the reliability of the conclusions you draw from it. Remember from the previous module when we discussed the case of Percival Lowell and the "canals" he saw on Mars? The canals he observed were a result of flawed experimentation. They turned out to be the result of inaccurate telescopes and eye fatigue. If he had used better telescopes and allowed more time for his eyes to rest between viewing sessions, he might not have imagined what really wasn't there. Even though he followed the scientific method, his flawed experimentation led to wrong conclusions.

So to do science well, you need to be very careful in designing your experiments and making your observations. You need to try to avoid flaws in your experiments and come up with various ways to test your hypothesis or theory so as to avoid missing data. Additionally, you need to carefully document your results in a way to make them easy to review. The better you are at that, the more reliable your conclusions will be.

Quaestio

Have you ever played the game where several people sit in a circle and one person whispers a sentence to the person sitting next to him, followed by that person whispering what he heard to the next one, and continuing until it reaches the first person again? Often, by the time the sentence reaches the first person again, it has been dramatically (and often hilariously!) changed. Well, reporting and communicating information can be a difficult process if it isn't done carefully. And when it comes to science, organization and clear communication is critical in exploring our world.

FIGURE 3.1
Experimental Setup

EXPERIMENTS AND VARIABLES

In designing an experiment, it is important to determine all the experimental variables.

> **Experimental variable**—An aspect of an experiment that changes during the course of the experiment

Identifying variables in an experiment will help you to avoid flaws in your work. For example, a part of the reason that Lowell saw what he thought were canals on Mars was the fact that as time went on, his eyes began to get tired. Eye strain was an experimental variable because it varied, or changed, over the course of his observations. Had he recognized that, he could have reduced that variable by taking several breaks during his observation hours so his eyes would be fresh. By not controlling that variable, there were defects in his experimental process.

Not all experimental variables are bad though. Often, scientists want to *include* variables in order to learn something by comparing the experimental results using them. For example, if you wanted to test which of 2 fertilizers was better for tomato plant growth, you would grow several tomato plants—some plants growing with one fertilizer and other plants growing with the other. In this case, the experimental variable is different fertilizers, but that is something you would want in the experiment. However, there are many different types of tomato plants, and they all might not respond to fertilizers in the same way. Therefore, this variable (different tomato plant species) is one you would want to remove. What does this mean? Well, it is important to make sure that all variables are considered when conducting experiments, removing the variables you don't want (such as different tomato plant species) and including the variables you do want (such as fertilizer types).

FIGURE 3.2
Tomato Plants

Explore experimental variables more by performing Experiment 3.1.

EXPERIMENT 3.1
DENSITY AND A FLOATING EGG

PURPOSE: To better understand the importance of variables in an experiment while observing how an egg floats in tap water and saltwater

MATERIALS:
- A tall, clear glass
- Measuring cups to measure 1½ cups of water
- A raw egg (It is best to use one that hasn't been sitting in the refrigerator for a long time.)
- A teaspoon
- A spoon for stirring
- Water
- Salt

QUESTION: How does an egg float in tap water as compared to how it floats in saltwater?

HYPOTHESIS: Write how you think an egg will float in tap water as compared to how it will float in saltwater.

PROCEDURE:
1. Fill a tall glass with 1½ cups of water. Use the measuring cups to measure the water.
2. Carefully place the egg into the glass of water. Write in your notebook whether it sinks or floats.
3. Use the spoon you have for stirring to pull the egg back out of the glass. Try to allow any water still on the egg to drip back into the glass so you don't lose much water. Set the egg aside for the moment.
4. Add one teaspoon of salt to the water and stir with your stirring spoon until the salt is dissolved.
5. Once the salt is dissolved, carefully place the egg back into the glass of water. Note the difference (if any) between how the egg behaved before and how it behaved this time.
6. Repeat steps 3–5 a total of 6 times, making the water saltier and saltier. Each time, write in your lab notebook any differences between how the egg behaves as compared to the previous time. If the egg's behavior does not change even after you have repeated steps 3–5 a total of 6 times, continue to repeat the steps until you see a difference. NOTE: Depending on the water in your area, you may have to repeat Step 6 more times.
7. Clean everything up. If the egg has not cracked, you can rinse it and put it back in the refrigerator to cook later.

CONCLUSION: Write why you think an egg floats in saltwater as compared to tap water, explaining how density plays a role.

WHAT TO DO

You are going to learn a few things from this experiment. First, I will go over what was going on with the egg and how it floated. Then I will discuss with you how variables are important in experimentation. Finally, I will walk you through how to record the data you obtained in this experiment in order to do a lab write-up.

What did you see in the experiment? If things went well, when you added the egg to the water-filled glass, it should have sunk. However, as you added more and more salt to the water, the egg probably didn't sink as quickly as it did before. At a certain point, the egg should have floated.

Remember Experiment 1.1? In that experiment, you had a ping-pong ball immersed in unpopped popcorn and a lead weight sitting on top. When you swirled the container, the denser lead weight sank into the popcorn, and the less dense ping-pong ball floated to the surface. Well, the same phenomenon is happening here. An egg sank in pure water but floated once a lot of salt was added to it. So we can say that saltwater is denser than pure water.

FIGURE 3.3
A Woman Floating in the Dead Sea

Have you ever heard of the Dead Sea located between the countries of Israel and Jordan? It is a saltwater lake located inland! The added salt makes the water much denser as compared to freshwater lakes. In fact, it is so dense that people can float without expending any effort because overall, their bodies are less dense than the saltwater (See Figure 3.3).

Experimental Variables

Now it's time to discuss the experimental variables in Experiment 3.1. First, you used the same glass throughout the whole experiment, and you used the same egg. The egg was always pulled out with the same spoon. So none of those things changed, and therefore they are not variables. To identify the variables, think about *what was changing*. Well, the first obvious variable is the amount of salt in the water. In step 2, there was no added salt to the water. Then you added salt to the water one teaspoon at a time. The amount of salt changed throughout the experiment, so it is a variable. The other experimental variable might be more difficult to identify. It had to do with the amount of water in the glass. You see, each time you pulled the egg out of the water, you pulled some water out, too. Even though you tried to minimize how much water was removed by allowing water to drip back into the glass, there was just no way to have returned *all* the water. So as you continued the steps in the experiment, the amount of water decreased, even if it was just a little.

The first variable greatly affected the experiment, didn't it? As the amount of saltwater increased, the egg eventually began to float. That helped us understand that adding salt to water helps eggs float. But think about the second variable. If you didn't add any salt at all, but just kept removing and returning the egg to the water, would that affect how it floats? No. But it *did* have a slight affect you couldn't see. Each time you removed the egg, you removed a bit of water, causing the glass to contain less water as compared to the salt being added. That made the concentration of salt, or the "saltiness" of the water, just a bit higher. Think about that. If you add a teaspoon of salt to ¼ cup of water and you add a teaspoon of salt to a gallon of water, which container would taste saltier? The one with the smaller volume of water is saltier. The ¼ cup of water with salt will have a higher **concentration** of salt per volume.

FIGURE 3.4
Experimental Variables in Experiment 3.1

FIGURE 3.5
Spoon with Water Droplets

Well, the same thing happened when you were removing a few drops of water each time you removed the egg. The volume of water was decreasing, even though it was decreasing by very, very small increments. Now, the effect was minor, but in an experiment, you need to consider all the variables and include those you want (increasing salt) while removing or minimizing those you don't want (removing water droplets). And you did that to the best of your ability by allowing the egg to remain over the glass while water dropped back in.

think about this

Often science involves the use of words you might not use in your daily vocabulary. That is because scientific terms are specific in order to be accurate for reporting and discussion. Think of the word *variable*. It is similar to the word *vary*. The word *vary* means to change or alter or to cause to be different from something else. Often when you break down scientific terms into their roots, it becomes easier to understand and remember them. *Experimental* variables are factors within an *experiment* that vary or change.

We can sum up by saying that when you want to design a good experiment, **you should always reduce the number of experimental variables that are not a necessary part of the experiment.** The amount of salt in the water was a necessary experimental variable, but it was helpful to use the same glass, same egg, and same amount of water (as best you could) so that you could only focus on how salt affects an egg's ability to float in water.

ON YOUR OWN

A student decides to test the effectiveness of different household floor cleaners. He marks off a section of the kitchen floor and scuffs it up with black heel marks. He then divides that section into 4 equal quarters, and he scrubs each quarter with a different brand of floor cleaner.

3.1 Identify the experimental variables in this experiment.

3.2 From what experimental variable will the student learn something, and which variables should he try to reduce or eliminate?

3.3 Describe ways to reduce or eliminate the experimental variables that need to be reduced or eliminated.

RECORDING EXPERIMENTAL DATA

Now it is time to discuss how to record the data you collected in Experiment 3.1 and then how to document it for a lab report. There are several ways to do this, and in this section, I will go over how to make a table. In the experiment, you first placed the egg in the tap water-filled glass. You should have noticed that it sank to the bottom. Then you removed the egg and added one teaspoon salt to the glass. Once the salt was dissolved, you added the egg back in the glass and noted what happened. The experiment instructed you to continue adding salt, one teaspoon at a time, and note what the egg did when it was placed in the water. So you should have 7 observations: 1 with no salt in the water and 6 with increasing amounts of salt.

FIGURE 3.6
Rows and Columns in a Table

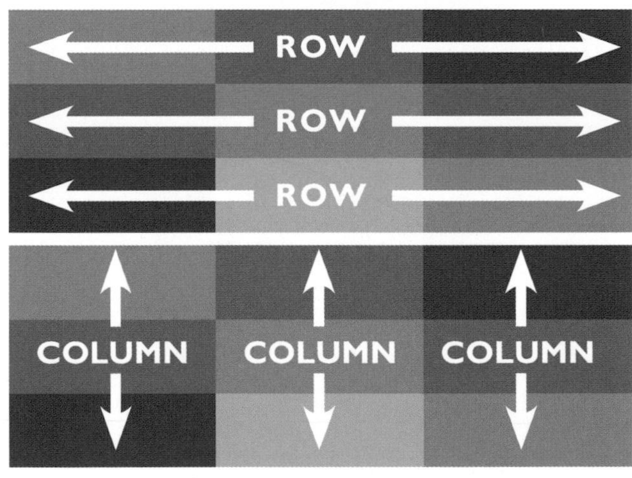

A great way to organize this information is to construct a table. A table contains spaces organized into horizontal rows and vertical columns (see Figure 3.6). You can create a table with as many rows and columns as you need. In our case, think about what you want to record. You have 7 observations, one from each trial. Repeated trials are when you do a similar measurement or action multiple times in order to gather information. You can place each trial into its own row. For the columns, think about what changed with each trial. You added salt each time, so you want to include a column showing how much salt was added. You also need to add a column where you mention what you observed when you added the egg. So we can initially set up our table like this:

No salt	Egg sank
1 tsp. salt	Egg sank
2 tsp. salt	Egg sank more slowly
3 tsp. salt	Egg sank slowly
4 tsp. salt	Egg sank slowly
5 tsp. salt	Egg sank slowly
6 tsp. salt	Egg floated

When you look at that table, *you* might understand what you did in the experiment, but others might not. It is important to record your information so that other scientists can identify what happened. That means you need to label the columns and rows.

Trial	Amount of Salt Added (tsp.)	Observation
1	0	Egg sank
2	1	Egg sank
3	2	Egg sank more slowly
4	3	Egg sank slowly
5	4	Egg sank slowly
6	5	Egg sank slowly
7	6	Egg floated

Because the uppermost row and the leftmost column contain labels, it makes it easier to view the table if we make the labels look different from the other information. Your table, therefore, might look like this:

Trial	Amount of Salt Added (tsp.)	Observation
1	0	Egg sank
2	1	Egg sank
3	2	Egg sank more slowly
4	3	Egg sank slowly
5	4	Egg sank slowly
6	5	Egg sank slowly
7	6	Egg floated

Notice how I removed some information from the columns because I included that information in the headings. For example, in the column titled "Amount of Salt Added," I was able to note that all the measurements in that column would be in teaspoons. That way, I could remove the units from the rest of that column. It makes it easier to read and understand the information.

Finally, I want to mention 2 more important things about tables. First, the column titles are just that: titles. Therefore, they should be capitalized like a proper title should be. They should be brief and not complete sentences. Second, *every TABLE should have a title*. It should explain what the information in the table contains and, again, be as brief as possible while not forming a complete sentence. So this is my final table from the data I collected when I performed Experiment 3.1:

Immersing an Egg in Varying Concentrations of Saltwater

Trial	Amount of Salt Added (tsp.)	Observation
1	0	Egg sank
2	1	Egg sank
3	2	Egg sank more slowly
4	3	Egg sank slowly
5	4	Egg sank slowly
6	5	Egg sank slowly
7	6	Egg floated

WHAT TO DO

Now it is time for you to do a lab report for Experiment 3.1. Include a table in the results section, following the instructions given in the text above. Remember to read through the information within the experiment and the discussion before and after to help you figure out what to write *in your own words*. I didn't highlight the important information in orange words like I did in the first 2 modules, but by now, you should know what to be looking for. You can do this!

ON YOUR OWN

3.4 A student was doing an experiment to explore what household items would be attracted to a magnet. He tested 6 different items and learned that the ones that stuck to a magnet were a steel rod, a paper clip, and a metal washer. Items that did not stick to a magnet were a pencil, a glass marble, and a piece of paper. Create a table using his information, making sure to label your rows and columns, and give your table a title.

USING A SERIES OF EXPERIMENTS

With a little experimental analysis under your belt, you need to understand that most scientists perform several experiments in order to develop a good conclusion about something. Thus, they perform a series of experiments to understand whatever they are studying. We will do the same in this section. First, perform Experiment 3.2.

EXPERIMENT 3.2
EXPLORING A FLAME'S OXYGEN USE

PURPOSE: To identify the presence of oxygen in air

MATERIALS:

- 3 glass containers of different sizes (You can use canning jars, drinking glasses, or food container jars.)
- A tea light candle (Make sure you use a small candle. A votive might be too large for your glass containers.)
- Matches
- A ceramic, glass, or metal pie plate
- A stopwatch (Many smartphones have a stopwatch feature.)
- A water-filled glass

QUESTION: How can we observe the presence of oxygen in air?

HYPOTHESIS: Write what you think will happen to the flame when it is placed under each of the 3 glasses.

PROCEDURE:

1. Place the candle in the center of the pie plate.
2. Hold the stopwatch in your hand, ready to start timing.
3. Light the candle with a match, and start the stopwatch as soon as the candle is lit. Drop the match into the water-filled glass.
4. After several minutes, note if the candle's flame has burned out. If not, blow the candle out and move to the next step.
5. Light the candle again and drop the match into the water-filled glass.
6. Hold the stopwatch in your hand, ready to start timing.
7. Carefully take the smallest glass container in your other hand and place it upside down over the candle. Start the stopwatch as soon as you set the container on the pie plate.
8. When the flame goes out, stop the stopwatch.
9. Record in your notebook the time it took for the flame to go out inside the smallest glass.
10. Repeat steps 5-9 with the midsize glass container and record the time it took for the flame to go out.
11. Repeat steps 5-9 with the large glass container and record the time it took for the flame to go out.

12. Clean everything up.

CONCLUSION: Write why the flame went out when it was under the glasses and why it took different amounts of time to become extinguished.

FIGURE 3.7
A Candle Burning Under Glass

What happened in the experiment? Well, the first time you lit the candle, it should have burned until you blew it out. It had plenty of the resources it needed to continue burning. But things were different once you covered the candle with a glass container. The flame should have eventually gone out. In fact, it should have died out the quickest when it was in the small glass container. It should have taken a bit longer in the medium container, and it should have taken even longer in the large container. Why is that? Well, when you light the candle, the heat of the flame melts the wax near the wick. Then the liquid wax is vaporized by the flame, turning it into a hot gas. The flame also needs oxygen in order to continue burning. The glass container was filled with air. Oxygen is one of the gases in air, along with other gases like nitrogen and carbon dioxide. When about a third of the oxygen in the air was used up, the oxygen concentration in the glass wasn't high enough and the candle could no longer burn. The larger containers had a greater amount of air, and therefore a greater amount of oxygen, enabling the flame to burn longer.

There's one more thing I want to discuss in regard to this experiment. Why do you think you were instructed to light the candle in step 2 without covering it? It actually was important. You see, by burning the candle without any covering, you were demonstrating that the candle had everything it needed in order to burn. The "normal" experimental conditions were such that a candle could burn for a long time. That way you had some information with which to compare the next 3 steps. We call that first trial the **control** of an experiment.

Control (of an experiment)—the variable of part of an experiment to which all others will be compared

WHAT TO DO

You are not required to do a lab write-up for Experiment 3.2, but I *do* want you to use the information you gathered to make a graph, following the instructions below. This is another way to record and present data in a way that is easy to read and understand by others. You will be instructed to create a bar graph. A **bar graph** is used to compare items or to show relationships between groups, such as how something changes over time. It's a fast way to show big differences in your data. Follow the instructions in the following paragraphs to create yours.

In the experiment, you had 3 glass sizes. You also recorded a time that the flame burned for each glass. We will use those 2 types of data (Glass Size and Flame Time) to create our bar graph. First, you need to draw a horizontal line (called an ***x*-axis**) and a vertical line (called a ***y*-axis**). The *x*-axis will always show your independent variable and the *y*-axis is your dependent variable. An independent variable is a variable that is not affected by the other variable. In this case, the 3 glass sizes will be placed along the horizontal *x*-axis. They will be evenly spaced to fill up the width of the axis. We will place Flame Time along the vertical *y*-axis.

Notice a few things about this setup. First, the *x*-axis is labeled Glass Size and has the 3 glass sizes evenly spaced and labeled along it. The *y*-axis is labeled Flame Time and in parentheses identifies that the numbers are measured in seconds. The numbers along the vertical axis are evenly spaced. But how did I know what numbers to use? Why did I count by fives instead of ones or hundreds? Well, I looked at my data. When I performed the experiment, the data I collected ranged from 10 seconds to 27 seconds. So I needed to create a range of numbers that will make that number-spread noticeable. If I used ones, then the graph would have to be extremely tall to reach number 27. And if I used hundreds, then the bars would all be about the same height in relation to each other.

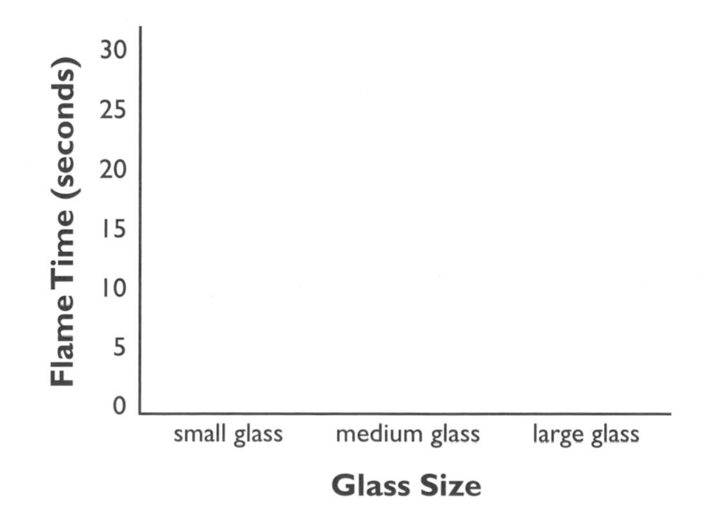

Now I can add the bars to the graph, based on the data I collected, and finish the graph by adding a title. Go ahead and make your own bar graph for Experiment 3.2.

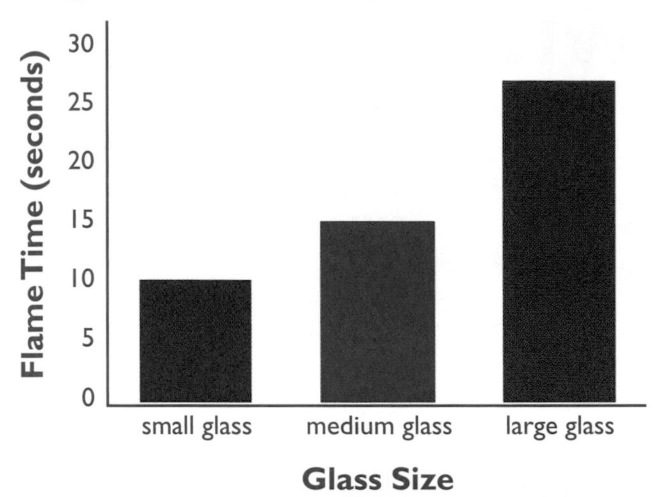

EXPLORE MORE

Bar graphs are often used to present information from surveys. Take a poll of your friends and family, asking them what their favorite ice cream flavor choice would be if they were given the options of chocolate, strawberry, and vanilla. Then create a bar graph with the flavor types on the *x*-axis and the number of people on the *y*-axis. Don't forget to give your graph a title!

Now perform Experiment 3.3 to further explore what is going on when a candle burns.

EXPERIMENT 3.3

THE EFFECT A BURNING CANDLE HAS ON AIR

PURPOSE: To identify what happens to air when a candle burns

MATERIALS:

- A medium glass container (NOTE: This experiment works better if the glass container is tall and thin. A drinking glass works well.)
- A tea light candle
- Matches
- A ceramic, glass, or metal pie plate
- Food coloring
- A measuring cup of water (It is helpful if the measuring cup has a pour spout.)
- A stirring spoon
- A paper towel
- A small lump of clay
- A medium-height candle that can fit in the medium glass container with room for a flame

QUESTION: What happens to the air inside the glass when a candle burns?

HYPOTHESIS: Write what you think happens to the air while the candle is burning and once the flame goes out.

PROCEDURE:

PART 1

1. Place the tea light candle in the center of the pie plate.
2. Add a few drops of food coloring to the water in the measuring cup and stir so it is well mixed.
3. Carefully pour water into the pie plate so it surrounds the candle. You only want a thin layer of water, so don't pour too much.
4. Light the candle and place the glass container over it.
5. Allow the flame to burn until it goes out.
6. Observe what the water does while the candle is burning and also what happens once the flame goes out.
7. Remove the glass container and set aside the tea light candle. To prevent stains, be careful not to get food coloring on any nearby cloth.

PART 2

8. Dump the water that is in the pie plate into a sink and dry the plate with a paper towel.
9. Take a small lump of clay and place it in the center of the pie plate.
10. Stick the tall candle into the clay so that it is firmly adhered to it and will stand on its own. Add more clay if you need to.
11. Carefully pour more colored water into the pie plate like you did in step 3.
12. Light the candle and place the glass container over it.
13. Allow the flame to burn until it goes out, paying close attention to how long it takes. **NOTE: Because the flame is closer to the base of the glass container, the glass could be HOT!**
14. Once the glass container cools, clean up everything and put it away.

CONCLUSION: Write why the water entered the glass once the flame went out and why it did not enter as high with the taller candle.

In the first part of the experiment, you should have noticed that the water in the pie plate did not do much while the candle was burning. You might have seen a bubble or 2, but not much else. But what did you see once the flame burned out? You should have seen that the water began to move *inside the glass*, maybe even building up higher than the water left in the plate (if there was any left).

What is going on here is that a burning candle requires air that is rich in oxygen. But it does not use up enough oxygen to cause water to move inside. So what happens at first is that the flame heats the air inside the container, and this hot air expands quickly. Hot air takes up more space than cool air. The expanding air pushes against the sides of the glass, creating higher pressure inside. Some of that expanding air might have escaped from under the glass, and that would explain some bubbles if you saw any. But once the oxygen levels decreased enough for the flame to go out, the air inside the container cooled. Cooler air contracts, taking up less space. This created a vacuum inside the container, representing less air pressure inside. With higher air pressure on the outside, the outside air pushed water into the container until the air pressure became equal on both sides of the glass.

FIGURE 3.8
Air and Water Vapor Clouds

Because air is not visible to the eye, it is difficult to observe what it can do. When it pushes on things, such as when air blows, you can see those things move. Air pressure also can cause things to move as it pushes on them.

When you did the same procedure in Part 2 of Experiment 3.3 using the taller candle, you might have noticed that the flame died out much more quickly. In fact, if I had asked you to time it, its burn time would have been less than the burn time for the tea light candle in the medium glass in Experiment 3.2. Why is that? Well, the burning process uses up oxygen but it produces carbon dioxide, which is another type of gas. That gas builds up at the top of the container, pushing down other gases, particularly oxygen, which causes the flame to go out. The taller candle burned at a higher level where it would be exposed to carbon dioxide sooner. That means the flame would go out sooner as compared to a shorter candle.

In the end we did a series of 2 experiments, or technically 3 if you consider Part 1 and Part 2 of the second one as separate experiments. Comparing their results helps us to better understand how candles burn and the gases involved in the process. This is typical of how scientists learn what they want to learn about creation. They look at a single variable's effect in many different experiments, hoping they can draw some general conclusions after several effects are studied.

ON YOUR OWN

3.5 The variable of part of an experiment to which all other variables will be compared is called the ______________.

3.6 A student is working on building a toy car out of wood and wants to see if adding a spoiler on the back of the car will make it move faster. He also wants to know what size spoiler will work best. He made a test car and 3 detachable spoilers of varied sizes. He will measure the time it takes the car to roll down a ramp on a test track he created. What will be his control trial?

RECOGNIZING EXPERIMENTAL VARIABLES WHEN THEY ARE NOT OBVIOUS

Experimentation is used in many fields, including marketing. Think about commercials you might have seen. Often the narrator will say something like this: "Our new product is preferred 85% of the time over the competitor's product!"

How do they know that? Is there a way to test that statement? Imagine that the new product is a brand of chocolate chip cookie. If you are responsible for creating a study to find out if, indeed, it is a better cookie, you would need to set up an experiment.

You could gather several people together and give them a new cookie, asking them if they like it. But to set up a better experiment, you need to have them taste the new cookie *and* the old cookie so they can compare them.

That might work, but it wouldn't give you the best results. That's because you need to consider all the experimental variables. If the tasters know which cookie is which, they might be biased. Some may have been big fans of the old cookie and feel loyal to it. Others might imagine one tastes better based on its name or its packaging. Oftentimes, the way a person thinks affects how he or she feels about a product.

FIGURE 3.9
Tasting Cookies

People have individual preferences and can be swayed by advertisements, labels, and even physical clues given by the person handing them food. These variables need to be minimized for better experimental procedure.

To eliminate this variable, you need to remove all packaging and just set the 2 cookies out on unmarked plates. This kind of study is known as a **blind experiment.**

Blind experiments—Experiments in which information about the test is kept from the participants to reduce bias

In other words, the participants are "blind" to some of the experimental information. Another way to improve your experiment is to set up a control group. What if it is difficult for most people to tell the difference between the cookies? To see if that is the case, you can gather a group of people to test 2 cookies; however, you give them 2 cookies from the same package. When asked if they have a preference or if they can't tell much of a difference, you should expect most of them to answer that they can't tell a difference.

If most of the people in your control trial report that the cookies taste the same, then you know that people are not affected by any bias just because you tell them there is a new cookie they are taste-testing.

So you can set up another group and prepare to do a blind experiment by giving them 2 unmarked cookies—one from each brand—to taste. But is that the best way to design a study? Not quite. You see, as long as *you* know which cookie is which, then it might affect the way you present the cookies to the tasters. It also might affect the way you report the data.

For example, if you really like the new cookie brand you might select a nicer looking sample of the new brand to give your taster. Or you might round your calculated percentages up or down so as to make the data better fit your expected outcome. So to minimize this variable, you need to become "blind" to the experiment, too. You need to have someone else keep track of the cookie brands and relabel them for you. Thus, you can present your testers with Cookie A versus Cookie B. You don't know which is the new brand, and thus that variable is removed. Studies like this, where both the participants and the people analyzing the results are unaware which product is which, are called **double-blind experiments.**

Double-blind experiments—Experiments in which neither the experimenters nor the participants know the objects' identities in the setup

FIGURE 3.10
Food Experimentation

Food presentation and the facial expressions of the person offering the food can sometimes sway a person's opinion of its taste.

Notice that there are at least 2 experimental variables that are not very obvious, and both have to do with people's preferences. Both variables can have dramatic effects on the results of the experiment, so both have to be controlled or eliminated. Think about why these variables exist in the experiment. They exist because the data are **subjective.** In other words, the data being collected depend on the *opinions* of people. Taste is a matter of opinion that varies from one person to another. Additionally, the analysis of such data is subjective, too. While some might like the new cookie, others might *really* like the new cookie, and the tester has to determine how to document that.

FIGURE 3.11
Blind Tests

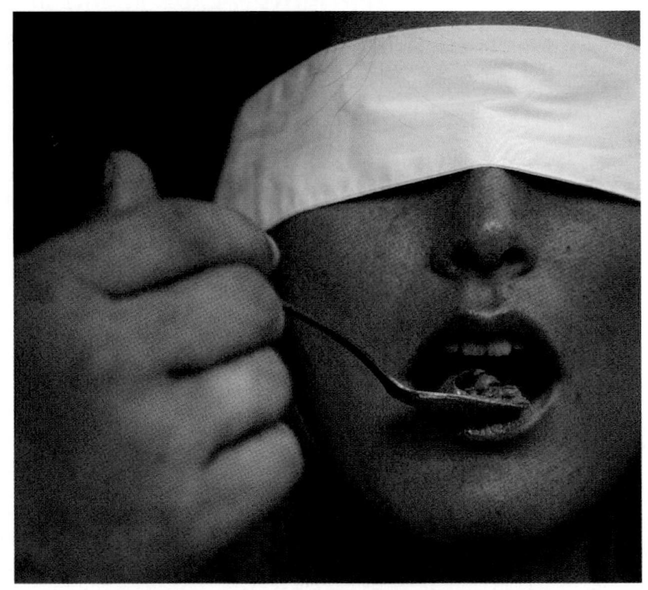

A blind or double-blind study does not mean the experimenters and participants are actually wearing blindfolds! They are "blind" to the actual identity of the materials used in the experimental procedure to help remove bias.

EXPLORE MORE

Taste-testing different food is a great way to explore blind experimentation. Try making a batch of homemade chocolate chip cookies, but when it is time to mix in the chocolate chips, divide the batter into 2 halves, adding one brand of chocolate chips to half and a different brand of chips to the other half. Make sure you can remember which batch is which, but don't let your test subjects know. Record the results of your delicious blind experiment in your notebook!

So when setting up an experiment you have to carefully consider whether the data taken are subjective. If the data are subjective only on the part of the subjects, then you might be able to do a blind study. If the data are subjective not only to the subjects but also to those running the tests and analyzing the data, then you should design a double-blind experiment.

Some experiments don't have subjective variables. If I wanted to test the effectiveness of different types of fertilizers, I can grow the same type of plant in several different pots that are all the same size and contain the same type of soil. I expose the plants to the same conditions, watering them with the same amount of water each day. To one plant, I give no fertilizer, and to the each of the other plants, I give a different brand of fertilizer. I use the same amount of fertilizer in each case. Then, I can measure the height of the plants each day to see which grows better. The results here are just a measurable number (plant height), not how someone feels about something. We call data like these **objective.** Objective data don't require the trouble of setting up a blind or double-blind experiment.

ON YOUR OWN

3.7 In the plant experiment description from this section, the process of testing the effectiveness of different types of fertilizers was described. What are the variables involved in this experiment, which are ones that need to be minimized or eliminated, which one or ones should be kept, and which situation is the control trial?

INTERPRETING AND RECORDING RESULTS OF EXPERIMENTS

At this point in the module, you have a good idea of how to design an experiment. You know how to use and recognize experimental variables. And you also know how to control or eliminate the experimental variables that might affect the results of your experiment in a negative way. Now it is time to dive deeper into how to record experimental results.

More on Bar Graphs

You have had some experience already in making a table and a bar graph, but there are many other ways to report data. Let's revisit the information about bar graphs. A bar graph enables you to show the relative size of different categories. So a bar graph makes it easy to compare amounts. Sometimes you will need to create a **double bar graph.** This graph compares the relative sizes of 2 sets of data. Say, for example, you wanted to record the rainfall in 2 cities over the course of the summer. You could easily report that information in a double bar graph. First, look at the data collected in the table.

2016 Monthly Rainfall in Inches

	New York City, New York	Miami, Florida
June	1.61	8.72
July	6.06	4.11
August	0.62	13.77

Information from https://www.wunderground.com/history/airport/

This table gives us a good report regarding the rainfall in 2 U.S. cities during June, July, and August in 2016. But now look at it in bar graph form in Figure 3.12. Notice a couple of things in this graph. First, the bars are one of 2 colors: blue or yellow.

FIGURE 3.12
A Double Bar Graph

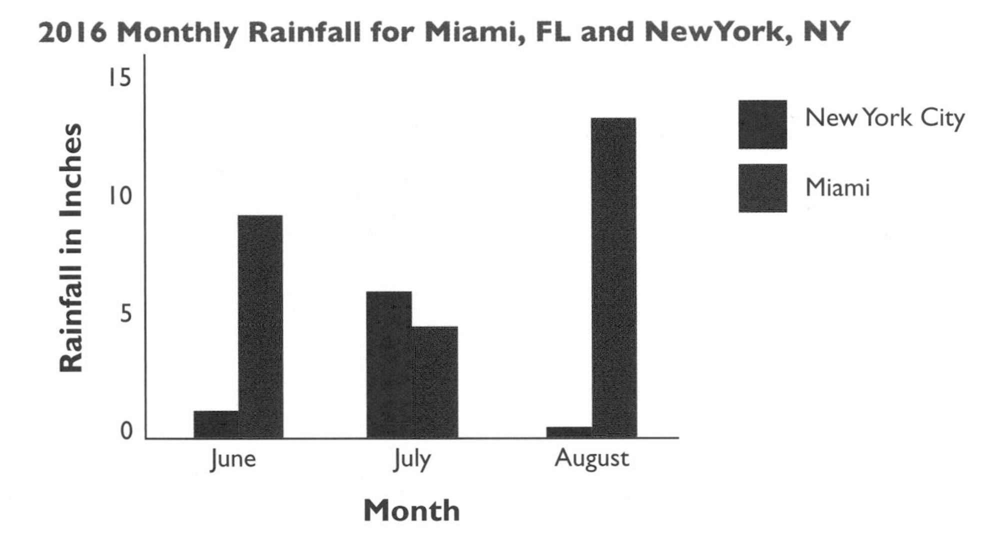

You can see on the upper right of the graph 2 small, colored squares. These are part of a **legend.** A legend gives you information about a graph so you can better read it. It identifies the different sets of data. This legend tells us that the blue colored bars represent rainfall in New York and the yellow colored bars represent rainfall in Miami. Now you can see why this is called a double bar graph. There are 2 bars for each month on the graph. So in June, New York had 1.61 inches of rainfall while Miami had 8.72 inches. Well, that information was also in the table, but can you see how much easier it is to view when it is presented in bar graph form? At a glance,

FIGURE 3.13
Rain in the City

By studying and comparing monthly rainfall in different cities, it is easy to conclude that rainfall dramatically varies from one city to another.

you can see that Miami had more overall rain, simply because there is more yellow on the graph. And the cities experienced the greatest difference of rain during the month of August. If you are not sure how I can tell that, look at the 2 bars over August on the x-axis. There is a short little blue bar and a very tall yellow one. They represent a much greater difference as compared to the 2 bars over June or the 2 bars over July.

To read a bar graph correctly you must look at the information given around the graph first. The title tells you what the graph is about. The axes (plural of axis) let you know which 2 parameters are being compared, in this case "Month" of the year and "Rainfall in Inches." Finally, you use the legend to help you determine which bar stands for which city.

Circle Graphs

Circle graphs are also used to report data. A circle graph, sometimes called a **pie chart,** is helpful when you want to easily visualize the size of parts of a whole. For example, let's say you had a bag of 100 marbles of varying colors. You wanted to report how many of each color are in the bag. First you have to count them all. You use tally marks to record your counting and come up with this:

Marbles in the Bag	
red	𝍸 𝍸 𝍸 𝍸 𝍸
blue	𝍸 𝍸 𝍸 𝍸 𝍸 𝍸 𝍸 𝍸 𝍸 𝍸
yellow	𝍸 𝍸 𝍸 𝍸 𝍸

Tally marks are lines you make in groups of 5 that make it easier to count items. Notice in the chart that the red row shows 5 groups of 5 tally marks which means the bag contains 25 red marbles. It also reports 50 blue marbles and 25 yellow marbles. To illustrate this in a circle graph you have to come up with percentages of the total number of marbles, which will be represented by a percentage of the whole circle. First consider the blue marbles. There are 50 out of 100 total, so 50% or half the marbles are blue. Therefore, we can make half of the circle blue. There are 25 red marbles out of 100 total, so 25% or one-fourth of the circle can be filled in red. And there are 25 yellow marbles out of 100 total, so 25% or one-fourth of the circle can be filled in yellow. We need to title and label our circle graph, of course, and we get this:

FIGURE 3.14
Circle Graph

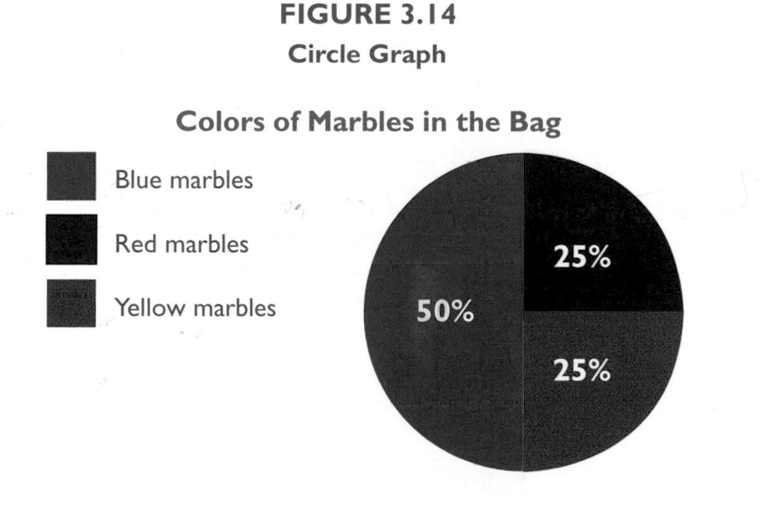

What if your numbers aren't so easy to figure out when it comes to dividing up the wedges in a circle? Well, that involves a bit more math, but the quick answer is that there are 360° in a circle. Once you determine the percentage of each of your items, you just take that percentage of 360°. So if you are making a pie chart showing how you spend your time each day, and you figure out that 19% of your day is spent eating, then you will take 19% of 360°, or 0.19 × 360 and get 68°. So you would use a compass to measure 68° on the circle and fill in that wedge for your time eating. Don't worry if you don't exactly understand how to *make* a circle graph. For this course, you just need to know how to *read* one.

Look again at the circle graph in Figure 3.14. Notice that, like the double bar graph, it also has a legend, telling you what each colored wedge represents. So the red wedge represents red marbles and is labeled 25% of the whole. Like bar graphs, circle graphs make the data easier to view so that conclusions are more easily reached. Just by glancing at the circle graph, you know which colored marble is in the largest quantity. You also can see that there are twice as many blue marbles as red ones, and there are an equal number of red and yellow marbles.

think about this

Circle graphs are often referred to as **pie charts** because they resemble a pie with wedges cut into it. In this module, I am referring to them as circle graphs because they are one of many graph types you are learning, and it is easier to remember this graph type if it is in the same word form as the rest. However, it is important for you to know their other name...which is a more delicious one, too!

Line Graphs

Line graphs record individual data as points on a graph. The line graphs we will be using have points that are connected so that any changes from point to point can be identified. For example, if a person started a business selling cakes, he or she would want to know how the sales have been from month to month. That way he or she can identify if the business is growing and also determine seasons of the year when business is busier. Look at the line graph in Figure 3.15.

Notice a few things about this graph. First, the title sums up what this graph is telling us. It shows the total sales of cakes for the year 2016. You can see how the months of the year are evenly spaced along the *x*-axis. Months are measurements of time,

FIGURE 3.15
Line Graph

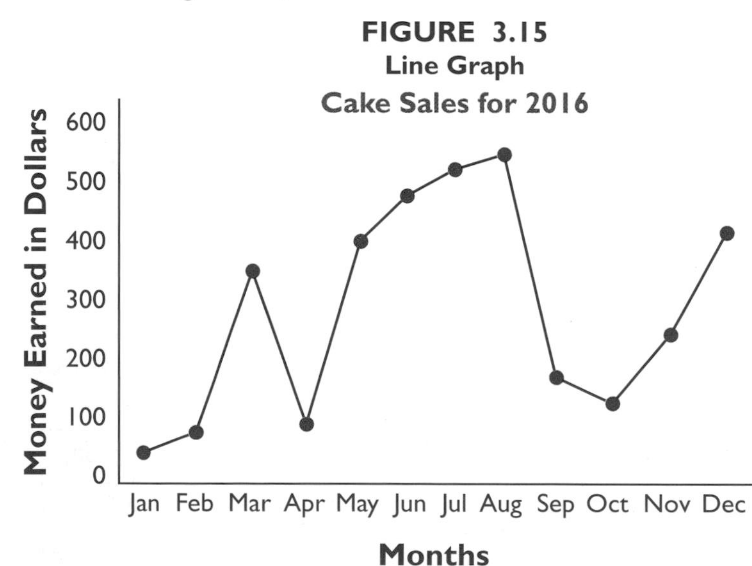

which is an independent factor. You see, no matter what the cake sales do, the months of the year will not change—they are independent. The *y*-axis represents the amount of sales in dollars for each month, and that value will change by month, so it is therefore a dependent value. In order to find how much money the person made in the month of May, for example, you look along the *x*-axis for the month of May. See Figure 3.17 to do that.

From the spot on the *x*-axis where May is, you follow that month upward in a vertical line until you find the point directly over it (See yellow dashed arrow). That is the point representing how much money was made in the month of May. To identify exactly how much, you then follow that point horizontally to the left until you reach the *y*-axis (See pink dashed arrow) and you would learn that $400 was earned in May.

FIGURE 3.16
Cakes

FIGURE 3.17
Reading a Line Graph

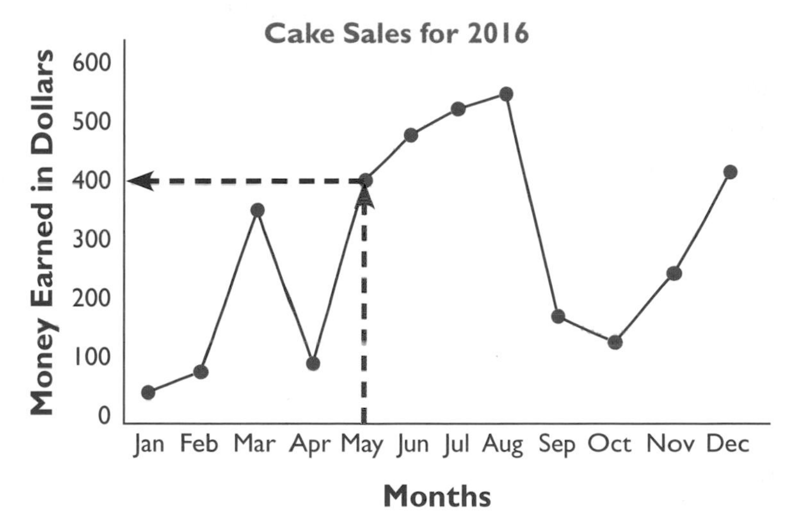

Line graphs also help to report trends in what is being studied. For example, you might notice that sales from May through August were much higher than they had been in previous months. They also *continued* to increase throughout the summer months. At a glance, you can identify the month that experienced the lowest sales (January) and the month that experienced the highest sales (August) for that year. To sum up, line graphs help us to see changes between any 2 points as well as identify trends from certain periods.

Creating a line graph is similar in procedure to creating a bar graph. In fact, the information in line graphs can often be reported as bar graphs. But line graphs are best used to find trends in information rather than just exhibit data.

Creating a Line Graph

In order to make a line graph, you first need to identify what information will go on each axis. Say, for example, you are creating a line graph of the high temperatures for your city during one week in the summer. You have the following data:

Sunday Jul 5	Monday July 6	Tuesday Jul 7	Wednesday Jul 8	Thursday Jul 9	Friday Jul 10	Saturday Jul 11
85 °F	86 °F	86 °F	69 °F	72 °F	76 °F	79 °F

FIGURE 3.18
Outdoor Thermometer

Notice that there are 2 rows in the table of data: day of the week and temperatures. Those will be the names of the 2 axes on the graph. You will place the days of the week along the x-axis because they mark the passage of time, which is an independent variable. The temperatures will be along the y-axis. But what increments of temperature should you use? Look at the range of temperatures. The highest is 86 °F, and the lowest is 69 °F. That represents a 17° difference. To easily mark it, you might want to note temperature in increments of 2°, beginning with a number below 69 and ending with a number above 86. It is always a good idea to use round numbers, even numbers, or increments of 5. So because we are using increments of 2°, let's start with 68 °F and end with 88 °F.

If you label the y-axis using degrees Fahrenheit within the label, then you do not have to include that unit with the numbers along the axis. Notice how the title informs us that the graph will represent the temperatures outside during the specific week when you took measurements.

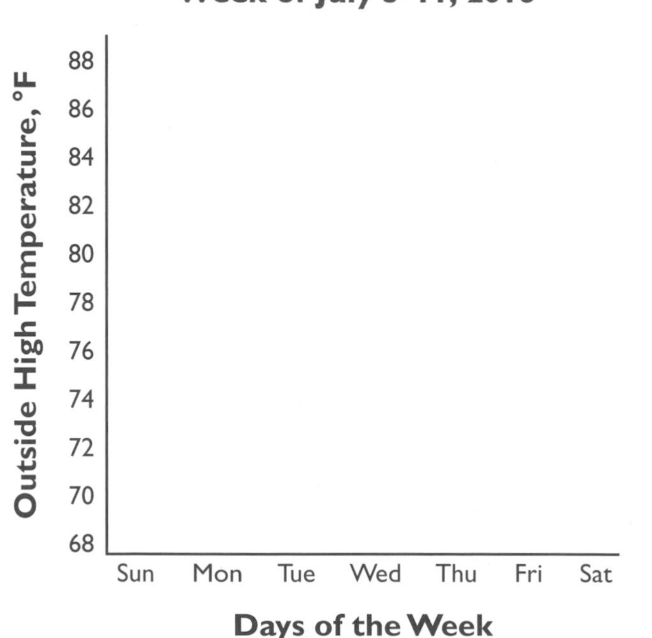

Now you can plot the points and connect the dots from one day to the next. So the first point will be right above Sunday and will be horizontal to the 85 °F temperature mark. The next will be above Monday and horizontal to the 86 °F temperature mark. After you finish marking the points on the graph, you can connect the points with lines because they are related to each other and will illustrate any trends.

Now that you have the information plotted, you can more easily identify any unique information. For example, with a quick look, you are able to tell what day of that week had the lowest temperature and what day had the highest. Actually, 2 days are tied with the highest temperature (Monday and Tuesday). Wednesday was the coolest during the week.

Can you see how graphs and tables help us to more easily record data?

FIGURE 3.19
Line Graph of Temperatures

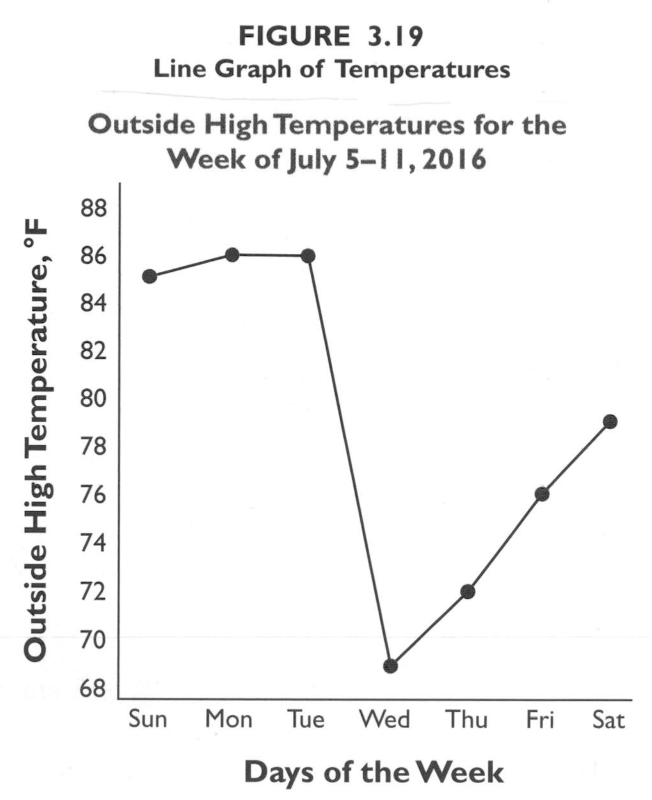

Infographics

Often lots of information needs to be given in a way that is concise, clear, and easy to read. Infographics help to take related information and put it in a visually interesting format. It can incorporate elements of line, bar, and circle graphs, tables, and timelines, all in a colorful diagram. The information within an infographic is related to a major theme in some way. For example, the infographic in Figure 3.20 has places to include lots of information about education. You can see flow charts to illustrate a process, perhaps showing how education progresses as a person gets older. Other groupings might explain the various subjects that can be taught within an education system. But all of the information is collected together in an easy-to-read, colorful way, using iconic images to make it easy to identify what is being presented. You can see in the figure how the sample infographic has several locations on which to place data. For example, if you were reporting the climate in a certain area, you could use one of those sections to record and illustrate high temperatures over the last 10 decades. In another area, you could mention businesses that benefit from that climate. (Mild weather in an area over many years

FIGURE 3.20
Sample Infographic

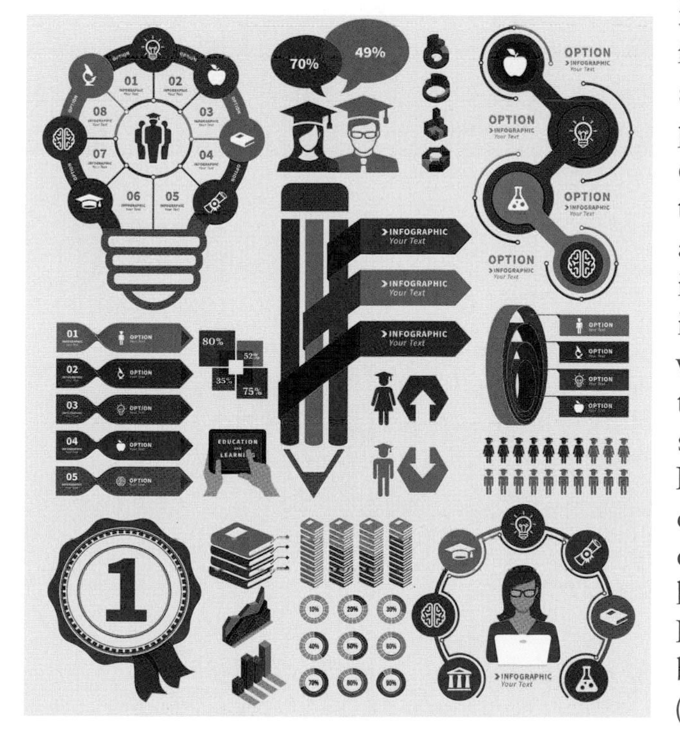

might mean good farming.) Another section might show the various ecosystems that exist within that climate. You could even include annual rainfall, types of scientific research, or practically anything else that is related to the climate in that area.

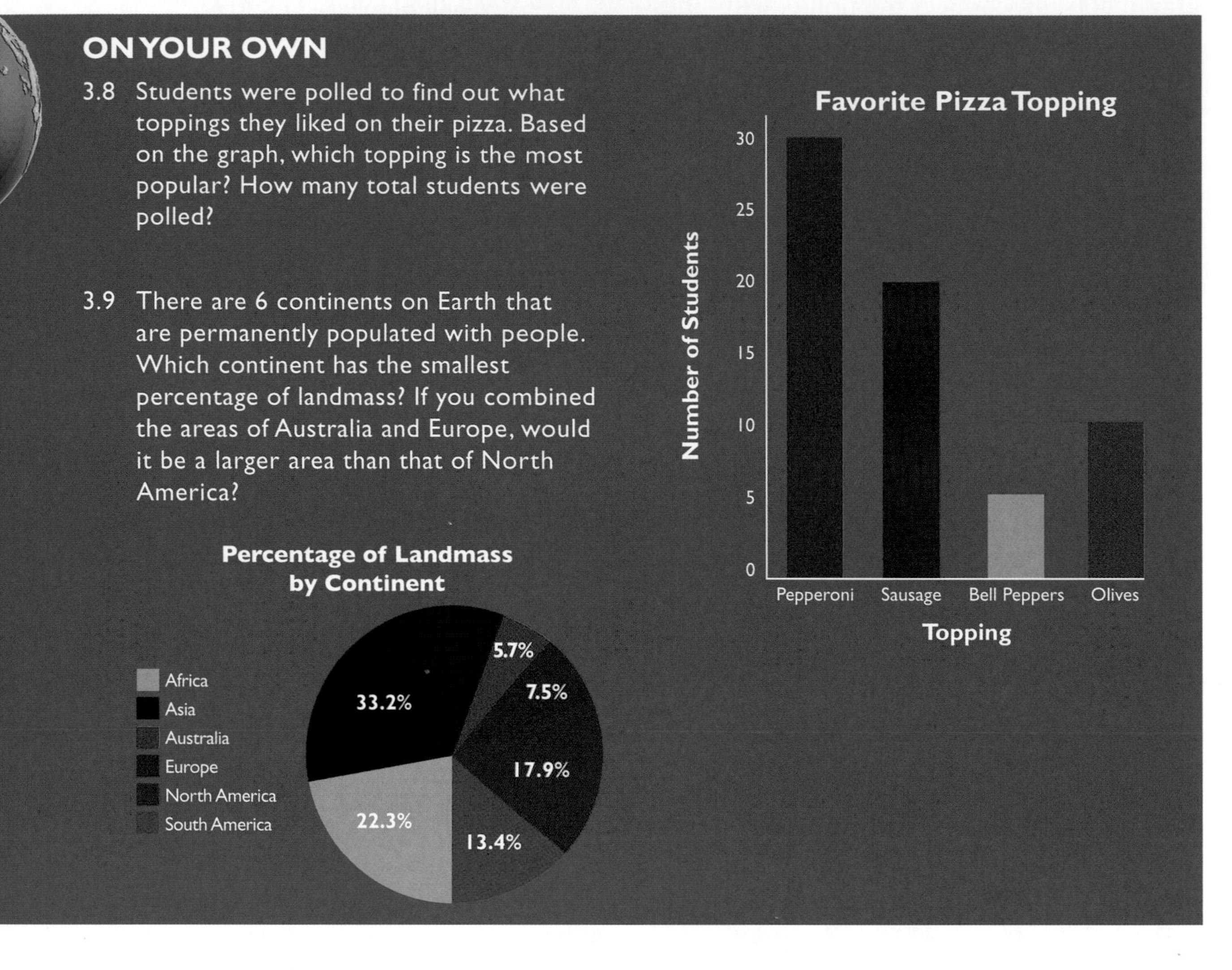

SUMMING UP

This module brought you through the process of designing and recording experiments. The process will help you to figure out the best procedure to explore a question you might have when studying a scientific subject. Using the scientific method to answer a question is most useful when it is done in a way to remove unwanted variables so your results are as accurate as possible. Reporting your results is also a critical part of the scientific process because it is important to convey the information so that others are best able to understand it.

ANSWERS TO THE "ON YOUR OWN" QUESTIONS

3.1 There are at least 3 experimental variables. First, **the brand of floor cleaner used** is a variable because he uses a different brand on each quarter of the floor. Second, **the amount of black heel marks in each quarter** will be different. There is just no way he can scuff up the floor equally on all quarters. Third, **the amount and effectiveness of the scrubbing** will vary. Most likely, he will get tired, and his arm will become fatigued as time goes on. Thus, he will scrub less vigorously in the last quarter than on the first quarter. There may be more, but these are the most obvious. Don't worry if you didn't get them all—just use this as a learning experience.

3.2 **The student will learn something from the brand of floor cleaner used.** That's the whole purpose of the experiment. The cleanest quarter will indicate the best floor cleaner. **He should reduce or eliminate the variable amount of black heel marks on each quarter and the variable amount and effectiveness of the scrubbing.**

3.3 **He can reduce the variable amount of black heel marks by examining each quarter closely and trying to even out the amount of black heel marks so they are the same on each quarter. He can reduce the variable amount and effectiveness of the scrubbing by taking breaks to ensure he is not tired. He could also count the number of strokes and make sure he scrubs with the same number of strokes on each quarter.**

3.4 **See the table below.** You might have a slightly different setup than I have. For example, you could have created 3 columns: Item, Attracted to Magnet, and Not Attracted to Magnet. As long as you have presented the data in an understandable way, with properly labeled rows and columns, it is fine if your table doesn't look exactly like mine.

MAGNETIC ATTRACTION

Item	Attracted to Magnet
steel rod	yes
pencil	no
paper clip	yes
metal washer	yes
glass marble	no
paper	no

3.5 The variable of part of an experiment to which all other variables will be compared is called the **control.**

3.6 **The student can time how long it takes for the car to go down the ramp without any spoiler at all.** That will be the control trial to which he can compare the other trials with spoilers.

3.7 The variables in this experiment include **plant type, pot size, soil type, environmental conditions, quantity of water, and fertilizer type. All of these variables, with the exception of fertilizer type should be eliminated** so that all plants are the same type, in the same-sized pot, with the same environmental conditions (light and temperature) and the same amount of water. **The type of fertilizer is the factor we want to explore, so *that* is the variable we want to keep. The control trial in this experiment will be the plant that has no fertilizer.** That way, you can compare the growth of the plants with fertilizer to the control to see if fertilizer helps them to grow better than the control plants without any fertilizer.

3.8 **Pepperoni** is the most popular topping because the bar extends up the highest with 30 students preferring it. **There were 65 students polled.** If you read the number that each bar reaches and add them up, you get 30 + 20 + 5 + 10, which equals 65 students in all.

3.9 **The smallest landmass is Australia,** because the smallest wedge on the graph is yellow at 5.7%, and the legend informs us that yellow represents Australia. **North America takes up more area on Earth than Australia and Europe combined.** The land areas of Australia and Europe are 5.7% and 7.5% respectively. We know this because Australia's area is the yellow wedge and Europe's area is the orange one. When we add those together, we get 13.2%, which is still smaller than the area of North America, which is represented by the green wedge at 17.9%.

STUDY GUIDE FOR MODULE 3

1. Match the following words with their definitions.

   a. Experimental variable

   b. Control (of an experiment)

   c. Blind experiments

   d. Double-blind experiments

   Experiments in which neither the experimenters nor the participants know the objects' identities in the setup

   Experiments in which information about the test is kept from the participants to reduce bias

   The variable of part of an experiment to which all others will be compared

   An aspect of an experiment that changes during the course of the experiment

Answer questions 2–3 based on this information: A scientist is testing if plants can grow well under fluorescent light bulbs. He places one tray of sunflower seedlings in a windowless room underneath a row of fluorescent light bulbs. He places another tray of the same number of seedlings in full sunlight. He turned off the light bulbs during the evening hours. The plants were each given the same amount of water each day, and at the end of 4 weeks, the height of each was measured.

2. Which variable in the experiment is being tested (and thus is the desired variable)?

3. What variables did the scientist try to reduce or eliminate?

4. Create a table from the information in the experiment below.

   A student performed an experiment to determine the time it took to freeze pure water as compared to water with 2 different amounts of salt. She measured 40 mL of water into 3 equal-sized measuring cups. She didn't add any salt to the first cup. She dissolved 5 g of salt into the second cup and dissolved 10 g of salt into the third cup. After placing all the cups in the freezer, she identified how long it took for each to become solid. The plain water froze after 40 minutes. The container with 5 g of salt froze after 67 minutes. The container with 10 g of salt froze after 115 minutes.

5. Multiple choice:

   The variable of part of an experiment to which all other variables will be compared is called the ______________.

   a. variable b. scientific method c. control d. hypothesis

6. Forensic science is when scientific practices are applied to solving criminal investigations. In some cases, a police officer will show a set of photos of people to a witness and ask him to identify a person he saw committing a crime. The officer is not from the city in which the crime was committed and has no previous knowledge of the crime. Is this a blind or double-blind procedure? Why do you think so?

7–9 **Multiple Choice. Answer questions based on the following graph:**

A group of students competed in a design-and-build model car race. They each constructed cars from recyclable materials and timed their speed going down a ramp. After the first round, they had the opportunity to upgrade or change the design of their cars and race them again. The results are in the graph below.

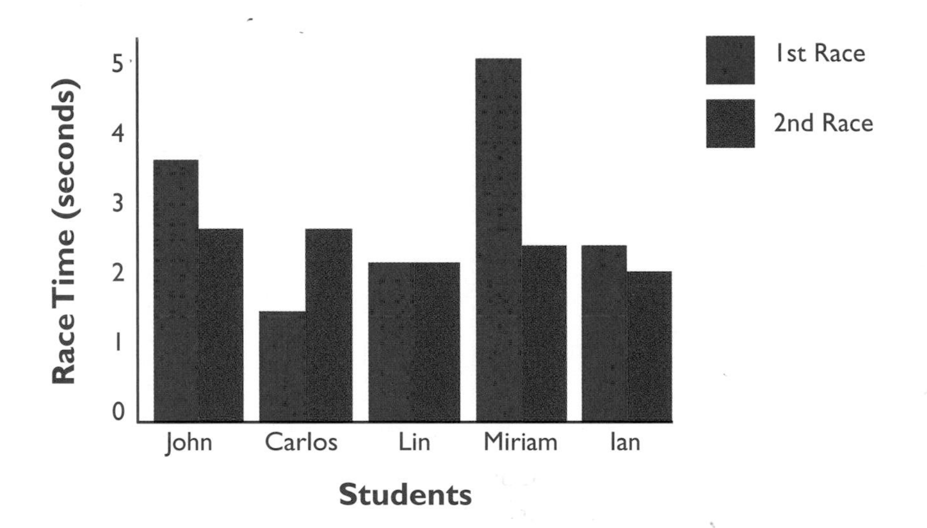

7. What type of graph is this?

a. circle graph b. bar graph c. line graph d. double bar graph

8. Which student won the first race?

a. Carlos b. Lin c. Ian d. John

9. Which student best improved his or her time between the first and second race?

a. Lin b. John c. Miriam d. Carlos

10–12 Multiple Choice. Answer questions based on the following graph:

Country Farms is a family business that began growing tomatoes in 2008. Each year, they kept a record of how many bushels (1 bushel = about 50 lb) of tomatoes they produced from their 5-acre plot of land.

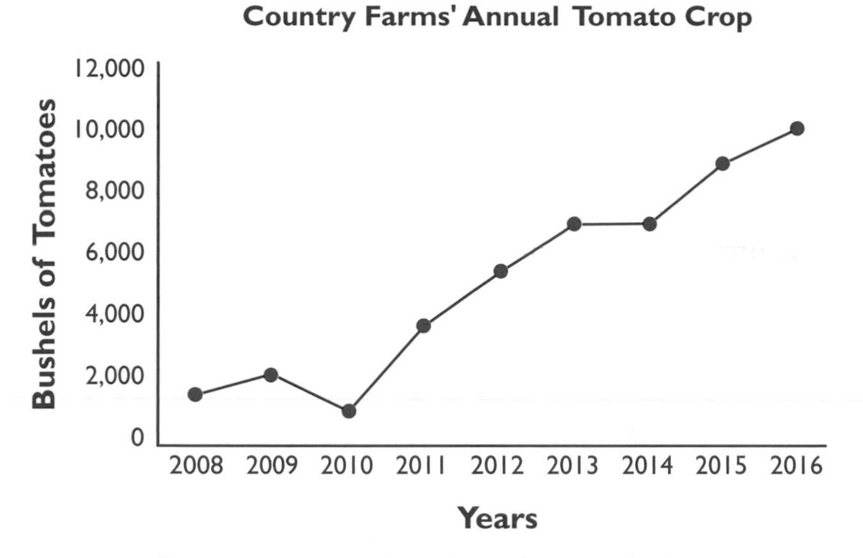

10. Which year was the tomato crop less than the year before?

    a. 2010 b. 2016 c. 2012 d. 2013

11. Which year did the farm produce the same amount of tomatoes as the year before?

    a. 2015 b. 2009 c. 2014 d. 2013

12. BONUS QUESTION: Based on the entire graph and assuming growing conditions were the same in 2017 as the earlier years, which of these numbers might be a good prediction for the number of bushels produced in 2017?

    a. 10,000 b. 8,000 c. 11,000

SCIENTIFIC ANALYSIS AND HISTORY

You might have figured out that we are systematically going through the process of science, beginning with its history, learning the proper way to practice it through the scientific method, and then documenting and interpreting results. Well, I am going to use this module to go deeper into how science can be applied in all areas, even history. You see, this course is taking you through a true study of *general* science. We will cover the major scientific areas of physical creation and living creation. In future modules, we will explore several branches of science, ranging from astronomy and ecology to chemistry and biology. But many of these fields are filled with controversy, particularly on how to approach the data we have in order to most accurately interpret and report them. This is a very important module in our course, and I believe it is one that all Christians should study (including parents!). Why? We all need to have a firm grounding in the nature of science in order to know how to deal with the controversies we will encounter.

Quaestio

How do we study things that happened in the past? Of course, people, places and events that happened 100 years ago are documented in newspapers, photos, and books. But what about events that occurred thousands of years ago? How do we study them from a scientific perspective? We will delve into these ideas in this module.

FIGURE 4.1
A Scientist at Work

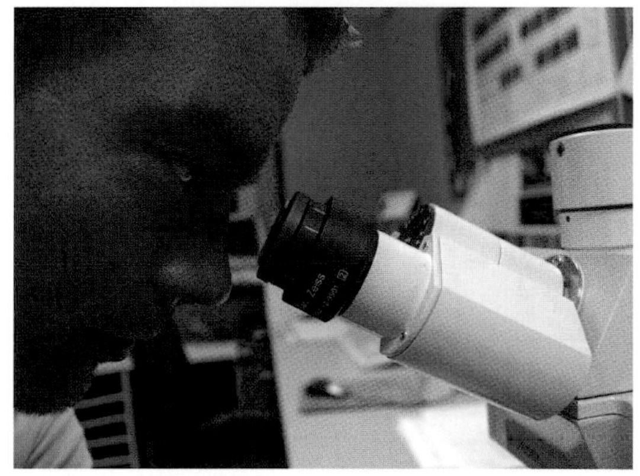

PURE SCIENCE, APPLIED SCIENCE, AND TECHNOLOGY

The title of this section lists 3 distinct scientific pursuits. Interestingly, the differences between them is rarely taught, so many people do not even know there is a difference. But they are uniquely different. It has to do with the motivation behind them. **Pure science,** for example, is motivated by curiosity to understand. So a scientist does experiments designed to explain some feature of creation. However, a pure scientist has no interest in whether the knowledge gained is *useful*. He or she just wants the knowledge to satisfy a personal curiosity.

Now, **applied science** is very different from pure science. In applied science, the experiments are designed to discover or identify something useful. For example, an applied scientist will look at a process and think, "There must be a faster way to do this." Or he might think "There must be a less expensive way to do this." Each thought can influence him to do experiments that are aimed at the goal of coming up with a machine or procedure that will make that process go at a faster rate or a lesser cost.

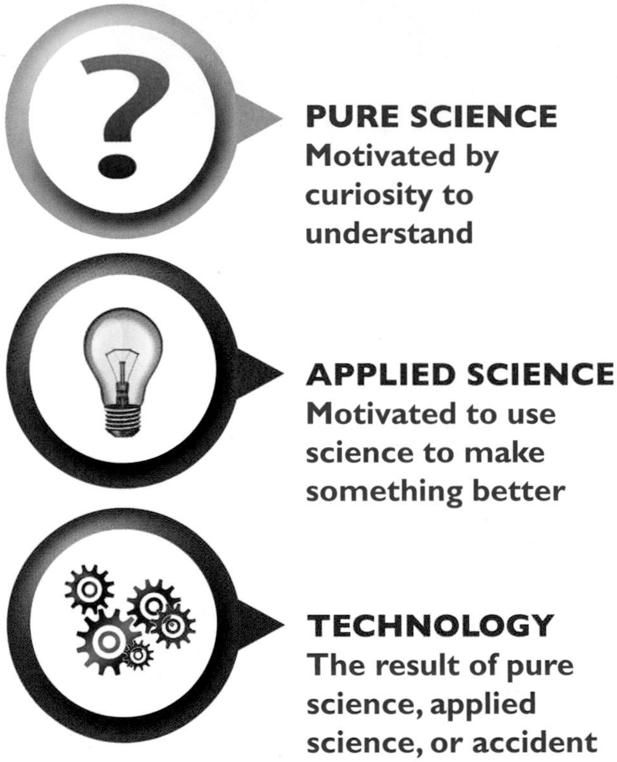

Pure science is primarily focused on asking questions with the goal of learning *why* something in creation happens the way it does. So scientists will make observations, do background research, form hypotheses, do experiments, and attempt to draw conclusions to explain the *why*. Applied science has a completely different goal. Applied science wants to use science *to make something better.*

FIGURE 4.2
3 Types of Science

PURE SCIENCE
Motivated by curiosity to understand

APPLIED SCIENCE
Motivated to use science to make something better

TECHNOLOGY
The result of pure science, applied science, or accident

Now, **technology** is different from both science and applied science. Technology is a new process or machine that makes life better or makes a job easier. It might sound very similar to applied science, but there is a distinction. You see, technology is the result of applied science or pure science. And it can be the result of an accident, too.

To make this easier for you to understand, think about what you learned about the ancient Egyptians. Remember that during their time, they had the best medical practices of anyone in their known world. One of those practices was to place moldy bread on open wounds to prevent infection. This discovery was a result of accident. The Egyptian doctors tried lots of treatments for open wounds, but many of those treatments made patients *worse*. Eventually, someone tried to use moldy bread and the wound healed quickly. So the practice became a regular medical procedure.

That account is an example of technology. The process of putting moldy bread on open wounds makes life better because it allows people to heal faster, and it was discovered by accident. You might be surprised to think of this as technology. That's because when most people think of technology, they think of machines such as computers, televisions, and airplanes. And, yes, those are examples of technology because they make people's lives better, but they are not the only examples. Any invention or process that makes life better or a job easier is technology. So the ancient Egyptians had lots of technology, even though much of it was the result of accident.

think about this

Science is, in many ways, dependent on technology. You see, the better our technology, the better the science we can do. For example, as telescopes get more powerful, we are able to see more of the heavens. In fact, science and technology do a bit of a circular dance...the more we see, the more we learn, the more we come up with new questions to ask and then develop ways to answer them.

EXPLORE MORE

Look through a drawer in your desk and see how many items you would consider to be a result of technology. Remember, technology is a process or machine that makes life better or makes a job easier. All items of technology are not necessarily machines, so you might be surprised to find more than you think!

ON YOUR OWN

4.1 Identify each of the experiments described below as a pure science experiment or applied science experiment.

a. An experiment designed to figure out why rainbows form in the sky
b. An experiment designed to determine how to make a field produce more crops
c. An experiment designed to make a television have a sharper picture
d. An experiment designed to determine the factors that influence the speed of wind

4.2 Which of the following would be considered technology?

a. An explanation of how clouds form
b. A microwave oven
c. A recipe to make cement
d. A description of the life cycle of a grasshopper

ARCHAEOLOGY

I began discussing science at the beginning of this course by covering the history of science. But to better understand all the branches of science, we need to go further. Until now, the historical information we used was recorded by historians. After all, there are historical records that are several thousands of years old. Many of these tell us about people, nations, animals, and plants that lived a long time ago. And that gives us some information, but we will need more if we are to get a good understanding of general science. **Life science,** for example, represents a big area of science.

Life science—A term that encompasses all scientific pursuits related to living organisms

In order to better study life science, we will need to go beyond historical records. That's because the further we go back in history, the increasingly scarce the records become. So we need something to help supplement the historical record. One tool we can use to accomplish this is **archaeology.**

Archaeology—The study of past human life as revealed by preserved relics

Scientists in the field of archaeology try to learn more about the people who lived in the past by studying what those people left behind.

History usually centers on what happened to people in the past. Archaeology concentrates on studying human relics and **artifacts.**

Artifacts—Objects made by people, such as tools, weapons, containers, etc.

FIGURE 4.3
The Archaeological Site of Kourion

The urban center of Kourion on the island of Cyprus was a bustling city during ancient Roman times. Ptolemy, an ancient author, mentions the city in his writings.

Therefore, history and archaeology are great tools for learning about the history of human life, but how do we learn about the animals and plants that have lived on Earth in the past? Well, to accomplish this task, we must focus on 2 more fields of science: **geology** (gee awl' uh jee) and **paleontology** (pay' lee uhn tall' uh jee).

> **Geology**—The study of Earth's history as revealed in the rocks that make up the Earth

> **Paleontology**—The study of life's history as revealed in the preserved remains of once-living organisms

Those 2 fields of science are fascinating and can reveal a lot about what happened in Earth's history. But you will soon see that they are also 2 of the most misinterpreted fields of science. That means it is extremely important that we carefully work to understand exactly what these interesting fields of science can tell us and the proper way to study them.

> **ON YOUR OWN**
>
> 4.3 Archaeologists study the past by looking at preserved items. Paleontologists also study the past by looking at preserved items. One major difference between these scientists is the type of preserved items they study. What are those items?

HISTORICAL RECORDS

Let's dig a little deeper into the field of archaeology. When it comes to history, archaeology is a bit limited because it focuses on the artifacts made by people. Yet it is a great way to learn about the history of civilizations.

Some civilizations have few or no historical records, and archaeology can provide some clues to how those people groups lived. It is best used, however, for uncovering and clarifying the history of civilizations for which we *do* have historical records. It helps to support those records and fill in the gaps of what we know.

A good example of this is the Roman Empire. It is likely you have heard of this ancient civilization, and you might already know several details about it. Or how about the accounts of ancient Egypt or the old Chinese dynasties? Is there a way to confirm that the historical facts you learned are really true? You might have learned about these civilizations by watching movies or reading historical fiction books.

But what makes something trustworthy? After all, anyone can record information about an ancient culture and then publish it. How can we make sure what they are writing is true? Well, we could compare their writing to a history

FIGURE 4.4
A Page from the Codex Vaticanus

This page from the Codex Vaticanus, one of the oldest existing manuscripts of the Greek Bible, has a note in the margin where a Medieval scribe criticized the previous scribe for changing the text. It reads "Fool and knave, leave the old reading, don't change it!"

textbook. But how do we know that history textbook is accurate? Our knowledge of history comes from books, so how do we know that the authors of the *history* books aren't in error?

Well, the field of **textual criticism** deals with just those questions. This field does exactly what the name suggests: critically examining texts to determine if they are accurate. There are many ways to do this, including looking at the "family tree" of the text, or in other words, how copies were made from the original document and whether they are accurate or not. Another way is the **copy-text method** where a critic looks at the base text and looks for corrections that may have been made to it in future copies.

In Figure 4.4, you can see how the copy-text method would identify that corrections were made in this text when comparing it to a copy that came before it. The scribe made a harsh comment in the margin regarding the previous copier having altered words, and this helps us to understand that there was a deep concern for preserving the Bible in its original condition!

Perhaps one of the most used methods takes any historical document (a clay tablet, a scroll, a book, etc.) and puts it through 3 tests using the critical process called **eclecticism** (ek lek' tih sizm). This fancy name just means that a wide variety of tests are used comparing the document in question to other documents, known historical facts, or even to itself. It is a good method because any questions identified by one test can be possibly answered with another.

FIGURE 4.5
Hieroglyphics

This is an example of ancient Egyptian writing known as hieroglyphics (hi' ruh glif' iks). In essence, it is writing that uses symbols and pictures to represent concepts and sounds. This series of symbols relates a story. Some of what we know about ancient Egypt comes from translating hieroglyphics.

The 3 tests are the **internal test,** the **external test,** and the **bibliographic** (bib lee uh graf' ik) **test.** Each of the 3 tests is designed to look at a document from a different angle. If a work passes all 3 tests, it is considered a legitimate work of history. If it fails even *one* of them, it is not considered an authentic historical work; it may have other uses, but as a historical document, it is not considered to be reliable.

These 3 tests compare the document in question to lots of other data. And that is a good thing. In the same way that we have to get rid of as many unwanted variables as possible in an experiment in order to have the most accurate results and remove bias, people have to be careful not to use bias when they look at historical documents, too. The more sources they use to compare, the less subjective their results can be.

THE INTERNAL TEST

The internal test looks at whether the document agrees with itself. That just means the document cannot make a statement and then disagree with that statement in another part of the document. That makes sense, doesn't it? After all, if a document disagrees with itself, it is not likely to be a reliable document.

Actually, using the internal test can be more of a challenge than you might think. That is because many ancient history documents are written in ancient languages. For example, if an archaeologist finds a scroll that is supposed to be a history of ancient Greece, it is likely written in ancient Greek. However, even though Greek is a language spoken today, modern Greek is very different from ancient Greek. That's because languages change over time, so the Greek language spoken today is very different from the Greek spoken ages ago.

Below is a good example to illustrate what I mean:

Whan that April with his showres soote
The droughte of March hath perced to the roote
And bathed every vein in swich licour
Of which vertu engendred is the flowr

Can you guess in what language that phrase is written? You might be surprised to know it is *English*! That passage is from the General Prologue of Geoffrey Chaucer's *The Canterbury Tales*. It is a collection of stories written in English about 600 years ago, but you can see how it barely resembles the English we speak today. And that is only over a period of 600 years. Imagine how much older documents differ in language from the modern version.

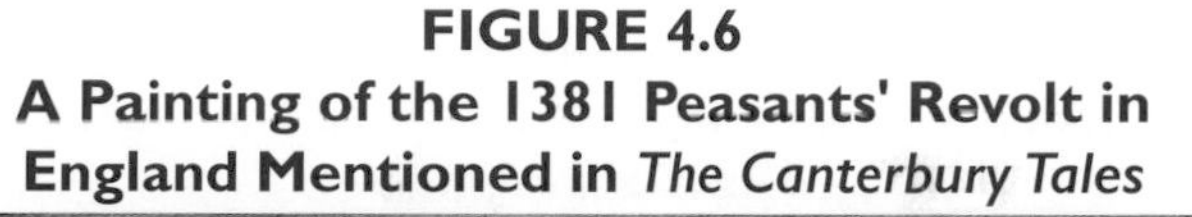

FIGURE 4.6
A Painting of the 1381 Peasants' Revolt in England Mentioned in *The Canterbury Tales*

Because languages change over time, the more time that goes by, the more difficult it will be to understand the language. That can make it difficult to identify inconsistencies within a document. What might look like a contradiction to us might not be once the original language is considered. So historians who apply the internal test to a document will often give some leeway to an inconsistency they find. If 2 passages seem to disagree, then they are not to be counted as a contradiction if there is a legitimate explanation that can resolve that contradiction. I'll talk more about that in the following section.

The Internal Test and the Bible

It's a good idea to see how historians evaluate historical documents using the internal test. So, I will go through some examples of applying it to the Bible. Some people say that the Bible contradicts itself. Well, that is a common misconception, particularly if those contradictions are further studied.

An example of a biblical contradiction often suggested has to do with the genealogies of Christ. The New Testament contains 2 genealogies: one in the book of Matthew, chapter 1, and the other in the book of Luke, chapter 3. At first, they appear to disagree with each other. For example, Matthew 1:16 says, "Jacob the father of Joseph the husband of Mary, of whom Jesus was born," and Luke 3:23 says Jesus was "being the son (as was supposed) of Joseph, the son of Heli." So who is Joseph's father: Jacob or Heli? Is this an inconsistency? Actually, it is not. When studied more carefully, these 2 genealogies are complementary, not contradictory. That's because Matthew's genealogy represents Joseph's family line, and Luke's represents Mary's family.

You see, you have to understand the culture of the writers of that time period. Women were not considered very historically important to the ancient Jews, so their names didn't appear in most genealogies. A historian would trace the family line of a woman by using the name of the woman's husband instead of her own name. We know that Luke was highly educated and knew that a person is Jewish based solely on the mother. If a person's mother is a Jew, then her children are Jews. But because women were not traditionally mentioned in genealogies, he used Joseph's name. So you can see that by taking a closer look at the *cultural context* of the passage, what might seem like an inconsistency is not. And that is true of many of the supposed contradictions in the Bible.

FIGURE 4.7
Paul's Conversion on the Way to Damascus by Caravaggio

Another supposed contradiction is a result of the difficulty in translation. The book of Acts has an account of Paul's conversion in chapter 9 which seems to contradict the account in chapter 22. But with an understanding of the original Greek language in which these passages were written, they are seen to be complementary and not contradictory.

These accounts have to do with the men accompanying Paul on his journey to Damascus. Acts 9:7 says, "The men who were traveling with him stood speechless, hearing the voice but seeing no one." So they *heard the voice* coming from the vision. But Acts 22:9 says, "Now those who were with me saw the light but did not understand the voice of the one who was speaking to me." This account seems to say that the men did not hear the voice coming from the vision. Is this a contradiction?

The Greek word *akouo* is used in both verses and is translated as "to hear." But in Greek, when verbs are constructed in different cases, their meanings differ. In Acts 9:7, *akouo* is in the genitive case, and in Acts 22:9, it is in the accusative case. The genitive case implies that only sounds were heard; but in the accusative case, it implies that speech was both heard *and* understood. So when we look at the passages together, understanding the verb usage, then we see that Paul's attendants did, indeed, *hear* sounds coming from Paul's vision (Acts 9:7), but they did not *hear and understand* those sounds (Acts 22:9).

ON YOUR OWN

4.4 The English language has changed a lot over time. Explore this phenomenon by drawing a line from a word's old definition through the correct "process of change" to the new definition.

	Old Definition	Process of Change	New Definition
Spinster:	a woman who spins	Lowest-ranking individual at university	Bad behavior
Fathom:	to encircle with one's arms	Unmarried women held jobs	Unmarried man
Bachelor:	a young knight	Having no morals	A piece of evidence to solve something
Naughty:	having nothing	Threading one's way through a maze	
Clue:	a ball of yarn	Measurement of outstretched arms to understand depth	Understand after much thought
			Unmarried woman

THE EXTERNAL TEST

The second test applied to historical documents is the external test. This test asks the question, "Does the document contradict other known historical facts?" So scientists will compare the document of interest to other documents that have already passed the 3 tests. Because those documents are considered to be historically reliable, then anything that contradicts them is likely not a reliable document. Keep in mind that the older a document is, fewer and fewer documents exist for comparison. Yet, the external test has another component. It also compares the statements in the document to *known archaeological facts*. So if a document references a city, then archaeology might be able to confirm or deny the existence of that city.

FIGURE 4.8
Archaeology and the External Test

Archaeology confirms this place in Athens, Greece, is the famous Areopagus (also called Mars Hill) where trials were held and people came to argue and debate. Its existence can be used to provide evidence for or against a historical document. For example, the Bible tells us that Paul went there to debate Christianity with the Athenians (Acts 17:16-34). The fact that it puts Paul at the proper place for debate in Athens provides external evidence for the truth of the account.

The External Test and the Bible

A document being studied should, to some extent, overlap with other accepted historical works. That makes it more credible. Additionally, it must be consistent with any archaeological discoveries for that time period. The more overlapping and more archaeological discoveries, the better the document passes the external test. However, it can be quite a task to do this for the Bible because it is a work that covers such a long time period. In fact, many parts of the Old Testament report on events that occurred so long ago that they have no external historical works to which they can be compared. In addition, there must be a good amount of skepticism when comparing documents written during the New Testament time period because many of the authors were sympathetic to the Christian church. That means those authors might not have been completely objective when they speak of matters reported in the New Testament. Conversely, many historical documents written during that time period were written by Jewish leaders who were anti-Christian, and therefore their accounts might also be biased.

Those reasons are why most historians consider archaeological discoveries as the primary data used in applying the external test to the Bible. However, there are some authors during that time period who can be considered objective.

Cornelius Tacitus was a Roman who wrote several works that are considered to be very accurate histories of the first century AD. His major work, *Annals*, mentions the existence of Christ and his death by Pontius Pilate, which perfectly agrees with the accounts written in the Bible. Tacitus also mentions specific cities and rulers who are discussed in the Bible. Each of these cases is consistent with what is written in the New Testament.

Another well-respected, non-Christian historian of that time period was Flavius Josephus. Josephus was a Jew who wrote a history of the Jewish people in an attempt to create better feelings between the Romans and the Jews. His major work, *Antiquities of the Jews*, mentions not only Christ's death at the order of Pontius Pilate, but also that some of his followers claimed to see him alive three days later.

The Bible also is demonstrated to be an accurate source of history when it is compared to archaeological discoveries. In fact, there is no way I can even briefly cover all the archaeological discoveries that have confirmed certain biblical passages. But I will give you 2 examples. The first has to do with the Old Testament book of Genesis, chapter 14. The text describes a series of ancient battles. During one of the battles, Lot, who was Abram's nephew, was captured. Abram took a group of men and fought against the group that captured Lot, defeated them, and rescued his nephew. Up to the early 1900s, this account was believed by many historians to be false. However, since that time, a number of archaeological discoveries have confirmed the historicity of this account. The discovery of the Mari Tablets in 1933 gives evidence that the kings mentioned in these battles did exist and that long-distance battles were fought at that time in history. Important archaeological evidence was discovered, also, confirming that the cities mentioned in the account were indeed at war during that time.

FIGURE 4.9
Depiction of the Separation of Abraham and Lot (by Wenceslaus Hollar 1607–1677)

FIGURE 4.10
One of the Mari Tablets

The Mari Tablets are stone tablets discovered by French archaeologists in 1933. There are 23,000 in all, and they contain quite a bit of information about the kingdom of Mari, an ancient kingdom on the west bank of the Euphrates River. It existed before and during the lives of Abraham, Isaac, and Jacob, so the tablets deal with much of the same history as the Old Testament. They describe the customs of the Mari kingdom, as well as giving names of people who lived during that time. These tablets mention King Arioch from Genesis 14, indicating that he was a real person. In addition, they mention Nahor, a city discussed in Genesis 24:10.

creation connection

In 1918, William F. Albright, an archaeologist, wrote an article in the *Journal of Biblical Literature* stating that he believed all of Genesis 14 was either borrowed from a legend or completely made up. However, after the supporting archaeological evidence for this chapter was discovered, he was forced to change his mind. He went from believing the story was a fabrication to being forced by the data to admit he was in error. In fact, Albright went on to say that archaeology has confirmed the historicity of the Old Testament. His conversion gives more support to the convincing ability of archaeological evidence.

The New Testament is well-known for its archaeological support. One of the best examples has to do with the historical details in Acts. Many scholars used to believe that because there was no evidence for many of the people or titles mentioned by Luke that they were errors. But since the late 1800s, first century inscriptions have been discovered that mention Sergius Paulus (13:7), Gallio (18:12), and Erastus (19:22). Luke was also criticized for wrongly calling the rulers of Thessalonika "politarchs" (17:6)." But since 1876, thirty-two inscriptions have been found that include that title.

There is a huge amount of archaeological evidence that helps the Bible to pass the external test. More archaeological attention has been paid to its contents than any other source of ancient history, so we can say that the Bible passes the external test better than any other ancient history text.

ON YOUR OWN

4.5 An archaeologist discovers a document that claims to be a history of the Sumerian people. It mentions a battle that was fought at a great fortress in a certain region of the Sumerian empire. Archaeologists look in that area and find the remains of a tiny village, but no indications of a fortress or a great battle. Which test does this document fail?

THE BIBLIOGRAPHIC TEST

In order to be a reliable document, a work should have either direct eyewitness accounts or a secondhand report *based* on those eyewitness accounts. However, those accounts are often recorded shortly after the events took place, so how can we know they haven't been changed over time? One of the problems is that we have practically no original documents from any ancient work of history. And this is an important thing. Virtually every document we have that has to do with the Roman Empire, ancient Egypt, ancient China, and other similar cultures is a *copy* of some original document that once existed.

So how do we know the words in a text are actually the words from the original work? Well, this is one of the biggest problems with historical works. You see, in those days, the only way to copy documents was to do it by hand. It took lots and lots of time, caused hand and eye fatigue, and was often filled with errors. Not many individuals could do it, either. To copy a document, a person who could read and write (skills that very few had in ancient times) would have to painstakingly read a few words at a time and then carefully write them. It could take hours to do just one page of work, so the cost of copying a document was very high.

FIGURE 4.11
A Scribe

Oftentimes, the person paying for the copy would suggest some of the information be changed. Perhaps a king wanted to change things he didn't like in order to make himself look more powerful. How can we tell whether a document that has been copied is indeed accurate?

Well, that is where the bibliographic test is used. This test asks 2 questions. First, it asks how many years have passed between the time the original work was written and the time of the first known copy. The shorter the time span, the more reliable the document is. That's because the shorter time span means there would have been less chance for alterations to occur. Second, the bibliographic test asks how many different copies made by different people exist for the document of interest. If there are many copies by many different people and they all are basically the same, then it is very unlikely that they are modified from the original document. That's because all of the copiers would have had to make the same changes, and because communication from one place to another was difficult in those days, that would be highly unlikely.

Thus, the shorter the time span between copies and the larger the number of copies made by different people, the more reliable a document is. We refer to the original document's copies as supporting documents because they support the validity of the document of interest.

The Bibliographic Test and the Bible

Remember, in order for a document to pass the bibliographic test, there has to be a relatively short amount of time between copy and original and there have to be several copies made by different people. If the document is very old it must have been copied several times in order to survive to the present day. Now before I go into how the Bible stands up to the bibliographic test, let's get an idea of how other ancient documents fare.

FIGURE 4.12
Portions of the Dead Sea Scrolls in the Amman Museum

Cornelius Tacitus has written histories that are considered to be accurate accounts of the events that occurred in the Roman Empire during the first century AD. In fact, his *Annals* are responsible for a great amount of the facts we know concerning the Roman Empire. His works exist in 2 manuscripts today. The first one is written sometime near AD 850, and the second one is from the mid-11th century. From those 2 manuscripts are 31 copies that we have today.

Like Tacitus, Pliny the Elder was a historian of the first century AD. His *Natural History* is considered to be a scientific authority up to the Middle Ages. It is supported by 200 manuscripts that mostly come from the 14th and 15th centuries, and a partial manuscript coming from the end of the fifth century, representing 500 years after the original writing.

This is pretty common for ancient works. Some works are supported by more copies than the examples I mentioned, and others are supported by fewer. The elapsed time between the original works of Pliny the Elder and the earliest existing copies represents one of the shorter time spans related to ancient historical documents.

Let's compare those numbers to the New Testament. It is supported by over 5,800 different copies in several languages, and the earliest was written only 40 years after the original! The differences between these 5,800 copies are extremely small, which indicates that the New Testament we have today is completely faithful to the original text. Think about those numbers. They indicate that the New Testament passes the bibliographic test *better than any other historical work of its time*!

Now let's consider the Old Testament. Does it pass the bibliographic test as well as the New Testament? Well, no, but you wouldn't expect it to because the Old Testament works are much, much more ancient. Yet, the Old Testament still passes the bibliographic test better than any other historical document of its time.

FIGURE 4.13
Bibliographic Test of Ancient Texts

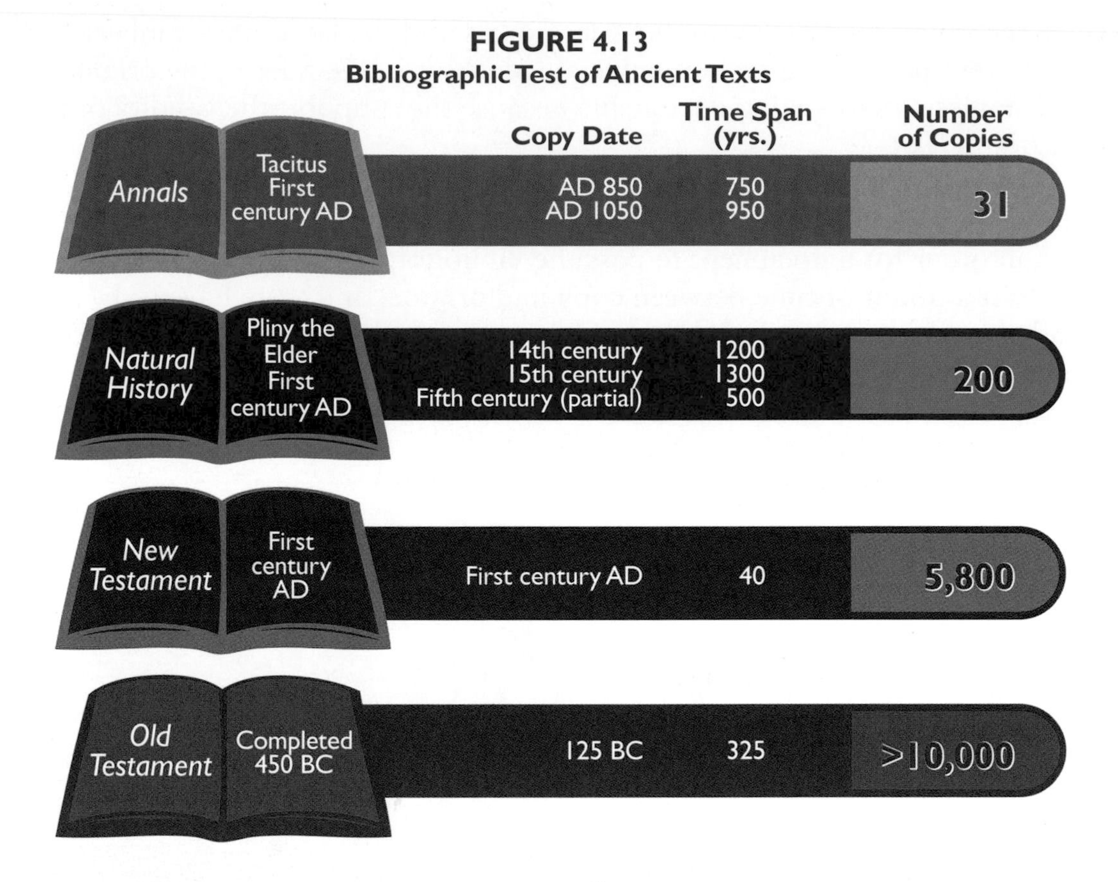

creation connection

Some accounts of events in the Bible are rather hard to believe from a scientific standpoint. For example, what about the worldwide Flood during Noah's time? The biblical account reveals that a worldwide Flood occurred as judgment by God, and the only people to survive were Noah and his family. But there are many reasons to believe this event occurred. First, the Bible is the most historically valid document of that time, passing all the historical tests with flying colors, and if you start to reject parts of biblical history, you are departing from the science behind it (let alone faith!) and are making up the rules as you go. However, there is plenty of evidence from other sources to support this event's occurrence. There is geological evidence as well as many stories throughout the world from many cultures giving accounts of a great flood. Babylonian tablets dating to 2000 BC have a story called the "Gilgamesh Epic" which tells of a wise man and his family who are the sole survivors of a great flood. Greek mythology mentions Deukalion and Pyrrha, the king and queen of northern Greece, who survived a great flood. The natives of Polynesia, Central America, South America, South Asia, China, and Japan all have similar stories, too. Isn't it interesting that so many cultures have a tale of an ancient, massive flood? The cultures had no contact with each other during those times, yet they share the same story.

A good way to illustrate this is with the example of the Dead Sea Scrolls (Figure 4.12). Before 1947, the earliest existing copy of some parts of the Old Testament came from the Cairo Codex, written about AD 895. Now, the last events of the Old Testament were supposed to have occurred sometime around 450 BC, which means that there is a notable span of time between the original writings and the first available copies. But in 1947, the Dead Sea Scrolls were discovered. They have copies of parts of several hundred ancient books. In fact, one of the scrolls has a complete copy of the Old Testament book of Isaiah. Archaeologists date that scroll as having been written in 125 BC, and the version of Isaiah it has is word-for-word identical with the standard Hebrew Bible in more than 95% of the text. The other 5% are variations that were obvious slips of the pen or variations in spelling. So this means in over 1,000 years, the book of Isaiah was copied faithfully. We can presume the rest of the Old Testament was copied with the same care, too. This greatly supports the already convincing data that support the bibliographic reliability of the Old Testament.

So the Bible passes the bibliographic test better than any other ancient work. When combined with the fact that the Bible passes the internal test just as well as other ancient documents in history, and it passes the external test better than any document of its time, you can come to the scientific conclusion that the accounts in the Bible are, in fact, more trustworthy than the written accounts of ancient Rome, ancient Egypt, or any other ancient life!

AGE TESTING AND DENDROCHRONOLOGY

Archaeological finds also have great value in helping us to learn about people and civilizations that are not recorded in historical documents. Artifacts can be found from almost every known civilization, and we can learn a lot about ancient people as long as we are careful to understand that these artifacts probably do not give a *complete* picture. That means all conclusions we come to are tentative.

Often, it is difficult to determine how old an artifact is. Sometimes the artifact itself can give us a clue. Ancient coins, for example, might bear the date or the name of the ruler at the time they were minted

ON YOUR OWN

4.6 The last several sections spent a lot of time explaining the 3 types of eclecticism, which consists of 3 tests that compare a document in question to other documents, known historical facts, or even to itself. This helps to thoroughly test a work in question. A good way to sum up these 3 tests is to create an infographic, but instead of providing one for you, you get to finish a partially completed one. Fill in the blank spaces that cover the 3 types of tests.

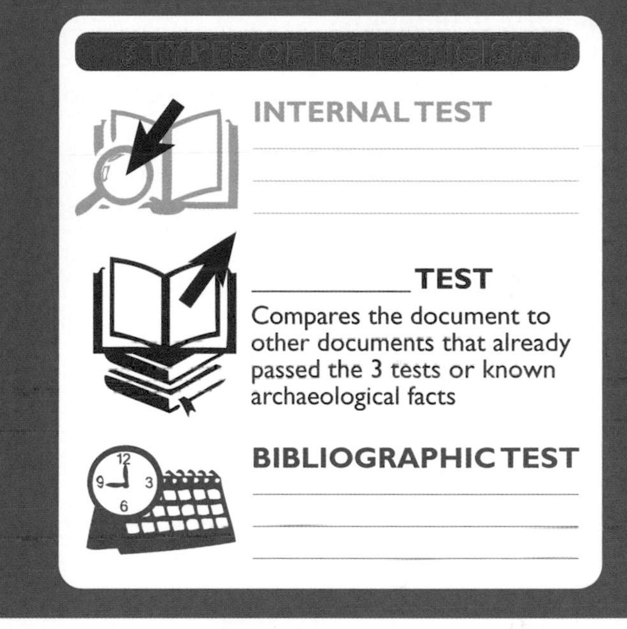

FIGURE 4.14
Ancient Coins

If artifacts, like these coins, have the image of a ruler, then archaeologists can reason they were from the dates of that ruler's reign. Of course, minted dates provide exact dates.

(Figure 4.14). An artifact might be mentioned in a historical document. So if there is a written record stating the date an Egyptian king died, for example, and an archaeologist is able to find that king's tomb, then the tomb and the artifacts it contains can be dated because of the reference in the historical document.

When the age of an artifact is determined by an actual date on it or by a reference in a historical document, it has a **known age.**

Known age—The age of an artifact as determined by a date printed on it or a reference to the artifact in a work of history

There are not many artifacts that have a known age, though. So archaeologists have to use other ways to determine how old they are. One of the more reliable methods is called **dendrochronology.**

Dendrochronology—The process of counting tree rings to determine the age of a tree

Now, to understand how this is done, you have to learn a little about how trees grow. Of course, during the life of a tree, its trunk expands not only in height but in width. So if you were to cut down a tree and look at the inside of its trunk, you would find a series of rings, called tree rings or **growth rings.** A tree typically grows one light and one dark ring each year. Therefore, if you cut a tree down and count its light rings, you can figure out how old that tree is. If there are 104 light rings, then the tree is most likely 104 years old.

How does that help us date artifacts in archaeology? Well, the appearance of the growth ring is dependent on several environmental factors for the year in which the ring was formed. The amount of rainfall, length of growing season, average temperature, and lots of other factors affect how well the tree will grow. A good growing season means the ring will be wider, and a poor growing season means the ring will be narrower. The darkness of the dark bands is also affected. As you look at the tree's rings you can notice patterns of varying thickness and darkness of the dark bands. Those patterns are due to weather patterns that happened in the tree's environment during the time it was alive.

FIGURE 4.15
Various Environmental Factors Causing Tree Ring Differences

Archaeologists use this information when they study a specific region. Because the weather in a specific area affects the appearance of tree rings, they can cut down an old tree that is still alive. Then they can look for unique patterns of rings that correspond to several years of the weather in that region. So counting from the outside of the tree to the start of the special pattern will tell the archaeologist how many years ago that weather pattern occurred. Archaeologists look for lots of these types of patterns and catalog them as **master tree ring patterns** for a specific region of the world.

Therefore, when archaeologists find a log that was used to build an ancient home, they can look at the growth rings in that log to try to find one of the master ring patterns. If they find one, they know when that ring pattern was formed. They can then count the remaining rings on the tree and figure out how long ago the tree was cut down. That will let them know when the people who cut down the tree were alive which will help to date the artifacts they left behind.

Let me give you an example. Let's say an archaeologist finds a log that was used to build a structure. She looks at the growth rings and finds a unique pattern in them that corresponds to a master tree ring pattern. She consults with dendrochronologists who have determined that this master tree ring pattern was formed from the weather patterns in that area during the years AD 200–300. That means the tree the archaeologist is examining formed those unique rings from AD 200 to AD 300, too. She then counts from the end of that unique ring pattern to the edge of the log and counts 200 more rings. So this tree stopped forming rings when it was cut down, 200 years after the end of the master tree ring pattern. Therefore, the tree was cut down in AD 500, when the structure was being built. Explore more about dendrochronology in Experiment 4.1.

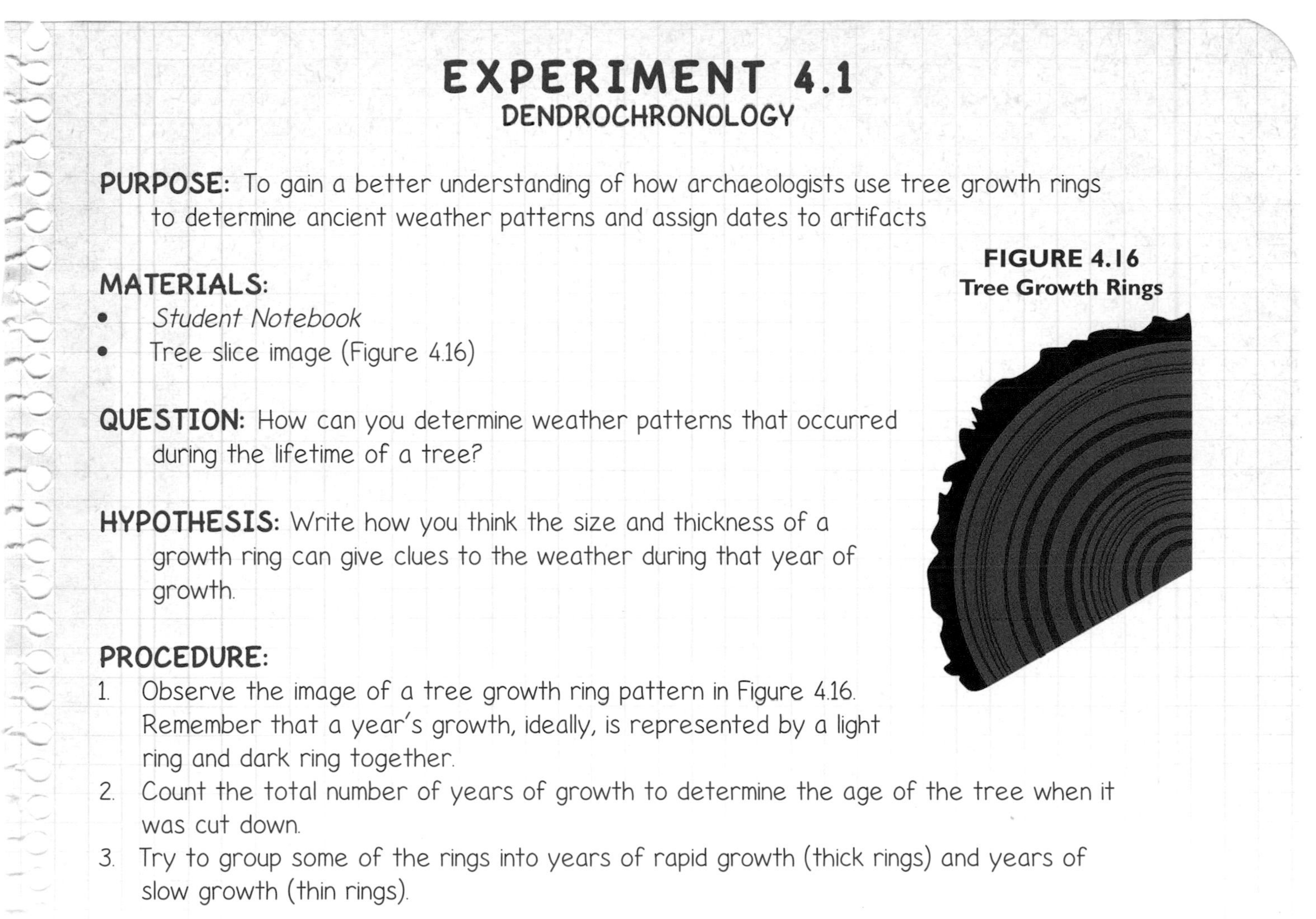

EXPERIMENT 4.1

DENDROCHRONOLOGY

PURPOSE: To gain a better understanding of how archaeologists use tree growth rings to determine ancient weather patterns and assign dates to artifacts

FIGURE 4.16
Tree Growth Rings

MATERIALS:
- *Student Notebook*
- Tree slice image (Figure 4.16)

QUESTION: How can you determine weather patterns that occurred during the lifetime of a tree?

HYPOTHESIS: Write how you think the size and thickness of a growth ring can give clues to the weather during that year of growth.

PROCEDURE:
1. Observe the image of a tree growth ring pattern in Figure 4.16. Remember that a year's growth, ideally, is represented by a light ring and dark ring together.
2. Count the total number of years of growth to determine the age of the tree when it was cut down.
3. Try to group some of the rings into years of rapid growth (thick rings) and years of slow growth (thin rings).

4. Write down the weather history for the tree, beginning at its first year (in the center). Show the number of years of good weather for rapid growth, then the number of years of poor weather which resulted in slower growth, then more years of rapid growth, etc.

CONCLUSION: Explain how weather histories can be gathered using tree growth rings.

Experiment 4.1 should have given you a good idea of how archaeologists can use logs or portions of trees to identify weather patterns for the time the tree was growing. By looking for a weather-pattern-match to master tree ring patterns, they are able to suggest a time period for when the tree was living and thus get a better idea of the age of the artifacts found with the tree.

Now, archaeologists have cataloged master tree ring patterns that have helped them to date certain artifacts as far back as 6600 BC. This is a fairly accurate tool to help date artifacts, but it still has some difficulties, which creates some uncertainties in dating. You see, one of the problems with dendrochronology is that trees sometimes grow more than one ring a year. That can lead archaeologists to think a tree is older than it actually is. And the further an archaeologist goes back in history, the greater this problem becomes. So dendrochronology dates represent the upper limits or the oldest an artifact can be. It can be younger. The older the artifact, the more error there will be in the process of growth-ring counting.

Another issue with dendrochronology is that it is limited to how much it can be used. After all, an archaeologist has to find a log that has identifiable rings. There also has to be a master ring pattern in the log so the archaeologist knows the age of some portion of the log.

In fact, the only ages that are certain in archaeology are the known ages. So unless the date is written on an artifact, or unless there is a reference to the artifact within a reliable historical document, then the age determined by archaeologists is not certain. Dates that are not known ages are referred to as absolute or **assigned ages.**

EXPLORE MORE

See if you can find some trees in your area that have been recently cut down. Often plant nurseries or even craft stores will have slices of tree trunks for sale. Try to count the rings of your tree sample to determine how old the tree is. Take pictures of it and add it to your notebook.

AGE TESTING AND RADIOMETRIC DATING

Archaeologists use other dating methods to try to determine an artifact's age. One very popular method is called **carbon-14 dating.** It is actually a type of a broader group of dating methods called **radiometric dating.**

Radiometric dating—Using a radioactive process to determine the age of an item

The radiometric dating method called carbon-14 dating is about as reliable as dendrochronology as long as the item being dated is less than about 3,000 years old (see Figure 4.17). We'll discuss more of this in a future module.

FIGURE 4.17
A Fossil Fish

Carbon-14 is a material that breaks down easily once a living organism dies. The amount of carbon-14 in a specimen will therefore become less with time. That principle helps archaeologists to try to determine a specimen's age by the amount of remaining carbon-14 it has.

So we can say that there are 2 types of dates an artifact can have. A known age is one that is certain. An assigned age is one that was given using dendrochronology, radiometric dating, or some other method and is not definite.

It is important to point out that certain history books or museums have artifacts that some archaeologists date to be hundreds of thousands or millions of years old. You need to be very skeptical of those ages. After all, the most reliable dating method is dendrochronology, which is only accurate to ages of about 8,000 years. And even though those ages are pretty reliable, they still provide the upper limit to the true age of an artifact. Radiometric dating methods sometimes produce ages that are hundreds of thousands of years old. But these are pretty unreliable methods. The problem is, many scientists love to use radiometric dating because they want to believe Earth is millions of years old and man has been living on it

creation connection

Since 1947, scientists have determined the ages of many old objects by measuring the amounts of radioactive carbon they contain. New research shows, however, that some estimates based on carbon may have erred by thousands of years. In 1990, scientists reported in the British journal *Nature* that some estimates based on carbon analyses were up to 3,500 years wrong! Contamination by outside sources of carbon has been one of the problems of mistaken dating estimates. Today, dendrochronology is considered the best dating method for an assigned age.

for hundreds of thousands of years. Radiometric dating techniques can provide ages that agree with that, so some scientists like using this method.

However, many scientists, myself included, do not believe radiometric dates are reliable beyond thousands of years. Therefore, any time you hear that some artifact has an assigned age of millions of years, you need to realize the dating method used to come up with that age is considered unreliable by many in the scientific community.

ON YOUR OWN

4.7 An archaeologist is trying to determine the age of an ancient village that has just been discovered, and he would like to use dendrochronology. What 2 things must he have in order to determine the age of the village in this way?

RELATIVE DATING AND THE PRINCIPLE OF SUPERPOSITION

Archaeologists have yet another way to help them get a good idea of how old an artifact is. If they cannot find the known age or an assigned age, there is a way they can determine the **relative age** of the object. A relative age is not an exact number but rather a determination of whether an artifact is older or younger than another artifact.

To do this, archaeologists employ the **principle of superposition.**

Principle of superposition—When artifacts are found in rock or earth that is layered, the deeper layers hold the older artifacts.

This method is used often in the field of archaeology and geology, so it is important for you to understand it.

You see, when an archaeologist or geologist digs into the earth, the soil or rock is often in notable layers, called **strata.** Archaeologists assume that when these layers were formed, they were laid down one layer at a time, and each layer took years and years to form. We will discuss this in a later module, but you will learn that this is not necessarily a good assumption in many cases. Yet, it is an assumption used often in archaeology and geology.

If the strata were, indeed, formed one at a time, we can conclude that the deeper layers are older than the shallow layers, right? After all, if they were laid down one by one, then the bottom layer would have to be formed first, the layer on top of it next, and so on. So the bottom layer of any formation would be the oldest layer, and the top layer of the bunch, the youngest.

If the principle of superposition is correct, then any artifacts found in a lower layer would be older than artifacts found in an upper layer. Therefore, even though an archaeologist might not be able to figure out a known date or an assigned date for a specific artifact in a layer, it could be said that the items in lower layers are older than items in upper layers. In Figure 4.18, the preserved firewood would be considered to be older than the stone tools, and the stone tools would be considered to be older than the pottery. Additionally, let's assume the archaeologist is able to use dendrochronology to come up with an assigned age for the firewood at 1,000 years old. Well, then it could be said that the animal bones in the layer below the firewood are older than 1,000 years because they are found in a layer below the firewood layer.

The principle of superposition gives archaeologists an idea of how old an artifact is relative to another artifact. And this can be useful, but you need to remember that it is not a definite fact. Why? Well, sometimes layers of rock and soil are not laid down one by one over time. Sometimes they form as a result of certain catastrophes, creating several layers at the same point in history. So the general assumption for the principle of superposition isn't true in every case. It is difficult to know when this technique will work and when it will not.

think about this

Think about how you would construct a 3-layer birthday cake. You would place the first layer on the tray and add some icing on top. Then you would place the second layer on top of the first, icing it.

And, finally, you would place the third layer on top of that and complete your icing job to make the birthday cake. Which layer was laid down first? The bottom layer. It is the oldest. Which layer was laid down last? The top layer. It is the youngest. This sums up the principle of superposition and is the assumption many archaeologists and geologists make when they observe layers of earth. However, the major issue with this idea is the *span of time* between each layer's formation. Think about the cake. How much time passed between the laying down of each layer when you were assembling it? Did you put it together within an hour? Did you wait a day, or a week, or a year (yuck!) between layers? It is difficult to know just by looking at them. That is the problem with the strata of the Earth. Some scientists believe each layer took a long time to form. Others believe layers can be laid down rather rapidly.

FIGURE 4.18
Stratified Soil or Rock

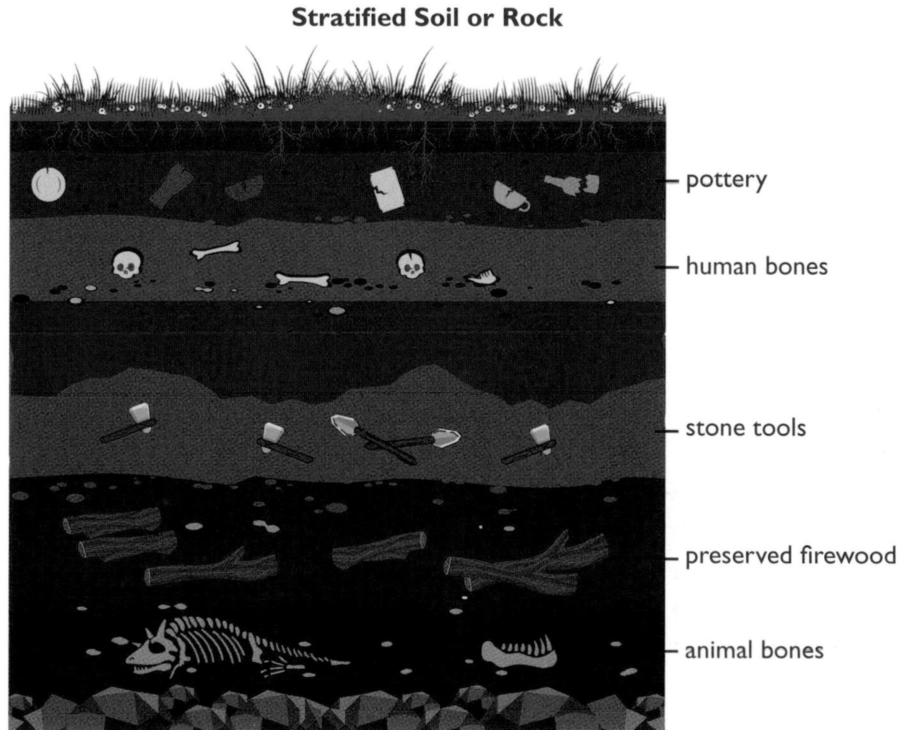

ON YOUR OWN

4.8 Based on the principle of superposition, list the artifacts pointed out in Figure 4.18 in terms of increasing age. In other words, list the youngest artifact first and the oldest one last.

4.9 What is the underlying assumption of the principle of superposition?

SUMMING UP

After reading through this module, you can see more clearly how science can be applied to any question as long as the correct methodology is used. For example, when we looked at the tests used to affirm the accuracy of documents, we applied those tests to the Bible which helped to indicate that science tells us we can believe the accounts in the Bible. The science behind archaeology and history is an important part of your science education to help you better understand how to interpret the things historians and archaeologists tell you.

ANSWERS TO THE "ON YOUR OWN" QUESTIONS

4.1 **Experiments (a) and (d) are pure science experiments, and (b) and (c) are applied science experiments.** The goals of experiments (a) and (d) are simply to gain knowledge. Now, that knowledge might be useful, but that is not the goal. The knowledge is the goal. Thus, these are pure science experiments. In experiments (b) and (c), making something useful is the goal. That makes it applied science.

4.2 **Options (b) and (c) are both examples of technology.** Options (a) and (d) are knowledge. Option (b) is a machine, which is obviously technology, and option (c) is not a machine, but it directly makes life easier by allowing you to make sturdy structures. Thus, a recipe for cement is technology, just like a microwave oven is.

4.3 Archaeologists study human life by looking at **preserved relics, or artifacts.** Paleontologists study the history of all life by looking at **preserved remains of organisms that were once alive.** These are slight differences, but they are important ones.

4.4

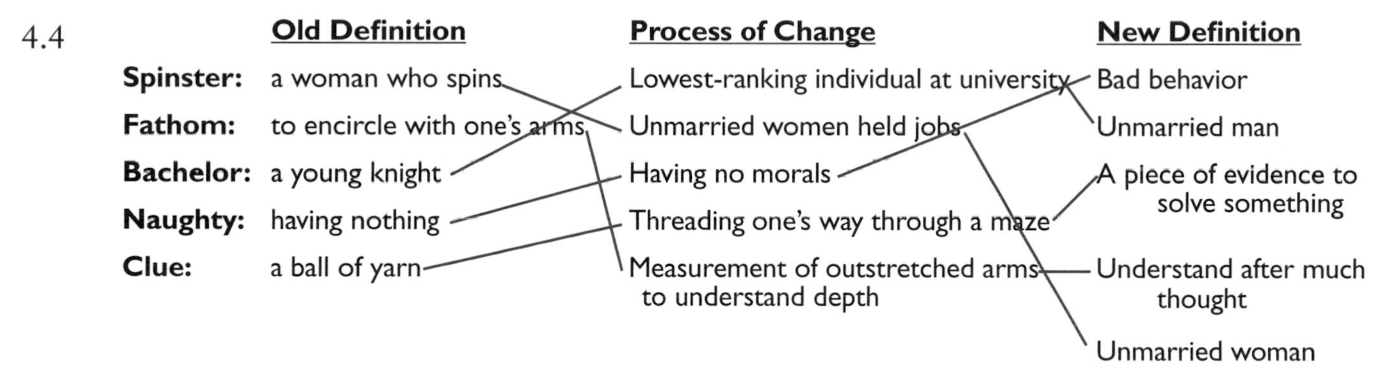

4.5 The document seems to be contradicted by archaeological research. Thus, it fails the **external test.**

4.6 See answers in the infographic below:

INTERNAL TEST
Compares the document to other information within the same document

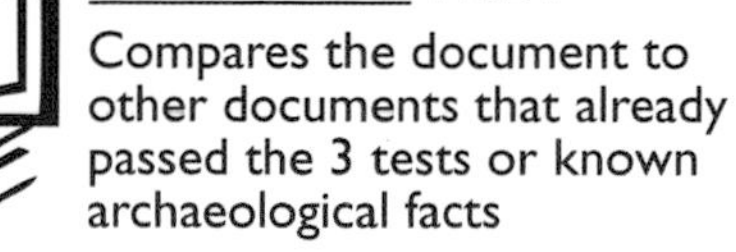

EXTERNAL TEST
Compares the document to other documents that already passed the 3 tests or known archaeological facts

BIBLIOGRAPHIC TEST
Determines time span between copies and number of copies

4.7 To use dendrochronology, **the archaeologist must find a preserved log with identifiable rings in the remains of the ancient village. He also must find a match to a master tree ring pattern within the preserved log.** The log gives the archaeologist something with which to use dendrochronology, and the master tree ring pattern allows him to figure out how old the log is.

4.8 The principle of superposition states that the artifacts found in the lower layers will be older than those found in the upper layers. Thus, in order of increasing age, you have **pottery, human bones, stone tools, preserved firewood, and animal bones.**

4.9 The principle of superposition assumes that **each layer of soil or rock is formed one at a time.** We know this is not always true.

STUDY GUIDE FOR MODULE 4

1. Match the following words with their definitions.

a. Life science	The study of past human life as revealed by preserved relics
b. Archaeology	The study of Earth's history as revealed in the rocks that make up the earth
c. Artifacts	The study of life's history as revealed in the preserved remains of once-living organisms
d. Geology	A term that encompasses all scientific pursuits related to living organisms
e. Paleontology	Objects made by people, such as tools, weapons, containers, etc.

2. Identify each of the experiments described below as a pure science experiment or applied science experiment.

   a. An experiment designed to figure out why clouds form as air rises over a mountain
   b. An experiment designed to determine how to cause tomato plants to produce more tomatoes
   c. An experiment designed to make a computer process information at a faster rate
   d. An experiment designed to determine how clouds affect air temperature

3. A document is subject to the internal, external, and bibliographic tests to determine if it is a legitimate work of history. It passes the first 2 tests, but does not pass the third one. Would it be considered a reliable historical document? Why or why not?

4. Match the types of document tests with their definition:

a. Internal test	Tests whether the document contradicts other known historical facts from other reliable documents or known archaeological facts
b. External test	Identifies how many years have passed between the time the original work was written and the time of the first known copy as well as how many different copies have been made by different people
c. Bibliographic test	Tests whether the document agrees with itself

5–6. Fill in the blank:

5. Known age is the age of an artifact as determined by a ________ printed on it or a reference to the artifact in a reliable work of history.

6. Dendrochronology is the process of counting ________ rings to determine their age.

7. Radiometric dating is a popular method of using a radioactive process to determine the age of an item. ________________ dating is one type of radiometric dating.

8. The principle of superposition says that which of the 3 layers of this cake is the oldest?

EARTH SCIENCE— ASTRONOMY

Why do you think it is important to study the heavens? One reason is that the universe is filled with created things. By studying these celestial objects, we get to see glimpses of the One who created them. The science of space includes studying the universe, the planets, and all other objects beyond Earth's **atmosphere**.

Atmosphere—The gaseous layer surrounding Earth or another heavenly body

This branch of science also involves the technology used to study space. That's because what we know about the objects in the heavens comes from telescopic images and observations of the behavior of light in space. Most scientists agree on the conclusions from these images and the physical laws that order their motions. There is also little dispute about how energy is transferred between them and how they stay in their positions. However, there is great disagreement about where these objects came from. I'll talk more about that subject at the end of this module.

Quaestio

As we dive into our first main branch of science, you will start to notice the order within our universe. Order in creation gives testimony to a Creator. For example, if you were walking through a forest and noticed a large stone with the word *Hello* etched in it, you would automatically know that it was carved by someone. There is no way that natural erosion of wind or rain could do that. So order and organization means there is one who made things that way. Once you understand that, you can see why a study of science is a great way to learn more about our God!

WHAT IS ASTRONOMY?

Let's start this section with a definition of **astronomy.**

Astronomy—The branch of science that deals with the physical universe beyond Earth's atmosphere

It involves the study of objects in space, mapping their locations and movements, and identifying the properties of the material in the universe. With a literal *universe* to study, you can imagine that we will only be able to cover the major highlights of this fascinating field within this module.

FIGURE 5.1
Observing the Sky at Night

Because it is such a broad field, there are several subfields of astronomy which allow scientists to specialize in the study of particular objects and events. For example, planetary astronomers focus on the study of planets; stellar astronomers observe the vast array of stars; galactic astronomers study galaxies; cosmologists focus on the entire universe and its history and future; and astrometric scientists measure the motions of the sun, Moon, and planets.

Genesis 1:14–19 says that God made the sun, Moon, and stars on day 4 of the Creation week. That includes all the bright lights we see in the night sky (and those we cannot see, too), as well as planets, comets (objects made of ice and dust), gaseous clouds, and even other galaxies (clusters of millions or billions of stars!). Many of these can appear to the naked eye as little dots of light in the sky. Yet God spoke them into being!

For centuries, people have studied the astronomical bodies in the sky and used their regular motions to tell time and build calendars. Day, month, and year are defined by the relative motions of the sun, Moon, and Earth. For example, an Earth year is the time it takes for Earth to completely **orbit** (or complete one trip around) our sun, and an Earth day is the time it takes for Earth to **revolve** once on its axis. Now, other planets have their own timetables when it comes to day and year. A year on Saturn is the equivalent of 29 Earth years because it takes Saturn much longer to orbit our sun!

FIGURE 5.2
Some Constellations in the Night Sky

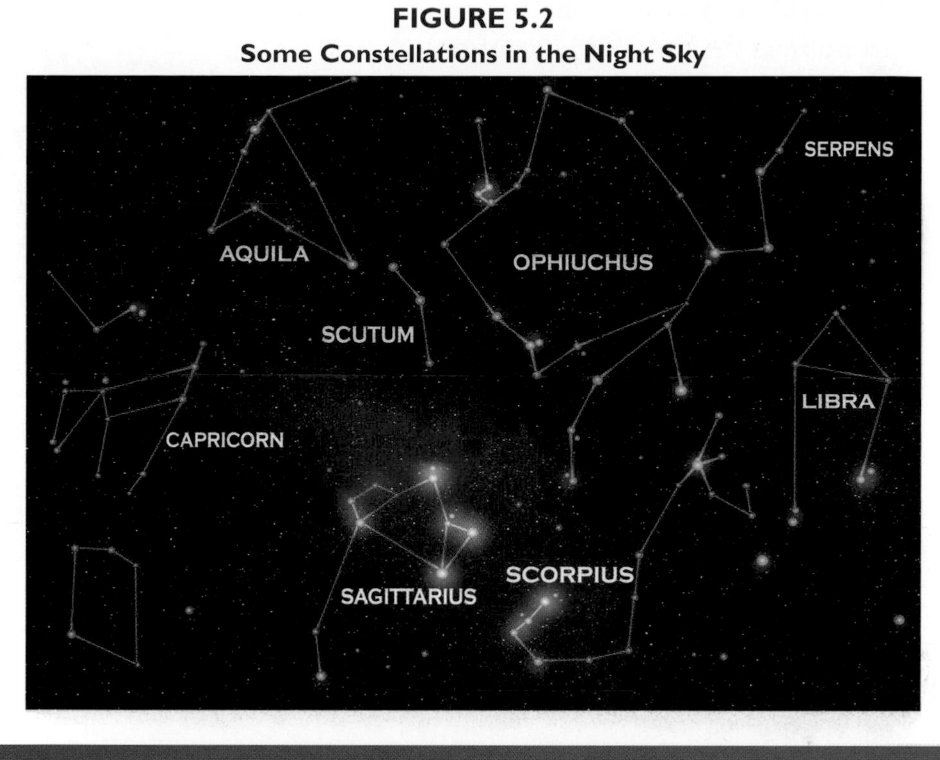

EXPLORE MORE

Genesis 1:14 tells us that the lights in the sky are "for signs and for seasons, and for days and years." We use the orbit of Earth around the sun to help mark years. In fact, we are best able to measure the orbits of the other planets in our solar system using Earth years, too. Make a bar graph of the number of Earth years it takes each planet to make a complete orbit around our sun. Mercury—0.24 Earth years; Venus— 0.62 Earth years; Mars—1.88 Earth years; Jupiter—12 Earth years; Saturn—29 Earth years; Uranus—84 Earth years; Neptune—165 Earth years.

Ancient astronomers noticed that the stars appeared to group together in noticeable patterns. Some of those patterns resembled animals or people, so they named many after them. These **constellations**, or patterns of stars, would be visible during certain seasons of the year as Earth orbited in its path around the sun. Constellations helped sailors navigate in the ocean and even helped astronomers to mark what year it was and how many years had passed since a specific event.

TOOLS TO STUDY THE HEAVENS

Have you ever watched your shadow on the ground when you stand outside during the day? You might have noticed that the direction of your shadow changes depending on what time of day it is. When people figured out that the shadow directions were predictable and could help to identify the time of day, they began to create objects that would intentionally create those shadows. The **gnomon** is one of the oldest devices that helped astronomers determine the location and motion of the sun in relation to Earth. Made of an upright pole, column of stones, or a pillar, the gnomon would cast a shadow in sunlight. By following the daily movement of the shadow, astronomers could estimate the time of day. Changes in the length of the shadow helped them to figure out the season of the year, too. In later years, a numbered dial was added to the gnomon to create a **sundial**. Perform Experiment 5.1.

FIGURE 5.3
A Sundial

EXPERIMENT 5.1
MAKE A SUNDIAL

PURPOSE: To better understand the rotation of Earth in relation to the sun and how that helps us to measure time

MATERIALS:
- A dark marker
- A paper plate (A thick paper plate works best.)
- A sharpened pencil
- A ruler
- A plastic straw (If you have a bendy straw, cut the bendy part off.)
- Cellophane or masking tape
- Paper clips if you will be setting your sundial on the ground

QUESTION: How can you determine the passage of time with a sundial?

HYPOTHESIS: Write what you think is happening between Earth and the sun in order for you to use a sundial.

PROCEDURE:
1. The best time to begin this experiment is 11:30 a.m. on a cloudless day. Use the ruler to find the center of the plate. Hold it across the plate and move it up and down until the distance measured across the plate is the longest. This is the plate's diameter. Draw a faint pencil line all the way across the diameter.
2. Turn the plate a quarter turn and find the diameter again, drawing a faint pencil line all the way across that diameter. The center of the plate is where the 2 lines intersect.

3. Use the sharp pencil to poke a hole in the plate's center. If the plate is too thick, use a pen or the point of a scissors to carefully poke a hole large enough for the straw to barely fit inside.
4. Now use the marker to write a 12 at the edge of the plate where you drew one of the diameter lines. Trace over the light pencil line, beginning at the 12 and back to the hole in the center. This will mark 12:00 noon.
5. Go outside and place your plate on a flat surface, either on a table or on the ground, where it will get full sun throughout the day and will not be disturbed.
6. Stick the straw through the hole in the center and secure it with tape if necessary.
7. Wait for the time to be exactly 12:00 and orient your plate so that the straw's shadow lines up with the line you drew from the plate's center to the 12. You might want to tape the plate to the hard surface so it doesn't move. If it is on the ground, uncoil a few paper clips and poke them through the plate in a few spots to anchor it. Double-check that the shadow is still at the 12:00 spot and your setup is complete.
8. Now come back to the plate at each hour. Mark the position of the shadow at 1:00 by placing a 1 at the plate's edge where the shadow is pointing. Continue to do this at the top of every hour until dark. Notice whether the shadow is moving in a clockwise or counterclockwise direction.
9. Remember, the shadow is moving because Earth is turning away from the sun after noon.
10. You need to complete your sundial marks for the morning hours, so you have to leave your sundial out until the following day at sunrise or shortly afterward. If you have to bring your sundial inside overnight, mark its spot using rocks or some other heavy item. Be sure to use a small rock to mark the 12:00 spot.
11. In the morning, set up your sundial in the same spot as the day before and in the same orientation. Now mark the times on each hour up until noon.
12. Your sundial is complete and will be able to mark time every day!

CONCLUSION: Write what you learned about how a sundial works.

Natural features such as mountain peaks and man-made structures were also used to help people align a star or the sun to a specific spot at a certain time of year. Stonehenge in England is believed to be an early observatory that did just that.

FIGURE 5.4
Stonehenge

Telescopes

The use of telescopes greatly helped people discover more about what is beyond our skies, allowing astronomers to view things with more accuracy and in greater detail. Now, there are 2 types of telescopes: refractors and reflectors. A **refracting telescope** contains 2 glass lenses (see top of Figure 5.5). The large lens bends light that passes through it, forming an image. When light bends, it is called **refraction**, and that is how this telescope gets its name. The second lens is located at the other end of the telescope and magnifies the image. It is called the eyepiece.

A **reflecting telescope** does just what you might think: it reflects light. So instead of a lens, this type of telescope uses a mirror to *reflect* light toward the direction it came into the scope (see bottom of Figure 5.5). Often, reflecting telescopes also have a little mirror to reflect that light to one side so the astronomer can view the image by looking into the side of the telescope, too. Their unique design makes a very long light path much shorter within a telescope by causing light to reflect in a shorter distance.

FIGURE 5.5
Refracting and Reflecting Telescopes

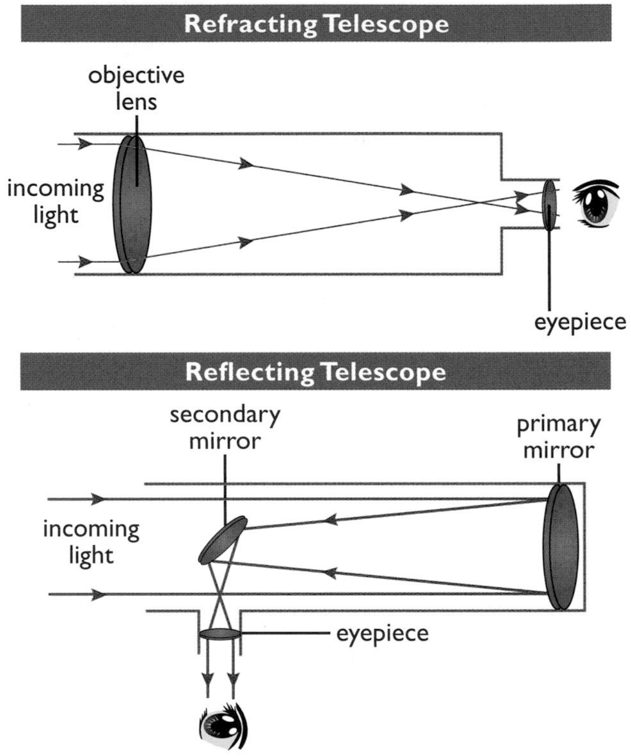

Refracting Telescope

objective lens
incoming light
eyepiece

Reflecting Telescope

secondary mirror
primary mirror
incoming light
eyepiece

Both refracting and reflecting telescopes are used to gather light energy and focus it so it can be directly viewed or recorded on photographs and computers.

The bigger the telescope lens or mirror, the more light it can collect, allowing scientists to identify more objects. Modern telescopes often have special instruments, such as cameras or computers, attached to them so they can collect data, record images, and analyze information in greater detail.

To make telescopes even better, scientists use higher quality glass and more finely shaped lenses to improve **resolution.** Better resolution helps us to see an image in greater detail. In fact, the larger the resolution of a lens (which technically is its diameter), the better the detail. High-resolution telescopes have helped astronomers learn that what they initially saw as a single star in the sky actually is 2 (or 3!) stars very close together.

Both refracting and reflecting telescopes can have a problem with something called **spherical aberration.** This is when not all the light coming in to the telescope is focused on the same point, so the image looks fuzzy. However, corrective lenses and computer programs are able to process these images to make them clearer.

FIGURE 5.6
The Hubble Space Telescope's View of the M100 Galaxy before and after Correction for Spherical Aberration

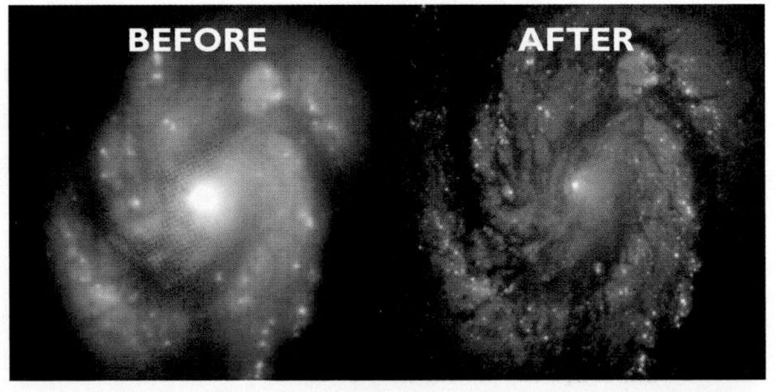

WAVELENGTHS OF LIGHT

When you think about it, astronomers are really looking through the universe, trying to identify light. Any object in the sky either is producing light (such as a star) or is reflecting light (such as a planet). Light is a wave, just like the waves you see in water. A **wavelength** is how long that wave is, or the distance between the crest (top) of one wave to the crest of the next one (see Figure 5.7). Light we can see with our eyes is called **visible light** and is made up of different wavelengths of light, each wavelength corresponding to a particular color (like what you see in a rainbow). The order of these colors from longest wavelength to shortest is Red, Orange, Yellow, Green, Blue, Indigo, and Violet. Using the first letters of each color helps us to remember the order: ROY G. BIV. You can think of these letters as a person's name, with G as the middle initial.

FIGURE 5.7
Light Wave Showing Wavelength

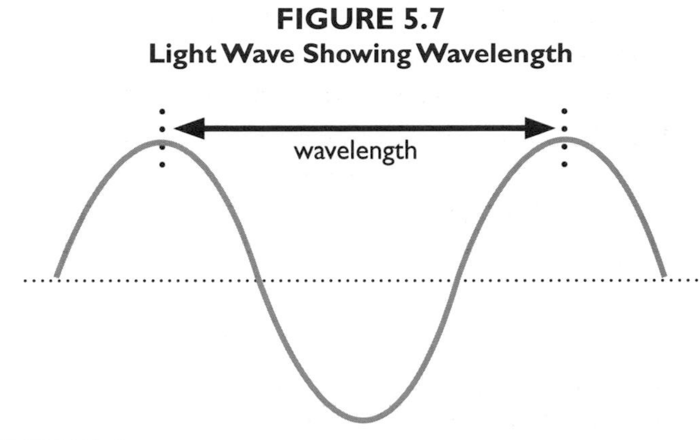

FIGURE 5.8
Wavelengths of Visible Color

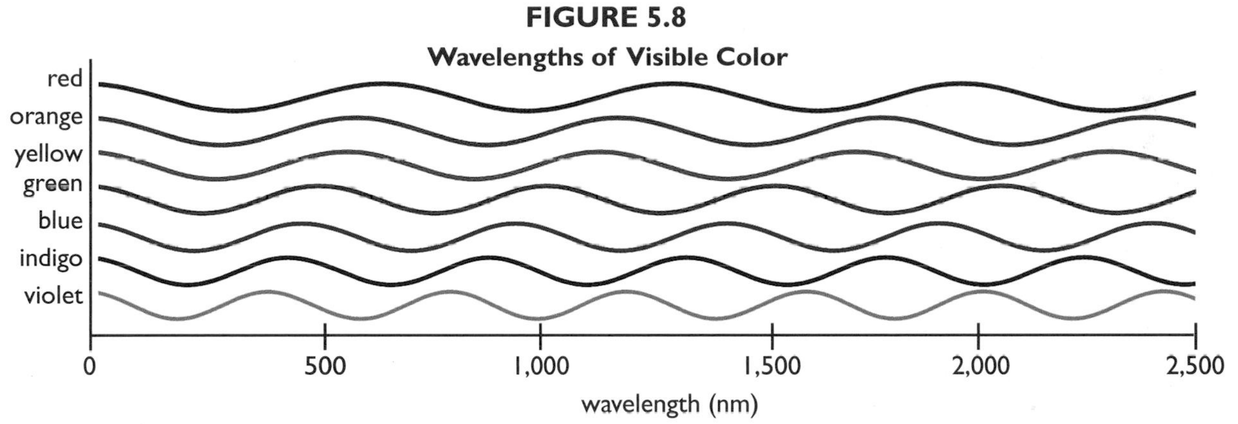

Now there are other wavelengths of light we *cannot* perceive with our eyes. Some are longer wavelengths, such as infrared light and radio waves, and others are shorter wavelengths, such as ultraviolet light, X-rays, and gamma rays. And scientists have developed non-optical telescopes to collect these. Radio telescopes, for example, collect the radio waves that some stars generate. Earth's atmosphere blocks many types of light waves, so astronomers use telescopes orbiting *above* the atmosphere to collect them. Telescope images have helped astronomers to create sky charts and catalogs of the stars we are able to identify. For example, the Tycho-2 Catalogue is an astronomical reference catalog

FIGURE 5.9
CSIRO's Parkes Radio Telescope in New South Wales, Australia

that contains the positions, motions, and colors for 2½ million of the brightest stars in the sky!

ON YOUR OWN

5.1 If you were to stand outside on a sunny day and noticed your shadow was very short, what time of day would it be? If your shadow was very long, what time of day would it be? (There are 2 possible answers to this second question.)

5.2 Some telescopes are sent into space to observe the skies. What advantage does a telescope sent in orbit around Earth have as compared to a telescope on land?

FIGURE 5.10
The Sun—Our Closest Star

THE SUN

The sun might appear as a circular light in the daytime sky, but it is an interesting heavenly object. First, it is extremely large. In fact, it is about 109 times larger than Earth. That means that over a million Earths would fit inside the space of the sun with extra space between them! That might surprise you because the sun doesn't appear to be very big in the sky. However, it is so, so far away—about 93 million miles from Earth. Second, the sun is very hot. It is estimated to be about 5,538 °C (10,000 °F) on its surface and 15 *million* °C (27 million °F) inside. Yet it is placed at a perfect distance from Earth. If it were much closer, the water in our oceans would evaporate and everything would burn up. If it were much farther away, we would freeze because Earth would not receive enough of the sun's warming energy. Third, the sun emits light. A lot of it! In fact, the light it produces is 4 septillion times brighter than a 60-watt light bulb (4 septillion is a 4 with 24 zeroes!).

Earth and other planets in our solar system orbit the sun. The sun is so large that it holds these objects in their orbits with a force called **gravity**.

Gravity—A force of attraction existing between any 2 masses

An orbit is one object revolving around another. In Module 1, you learned that many years ago, astronomers believed the sun revolved around Earth. You see, they observed the sun rise in the east, travel across the sky, and then set in the west, so it seemed to be revolving around or orbiting Earth. However, more observations demonstrated that Earth actually was orbiting the sun.

EXPLORE MORE

Explore orbits by getting a friend to help you. Pretend to be Earth by standing in one spot, facing forward. Use your hands to prevent your eyes from seeing sideways. Now have your friend pretend to be the sun by slowly walking around, or orbiting, you. In this activity, what you are viewing makes it seem like the sun is orbiting Earth. Now instruct your sun-friend to stand still. You face your friend, shielding the sides of your eyes like before. Now you slowly spin in place the same way Earth would turn on its axis. Do you see the sun seem to rise on one side of your vision field and set on the other just like before? It took other observations by early astronomers before they realized that was a more accurate model of how we observe sunrise and sunset.

Earth is considered a **satellite** of the sun.

Satellite—A natural or artificial body orbiting a planet or star

Earth is a natural satellite, revolving around it. The Moon is another example of a natural satellite; however, it orbits Earth instead of the sun. There are artificial satellites, too. Man-made telescopes, rockets, and other mechanical devices are sent into orbit around Earth.

We now know the sun is in the center of our solar system, and Earth and the other planets orbit it. A complete revolution around the sun is one trip around it. On Earth, we call that a year.

FIGURE 5.11
Artist's Drawing of a Communication Satellite

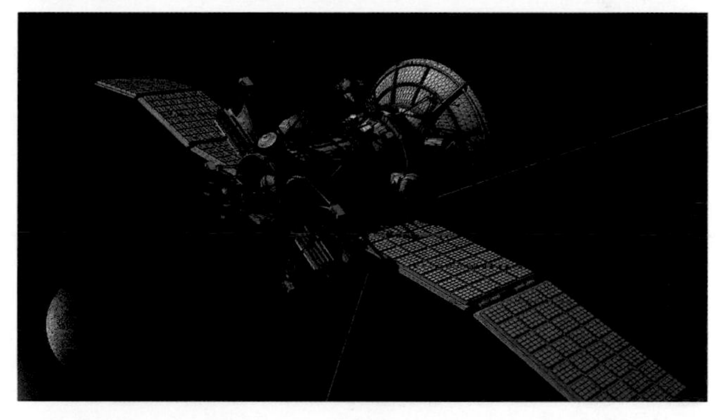

think about this

We may know much more about the sun very soon. NASA's Parker Solar Probe is the first mission ever sent to reach the sun's surface. The relatively tiny spacecraft, about the size of a small car, probes into the sun's atmosphere, which is about 4 million miles from its surface. Who knows what wonders this probe may discover?

THE SUN'S SURFACE

Even though we have not yet traveled to the sun (If we could, we would burn up!), astronomers use a tool to help figure out what it is made of. A device called a **spectroscope** can determine the wavelengths of light that come from an object. That helps them learn what materials are present because of the unique types of light each material emits. Spectroscopic readings show that the sun contains the same elements as Earth, but in different proportions. The most abundant is hydrogen, and the second is helium. Yet these are not present in the form of gas, like they are on Earth. You may have held helium balloons that float in the air. Helium balloons are filled with a high concentration of helium *gas*. However, the surface of the sun is **plasma**, which consists of super-hot matter that is neither solid nor liquid nor gas. So helium on the sun is in a different form. The visible surface of the sun where the plasma is found is called the **photosphere.** This is the part of the sun from which we receive its solar energy.

Now, the sun's surface is constantly churning and moving. Sometimes large towers of fire, called **solar flares,** shoot out from the photosphere. Solar flares can extend millions of miles from the sun and throw so much energy and electrically charged plasma to Earth that it can affect the sky at night. To get a good idea of how large they are, compared to the photo in Figure 5.12A, Earth would be the size of one of the commas in this sentence! Sometimes the energy from a solar flare occurrence is so great that it does something special on Earth. A few days after an intense flare occurrence, colorful nighttime light displays are seen near the poles. The Aurora Borealis in the north and the Aurora Australis in the south are caused by solar flare particles colliding with atoms in Earth's atmosphere. These high-energy particles that are emitted aren't just pretty to look at. Occasionally, they can also destroy delicate communication satellites orbiting Earth or disrupt power supplies and radio wave reception.

FIGURE 5.12A
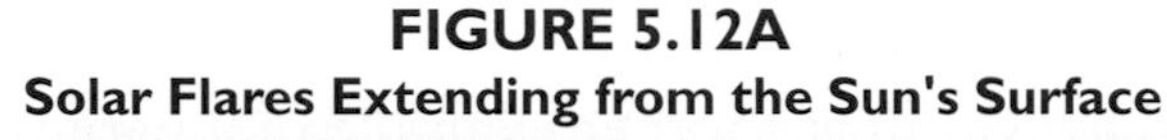
Solar Flares Extending from the Sun's Surface

FIGURE 5.12B
Aurora Borealis Caused by Solar Flares

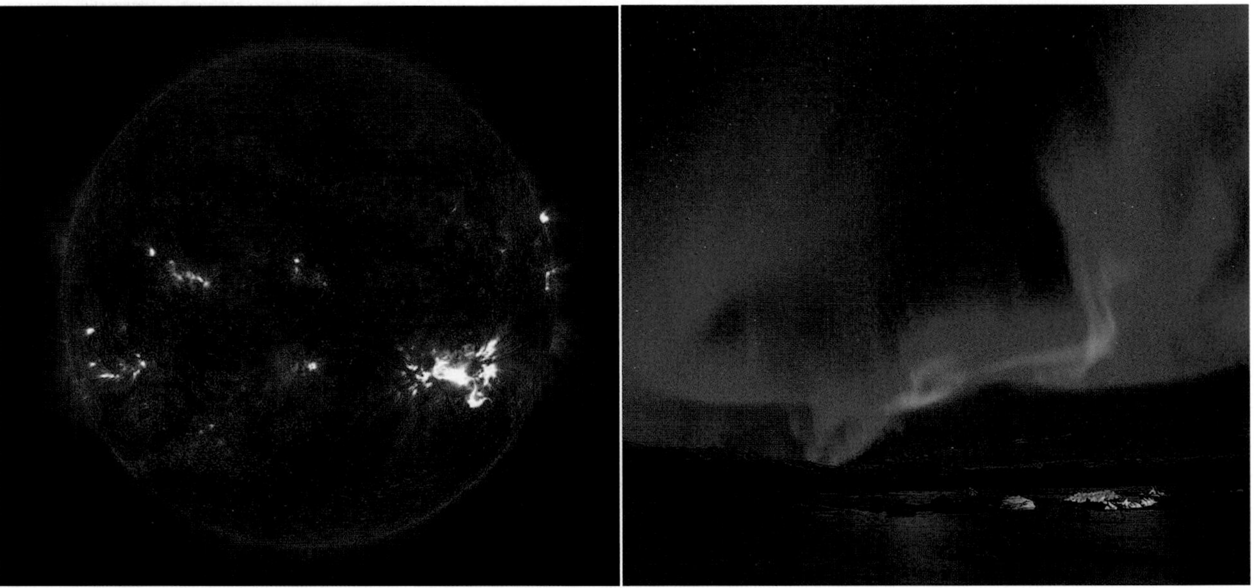

The sun's surface often is dotted with **sunspots.** These are darker areas of the sun that are cooler. Now, the words *darker* and *cooler* are relative. Dark sunspots only appear dark as compared to the *very* bright sun. And cooler sunspots are only about 3,000 °F cooler. So they're still much hotter than lava on Earth, even though they are a bit cooler than the sun's photosphere. And although they look like small dots on a large sphere, many sunspots are much, much bigger than Earth! They can last from a few days to several weeks and often change in size and shape from day to day. We can learn a lot from studying sunspots. Their presence helps scientists to observe the sun's rotation. You see, scientists noticed that these spots move across the sun from left to right, and when one disappears on the eastern edge (from Earth's vantage point), it reappears on the western edge about 2 weeks later. This demonstrates that the sun is rotating.

FIGURE 5.13
The Earth-facing Surface of the Sun during February 2013, Showing a Few Sunspots

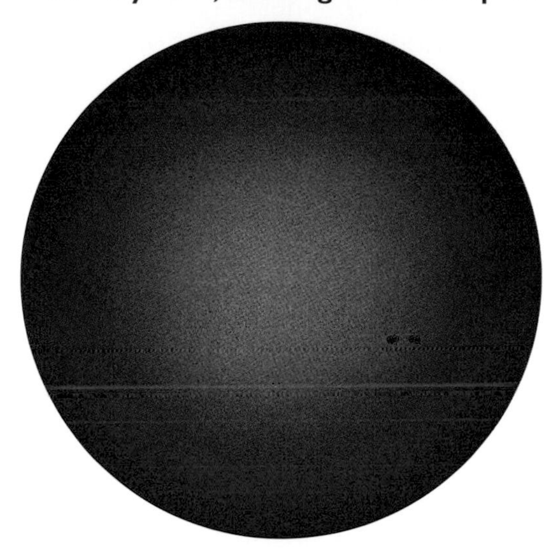

Sunspots are important to study. Many scientists believe they affect our weather. When there are lots of them, the sun is actually hotter because it is suggested that the sun is more active during these times. Additionally, dendrochronologists noticed that tree rings have shown that reduced sunspot activity seems to be historically linked to droughts and cold weather. So the more sunspots there are, the more favorable the weather conditions. Fewer sunspots mean extreme cold or droughts. A good example of this is during the years 1645 to 1710 when astronomers could not find any sunspots. At the same time, the weather on Earth was much cooler than normal. It also seems to be cyclical. You see, when astronomers plot the number of sunspots over time, they notice a pattern, with the number of sunspots reaching a maximum approximately every 11 years.

THE SUN'S INTERIOR AND EXTERIOR

Remember, everything we know about the sun is based on what we can see through devices. No one can visit the sun to observe what it is made of. Scientists observe the sun through special protective lenses to prevent its massive energy from causing eye damage, too. And what they have seen helps them to come up with a good model of the sun's interior.

The inside of the sun is believed to be made up of 3 sections. The **core** is the innermost section and is the location where most of the activity generating the sun's heat takes place. That energy travels to the next layer called the **radiative zone.** Here, the energy is in the form of photons, which are small energy packets of light. The pressure and density in the radiative zone are so great that there is very little movement of its plasma particles. Once they inch their way to the outer edges of this section, the pressure lessens enough so they can more easily move. This marks the beginning of the outermost layer: the

FIGURE 5.14
The Sun's Interior

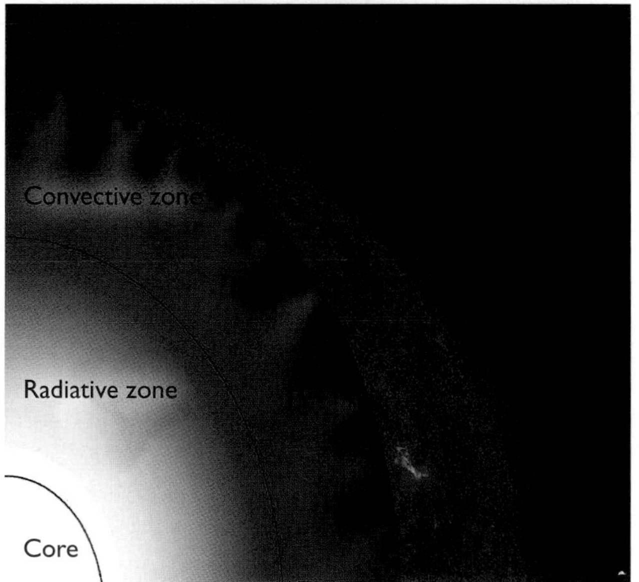

convective zone. Plasma particles in the convective zone get lots of heat from the zone below and then rise to the surface of the photosphere.

There are 2 layers in the atmosphere above the sun's photosphere. The first layer is the **chromosphere**, which is a layer of plasma about 3,000 km (1,864 mi) thick. The chromosphere is extremely hot, reaching up to about 10,000 °C (18,000 °F). The **corona** is the outermost area of the sun's atmosphere. It is much, much larger than the chromosphere, radiating outward for millions of miles. It is much hotter than the chromosphere, too, reaching several million degrees Fahrenheit.

Scientists are able to identify many of these solar features during an **eclipse.**

SOLAR ECLIPSES

When the sun, Moon, and Earth line up in just the right way, the Moon blocks our ability to see the sun. Called a solar eclipse, this event is only visible from certain parts of the world at specific times. Total solar eclipses result in near darkness during the middle of the day and can last up to about 7 minutes. Now, when the Moon moves between the sun and Earth, you might not think it is big enough to block such a huge thing as the sun, because the Moon is much smaller. However, the Moon is also much closer to Earth, so it appears to us to be bigger. What is interesting is that the sun is 400 times larger than the Moon and it is also 400 times farther away from Earth as compared to the Moon. This makes the sun and Moon appear to be the same size when we view them. The Moon's shadow on Earth is called an **umbra** and is just a few hundred miles in diameter. During a solar eclipse, any person in the path of the umbra is able to see the Moon covering over the sun for a short period of time. (Of course, they have to use special protective lenses so they won't harm their eyes.) In a total solar eclipse, the Moon just barely covers the sun, enabling us to see the corona and loops of gas sticking out (see Figure 5.15). These prominences extend outward from the sun, following its magnetic field. If the Moon were just a bit smaller, just a bit bigger, a little farther from us or a little closer to us, we wouldn't be able to view these solar features.

FIGURE 5.15
Total Solar Eclipse

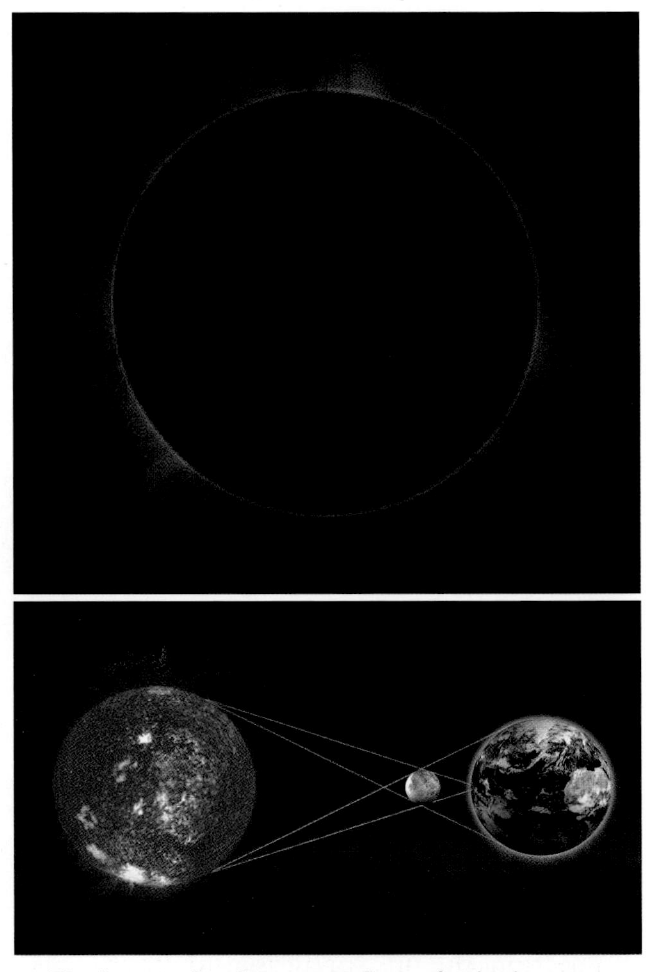

The lines in this diagram are lines of sight. A person standing on Earth at the "V" cannot see the sun because the Moon is perfectly blocking it.

Power of the Sun

The material that makes up the sun is so massive that it provides the fuel to heat and light the entire solar system of planets that orbit it. Scientists think the source of the sun's energy is nuclear powered, involving **fusion.**

Fusion is when small atoms combine into larger ones. In the sun's case, it is believed that hydrogen atoms are fused together into helium atoms. This fusion releases more energy than the processes we use at nuclear power plants on Earth.

I already mentioned how the sun is rotating on its axis, but we also know it is moving through space. As it travels, its orbiting planets (including Earth) move along with it.

ON YOUR OWN

5.3 What is one evidence of the sun's rotation?

PLANETS

Our solar system is made up of the sun along with planets and everything else in orbit around it. First, let's talk about what a planet is. A **planet** is a large object that orbits the sun. Early astronomers noticed that planets moved slowly among the stationary stars. Planets also appeared as defined disks in their telescopes as compared to stars that looked like points of light. Planets are not the same, but we can place the known planets within our solar system into 2 major groups. Before I do that, let me go over some of their general features. In order of increasing distance from the sun, there are Mercury, Venus, Earth, Mars, Jupiter, Saturn, Uranus, and Neptune. Our solar system is so large that using conventional units of distance such as miles or kilometers would not be useful. It would be like measuring the distance between New York City and Tokyo in inches. So astronomers defined a new unit of distance, called the **astronomical unit**, abbreviated as **au.** This represents the average distance between Earth and the sun. Thus, the distance from Earth to the sun is 1 au. Mercury, which is the closest planet to the sun, is 0.39 au from the sun. Neptune, which is the farthest planet, is 30.20 au from the sun.

FIGURE 5.16
Heavenly Bodies in Earth's Solar System

Planets differ in their size and mass. Each planet rotates around its axis at a different speed, has a different number of satellites (moons), and travels around the sun at different rates. Two planets, Venus and Uranus, actually rotate backward as compared to the other planets, moving in a *clockwise* rotation. Scientists really don't know why that is, but some suggest that they were hit by very large objects during their formation. However, that collision should have caused them to have a more elliptical orbit around the sun, yet they have very circular orbits. Table 5.1 summarizes key facts about our planets.

TABLE 5.1
Characteristics of the Planets

Planet	Name Origin	Distance from Sun (au)	Rotation Rate (Earth Hours)	Revolution Rate (Earth Years)	Atmosphere	Known Satellites	Rings
Mercury	Roman god of travel	0.39	1,408	0.24	N	0	N
Venus	Roman goddess of beauty	0.72	5,832 (opposite spin as Earth)	0.62	Y	0	N
Earth	Unknown: English/ German root	1	24	1	Y	1 natural; 2,271 man-made	N
Mars	Roman god of war	1.52	25	1.88	Y (thin)	2	N
Jupiter	Roman king of gods	5.20	10	12	Y	67	Y
Saturn	Roman god Saturnus	9.58	11	29	Y	53	Y
Uranus	Greek god of the sky	19.3	17 (opposite spin as Earth)	84	Y	27	Y
Neptune	Roman god of the sea	30.2	16	165	Y	13	Y

Based on their size and density, we can group planets into 2 major groups. The first group, called the **terrestrial planets**, are Earth-like. The 4 planets closest to the sun (Mercury, Venus, Earth, and Mars) are terrestrial planets. The rest of the planets are in a group called the **Jovian planets.** This term means they are Jupiter-like. That's because the planet Jupiter was named after the Roman mythological god, Jove. Jovian planets include Jupiter, Saturn, Uranus, and Neptune. Terrestrial planets have less mass and are smaller than Jovian planets. They are closer to the sun and are denser than Jovian planets, too. In fact, Jovian planets have thick, gaseous atmospheres and are often referred to as **gas giants.** Jovian planets rotate very rapidly, and terrestrial planets generally rotate slowly. Jovian planets have many satellites, and terrestrial planets have few, if any at all. Lastly, all the Jovian planets have rings, but none of the terrestrial ones do. We don't know exactly why these planet types have the features they do, but it is interesting to classify them this way.

The planets all seem to orbit the sun on approximately the same plane and in an elliptical, or oval, shape.

EXPLORE MORE

An ellipse is a closed curved shape, like a circle. But unlike a circle, where all points on a circle are the same distance from its center, an ellipse is shaped so that when you add together the distances from 2 points inside (called **foci**), the distances always add up to the same number. Draw an ellipse by gathering a sheet of corrugated cardboard or a corkboard, a sheet of white paper, 2 thumbtacks, a pencil, and some string. Place the paper on top of the cardboard and push the thumbtacks into it about 2 inches apart. Cut a piece of string about 8 inches in length and tie each end to one thumbtack. The thumbtacks represent the 2 foci of the ellipse you draw. Place the tip of your pencil against the string and pull outward along the paper so the string is taut. Now touch the pencil to the paper continuing to pull outwards from the foci as you move the pencil around them. You might have to adjust the string so it doesn't catch on the thumbtacks as you go around, but try to complete the pathway all the way around the foci. You now have an ellipse!

Most planets have more elliptical orbits, with Venus and Neptune having the most circular-like orbits. The point where a planet is closest to the sun is called its **perihelion** (pear' ih hee lee on). The point where it is the farthest is called its **aphelion** (af' fee lee on).

Each planet reflects sunlight, and the brightness (or magnitude) of the reflected light that we see is related to the planet's distance from Earth. Two other factors that determine a planet's brightness in the sky are the reflective ability due to its atmosphere and a planet's size.

ON YOUR OWN

5.4 What are the 2 types of planets in our solar system and which type is Earth?

THE MOON

The Moon is a satellite of Earth and is the closest of all the astronomical bodies. It is in orbit around Earth as Earth orbits the sun. The Moon doesn't create its own light, but rather reflects the sunlight shining on it. This reflection is called its **albedo**.

Albedo—The amount of light or radiation reflected by a surface, typically that of a planet or moon

So if the sun is shining on a planet or Moon, the percentage of its solar radiation that is reflected is that planet's or moon's albedo. Albedo can range from a value of zero, which means no reflection, to a value of 1, which means 100% reflection.

FIGURE 5.17
The Moon

For example, Earth's average albedo is about 0.30, or 30% reflection. Fresh, white snow reflects about 95% of the solar radiation, which means it has a high albedo of 0.95. The Moon has an albedo of 0.11, and that enables us to observe it pretty well.

The Moon is just over ¼ the size of Earth and is nearly a perfect sphere. Its rotation rate affects its overall shape. You see, the faster an astronomical object spins, the more bulged it becomes at its equator and the more flattened at its poles. That's because even though the Moon is made of solid material, that material is still able to be shaped if the forces are strong enough. Therefore, because the Moon rotates more slowly on its axis as compared to Earth, it is more spherical in shape.

The Moon has less mass as compared to Earth, too: about 1% of its mass. This means its gravity is about one-sixth as great. Lower gravity means you would weigh less on the Moon, too! It also means that gas particles that are required to form an atmosphere easily escape the Moon's surface. Thus, the Moon has a very thin atmosphere with few gases.

think about this

Why do we capitalize Moon? Well, when we say "moon" we mean our Moon. Other planets have moons, and the majority of those moons have specific names. The capitalized term Moon, then, refers only to our Moon.

FIGURE 5.18
The Moon's Distinct Terminator

The Moon's Atmosphere

Astronomers were able to identify that the Moon had little atmosphere even before people were able to travel to the Moon. That's because of a few observations. They noticed that when the Moon passed in front of a star, the star would not gradually get dim as it got close to the Moon's surface. If there were an atmosphere, the gases in it would cause the star to dim a bit because the light coming from that star would be scattered by the material in the Moon's atmosphere. Another evidence of the Moon's thin atmosphere has to do with something called a **terminator.** This is a line dividing the lighted side of the Moon from the dark side. If there were a dense atmosphere, the terminator line would be fuzzy. But on the Moon, the terminator line is distinct.

Because there is such little atmosphere, the Moon's temperature changes drastically between day and night. Surface temperatures near the Moon's equator can get to –160 °C (–250 °F) in the night and then swing up to 120 °C (250 °F) in the day.

The Moon's Features

The Moon is full of unique physical land features, such as craters, "seas," and mountains. Craters dot the entire surface of the Moon, ranging in diameter from centimeters to hundreds of kilometers. Most astronomers believe that craters are primarily formed by impacts from smaller astronomical objects colliding on the surface. A few craters are believed to have formed from volcanic activity.

The Moon has varied coloring. Lighter areas are due to rock that better reflects sunlight and is higher in elevation. Darker areas are composed of rock that is denser and at lower elevation. These darker areas also have fewer craters. Early astronomers thought that the darker Moon areas were oceans, so they called them seas. They used the Latin word **mare** (mah' ray). Scientists now know that these **maria** (mah' ree ah), the plural of *mare*, are not filled with water but are smoother because volcanic material likely filled in these areas, covering over any existing craters. The few craters that are present in the maria today are a result of impacts that happened since the molten material cooled.

The Moon orbits Earth in a slightly elliptical orbit, which means its distance from Earth changes. The average distance from the center of the Moon to the center of Earth is about 384,472 km (238,900 mi). The closest point to Earth is called the Moon's **perigee** (pear' ih jee), and the farthest point is its **apogee** (ap' oh jee). It takes the Moon about a month (approximately 29½ days) to complete a single trip. In fact, the word *month* comes from the Old English word for Moon.

Interestingly, the Moon rotates on its axis at the same rate as its revolution around Earth. That means the same side of the Moon is always facing Earth. Scientists didn't even know what the far side of the Moon looked like until rockets were able to travel there and take pictures. The term for same rotation and revolution rates is called **synchronous rotation.** *Syn-* is a prefix meaning together, and *chron* is a Greek root word that refers to time. So the Moon

creation connection

There are relatively fewer maria on the far side of the Moon as compared to the side that faces Earth. Maria are believed to have been caused by large astronomical impacts, creating huge basins that were then filled by molten material. So it seems that the Moon was struck at one point by a large amount of material coming from the direction of Earth during a short amount of time. Of course, we don't know when or how this happened, but if lots of material was hitting the Moon, it is likely that much of it was also striking Earth, and the material that missed Earth hit the Moon on one side. If that is the case, then there would have been global-scale changes on Earth from all those impacts. Some scientists believe these Earth impacts might have been the cause or part of the cause of the global Flood and dinosaur extinction.

FIGURE 5.19
The Moon's Synchronous Rotation to Earth Viewed from Earth's North Pole

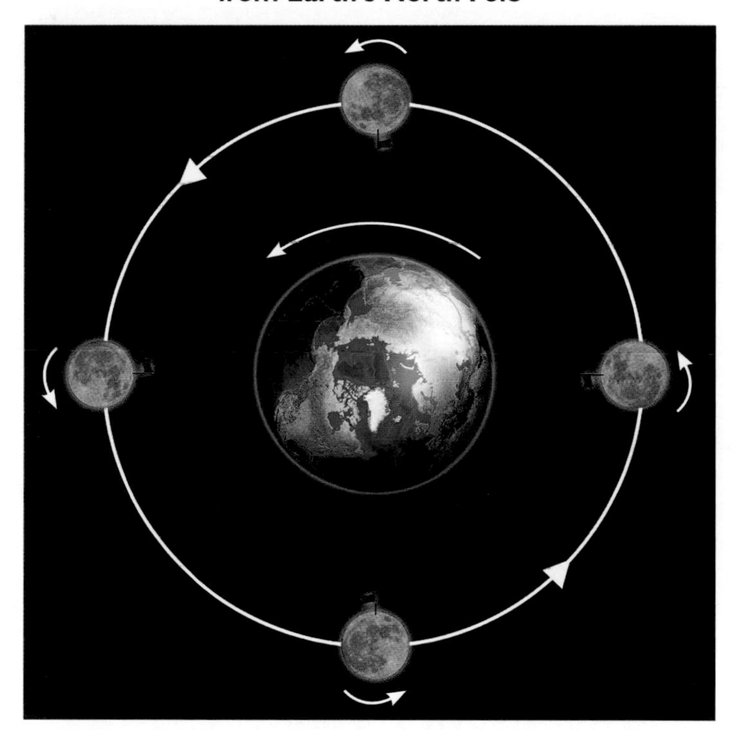

The flag on the Moon represents the near side of the Moon. Notice how it is always facing Earth, even though the Moon is rotating on its axis. The direction of the Moon's rotation, Earth's rotation, and the Moon's orbit are synchronous. That's why you only see one side of the Moon.

rotates and revolves at the same rate of speed. Actually, most satellites (or moons) of other planets also have synchronous rotation, too.

You may have heard someone refer to the dark side of the Moon. Well, that is an incorrect term that comes from the fact that we only see one side of the Moon from the vantage point of Earth. But as the Moon rotates on its axis, it receives sunlight on every side.

The Moon's Phases

Because the same side of the Moon faces Earth as it orbits us, we are able to see the sunlight reflecting off of it from different angles. Remember that the sun always lights up half of the Moon, but that lit half changes position, creating lunar phases. When the Moon is between Earth and the sun, we see no reflected sunlight. This is referred to as a **new moon.** As the Moon moves along its orbit around Earth, we can begin to see a thin slice of it that continually increases each day. This is referred to a **waxing** (growing) **moon.** A **full moon** is when the Earth is between the Moon and the sun; the light side of the Moon is completely facing us. Then as the Moon continues in its orbit, we see less and less of its lighted side. This is a **waning** (shrinking) **moon.**

EXPLORE MORE

Take a Styrofoam ball and stick a straw or pencil into it so it looks like a lollipop. Now insert a push pin or a bent paper clip into one side of the Moon to mark a spot as if it was on the Moon's equator. In a dark room, hold your model Moon at arm's length near a bright lamp, making sure the push pin side is always facing you. Now slowly turn around so the lamplight hits your Moon from lots of different directions. You represent Earth, always facing the same side of the Moon. The lamplight represents the sun. So as the sunlight hits the Moon from various angles during its orbit around Earth, only certain parts of it are visible. These are the Moon's phases.

FIGURE 5.20
Moon Phases

New	Waxing	Full	Waning

MORE ABOUT THE MOON

Tides

Although the Moon is far away, its gravitational force has an important effect on Earth. It pulls on Earth in a way that causes our oceans to bulge. This results in ocean tides. Tidal bulges line up with the Moon, creating **high tides** in areas where water is moving toward the Moon and **low tides** in areas where the water has moved from. Of course, the location of landmasses and the varied water depths also play a part in how much the ocean water moves in and out as compared to the shore. For the most part, each part of Earth passes through high tide twice a day and low tide twice a day. Tides are very important to cleanse the shorelines and help ocean organisms maintain life cycles.

Lunar Eclipses

Sometimes Earth is in just the right position between the Moon and the sun that it casts a shadow on the Moon. This is called a **lunar eclipse.** It occurs during a full Moon, but it doesn't happen with every full Moon; in fact it is quite rare. You see, the Moon's orbit around Earth is slightly tilted as compared to Earth's orbit around the sun. So Earth's shadow doesn't often fall on the Moon when it is full, sometimes passing above it or below it.

Earth's shadow, called an **umbra,** is just a bit larger than the Moon. Sometimes the shadow partially covers the Moon, and other times it completely covers the Moon. When the umbra completely shadows the Moon, it is called a **total lunar eclipse** (see Figure 5.21). Now, the Moon is not completely dark during a total lunar eclipse because Earth's atmosphere scatters the sunlight into its umbra, causing the Moon to range from a dark gray to even red or orange.

FIGURE 5.21
Progression of a Total Lunar Eclipse

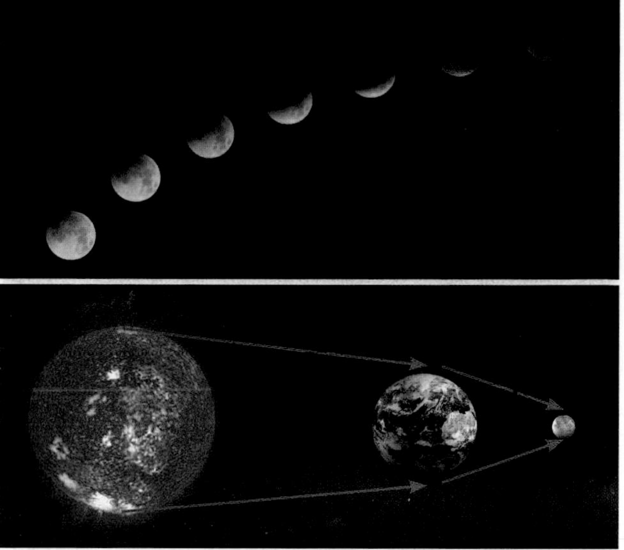

Notice how Earth's curved shadow starts to cover the Moon in the top photo. Once it has completely shaded the Moon, sunlight bends (refracts) as it passes through Earth's atmosphere, bending just enough so some of it hits the Moon.

Moon Exploration

During the 1960s, there was a lot of interest in exploring space, in particular, the Moon. NASA started the Mercury program to send one astronaut per mission in to space. Then the Gemini program was started to send 2 astronauts into space at a time. The Apollo program was developed to test and prepare for 3 astronauts to go into space and eventually travel to the Moon. Apollo 11 is the spacecraft mission that took Neil Armstrong, Michael Collins, and Buzz Aldrin to the Moon on July 20, 1969. Neil Armstrong was the first to actually set foot on the Moon. There were 9 Apollo missions sent to explore the Moon and 12 men walked there; some even explored using a wheeled craft called a **lunar rover.**

FIGURE 5.22
Apollo 17 Mission Commander Eugene A. Cernan Driving Lunar Rover

ON YOUR OWN

5.5 Which term is incorrect: the dark side of the Moon or the far side of the Moon? Why?

5.6 Explain the difference between a total lunar eclipse and a total solar eclipse. You can make an illustration if you want.

NON-PLANETARY BODIES

We have looked at the sun, its planets, and our Moon, but there are also many types of smaller objects in our solar system. We can group these non-planetary bodies into 3 basic groups: minor planets, comets, and meteors.

MINOR PLANETS

Minor planets are the largest of the non-planetary bodies. Although minor planets move across the sky as they orbit the sun, they look so small through a telescope that they appear to be stars instead of planets. Therefore, they are sometimes called **asteroids,** a word that means star-like, even though the preferred term is minor planets.

FIGURE 5.23
Illustration of Dwarf Planet Ceres within the Asteroid Belt

Astronomers in the early 1800s first discovered minor planets when they noticed that the distance between Mars' and Jupiter's orbits was quite large. Looking for a missing planet in that space, they discovered 4 small planets they called minor planets. By the end of the 1800s, more than 300 minor planets had been identified. Because of improvements in the techniques of studying the heavens, hundreds of thousands of these celestial bodies have been identified and their orbits are known. Interestingly, most of them have been discovered by professional and amateur astronomers using time-lapse photographs, looking for streaks of light as they move across the sky. There are so many minor planets and celestial bodies located between Mars and Jupiter that this region is called the **asteroid belt.**

think about this

Isn't it interesting that there are so many minor planets located between Mars and Jupiter? Many astronomers believe that there was once a planet in orbit there and sometime in the past, it may have exploded, sending pieces of rock and ice flying through space. These planetary bits remained in orbit around the sun, creating what is now called the main asteroid belt. Additionally, there are crater scars on many planets and moons, but they exist mostly on one side of the spheres. Well, if you imagine a planet located between Mars and Jupiter and then think of it exploding, you would expect that much of the resulting debris could have hit the surrounding planets and moons, but *only on the side facing the explosion*. Of course, we don't know for sure if that's what happened, but there seems to be lots of evidence to support that idea.

Minor planets range in size from a few meters in diameter to over 1,100 km (680 mi). They are not large enough to have the necessary surface gravity to hold an atmosphere. Some do have enough gravity to keep a small satellite of their own, and others exist as **binary asteroids,** where 2 asteroids orbit each other. The larger minor planets seem to exist as a solid piece of material, and the smaller ones are made up of smaller pieces held together by their weak gravity. Most of them are pretty irregularly shaped because they don't have enough gravity to form a spherical shape. Minor planets orbit the sun in a similar way as the planets do, traveling in a mostly circular-shaped orbit and in the same plane as the planets, too.

Now let's talk about **Pluto**. Pluto was discovered in 1930 and was considered to be the ninth planet in our solar system. It was considered the farthest planet from our sun, except for a short time during its elliptical orbit that brought it closer to the sun than Neptune. But there were some problems. First, Pluto never really fit into either of the 2 major types of planets. You see, it is far from the sun, has low density, and has many satellites, which would make it a Jovian planet. But its small size and slow rotation make it more like a terrestrial planet. Then, astronomers began to discover more and more similar-sized celestial bodies. That meant that they either needed to designate all of them as planets or reassign Pluto. In the end, Pluto was "demoted" to the realm of the minor planets. But it and at least 4 other of the larger minor planets (Eris, Ceres, Haumea, and Makemake) are given a more specific title: the **dwarf planets**. Dwarf planets are large enough to have enough gravity to make them spherically shaped.

Kuiper Belt and Oort Cloud

The **Kuiper** (ky' per or koy' per) **belt** is named after astronomer Gerard Kuiper, who studied the possibility of other planetary objects near Pluto's orbit. The first object actually discovered there (besides Pluto) was found in 1992 and named QB1. This belt of celestial bodies located just beyond Neptune's orbit is similar to the asteroid belt with the exception that the objects in the Kuiper belt are mostly larger and made of lots of ice instead of rocky material. Many dwarf planets are within this area, and it is believed that the Kuiper belt is a source of many of the comets within our solar system.

The **Oort cloud** is a shell of objects made of lots of ice. This belt is located in the farthest points of our solar system. Named after Jan Oort, who first suggested its presence, the Oort cloud is still yet to be explored in detail.

COMETS

Comets differ from minor planets in several ways. They do not have circular orbits, rather traveling around the sun in a noticeable elliptical path. The sun is near one end of the ellipse, so a majority of a comet's travels take it a far distance from the sun.

FIGURE 5.24
A Comet's Parts and Its Orbit

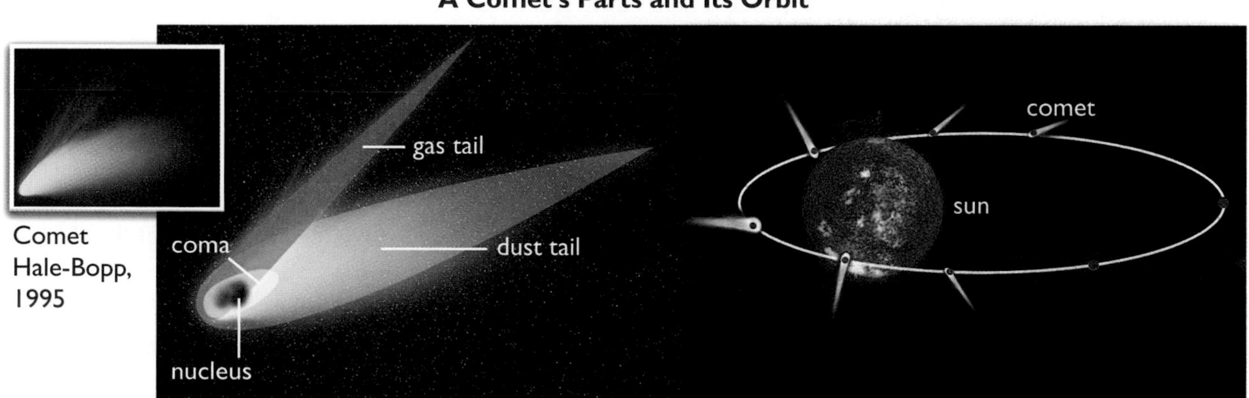

As it gets closer to the sun, a comet's tail grows in size. However, most of its time is spent away from the sun.

Comets have lots of ice, with fine, dusty material at their center, called the **nucleus.** As compared to the minor planets, comets are very small, with nuclei only about a few kilometers in diameter.

When a comet is close to the sun, the ice begins to heat up and evaporate, dispersing some of the dust, too. This forms a cloud, called a **coma,** that can extend thousands and thousands of kilometers in length. It glows because of the sunlight lighting up the gas.

If you think about it, every time a comet passes close to the sun, it will get a little smaller. That's because some of its ice melts and its dust particles are pushed away. So some comets end up being just rocks "flying" around in space. Comets also can collide with a planet if they are pulled in by the planet's gravitational force. An example of this is when a comet crashed into Jupiter in 1994 (see Figure 5.25).

FIGURE 5.25
Comet's Impact on Jupiter

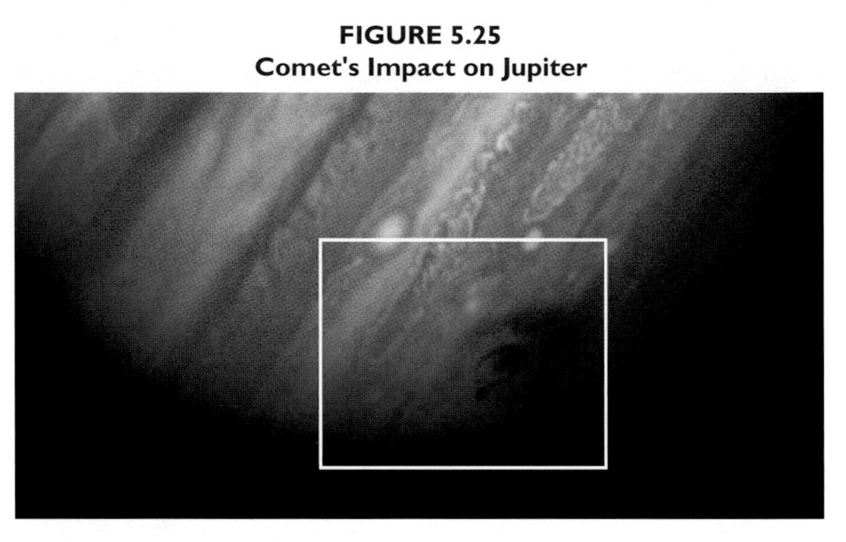

Comets can sometimes leave our solar system if they are pulled out of their orbit by a large planet in a way that causes them to leave the sun's gravitational pull. Then they travel out into deep space.

For thousands of years, astronomers have identified comets. Many written descriptions describe their long tails trailing in the sky. Short-period comets have orbits around the sun that take less than 200 years, and long-period comets have orbits up to thousands of years. It is believed that short-period comets come from the Kuiper belt and long-period comets originate from the Oort cloud.

METEORS

There are actually 3 names for the same celestial object that you might think of as a meteor. When a piece of rock or dust orbits the sun, it is called a **meteoroid.** What makes a meteoroid different from a minor planet or comet is just its size. Meteoroids are much smaller. When a meteoroid moves into Earth's atmosphere, it starts to glow as a result of the immense **friction** as it moves past the molecules in the air.

Friction—The action of one surface, material, or object rubbing against another

At this point, it gets a different name: a **meteor.** Most meteors are first identified when they are about 100 km above Earth and completely burn up by the time they reach about 80 km. Technically, you might be able to see a meteor on any night, but it really depends on being at the right place at the right time and looking at the right spot in the sky before the few moments it takes for them to burn up. However, there are a couple times during the year that meteor formation tends to increase. That's because there are meteoroids that exist in specific orbits and cross Earth's orbit at specific places. So when Earth arrives at these spots, the meteoroids that are there will be pulled into our atmosphere, creating a shower of meteors. During these times, the number of visible meteors increases. For example, during mid-August, the Perseid (pur' see id) meteor shower is visible. This phenomenon is given its name because the meteors seem to come from the Perseus constellation of stars (even though they don't). What really is happening is that the Comet Swift-Tuttle passed by Earth during its orbit around the sun in 1992. It left lots of dust and debris in its path, and when Earth moves through that material each year, we see the annual Perseid meteor shower. Perform Experiment 5.2 to observe the effects of friction.

EXPERIMENT 5.2

FRICTION

PURPOSE: To better understand how friction affects materials

MATERIALS:

- A piece of chalk
- A sheet of corrugated cardboard
- Masking tape
- A piece of sandpaper about half the size of the cardboard

QUESTION: How does friction affect objects?

HYPOTHESIS: Write what you think will happen to a piece of chalk when it experiences friction.

NOTE: This experiment produces a lot of dust, so it might be a good idea to do it outside.

PROCEDURE:

1. Attach the sandpaper to the center of the cardboard using a piece of masking tape on each corner.
2. Feel the surfaces of the sandpaper and the chalk and write whether they feel cool, warm, or hot.
3. Now take the chalk and rub it in a rapid back-and-forth motion on the sandpaper for about 30 seconds.
4. Immediately feel the rubbed surface of the chalk and write if it changed temperature. Do the same thing for the sandpaper.
5. Notice what happened to the chalk's size and write it in your notebook, too.
6. Clean everything up and put it away.

CONCLUSION: Write what you learned about friction.

What happened to the chalk in the experiment? Well, first, you should have noticed that as you were rubbing it against the sandpaper, it started to get smaller and form chalk dust. Second, after you stopped rubbing the chalk against the sandpaper, it felt a little warm (the sandpaper might have felt warm, too). When an object experiences friction, its material rubs against another material—in this case, the chalk material against the sandpaper material. As these surfaces experience friction, 2 things can happen: material starts to break up and heat is produced. That is what happens when a meteoroid enters Earth's atmosphere. Remember, the atmosphere is made up of material; gases like oxygen and nitrogen are rubbing against the meteor. This creates a great deal of friction, causing the meteor to heat up and lose material. If it is small enough, the meteor completely burns up before it reaches the ground.

FIGURE 5.26
Meteoroid, Meteor, Meteorite

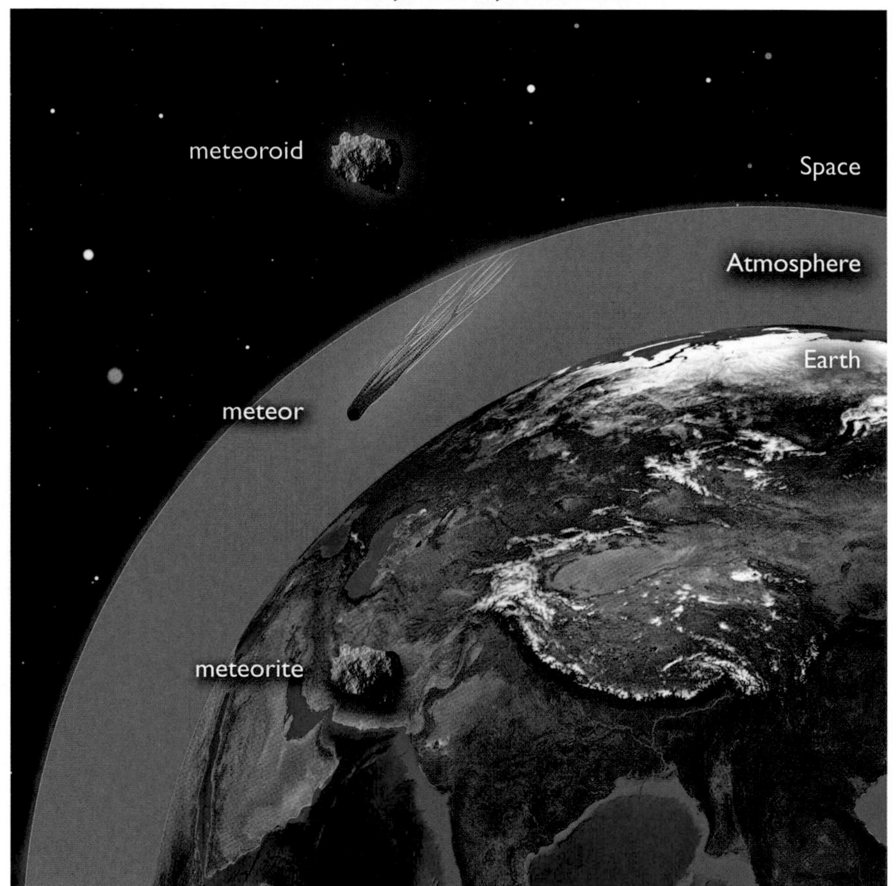

Now, most meteors *do* completely burn up as they fall through our atmosphere, but if they are large enough, there is enough of them left to strike Earth. When a meteor hits the ground it is referred to as a **meteorite.** The largest meteorite ever found was discovered when a farmer was plowing a field near Namibia, Africa. The large metal meteorite remains in its original spot today because it is so massive, weighing 66 tons. (That's 132,000 lb!) It's called the Hoba meteorite because it was discovered on a farm named Hoba West. Interestingly, this meteorite is not surrounded by a crater. You would think that an object as large as Hoba would create some sort of depression when it hit Earth, but it seems that it fell at a slower rate of speed. Scientists still cannot explain why. Perhaps it fell during a time of a large flood? The water would definitely slow the impact of the meteor.

Well, when a meteor does strike the planet, it often leaves a large crater. Meteorite craters have been found all over Earth, some thousands of feet in diameter. The craters often have meteorites located below the material at the bottom of the crater, though it is sometimes difficult to find them.

FIGURE 5.27
The Hoba Meteorite

ON YOUR OWN

5.7 Why does a comet's tail always point away from the sun?

5.8 Explain the difference between a meteoroid, a meteor, and a meteorite.

STARS

Our sun looks very different from the stars in the sky, yet astronomers have lots of evidence to show that it is a star, too. Stars look so much smaller because they are very, very far away from us. In fact, to express how far they are, we have to use the term "**light years.**" A light year is the distance that light can travel in a year.

EXPLORE MORE

You might not think of light traveling. After all, when you turn on a light switch in a room, the room lights up almost instantaneously. But the light from the lamp actually travels from the light bulb to the walls. It just moves so fast you cannot see it. Grab a flashlight to explore this phenomenon. Go into a dark room and turn on the flashlight. Try to see if you can watch the light travel from the flashlight bulb to the walls. After a few tries, you will realize that you just cannot see any span of time from when you turn on the light and the walls light up. That is because light travels so quickly. In fact, scientists have determined that it travels 299,792,458 m every second! Imagine how far light can travel if it goes at that speed for a year!

The closest star to Earth, besides our sun, is Proxima Centauri, which is one of a group of 3 stars bound together by gravity. It is about 4.22 light years away. Some stars are hundreds or even thousands of light years from us. How do we know? Astronomers use something called **stellar parallax.** It involves 2 type of maths, called trigonometry and geometry. Astronomers measure a star's movement against the background of stars farther away as Earth revolves around the sun. By measuring 2 angles and the included side of a triangle formed by the star, Earth on one side of its orbit, and Earth 6 months later on the other side of its orbit, astronomers can mathematically figure out the star's distance from us. So far, stellar parallax works for stars several hundreds of light years away.

Stars vary in their brightness, referred to as magnitude. The brightest-appearing stars are first magnitude, those that are a bit fainter are second magnitude, and so on. The faintest stars we can see in the night sky are about 6 magnitude. With improved telescopes, we are able to detect stars so faint that they reach a magnitude over 30. And the scale can go the other way, measuring brighter than first magnitude. Sirius, the Dog Star, is a magnitude of –1.4, and the planet Venus appears with a brightness of magnitude –4.4. Our sun can even be categorized by its brightness in the sky as a magnitude of –27!

FIGURE 5.28
Stellar Parallax

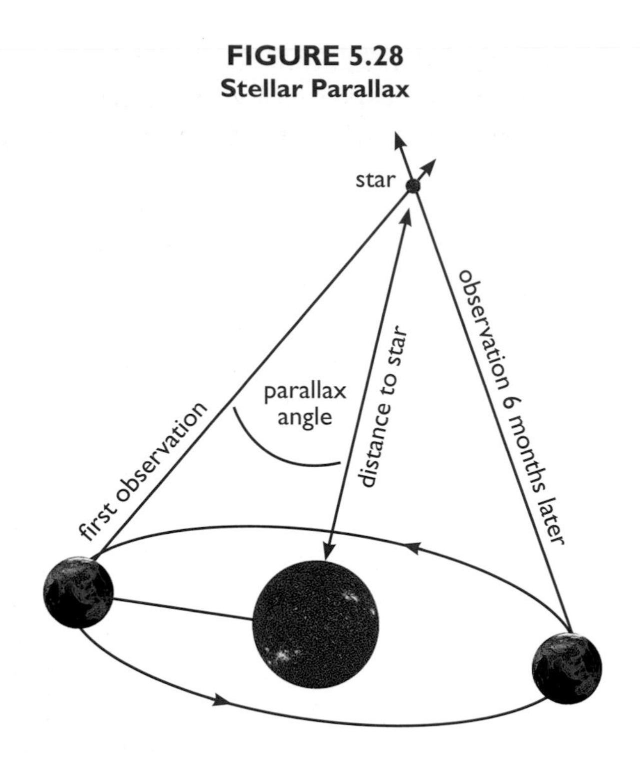

Stars have varied colors, too. A star's color can range from white to blue to orange to red, depending on its surface temperature. Hotter stars are more bluish in color, and cooler stars are red. As a rule, the hotter, brighter stars are also more dense, though there are some exceptions. The coolest stars are about 3,000 °C (5,000 °F), which might seem pretty hot, but the hottest known stars approach temperatures up to 100,000 °C (180,000 °F)!

One of the best ways astronomers determine a star's size is to look for a specific type of **binary star.** A binary star is a system of 2 stars that orbit one another because of their mutual gravity. If their orbits are oriented just right, we will see the stars blocking each other's light as they orbit one another. It is kind of like an eclipse, and by timing how long it takes for the eclipse to last, scientists can measure how large the stars are.

FIGURE 5.29
Illustration of a Newly Discovered Planet Orbiting One Star of a Binary Star System

Now, some stars can be huge. These **giants** and **supergiants** can be up to 1,000 times larger than our sun. Yet the giants are not very dense. Other stars are comparatively small. **White dwarfs** are very hot stars the size of Earth, and they are very dense. **Neutron stars**

are even smaller than white dwarfs, being 1/1000 the size of Earth. And they are *extremely* dense. All normal matter in the universe is made up of **atoms,** which are the smallest building blocks. Atoms consist of neutrons and protons, located in a central nucleus while electrons spin around it. But neutron stars are made of just neutrons organized into one giant mass. A neutron star spins very rapidly and has a strong magnetic field. So as it spins, its magnetic field spins along, too. And as it does, any charged particles nearby emit strong amounts of radiation in a long beam. If that beam is aligned the right way, astronomers are able to see it in the form of flashes, or pulses, of light. That is why these stars are sometimes called **pulsars.** We can only identify those pulsars that are lined up just the right way, so astronomers are not able to see all of them that are within our telescopic ranges. However, they have discovered over 2,000 pulsars already.

FIGURE 5.30
Hertzsprung-Russell Diagram Showing Star Characteristics by ESO

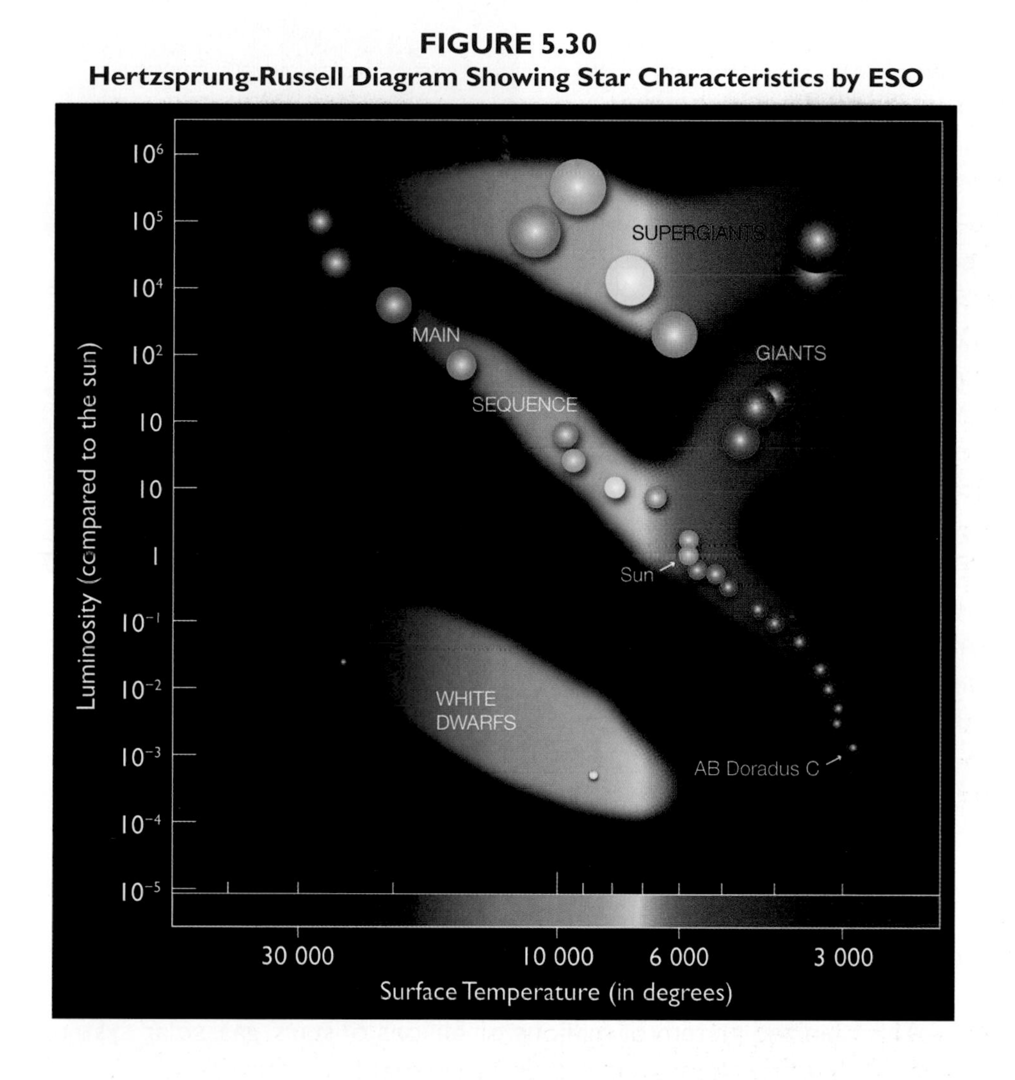

A **black hole** is a star that has much more gravity than a neutron star. And it is even smaller. You probably have noticed a pattern with a star's size, its density, and its gravitational pull. The largest stars are not very dense and have less gravity. The smallest ones are extremely dense and have a large gravitational pull. Black holes have a strong enough pull that even something going as fast as light, which is the fastest known speed, cannot escape their pull. Therefore, anything that comes near to them is pulled in, including light. That's why black holes appear dark. So how can we see them? Well, we can't directly observe them, but we *can* see their effects on the space around them.

Finally, some stars experience times of massive eruption, creating larger amounts of light than they normally do. This is called a **nova,** which is Latin for "new star." The stars weren't new, but they were not noticeable before they went nova, and therefore ancient astronomers called them new stars. Stars going nova don't stay at their new brightness forever, but eventually fade back to about the same intensity as before. Astronomers think that a nova occurs in a binary star system where the stars are very close together, and one of the 2 stars is a white dwarf while the other is a medium-sized star. The higher gravitational force of the white dwarf pulls material from the other star, causing increased pressure on that new material. The release of the resulting heat increases the star's brightness for a while. Some binary stars are structured so that they experience even greater emissions of light. We call these **supernovae** (singular supernova). You see, a white dwarf star can only get so large...somewhere about 1.4 times as massive as our sun. If it gains enough mass from the other star, it can explode, which completely destroys the star. That energy release is the supernova. The core that the star leaves behind is believed to be a black hole or a neutron star, depending on how much mass is left. The explosive energy also leaves behind a **nebula,** which is a cloud of gas and dust.

FIGURE 5.31
Crab Nebula

The Crab Nebula is the result of a supernova observed by scientists in AD 1054. It is about 10 light years in width and has a pulsar at its center. The pulsar is believed to be a neutron star as massive as the Sun but the size of a small town!

GALAXIES

When you look at the night sky, you might think that stars are evenly dispersed across the universe, but that is not true. The stars we see with the naked eye are those that exist within our **galaxy.**

Galaxy—An organized system of millions or billions of stars, gas, solar systems, and dust that are held together by gravitational attraction

Stars are found in groups, clustered together within the expanse of the universe. These galaxies exist in many shapes, including spiral and elliptical. Our sun is a star within the **Milky Way galaxy,** which is a spiral galaxy. If you are in a dark area at night, sometimes you are able to see a stretch of one of the arms from our spiral galaxy (see Figure 5.1).

You see, galaxies are very large. Think about what you know about our solar system and the planets and other celestial bodies that orbit our sun. It is just *one star system* within the Milky Way galaxy which has millions of stars. So it is very difficult to even imagine our galaxy's size! And astronomers believe there are millions or even billions of galaxies within the universe. When you think of God's creative power when He created all things, you can now better appreciate His omnipotence when He said, "Let there be lights in the expanse of the heavens to separate the day from the night" (Genesis 1:14a).

FIGURE 5.32
Galaxies

EXTRASOLAR PLANETS

In the late 1900s, astronomers discovered planets that orbited other stars. These are **extrasolar planets**, or **exoplanets.** It is very difficult to see them, particularly if astronomers are looking for the light these planets reflect from their sun. A better way to find them is to look for a star's change in brightness as a planet orbits it. If the planet is large enough, its gravitational force will affect the star just enough for us to identify it. These planets are then named by adding a lowercase letter to the name of the star they orbit, starting with the letter "b." In 2008, for example, Fomalhaut b was discovered orbiting the star Fomalhaut, which is a much hotter sun than ours and is located about 25 light years from our solar system.

FIGURE 5.33
An Artist's Illustration of the Extrasolar Planet Fomalhaut b in Orbit around Its Sun

The Kepler spacecraft was launched to survey our area of the Milky Way galaxy, looking for Earth-sized or smaller planets. It has found over 1,284 extrasolar planets, but there are likely many more it hasn't discovered. Often when it scans a star, it is not able to see those planets that are far in orbit from their star. So far, we have not found any planets that are similar to Earth. That's because there are several requirements for life as we know it. Orbital distance from the sun needs to be just right (not too close or too far), liquid water needs to naturally exist, and an oxygen-rich atmosphere is required. The sun cannot be too large or too small to emit the right amount of solar energy. The planet itself has to be just the right size for proper gravitational force. And there are many more requirements, too! So although there are likely many more extrasolar planets to find, we have not yet found one that has anywhere close to all the requirements to support life. Indeed, Earth is rare!

ON YOUR OWN

5.9 Our sun is a yellow dwarf main sequence star. If you refer to Figure 5.30, it would be located along the center diagonal strip of the graph and just to the right of the white ones. What do you think would happen to Earth if our sun was a neutron star? How about if it was a supergiant?

EXPLORATION OF SPACE

Man has always dreamed of exploring the heavens. So far, we have only been able to send people to the Moon. We've even traveled several times to the Moon. And we have been able to send unmanned telescopes to the far ends of the solar system, taking photos and sending them back to Earth. But is it possible to do more?

The first problem with manned space travel is that space is big. It would take up to 300 days just to reach Mars, so a round-trip visit to that planet would involve a couple years. You can imagine that it would be even more difficult to send people to the edges of our solar system and even more challenging to go to the nearest star. For example, the Voyager 2 unmanned spacecraft was launched from Earth on August 20, 1977. It reached Neptune 12 years later. Imagine how difficult it would be for a person to travel there. The spacecraft would have to be much larger to provide enough living space, and there would be difficulties in supplying enough water, food, medical supplies, and other physical needs. Of course, for a round trip, the time would be more than doubled because of the time spent on or near the planet.

To send people farther distances, rockets have to be designed that can travel much, much faster than they are now able. So far, the technology has not yet been developed, but that hasn't stopped people from dreaming.

SUMMING UP

In this module, we have traveled from our solar system, through our galaxy, and to the universe surrounding it. As you read about the vastness of space and all the heavenly bodies there, I hope you come away with an awe for the One who created it. Scientists who do not believe the universe was created have a difficult time trying to explain how it formed. Astronomers have identified how galaxies are oriented in clusters, separated by strands, making the universe kind of like Swiss cheese. The universe also seems to be expanding. They once suggested that as the universe expands, new galaxies pop up in the new space (though they couldn't explain how). This is called the steady-state theory. Other scientists suggest that the universe had a beginning, starting with a super-hot, dense state that exploded and now is cooling as it grows. This is called the Big Bang theory. These theories were debated for years until about 1965 when a cosmic microwave background was identified in the universe. This radiation comes from the microwave part of the spectrum of light. However, a cosmic microwave background can't exist in a steady-state universe, so today, many scientists believe the Big Bang theory is true. The Big Bang theory has changed over the last few decades to make it better fit new information as astronomers discover things. Yet it is still a theory that cannot stand without making several major assumptions. And assumptions are not proof. Remember, science cannot prove something is true, but we can use our observations to help us better understand the universe. Genesis 1:14–15 says, "Let there be lights in the expanse of the heavens to separate the day from the night. And let them be for signs and for seasons, and for days and years, and let them be lights in the expanse of the heavens to give light upon the earth." We know that these words are true, don't we? People use the lights in the sky to measure seasons, days, and years. They give light to Earth. And they are ordered in their movements. The elegant order of the universe gives good testimony that it was created, made by an omnipotent Creator!

ANSWERS TO THE "ON YOUR OWN" QUESTIONS

5.1 When your shadow is very short, it means the sun is directly above you. That means it is close to 12:00 noon. When your shadow is very long, it means the sun is off to one side of you. So it is either early morning right after sunrise or early evening just before sunset.

5.2 There is less atmospheric material in orbit so the light coming into the telescope will not be as scattered.

5.3 Sunspots on the sun's surface move across the sun from east to west. When one disappears on the western edge, it reappears on the eastern edge a few weeks later.

5.4 The 2 types of planets are terrestrial planets and Jovian planets. Earth is a terrestrial planet.

5.5 There is no dark side of the Moon. Because the Moon has a synchronous rotation, it rotates and revolves at the same rate of speed. That means the view from Earth is always of one side. The other side is the far side of the Moon. All sides of the Moon eventually receive sunlight as the Moon rotates on its axis.

5.6 A total lunar eclipse is when Earth is between the Moon and the sun so that it casts a complete shadow on the Moon. A total solar eclipse is when the Moon is between Earth and the sun, casting a shadow on Earth. During this time, the Moon barely, but completely, covers the sun so that viewers on Earth see just the sun's corona.

5.7 As a comet nears the sun, solar energy heats up its dust and ice, causing a gas cloud coma. The solar energy then pushes the gas and dust particles away from the sun, which means the comet's tail will always point away.

5.8 When a piece of rock or dust orbits the sun, it is called a meteoroid. Then, when the meteoroid enters Earth's atmosphere it is a meteor. Finally, when the meteor lands on Earth's surface it is a meteorite.

5.9 If our sun was a neutron star, it would be very small, but very dense. That means it would have strong gravitational force. At the very least, that could affect the ocean tides by pulling on them too hard, making the tidal changes more severe. It could also affect Earth's orbit, pulling it closer to the sun. But most likely, its massive heat would scorch Earth, harming life. If our sun was a supergiant, it would be so large that it might extend past Earth's orbit, burning up the planet. It also would greatly affect Earth's orbit (if the Earth didn't burn up!), changing our days, months, and years. The short answer to this question is that *Earth could not support life as we know it!*

STUDY GUIDE FOR MODULE 5

1. Match the following words with their definitions.

a. Atmosphere	A force of attraction existing between any 2 masses
b. Astronomy	The branch of science that deals with the physical universe beyond Earth's atmosphere
c. Gravity	A natural or artificial body orbiting a planet or star
d. Satellite	The gaseous layer surrounding Earth or another heavenly body

2–4. Complete the definitions by using the correct word or words from the list below.

moon stars rubbing gravitational light

2. An albedo is the amount of ______________ or radiation reflected by a surface, typically that of a planet or ______________.

3. Friction is the action of one surface, material, or object ______________ against another.

4. A galaxy is an organized system of millions or billions of __________, gas, solar systems, and dust that are held together by _________________ attraction.

5–6 True or false.

5. Although a sundial is a simple object, and a telescope is a more complex one, both are forms of scientific technology.

6. Using a telescope on land provides a better advantage for observation as compared to using a telescope placed in orbit around Earth.

7. What name, including a middle initial, works as a good device to remember the order of the visible wavelengths of light?

8. Give one example each of a natural and an artificial satellite of Earth.

9. Which of the following is NOT related to sunspots.
   a. Sunspots are darker and cooler areas of the sun.

   b. Sunspots can extend millions of miles from the sun and throw so much energy and electrically charged plasma to Earth that it can affect the sky.

   c. Sunspots seem to affect Earth's weather, causing extreme cold and drought-like conditions when there are fewer of them and warmer conditions when there are many of them.

   d. The observation of sunspots moving across the sun and reappearing on the other side of the sun a few weeks later suggests the sun is rotating on its axis.

10. What event enables scientists to learn more about the sun's atmosphere, including its corona and loops of gas extending outward?

11. Using the information in the following paragraph, make a chart with 2 columns: Terrestrial Planets and Jovian Planets. Then write the characteristics of each planet type in its respective column.

    The **terrestrial planets** are Earth-like. The 4 planets closest to the sun (Mercury, Venus, Earth, and Mars) are terrestrial planets. The rest of the planets are in a group called the **Jovian planets**. Jovian planets include Jupiter, Saturn, Uranus, and Neptune. Terrestrial planets have less mass and are smaller than Jovian planets. They are closer to the sun and are denser than Jovian planets, too. In fact, Jovian planets have thick, gaseous atmospheres and are often referred to as **gas giants**. Jovian planets rotate very rapidly, and terrestrial planets generally rotate slowly. Jovian planets have many satellites, and terrestrial planets have few, if any at all. Lastly, all the Jovian planets have rings, but none of the terrestrial ones do.

12. Because the Moon rotates on its axis at the same rate as its revolution around Earth, the same side of the Moon is always facing Earth. Thus, we can only observe one side of the Moon from the vantage point of Earth. Why is the term "dark side of the Moon" an incorrect one in reference to this phenomenon?

13. Which diagram correctly orients a comet's tail when the comet is near the sun?

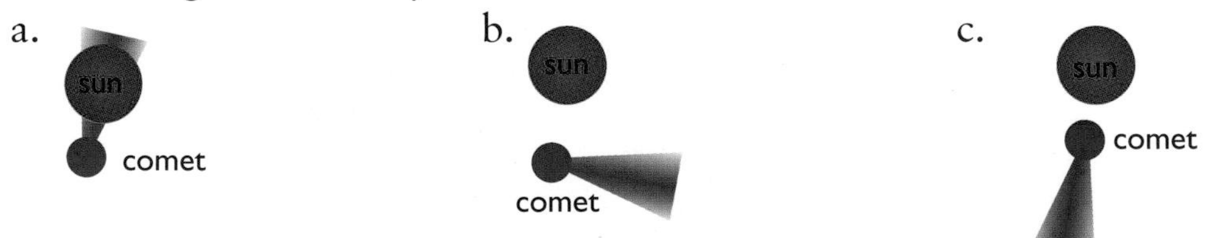

14. Place these terms in order from the farthest distance from Earth until the object lands on Earth: Meteor – Meteoroid – Meteorite

EARTH SCIENCE— GEOLOGY AND PALEONTOLOGY

Last module, you learned about the science of astronomy. Your journey took you from the surface of Earth through the atmosphere, solar system, galaxy, and, finally, the universe. It was actually the beginning of a study of Earth science, a field that includes astronomy, geology, paleontology, meteorology, and oceanology. That's a lot of "*-ologies*," isn't it? Well, that suffix simply means "the study of," and it is attached to prefixes that involve some of the various branches of science to study. In this module and the next one, we'll be looking at Earth's surface and digging downward to continue our exploration of all the major fields within Earth science.

Quaestio

Earth is our home. God has given us Earth so we can live on it and care for it. A good way to care for it is to know more about it—what it's made of and how it behaves in the universe. After a solid study of astronomy, you learned a bit about how our Earth behaves in relation to other celestial bodies. Now we need to turn our observations to Earth itself, trying to better understand its composition and get some clues to its history. This will help us to be better stewards of what we are called to care for.

FIGURE 6.1
Earth Science: A Study of Earth

THE EARTH'S STRUCTURE

Let's start with a more formal definition of geology.

Geology—The study of Earth's physical structure, its history, the processes acting on it, and the rocks of which it is composed

In Module 5, you learned how Earth is the third planet from the sun and is part of the terrestrial planets, with a solid composition. Now, although scientists believe we have a pretty good idea of what Earth's structure is, you need to realize that no one has ever been deeper than about 3 km (2 mi) below its surface, and the deepest we have been able to drill is less than 13 km (8 mi) down. You might think that is pretty deep, but scientists have calculated it is about 6,440 km (4,000 mi) to the center of Earth, so we literally haven't even scratched the surface! However, we do have the technology to determine a general idea of what this planet is made of. Earth is made of 3 major layers, based on their composition: the crust, mantle, and core.

Earth's Crust

The crust is the first layer and is comparatively thin in relation to the other 2 layers. It is made up of solid rock and is the only layer we have been able to sample and explore. The crust ranges in thickness from 6 to 11 km (3.7–6.8 mi) in the ocean and 25 to 90 km (15–56 mi) on the continents. That might sound pretty thick, but if you were to take a large cantaloupe to represent Earth and then stick a postage stamp on it, the stamp's thickness would represent the average thickness of Earth's crust! Now most of the crust is not directly visible. It is covered by soil and other material. In fact, in some parts of the world, heat and pressure compact these soil materials into rock. Yet, there *are* a few places on the planet where the soil and rock have worn away, revealing the crust material below.

FIGURE 6.2
A Cross Section of Earth Showing Its Layers

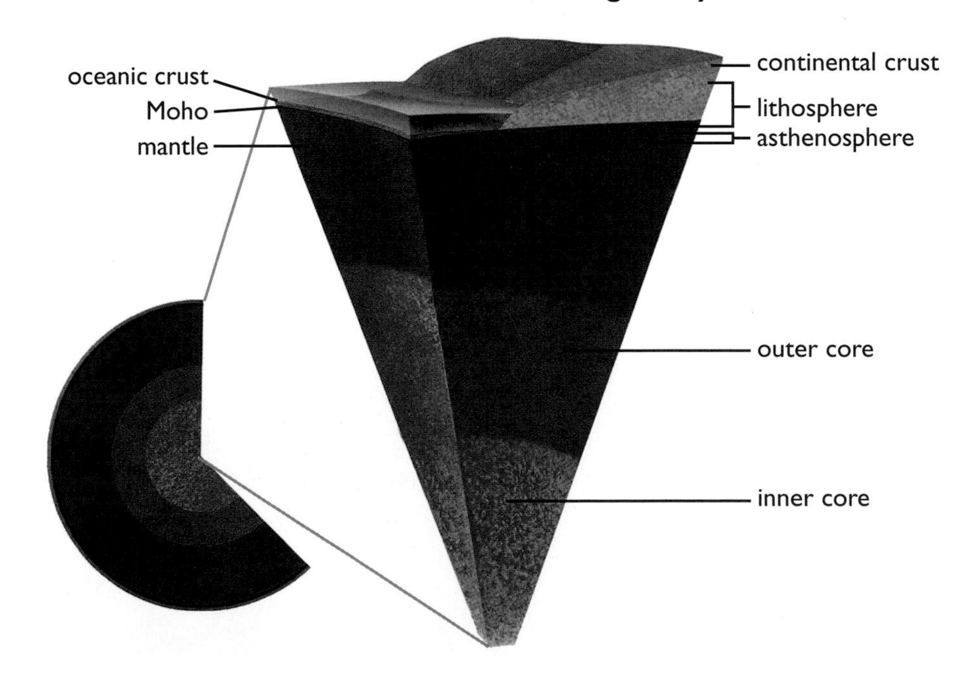

Earth's crust can be divided into 2 types: continental crust and oceanic crust (see Figure 6.2). Continental crust is primarily made of **granite** (rock mostly made of silica and aluminum oxide) and oceanic crust is primarily made of **basalt** (rock containing lots of magnesium or iron). Granite is not as dense as basalt and is located underneath the continents. Basalt is a bit denser and lies below the oceans. You'll learn why in just a bit.

Earth's Mantle

The **mantle** is the middle layer of Earth right below the crust and is the layer with the largest mass. Remember, we have never directly explored the mantle, so what we know of it comes from the study of geologic events such as earthquakes. Earthquakes are sharp movements in Earth's crust, and they create seismic waves. These waves move through Earth's interior as they radiate outward, much the same way that ripples of water move outward when you drop a rock in a still pond. The waves bend when they come in contact with different materials, such as liquids or solids, and that helps scientists to figure out what material is in the waves' paths.

There is a noticeable change in density at the bottom edge of Earth's crust. This spot is called the **Moho**, named after Andrija Mohorovičić, who discovered it. Directly beneath the Moho is where the mantle begins. It extends down to about 2,900 km (1,800 mi) below Earth's surface. Now, the mantle is made up of the same components as the crust but in different proportions, and it experiences much higher temperatures and greater pressure than the crust. Because of this, the rock of the mantle is not always solid. It behaves more like a thick, syrup-like material, called **plastic rock.** Plastic rock normally flows like thick molasses does; however, if it is hit with a quick, sharp force, it becomes like a solid.

think about this

What is a continent? You may have learned there are 7 continents, but did you know that some scientists disagree on that number? Most scientists define a continent as a large, continuous landmass, separated by an expanse of water. However, some people consider Europe and Asia as 2 different continents even though they are connected. (North and South America are also naturally connected, too!) And the word *large* is not really helpful because Greenland is considered an island, even though it is larger in area than the *continent* of Australia. Geographers (scientists who study Earth, its land, and inhabitants) mostly prefer the 6-continent model, combining Europe and Asia into a large Eurasian continent. However, in Latin America, students are taught a 6-continent model which combines North and South America instead. Therefore, the designation of a continent is more by general agreement than by definition.

FIGURE 6.3
Lava

The only time we can see material of the mantle is when it escapes through cracks in Earth's crust. This lava flow was once material in the mantle.

EXPLORE MORE

It might be difficult to imagine how plastic rock works, so try this simple activity. Take a 16-oz. container of dry cornstarch and dump it into a large bowl. Gradually add water a little at a time and stir the mixture with a spoon. Make sure you are stirring slowly. Once the mixture is thick and syrupy in consistency, stop adding water. Now, with a clean hand, scoop up some of the goo. Holding your hand over the bowl, rapidly and firmly squeeze the material, and then quickly open your hand. The liquid should have become a solid for a short time and then slowly "melted" back into a liquid in your hand. Punch the mixture in the bowl (not too hard, or you could hurt your fist!). Notice how the impact makes it hard. This is like how the plastic rock of the mantle behaves. It is referred to as a **non-Newtonian** fluid because it is a liquid that doesn't follow the fluid laws suggested by Sir Isaac Newton. You see, most fluids become thinner when they are warmed and thicker when they are cooled, but non-Newtonian fluids can change their flowability (called viscosity) by a change in pressure. **NOTE: Do NOT dump this mixture in the sink when you are finished; it will clog your pipes. Throw it away instead.**

The deeper you go in the Earth, the higher the temperature and the greater the pressure. In fact, at the Moho, the temperature is about 480 °C (895 °F), and at the bottom of the mantle, temperatures can reach as high as 3,700 °C (6,700 °F). Now you can better understand why we have not been able to directly explore this layer of Earth! Geologists believe that large amounts of plastic rock move through the mantle. Hotter rock rises to the top and then slowly sinks back down as it cools. This means the mantle is a dynamic layer with lots of movement (even though it is made of rock).

Earth's Core

The lower edge of the mantle is the core-mantle boundary. At about 2,900 km (1,800 mi) from Earth's surface, this is where the next layer of Earth begins: the **core**. The core extends down to Earth's center 6,400 km (4,000 mi). It has 2 layers: the **outer core** and the **inner core**. Geologic data suggest the outer core is made up of liquid because of its extreme heat of 5,000 °C (9,000 °F). It is believed to be made up of iron and nickel, and because it is fluid, currents of molten material run throughout this sub-layer. The inner core is, well, *inner*. It is believed to be made up of the same material as the outer core but in a solid phase. Now, you might be wondering why that is. After all, I said the deeper you go into the Earth, the hotter it gets. And, indeed, that seems to be true. So why aren't the iron and nickel in the inner core melted? After all, the inner core is hotter than the outer core. Well, there is another thing happening here. The deeper you go into the Earth, the greater the pressure, and the pressure is so great at the inner core that the iron and nickel atoms

FIGURE 6.4
Phases of Materials in the Earth

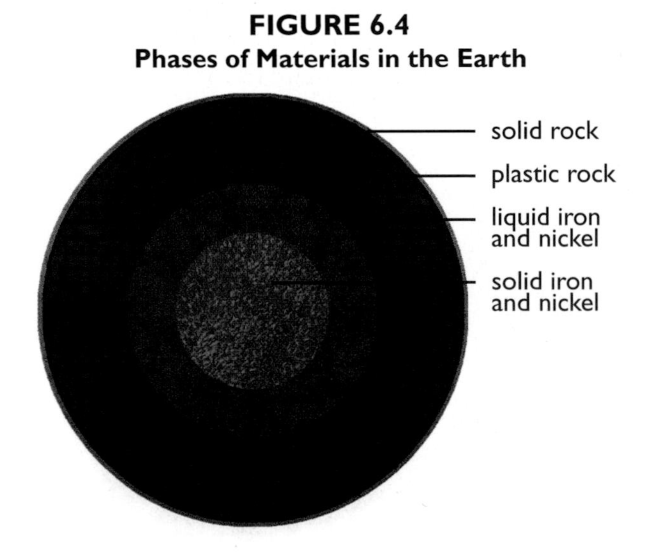

are not able to move around, even though they are *very* hot. Thus, they are forced into a solid phase.

THE LITHOSPHERE

With a good understanding of the layers within the Earth, I can start to describe some of the land formations we see on its surface. The very upper part of the mantle is solid rock. This and the crust above it make up Earth's **lithosphere** (lith' uh sfear). Directly below the lithosphere is a thin mantle sub-layer called the **asthenosphere** (as then' uh sfear). Here is where the rock is more plastic-like. It is believed that the solid lithosphere floats on the plastic asthenosphere (see Figure 6.2).

Remember that there are 2 types of crust? Well, the mostly-granite continental crust is not as dense as the mostly-basalt oceanic crust. This means the denser oceanic crust "floats" a little lower on the plastic rock of the mantle as compared to continental crust. That's why oceanic crust is covered by oceans and continental crust is not. Both crust types float around based on the movements of the plastic rock as it shifts and changes. They move around because Earth's lithosphere is believed to be broken up into pieces, called **plates.**

This theory is called **plate tectonics.** It is based on evidence that seems to support the idea that as the plastic rock of the mantle moves around, the plates move along with it (see Figure 6.5). A good way to think of this is to imagine yourself standing waist high in a pool, holding a large, rectangular sheet of Styrofoam that floats on the water's surface. You then break the sheet into pieces but still hold it together for a moment. Now, when you let go of the sheet, you would notice the individual pieces start to drift around, based on the movement of the liquid water below. That is similar to how scientists think the rocky plates of the Earth move around on the plastic rock below.

FIGURE 6.5
Plates of the Earth's Crust

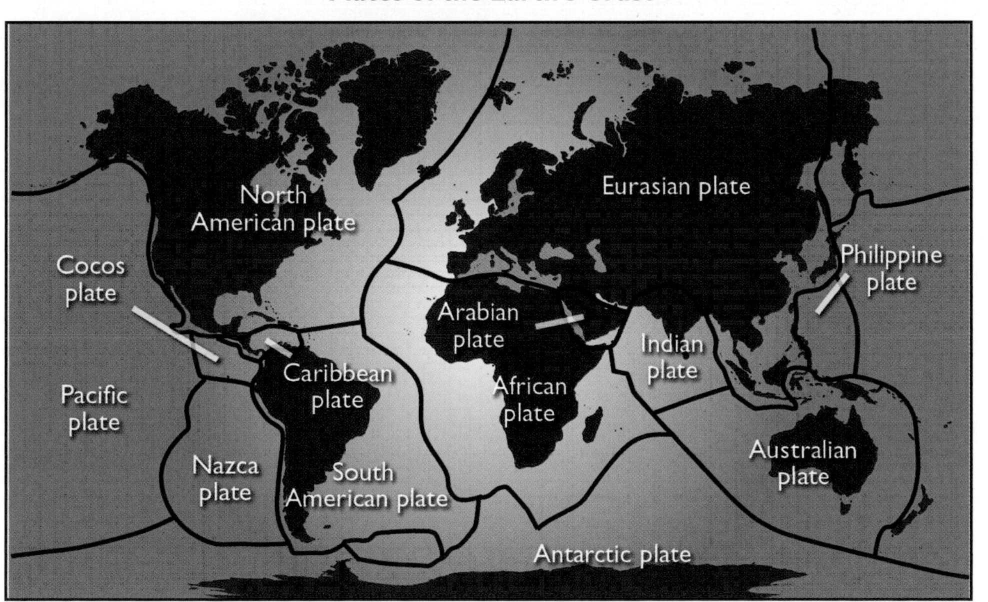

Well, as the plates move around, they push past one another and bump into each other. And this is believed to be what creates land formations. Sometimes plates will collide and buckle, forming mountains. In other instances, one plate may move below another as they are pushed together. This can form a deep trench. Remember, these are *very* large rock masses we're talking about, some the size of continents. So you can imagine that when they move against each other the results can be quite violent and create earthquakes or volcanic events.

There is a lot of evidence to support the idea of plate tectonics. In fact, many of our observations of earthquakes, mountains, and volcanoes support it. Most geologists believe the movement of Earth's plates is occurring, but the speed of their movement, both today and in the past, is debated. It is true that the plates seem to move pretty slowly *today*. But they may not have always moved at this speed. In fact, scientists have observed recent evidences of rapid movement in certain parts of the world. For example, in 2005, a crack suddenly formed in the desert of Ethiopia. It was 56 km (35 mi) long and is believed to be the beginning of a new ocean! Studies show that the processes creating this rift are nearly the same as what is happening in the deep ocean. Because it is evident that tectonic movements can occur at a faster rate, it is scientifically sound to suggest that all of Earth's plates may have moved at a faster rate in history, too. In fact, if a global cataclysm like Noah's Flood occurred, then the plates would have *rapidly* moved around!

FIGURE 6.6
Afar Region of Ethiopia

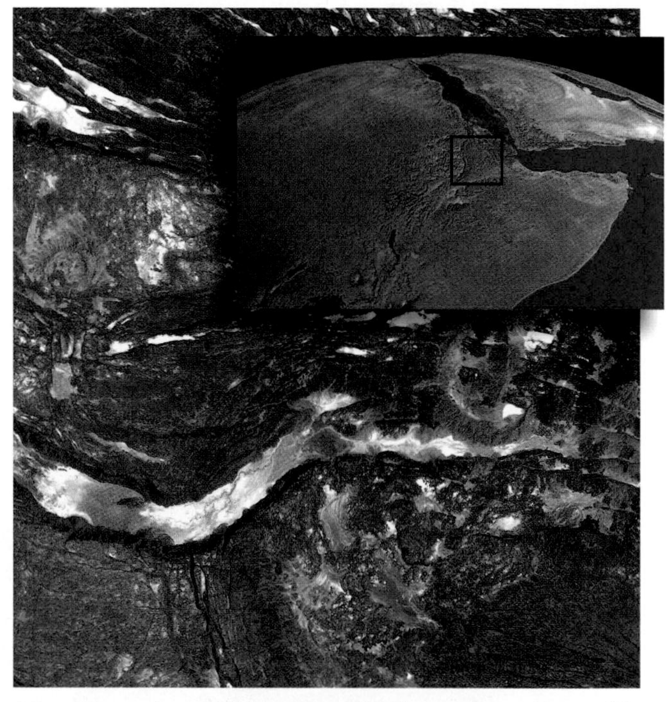

The Afar region of Ethiopia marks the meeting place of 3 separate pieces of Earth's crust. As they pull away from each other, they are creating a large body of water (lower third of photo).

Now, if the large rock masses of Earth's surface move relative to each other, something should be noticeable where those masses meet. And, indeed, lots of things can be seen! We call the boundary between 2 plates a **fault**. And when these large rock masses move in relation to one another, things like earthquakes can occur there. Earthquakes are vibrations of the Earth as a result of volcanic activity or plate movement.

So wherever there is a fault, there is the possibility of an earthquake. That's because rocks are not really smooth. When they move, they tend to get caught up on each other, even though the forces are still pushing on them. You cannot really notice anything is happening as this pressure builds up, but the rock actually starts to bend a bit. Eventually the forces become too great, and the rock finally breaks free of the rough edges at the fault holding it in place. And when this happens, the rocks unbend, rapidly returning to their original shapes. The vibrations from this phenomenon are what we know as an earthquake.

ON YOUR OWN

6.1 Label the diagram to the right:
Oceanic Crust, Continental Crust, Mantle, Outer Core, Inner Core, Moho, Lithosphere, Asthenosphere

A.
B.
C.
D.
E.
F.
G.
H.

6.2 Plate tectonic movement is believed to be true by most scientists. However, most of our data to support this phenomenon come from **indirect observations**. Explain in your own words what you think an indirect observation is. (Remember, no one has ever seen below Earth's crust.)

THE HYDROPLATE THEORY

Plate tectonics is a commonly taught theory that attempts to explain the formation of the geological features of Earth we see today. Because no one was present to observe what happened long ago, scientists make observations and perform tests to try to understand the processes that are occurring today as well as those that occurred in the past. Therefore, there are different views even among creationist scientists.

Over the last several decades, creationists have suggested a number of geological models using the mechanisms of the worldwide Flood to explain the features we see today. Secular geologists also have developed different models to explain geological history. In fact, about 50 years ago, very few geologists accepted the idea that continents moved around at all. Today, many geologists do.

Creationist scientists who hold to plate tectonics believe that much of the movement of Earth's plates occurred rapidly during the time of the Noahic Flood. This catastrophic plate tectonic theory suggests a runaway movement that accounts for the main tectonic changes associated with the Flood. Scientists that accept this theory believe it is the best framework available to understand the massive amounts of observed geological data.

Yet other scientists believe that the data better fit another theory: the hydroplate theory. The hydroplate theory suggests that before the Flood of Noah's time, a massive amount of water existed beneath Earth's crust, and Earth at that time had only one large supercontinent.

Before the Great Flood, it is suggested that about half of Earth's water was contained in underground, interconnected chambers about 16 km below Earth's surface. This water layer (called supercritical water as a result of the enormous pressure exerted on it by the overlying crust) was experiencing increased pressure over the centuries due to the daily gravitational pull of the sun and moon, the same way that tides are pulled and pushed in above-ground oceans today. So, the increasing pressure created by the back-and-forth underground tidal stress caused the crust above to stretch.

Eventually, the crust rapidly cracked along a line that circled the globe. As the cracks reached the water layer, the pressurized water violently spewed up into the atmosphere, causing rain to fall in a way that it had never done before. In fact, when the waters erupted from these underground chambers, a massive amount of energy would have been released, too, possibly approaching the strength of 30 trillion hydrogen bombs exploding!

Seafloor Features as Revealed by Slight Differences in Measured Gravity

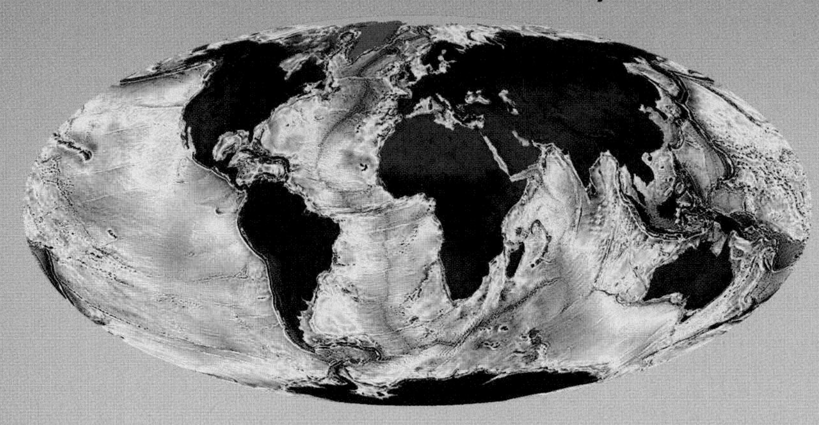

This event is mentioned in Genesis 7:11: "In the six hundredth year of Noah's life, in the second month, on the seventeenth day of the month, on that day all the fountains of the great deep burst forth, and the windows of the heavens were opened."

As the water moved up through the widening crack, lots of crust material would have eroded, creating massive amounts of sediments that moved with the floodwaters. These sediments rapidly buried plants and animals to form the fossils we see today.

Additionally, when the water pushed upward, the rock structures around the crack rose with it, forming high ridges which are called mid-ocean ridges today. The plates on either side of these ridges then slid down and away from them, gliding smoothly on the layer of water that remained below. As the plates moved, they eventually experienced friction and began to slow down, buckling and bunching up until they stopped. Upward movement would have formed high mountains. This could explain why the major mountain ranges of the world today are parallel to the ocean ridges from which they slid.

Large, deep ocean basins would also have formed when the plates moved away from the ridges. That would have provided areas into which the floodwaters could recede.

Now, there are studies today that support the hydroplate theory, including evidence of a layer of electrically conductive material (such as saltwater) lying below the Tibetan Plateau.

Meteorites have been discovered containing salt crystals and liquid water, suggesting that perhaps large Earth rock fragments were ejected into orbit around the sun when those massive cracks formed and the water erupted. These fragments could be returning to Earth today as meteorites.

Additionally, when scientists recently drilled a 12-km-deep hole down into Earth's crust in Russia, they expected to find a layer of basalt, but instead they found heated saltwater flowing among crushed granite rock.

You should not be surprised to learn that more than one theory exists to explain how Earth's formations came to be. That's because Earth is huge, and the data we have are comparatively limited. Scientists continue to have discussions and debates to try to best understand the data they have. And when

Kola Borehole in Russia Reaching 12,262 m (40,230 ft) into Earth's Crust

new data are recorded, they then need to adjust their models so that the new facts are considered.

Creationist scientists know that we can't be careless in handling scientific data and should not pick and choose data to accept or ignore. And they realize that we all need to be discerning as we draw on the work done by researchers who have a secular worldview.

However, Christians should never base their faith on a single scientific model because models change as more and more information is gathered. *Instead, we need to place our faith on God's Word.* The Bible is infallible and never changes because it is Truth!

In fact, among creationist scientists, most agree on many aspects of Earth history. They agree (and there is a lot of scientific support) that there was a global Flood. They also agree that dynamics at locations where modern plates meet are much more complex than what is often taught.

Isn't it amazing that science always allows us to expand our knowledge? The important thing is to continue to explore, investigate, and ask questions. Perhaps one day, you will study geology more in depth, enter the discussion, and add to this grand adventure!

SOIL, ROCKS, AND MINERALS

Plate movement is believed to have caused many of the land formations we see today. But before we get into some of those formations, let's first take a closer look at the rocks that make up the lithosphere.

What are the rocks of the lithosphere made of? If you were to go outside and start digging, you would first be digging through dirt. This material is called soil. Soil is made up of different components in varied amounts. The topmost layer of soil is full of **humus.**

Humus—The decayed remains of once-living creatures

Humus is rich material, filled with nutrients that nourish plants. Besides humus, soil also can contain **gravel, sand, silt,** and **clay.** Not all soil has all 5 of these components, but most does, and the types and percentages of these major materials are why soils differ all over the world.

Below the soil is a layer of rock—not single large rocks, but an actual rock layer of Earth's crust. This layer is probably too deep for you to find if you were to dig with a shovel, so I don't recommend you try.

FIGURE 6.7
Large Rock Formation Made from Several Rock Types

Now there are 3 basic types of rock that make up Earth's crust: **sedimentary** (sed uh men' tuh ree) **rock, igneous** (ig' nee us) **rock,** and **metamorphic** (met uh mor' fik) **rock.** Sedimentary rock is made from sediments, which are sand, minerals, and other materials that are primarily laid down by water. They pile up on top of each

FIGURE 6.8
Magma on Earth's Surface is Lava

other, often in layers, and eventually can be cemented together by chemical reactions, heat, and pressure. The sediments turn solid, creating sedimentary rock. Now, sedimentary rock covers over much of the surface of Earth and technically is the uppermost layer of Earth's crust. That means it is the most common type of rock people find. Igneous rock is made from melted, or molten, rock. We call molten rock **magma.** So a volcanic eruption that is releasing lava is actually releasing magma; the only difference between these words is where the melted rock is located. Lava is on Earth's surface, and magma is below the surface. More commonly, magma flows underground and sometimes will harden there. That is why most igneous rocks are formed beneath the surface of Earth. The only igneous rocks people tend to find are those that are hardened from lava after a volcanic eruption.

The third rock type is metamorphic rock. *Meta* is a word form meaning "transform," and *morph* means "form." So metamorphic rock is rock that has changed its form, often due to extreme heat or pressure. Both sedimentary and igneous rocks can form metamorphic rock. For example, when sedimentary rock is transformed, it forms limestone, which is much harder. If it experiences even greater temperature and pressure, limestone can change to marble, which is even harder than limestone.

What makes rocks different from each other is the materials they are made of. These include **minerals.**

Minerals—Inorganic crystalline substances found naturally in the Earth

Let's break that definition down to better understand it. First, *inorganic* means the material did not come from a living organism. That means it is not made up of materials from dead creatures or from materials produced by living ones. *Crystalline* refers to a specific kind of structure. Perform Experiment 6.1 to see what I mean.

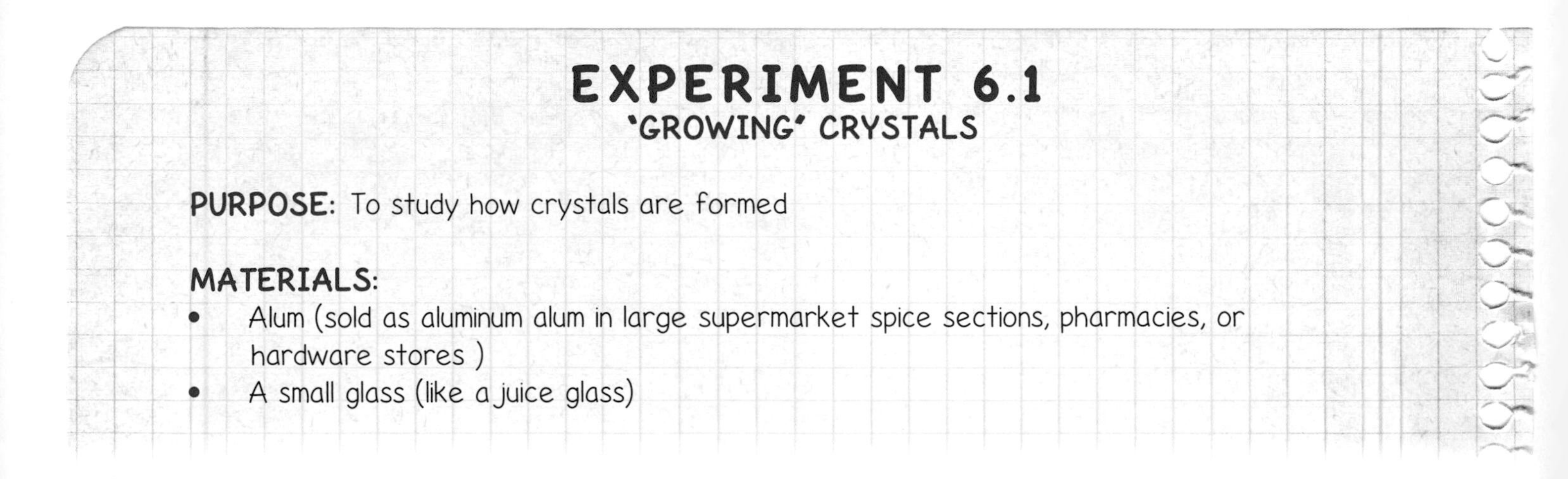

EXPERIMENT 6.1
'GROWING' CRYSTALS

PURPOSE: To study how crystals are formed

MATERIALS:

- Alum (sold as aluminum alum in large supermarket spice sections, pharmacies, or hardware stores)
- A small glass (like a juice glass)

- A liquid measuring cup
- A small spoon for dispensing the alum
- A large spoon for stirring
- Some thin, rough string (Thread will work, but the rougher the string, the better the results.)
- 2 weights (washers, nuts, fishing sinkers, etc.)
- A large plate
- A few rocks from outside (Small pebbles work best.)
- A sheet of dark-colored paper
- A magnifying glass
- A stove
- A pot to heat water
- Oven mitt
- Eye protection such as goggles or safety glasses

QUESTION: What does the term "crystalline" mean?

HYPOTHESIS: Write what you think will happen once the powdered alum is dissolved into water and allowed to cool.

PROCEDURE:

1. Add about 2 cups of water to the pot and heat it until it is boiling.
2. While you are waiting for the water to boil, cut a piece of string so it is 3 times as long as your juice glass is tall. (If your glass is 3 inches high, you would cut a length of string 3 x 3 = 9 inches.)
3. Attach a weight to each end of the string.
4. Once the water is boiling, take it off the stove and wait for the boiling to stop.
5. As soon as the boiling stops, add alum to the hot water with the small spoon. It should easily dissolve. Stir it with the large spoon to help it dissolve.
6. Continue to add alum until you cannot get any more to dissolve. You will know you have reached that point when the water gets cloudy and will not clear up regardless of how much you stir.
7. Let the pot stand for a few minutes, and the undissolved alum will settle to the bottom of the pot, making the solution above it reasonably clear.
8. Once the solution in the pot is pretty clear, carefully pour some of the liquid into the empty glass. Do this slowly and carefully, trying not to disturb the alum that has settled to the bottom of the pot. (You might want to set the glass down in a sink in case some of the liquid spills.) Pour until you have filled the glass ½ full. Try to avoid pouring any of the alum that has settled to the bottom of the pot into the glass. This process is called decanting, and it is often used in chemistry.
9. Now you should have a reasonably clear solution of alum in the glass. Use an oven mitt to protect your hands from the heat, and set the glass on the plate.
10. Drop one end of the string into the glass. The weight will keep that end in the glass.

11. Put the other end on the plate. Your setup should look like this:

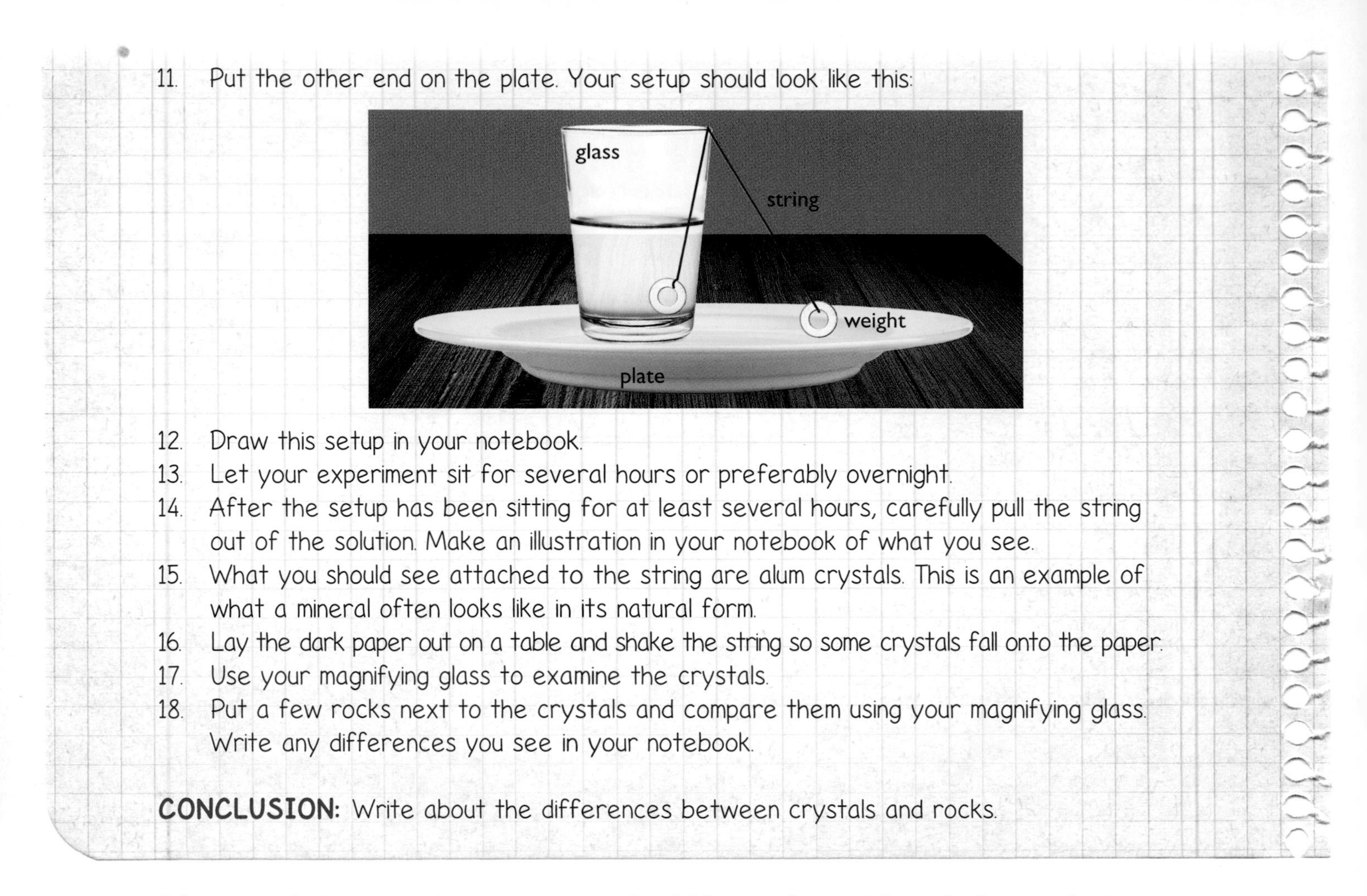

12. Draw this setup in your notebook.
13. Let your experiment sit for several hours or preferably overnight.
14. After the setup has been sitting for at least several hours, carefully pull the string out of the solution. Make an illustration in your notebook of what you see.
15. What you should see attached to the string are alum crystals. This is an example of what a mineral often looks like in its natural form.
16. Lay the dark paper out on a table and shake the string so some crystals fall onto the paper.
17. Use your magnifying glass to examine the crystals.
18. Put a few rocks next to the crystals and compare them using your magnifying glass. Write any differences you see in your notebook.

CONCLUSION: Write about the differences between crystals and rocks.

After completing Experiment 6.1, you should have a better idea of what geologists mean when they use the term *crystalline*. Crystalline substances often have sharp, geometric shapes. That means they have flat surfaces, or **faces**, and well-defined edges. That should have been what you noticed when you compared the alum crystals to the rocks. The alum crystals have a definite geometric pattern.

Now we can get back to our discussion of minerals. A mineral is a crystalline substance that is the same material throughout. So the chemical makeup of a mineral doesn't change no matter where you sample it. The alum you used was pure powdered aluminum alum, with no other chemicals present. It was just crystals of alum salt smashed into a powder. When you made alum crystals, they were pure alum salt, too. The only difference between the powder you started with and the crystals you ended with is their appearance; both were still alum.

FIGURE 6.9
Minerals and Rocks

The purple crystals are made of amethyst. No matter where you take a sample, the only chemical you find is the mineral amethyst. The rocks on the right are granite. Samples of these rocks will give you several chemicals. That's why they don't have a crystalline shape.

Often, when you find a mineral in the Earth, you find it as a crystal. Now the rocks you used for comparison most likely had at least 2 (and probably more) separate chemicals in them. Rocks typically contain many minerals. Because of this mix, rocks will not form a distinct geometric pattern like you see in a crystal. So we can say that minerals are pure substances; no matter where you look in a mineral, you will always have the same chemical. A rock, however, is most often a combination of 2 or more minerals, so it is composed of 2 or more chemicals. But the easiest way to tell them apart is by their appearance: minerals often form crystalline shapes, and rocks do not.

Interestingly, minerals also can be metals, such as gold, silver, copper, and iron. But in their natural state, most metals are bonded to other minerals, so they don't have a natural crystalline structure.

creation connection

Precious metals, such as gold and silver, are often found in rocks with other materials. To extract them, we must put the metals through a refining process that includes high heat to remove the unwanted chemicals. The refining process to produce a perfectly pure silver substance is mentioned in the Bible in an analogy of how God refines His people through difficulties in order to build our character and bring us closer to Him. Psalm 66:10-12 says, "For you, O God, have tested us; you have tried us as silver is tried. You brought us into the net; you laid a crushing burden on our backs; you let men ride over our heads; we went through fire and through water; yet you have brought us out to a place of abundance." Pure like silver!

ON YOUR OWN

6.3 List the 3 basic types of rock that make up Earth's crust.

6.4 While digging on a site where a large building will be constructed, a worker discovers what he calls a "large, clear rock." It has several faces and looks like a big, angular crystal. Is this a rock or a mineral?

THE EARTH'S SURFACE

With a better understanding of what Earth is made of, we can now look at the shape it is in, particularly its features and the processes that create them.

Most of Earth's sediments have been laid down by water. Moving water is transported by gravity so once it reaches a low point near sea level, it loses much of its moving force and then the sediments suspended within it will settle out. That forms flat **plains**. **Alluvial plains** are formed by rivers carrying along large amounts of sediments as they flow, and then slowing down when the river path forms a bend or empties into the ocean. Slower flow allows the sediments to settle onto the river floor. At the ocean boundary, this can form a **delta**. If the river is large, like the Nile in Africa or the Mississippi River in North America, the delta can

FIGURE 6.10
Lena River Delta in Russia

cover a vast area. There are also **coastal plains** that are found uphill from an alluvial plain, possibly being formed at a time when sea levels were higher. **Lake plains** are created in large lakes as sediments are carried in from water running off the surrounding land. And **glacial plains** are formed when a glacier (a slowly moving mass of ice formed by the buildup and compacting of snow) scrapes along the ground and then melts, leaving its sediments behind.

When you think of mountains, you probably think of sharp, pointed, snow-covered peaks that are very high in elevation. But there are several other mountain types on Earth. Earlier in this module, you learned a little about plate tectonics. Well, the presence of various mountain types helps to support this theory. Mountains are formed several ways. For example, at a fault area, if one plate is moving up while the other is stationary or moving down, the upward-moving mass of rock forms a mountain. This is called a **fault-block mountain.**

FIGURE 6.11
Three Mountain Types

The Sierra Nevada mountain range (left) in the western United States contains examples of fault-block mountains. The Appalachian Mountains (center) in the eastern United States are an example of folded mountains. Mount Fuji (right) in Japan is an example of a volcanic mountain.

A second mountain type can form when 2 moving rock masses push against one another. When this happens, the crust buckles into an up-and-down rolling pattern. This creates **folded mountains.** A third mountain type can appear when a crack forms in Earth's crust. Magma from the mantle can rise up into that crack, and if the crack reaches the surface, the magma can pour out as lava. If the lava accumulates, a **volcanic mountain** results. Now, there is a lot of research being done on volcanoes. One reason is so we can possibly predict if and when they will erupt in order to protect people; the other reason is to learn more about the hard-to-reach material below Earth's crust. A fourth mountain type can form when there is a crack in the crust but it does not go all the way to the surface. In this case, the magma cannot escape and instead builds up, pushing the crust up along with it. This forms a **domed mountain,** which is similar to a volcanic mountain but rounder in shape.

TYPES OF WEATHERING

You may have heard the phrase "hard as a rock" before. And, indeed, rocks are hard. But they also can be broken down. Through the work of ice, water, wind, and temperature changes, the rocks of Earth's crust can be crumbled into bits of minerals or even transformed into other materials. This process is called **weathering.**

Weathering can occur physically and chemically. **Physical weathering** is when large rocks are broken into small rocks from physical forces such as ice, temperature changes, and abrasion of sand or running water. So physical weathering doesn't change the chemical composition of rocks; they are still the same material, only differently shaped or in smaller pieces. For example, sometimes water will creep into small cracks within a rock and then freeze. Well, frozen water (ice) takes up more space as compared to liquid water, so it expands and causes the rock to break up. Rapid temperature changes also can break rocks. When they are exposed to high daytime temperatures and low nighttime temperatures, rocks can expand in the heat and contract in the cold, eventually cracking from the stress. Plants can physically break up rocks, too, as they send their roots down into the ground.

Chemical weathering is when the minerals in rock chemically react with air or water, changing their composition. Rainwater often becomes acidic when it combines with carbon dioxide gas in air, creating carbonic acid. That acid can break down rock material by reacting with it. Oxygen affects rocks by reacting with minerals inside them. You may already know that iron can rust if it is exposed for a long time to the oxygen in air. Well, iron naturally occurs in rocks, and when exposed to oxygen it can rust, causing the rock to chemically change (see Figure 6.12).

FIGURE 6.12
Rock with Rusting Iron

Erosion

Other physical processes can affect rock formations. Wind or running water can carry away bits of rock via **erosion.**

Erosion—The process of wearing or grinding something down by wind, water, or other natural agents

Erosion most often occurs by the movement of water. It can wash away soil and vegetation, changing the face of the landscape. When water flows beneath the Earth's surface, erosion can create networks of caves.

Some of the most amazing geological features on Earth are due to erosion. Canyons, for example can be carved by rivers and large-scale moving water. The Grand Canyon in North America is one of the most striking canyons on the planet, created after layers and layers of sediment had been eroded away. Sometimes enough water flows over an area that the erosion moves most of the layers of sedimentary rock, leaving only isolated high spots. **Mesas,** for example, are large, flat-topped hills surrounded by flatlands. **Buttes** are smaller steep-sided prominences. Though they might look like it, these are not mountains because of the way they were formed. A great deal of the western United States shows evidence of this type of large-scale water erosion.

FIGURE 6.13
Remnants of Large-Scale Erosion

Rivers can carve wider paths as they flow, breaking off bits of material and eroding the shores. Some rivers carry those sediments with them and dump them into the ocean or large lakes, creating river deltas. Delta deposits are often triangle-shaped and look like the Greek capital letter, Delta (see Figure 6.10).

Rainwater can seep underground, feeding rivers that flow beneath the surface. As the water moves through small cracks and veins in the rocks, it can erode these areas, forming large underground caverns. Then, if the water levels are reduced, these caverns can experience water seeping through the soil and slowly draining into them. The minerals dissolved in the water can be deposited as the droplets fall, creating stunning cave formations.

FIGURE 6.14
Cavern Deposition Formations

Stalactites are created when mineral-rich water seeps down through cracks in the cavern roof. The minerals are deposited as the water drips down. Stalagmites are formed below stalactites as the water hits the cavern floor. When the 2 formations meet, they create a column. A good way to remember the difference between stalactite and stalagmite is to think that *-tite* comes from the *top*.

EXPLORE MORE

Make your own stalactites by mixing 2 cups water with 2½ cups Epsom salt in a saucepan. Bring the mixture to a boil, stirring constantly. When the crystals stop dissolving, remove the saucepan from the heat and allow it to cool. Take a 2-ft length of rough twine and tie 2 washers to each end. Immerse the string in the salt solution for at least an hour. After an hour, fill 2 juice glasses about ¾ full with the salt solution and place the glasses on either side of a small plate. (Store extra solution in an airtight container for later.) Place one end of the string in one glass and the other end in the other glass, allowing the string to drape downward between the glasses toward the plate (but not touching it). Make sure the string's center is hanging below the level of the solution in the glasses. Let your setup sit for up to a week. Add extra solution to the glasses as needed to keep the string's center below the liquid levels. Watch your stalactites (and maybe stalagmites) form!

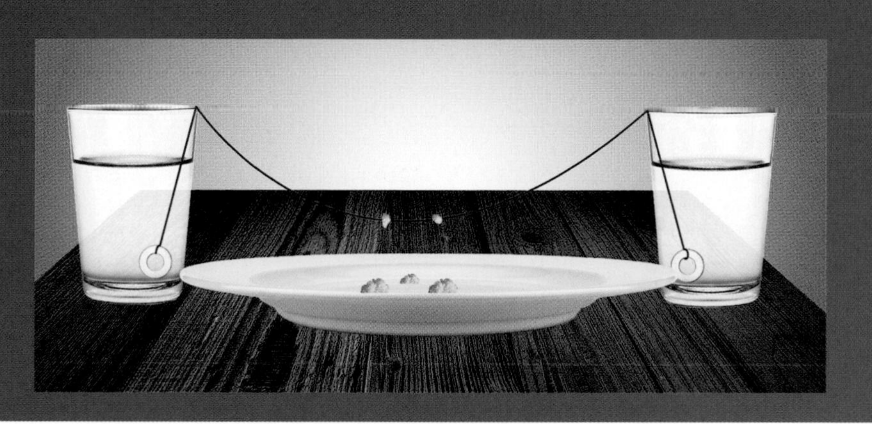

Oceans can also cause tremendous erosion as powerful waves and currents affect the shoreline. Glaciers move across the land as they are pushed along when continual glacier material is formed in high mountain areas. They can scrape out deep valleys and move huge boulders as they go. Many areas of the world were believed to be once covered by glaciers. The Finger Lakes in New York are a series of deep lakes believed to be carved out by glacial movement.

Finally, wind is a force of erosion, blowing around sediments and fine particles. Huge dust storms can carry sand and soils from one area to another, greatly affecting both landscapes. Additionally, as the sand is blown through the air, it can behave like sandpaper, eating away at rock formations it passes.

ON YOUR OWN

6.5 Is erosion a type of physical or chemical weathering?

6.6 When iron material in rocks starts to rust, is that a type of physical or chemical weathering?

SEDIMENTARY ROCK STRATA

Let's go further in our discussion of the rock and mineral arrangement of Earth's crust. Perhaps the best way to do that is to look at one of the most famous geological features on the planet: the Grand Canyon. This 446-km-long (277 mi) canyon is located in Arizona and ranges in width from 6 to 29 km (4–18 mi). The deepest point in the canyon is about a mile. Now, the Grand Canyon is known for its beautiful and awe-inspiring landscape, but it also presents us with an excellent way to study geology. The canyon walls are mostly composed of sedimentary rock, so this geologic feature gives us a great idea of some of the basic characteristics of this rock type. As you look at the Grand Canyon, one question comes directly to mind: How did these layers actually form? And from a scientific standpoint, we cannot know for sure because there was no one there to observe their formation. Yet, Experiment 6.2 will demonstrate one way such layers might have been created. Note that this experiment must sit overnight.

FIGURE 6.15
The Grand Canyon

EXPERIMENT 6.2
SEPARATION OF SEDIMENTATION

PURPOSE: To see how water can separate sediments into layers

MATERIALS:

- A large glass jar with a lid
- Some dirt from outside (Dig straight down into the ground to get dirt from many depths.)
- Some sand
- Some gravel composed of various sizes of rocks
- Water

QUESTION: What happens when various sediment sizes are suspended in water and allowed to settle?

HYPOTHESIS: Write what you think will happen when the suspended sediments settle out.

PROCEDURE:

1. Fill the jar about ⅕ of the way with dirt. Add an equal amount of sand and an equal amount of gravel.
2. Put the lid on the jar and then gently invert the jar to mix the contents. Invert the jar several times so the dirt, sand, and gravel are well mixed.

3. Draw a picture of the jar and its contents in your lab notebook.
4. Add water to the jar so the water level is about an inch from the top of the jar.
5. Put the lid back on and invert the jar to once again mix up the contents. Do this several times to make sure they are well mixed.
6. Let the jar sit for about an hour.
7. After about an hour, invert the jar again several times to once again mix everything up.
8. Repeat step 7 at least twice more before you go to bed. Be sure to let the jar sit for at least an hour between each repetition.
9. Draw a picture of the jar and its contents after it has settled undisturbed overnight.
10. Dump the contents of the jar outside wherever your parents suggest, and clean everything up.

CONCLUSION: Write what you learned about how sediments settle out when suspended in water.

What happened to the contents of the jar after they sat overnight? Well, you should have noticed they looked very different as compared to how they looked before you added water. Most likely, the gravel is now at the bottom, and the soil and sand have settled into layers. This means the lighter substances are probably on top, and the heavier substances are probably on the bottom.

Experiment 6.2 helps you to understand that water has the ability to separate sediments into layers. When you mixed the contents of the jar, you simulated a body of water in motion. You were modeling currents in rivers, tides in the ocean, and other natural water movements. Well, as water moves, it can separate sediments. The sediments settle out of the water (called **deposition**—the sediments are *deposited* onto the floor below) and often do it in layers, with the heavier materials settling out first and the lighter materials settling out later. Now, there are other processes that deposit sediments onto the ground, but water processes are, by far, the most common. Once water has deposited sediments, they can then form sedimentary rock as they are cemented together primarily by chemical reactions. As you look at these layers, called **strata**, you might notice that they differ greatly in thickness and appearance. The layers in Figure 6.16, for example, have various thicknesses, some being *extremely* thin.

FIGURE 6.16
Close-up of Some Grand Canyon Strata

ON YOUR OWN

6.7 The Grand Canyon is in the northwestern part of Arizona, a state with many desert-like characteristics. There is little rain and a few lakes. Does it really make sense to think that the sedimentary rock in the Grand Canyon was laid down by water? Why or why not?

THE BASIC STRUCTURE OF THE GRAND CANYON

Take a look at Figure 6.17, showing an illustration of the Grand Canyon. We're going to study it because it contains all 3 basic rock types and many of the geological features you'll find on Earth. Notice first how most of the rocks are in strata. Igneous and metamorphic rock are labeled so you can see their limited locations in the canyon. This means a majority of the rock in the Grand Canyon is sedimentary, and the sedimentary rock is situated in layers. Now take a look at how the upper strata are horizontal and the lower strata are tilted compared to the upper ones. The boundary between these is called an unconformity.

Unconformity—A surface of erosion that separates one layer of rock from another

FIGURE 6.17
A 3-Dimensional Sketch of a Portion of the Grand Canyon

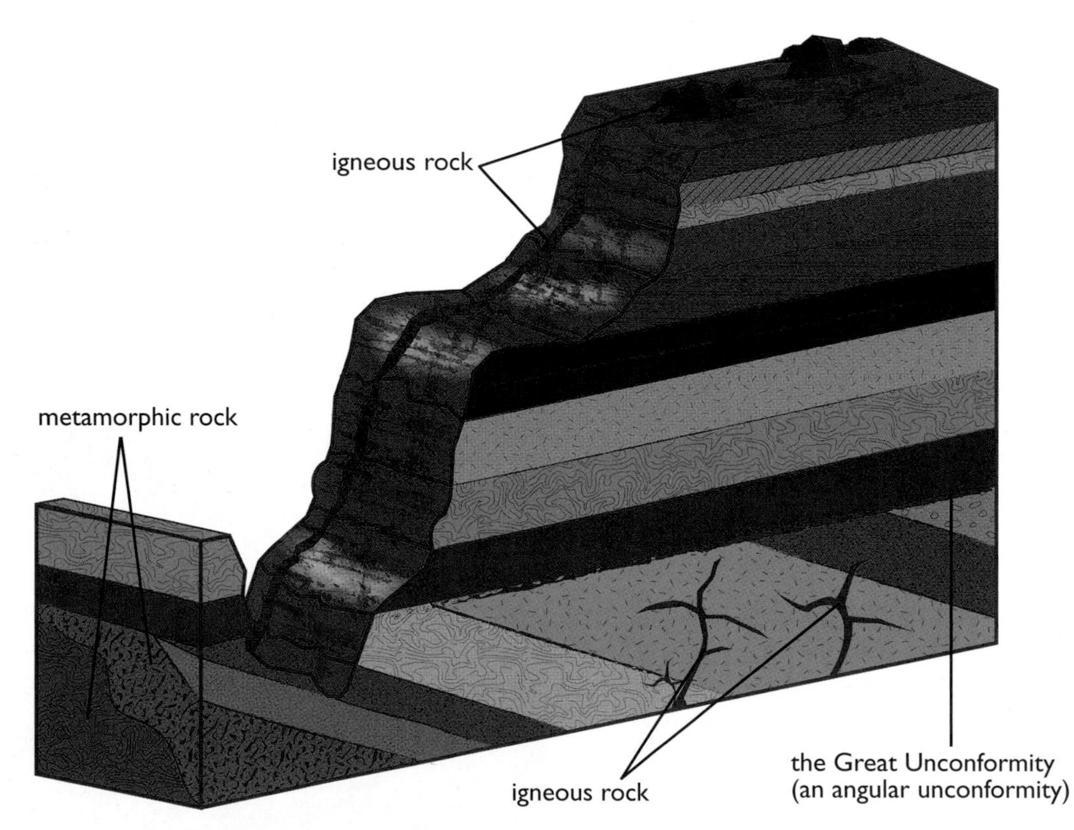

An unconformity is more than just a separation between rock strata. It is a separation where the top of the layer *below* the unconformity was significantly eroded before the

layer *above* the unconformity formed. Now this is not the case with many geological strata. Often, one layer of rock sits smoothly on top of another (like most of the upper layers of the Grand Canyon); there is often no evidence of erosion in between. Thus, an unconformity is a special kind of separation between strata—one that is marked by all the indications of erosion.

There are lots of types of unconformities in the geological record. The one I am referring to in the Grand Canyon is called the **Great Unconformity**. That is because it is arguably the most striking unconformity found there. What makes it so interesting is the *orientation* of the strata above and below it. We call this an angular unconformity because the strata of rocks below it lie at an angle relative to the strata above. There are a few other locations between strata with evidence of erosion before the next layer was laid down, but they are not as striking, are given different names, and are infrequent among the Grand Canyon strata. You saw in Experiment 6.1 how layers can be created without any erosion or major water movement occurring as they were laid down.

So how did the Great Unconformity form in the Grand Canyon? Well, before I answer that question, I need to first discuss 2 major views of how Earth's features may have formed. Remember how I said that no one was around to actually see how the rocks of Earth came to be? We do not have any direct observations of that. But we can use the scientific method to help understand what happened, using questions, hypotheses, experiments, and observations. There are (at least) 2 major viewpoints when it comes to forming hypotheses about Earth's past. In the 19th century, some scientists suggested that every natural process we see today has been operating in the same manner and at the same rate throughout Earth's history. This idea is called **uniformitarianism**, which basically states that "the present is the key to the past."

FIGURE 6.18
The Colorado River in the Grand Canyon

What do I mean by that? Well, what do you see at the very bottom of the Grand Canyon today? The Colorado River flows along the canyon floor, and as it flows, it erodes small portions of the river bed, making the canyon deeper and deeper, one small bit at a time. Uniformitarianism says that this river is responsible for slowly carving out the entire canyon. There is a problem with this idea, though. The natural processes seen today have likely not proceeded at the same rate or on the same scale as in the past. So as scientists, we just cannot be sure that the present rate is the same rate that occurred in history. For example, we have observed rapid canyon formation in recent history. Mount

St. Helens erupted in 1980, creating a massive landslide of ice, water, and materials. This created nearly 183 m (600 ft) of layered sediments in just a few days! If scientists had not observed the volcano before and after that huge landslide, they may have thought the layers of sediment came from many different eruptions over many years.

The strata from the Mount St. Helens eruption (Figure 6.19) are starting to compact and chemically change to sedimentary rock. What a fascinating match to the Grand Canyon!

FIGURE 6.19
Mount St. Helens Canyon

This is just one natural example of how sedimentary layers can be deposited rather quickly. However, many geologists who believe in the process of evolution (a theory that tries to explain the existence of life without reference to God—something we'll study later in this course) believe the sedimentary layers of the Grand Canyon were deposited over millions of years as inland seas covered present-day Arizona at many different times in history. They then suggest the land was lifted up to a great height, and the flowing water from the Colorado River slowly carved the canyon.

Other geologists believe that Earth has experienced many catastrophes, the last of which is the global-scale flood of Noah's day. This idea that one or more catastrophes are the *main* reason for Earth's geological features is called **catastrophism.**

There are several visible examples of geologic formations that are best explained by catastrophes. In fact, as evolutionary geologists began reevaluating the geologic record, they found that slow and steady processes could not have formed all of the geologic features we see today. So they adjusted the uniformitarianism theory to include short periods of catastrophe. This adjustment to uniformitarianism is sometimes called **neo-catastrophism,** although it is basically still uniformitarianism that allows for occasional catastrophes. So in my explanations of the 2 theories I will use the terms *uniformitarianism* and *catastrophism*. Just be aware that many geologists who hold to uniformitarianism often call themselves neo-catastrophists, recognizing that the rates of geologic processes (such as erosion and deposition) vary greatly. They hold to a geologic record that shows a series of catastrophes (like massive volcanic eruptions, floods, asteroid impacts, or multiple ice ages) between long, slow processes occurring over a period of millions of years to form the many geological features we see today.

Now, let's go back to Figure 6.17. Notice how igneous rock is pointed out in the center of the figure near the bottom. These veins of igneous rock shoot right through several layers of sedimentary rock. They are called **intrusions,** and they form when magma from below the sedimentary rock gets injected into its cracks and crevices.

ON YOUR OWN

6.8 Label the basic diagram of Figure 6.17 to to show the 4 major rock groups listed in this section.

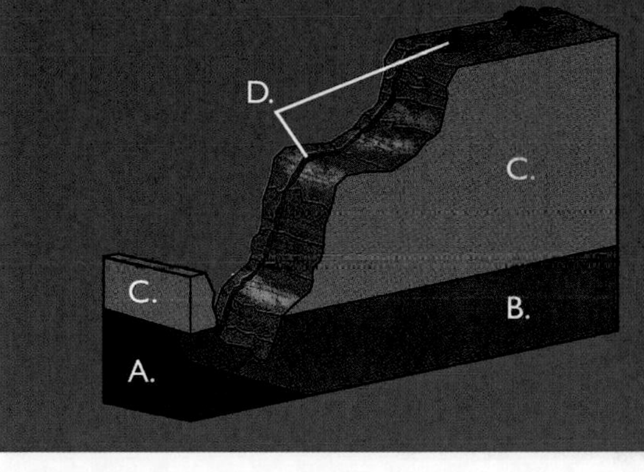

There is one more major igneous rock formation I want to mention. It is on the surface of the Grand Canyon and is the result of volcanic activity. So now you can see why I said earlier how some igneous rock forms as a result of magma flowing under the ground (intrusions) and some igneous rock forms as a result of volcanic activity (on the surface).

I can sum up this section by placing the rocks of the Grand Canyon into 4 basic groups. The first group is made up of the igneous and metamorphic rocks forming the base of the canyon. The second group consists of the sedimentary (and one layer of igneous) rock strata that lie below the Great Unconformity. The third group contains the sedimentary rocks that form the horizontal strata above the Great Unconformity. And the fourth group consists of the igneous rocks formed at the surface due to volcanic activity. Uniformitarians and catastrophists strongly disagree as to how these rock groups came to be. In the next few sections, I will talk about this debate as well as the fossils that exist in many of these strata.

THE FOSSIL RECORD AND ITS FEATURES

I have mentioned fossils a few times up to this point, but it would be good to give you a definition.

Fossil—The preserved remains of a once-living organism

So we can say a fossil gives us information about what happened in the past because it is a preserved record of something that was once alive. And if a fossil is old enough it can give us information about a time in Earth's past before there was a lot of recorded history.

A fossil is preserved remains. That means in order to become fossilized, an organism's body cannot decay like it *normally* would. However, decay is what normally happens when a living thing dies. So you need unique conditions to create a fossil as this is not what usually occurs. And that means fossil formation is quite rare. Therefore, only a tiny fraction of once-living organisms gets fossilized.

Fossil Formation

Consider a seashell, for example. If it gets buried in sediment and that sediment hardens and turns to rock, the rock hardens around the shell. As time goes on, water can seep through the sedimentary rock and weather away the rock and the shell. If the shell is affected by weathering more than the rock is, it's possible that the shell will disintegrate before the rock. If this happens, it leaves a **mold** where the shell originally was. Paleontologists sometimes find molds like this in sedimentary rocks. More commonly, though, paleontologists will find a **cast.** This is when other material comes in and fills the mold left behind by the eroded or decomposed shell.

FIGURE 6.20
Fossilized Shell Cast

EXPLORE MORE

Create your own cast by taking a shell or other similar item and covering the backside with some petroleum jelly. (You might want to wear surgical gloves to keep your hands clean.) Then roll some clay in a thick layer onto a paper plate. Press the backside of the shell into the clay and carefully remove it to leave behind a mold. Now mix some plaster of paris (following package directions) in a disposable cup and pour the plaster into the mold. Allow it to harden and remove the clay from the cast you made.

Molds don't often last long. For example, if an animal leaves a footprint in the mud, that is a mold, but it is often washed away by rain or will dry and be blown away by the wind. But, even though they are rare, fossil footprints have been discovered. In order for them to be preserved, material such as a thick layer of sediment or a layer of magma has to quickly be laid down right after the footprints have been made but before they have time to be washed away.

Now, besides molds and casts, there are 2 other ways fossils can form. **Petrifaction** is when organic material *chemically changes* into rock. This happens when mineral-rich water swirls around a dead animal, tree, or other object and fills in the pores. Over time the water evaporates, leaving behind the minerals.

FIGURE 6.21
Petrified Tree Trunk and Carbonized Fossil Fish

You already learned that minerals are a type of rock, so these minerals form rock in the shape of the material they filled (see Figure 6.21 top).

Sometimes, when an organism is buried in sediment, the pressure can cause liquids and gases in the organism's remains to be forced right out of it. And because water makes up a large part of any organism, this means most of the organism's remains are lost. Next, chemical reactions occur, and a thin, filmy residue made up of mostly carbon is left. This process is called **carbonization,** and it creates carbonized remains of an organism, almost like a detailed drawing of it. Plant fossils are commonly carbonized.

The biggest problem with fossils is that it is difficult for soft parts of an organism to survive long enough to be fossilized. Most fossils are created from the hard parts of an organism, like bones or shells, and even then most are only a few parts of the animal. Now, carbonization can leave great detail, although it only gives us an idea of a "pancake" version of the organism (Figure 6.21 bottom). We cannot know exactly how thick it was when it was once living.

Only in very rare cases is an entire fossilized organism discovered. In 1977, for example, in a remote area of Siberia, the complete preserved remains of a baby mammoth were found, including its skin, hair, and many soft body parts.

This is because it was found within frozen mud, and the ice protected its remains from decaying. Other cases of entire preserved organisms include small insects that have been trapped in **amber.** Amber is a plant resin that becomes fossilized into a solid material. If an insect becomes trapped in the honey-like resin and the resin turns to amber, the trapped organism is preserved intact.

FIGURE 6.22
Plant Material Trapped in Amber

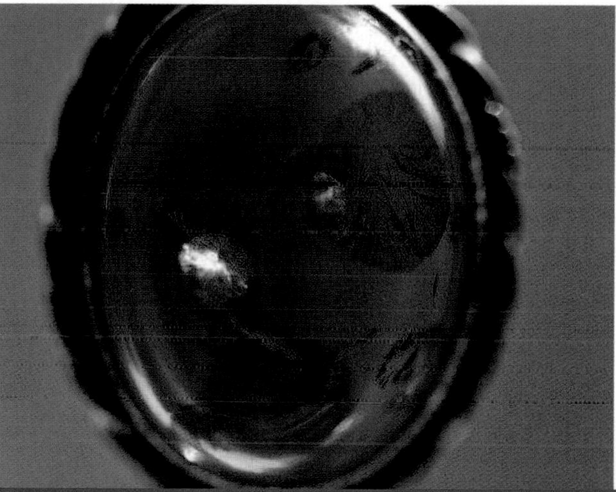

ON YOUR OWN

6.9 If a paleontologist unearths a fossil that is preserved 3-dimensionally and is completely made of rock, which fossilization process formed it?

GENERAL FOSSIL RECORD FEATURES

Before we get into this section, let me explain what a fossil record is. The fossil record refers to the sum total of all discovered fossils. That's because fossils are really a record of life in Earth's past. I want to go over 4 notable features of the fossil record.

The first feature of the fossil record is that **most fossils are found in sedimentary rock.** And that makes sense. Igneous rock is formed from magma or lava, which would burn up most materials (though a few fossils have been found in igneous rock!). The same caustic situation happens with metamorphic rock, formed from extreme temperature and pressure. Because sedimentary rock is mainly laid down by water, we can also say that most fossils are formed in conjunction with the action of water.

The second feature of the fossil record is that **the vast majority of all fossils on this planet are of hard-shelled organisms, like clams.** This is a *very* important point…not a boring one. Clam-like fossils are found in every region of Earth. That makes sense, doesn't it? The harder something is, the more likely it is to fossilize. Clams and similar organisms have hard shells, are in water, and often live buried in sediments, so therefore they are in the best situation to be fossilized. The rest of fossils are mostly bony marine animals, like fish. And of the tiny fraction of fossils that remain, most of those are insects. So only a very, very *tiny* fraction that is left is made up of reptiles, birds, plants, and mammals. Yet if you read a book about fossils, what do you see most photos of? The "fun" ones… dinosaurs! But you need to know these are an extremely small percentage of all the fossils that we have discovered.

A third notable feature of the fossil record is that **it contains the remains of some organisms still living today.** And when paleontologists compare a fossil like this to its living counterpart, they look very similar (see Figure 6.23). We can thus say that organisms that have survived throughout Earth's history experience little change. They change a bit, with slightly longer tails or shorter fins, but they are primarily the same.

FIGURE 6.23
Fossilized Coelacanth and a Preserved Living Counterpart

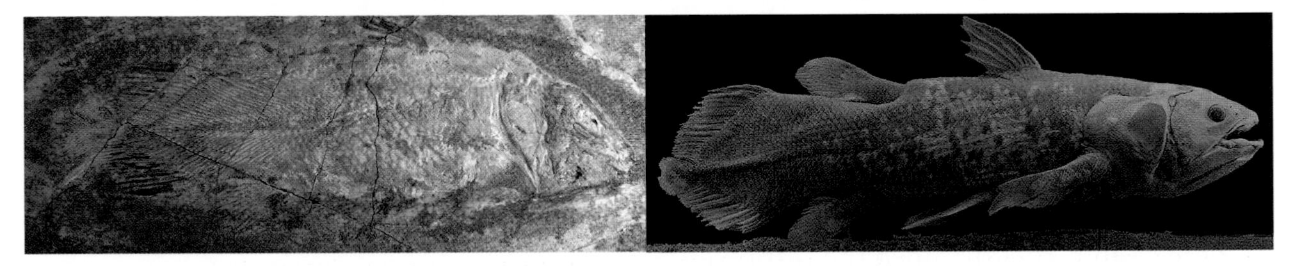

Now there *are* some fossils, like the wooly mammoth, that have no known living counterparts. We call these organisms **extinct**, meaning they were once living and now are not. Extinction doesn't happen often. From the literature of the scientists who are actually doing research on extinctions throughout history, we know that in the last 400 years, just over 1,100 species of plants and animals have become extinct, and many of those extinctions have no apparent connection to human activity. You may have heard otherwise because this is a commonly misinformed topic. Many people calling themselves environmentalists throw out claims that tens of thousands of species go extinct each year. They are overenthusiastic to preserve the environment, but their facts are not accurate. This is why it is a good idea to do some fact-checking when you study scientific claims.

There is one more fossil record feature I want to cover. It turns out that **the fossils found in one layer of stratified rock can be considerably different from the fossils found in another layer of stratified rock.** Remember I said that a majority of fossils are of clams and similar animals, located throughout several strata of the Grand Canyon. But if you remove all of those fossils, you notice that there are very few organisms below the Great

Unconformity...just a few microscopic creatures like algae and bacteria. There are trilobites in many layers above the Great Unconformity. These are extinct, bottom-dwelling ocean organisms with a hard, outer shell. The 3 layers just above the Great Unconformity have fossils of worm burrows. A single layer above them has placoderm fossils (extinct, bony plated fish). Fish like the modern fish we see today are found in the upper layers, and there are fossils of amphibians and reptiles in 3 layers just below the fish. There are no mammal or bird fossils that have been found in the Grand Canyon. Now, the reasons why fossils are found in some layers of rock and are not found in others is greatly debated. Uniformitarians have one explanation and catastrophists have another.

ON YOUR OWN

6.10 List 4 notable features of the fossil record.

GEOLOGY AND PALEONTOLOGY PERSPECTIVES

The Uniformitarian Perspective

Because fossils are found in rocks, the formation of rocks obviously affects the formation of fossils. That means we have to understand the geological record and the fossil record together. Remember, uniformitarians believe sedimentary rock formed through slow processes, much the same way we see it forming today. Yet, we *do* know that it can be formed by catastrophes. (And there is so much evidence to that fact that many uniformitarians altered their theories to rename themselves neo-catastrophists.)

To explain the strata of the Grand Canyon, uniformitarians suggest Arizona was once (at least partially) covered by a body of water, such as a small ocean. The ocean deposited a layer of sediment and then the ocean retreated later on in history, leaving Arizona dry again. And this happened again and again. Thus, each layer of sedimentary rock in the Grand Canyon, according to uniformitarians, represents a time when that part of Arizona was covered by a body of water. And because these bodies of water changed, disappeared, and reformed because of differing conditions, the sediments they deposited on Arizona were different in composition. This could explain why there are so many different kinds of rocks in the strata of the Grand Canyon.

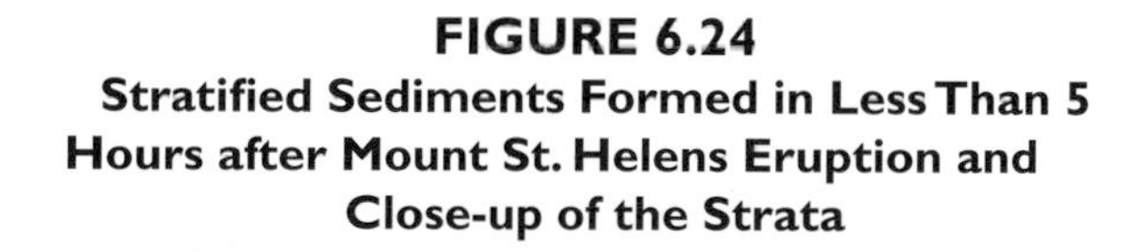

FIGURE 6.24
Stratified Sediments Formed in Less Than 5 Hours after Mount St. Helens Eruption and Close-up of the Strata

However, this view of geology requires huge amounts of time. Based on sedimentary rates today, it could take over 1,000 years to produce a 1-ft-thick sedimentary layer, plus up to 100 million years of exposure once that body of water was gone. This framework could then explain the Great Unconformity. For example, after several layers of sediments were laid down over time, perhaps there was a great earthquake that shifted the land, followed by centuries of time where erosion could have smoothed out the exposed and tilted edges. Then when a new ocean covered Arizona, new sedimentation would have been deposited horizontally. Finally, once all the Grand Canyon strata formed, something had to happen to cut out the canyon. Uniformitarians believe the Colorado River that is now flowing at its bottom is responsible, having started the slow erosion process about 6 million years ago.

If this view were true, it *might* be able to explain why you only find certain fossils in certain layers of rock because each layer of rock was believed to be laid down during a different time period. So because paleontologists can only find fossilized algae and other such organisms below the Great Unconformity, one could think this indicates that only *those* kinds of organisms lived in the oceans of Arizona during that time in Earth's ancient history. Trilobites are found in many layers of the Grand Canyon above the Great Unconformity because they were living in the waters of Arizona during the time *those* strata were deposited. They are not found below the Great Unconformity because it is suggested that none were living during the period when those sediments were deposited. So each layer of rock in a geological formation is, according to uniformitarians, a record from a certain period in Earth's history, representing a suggested 10 million to a few hundred million years.

The Catastrophist Perspective

While the uniformitarian essentially believes that the same processes we observe today are responsible for forming most of the geological features of Earth, catastrophists believe much of the geology we see today is the result of processes that occurred once in Earth's past and will not be repeated. And this different view results in a huge difference in what is concluded from the geological and fossil record.

The geological record can be viewed through the Bible's account of the creation of the world and the worldwide Flood. Many catastrophists think the layers of rock below the Great Unconformity were formed when God first created Earth. The igneous and metamorphic rocks there are believed to have been formed as a part of the initial creation while most of the sedimentary rock strata below the Great Unconformity were made during the time dry land was formed. Obviously, right after Earth's creation there would have been a lot of erosion and deposition, along with earthquake-like movements, forming sediment layers very quickly.

FIGURE 6.25
Swirling Water Carrying Materials As It Moves in the Black Sea

After the Creation week and before the Great Flood, it is likely that there was not a lot of geologically important activity.

Layers above the Great Unconformity are believed to have been formed during and after the worldwide Flood. Before the Flood or perhaps as a part of its early stages, the layers of rock that were already formed could have tilted as the result of earthquakes and waters coming up from the depths of the Earth. Earth's surface was eroded by enormous amounts of wind, rain, and rushing water that began the flood formation. Water trapped in underground rocks began to be released, and the great landmasses began to sink and move as great walls of water came in from the sea. Mountains were formed, and the mantle melted as basaltic lava flowed. This resulted in the current position of the continents as well as the land formations under the ocean. The majority of the strata above the Great Unconformity could have then been deposited by the floodwaters themselves.

Now, these are not believed to have been calm waters. God opened the "fountains of the great deep" and the "floodgates of the sky" (Genesis 7:11) to create the Flood. Earth was covered in surging, rushing water likely containing violently shifting currents. These varying speeds and directions of floodwaters could cause varied sedimentary layers. When the waters were deep and advancing, that's when one kind of sediment was deposited, forming one type of rock layer. As the waters settled down a bit, another kind of sediment would form, creating another type of rock layer. Shallow and retreating floodwaters could have created other rock layers depending on their direction and the types of sediments they contained. Therefore, the different rock layers you see above the Great Unconformity were laid down during different stages of the Flood, based on the floodwater direction, depth, and speed.

think about this

Recent research has revealed that there is likely a large amount of water held in Earth's mantle. At locations where 2 plates of Earth's crust meet, if one moves below the other one, it can carry with it a large amount of water. This means massive amounts of water could exist in the form of tiny droplets caught in microscopic spaces within the mantle material.

FIGURE 6.26
Mount Everest

It is likely that before the worldwide Flood, Earth did not have large mountains and deep valleys. Much of these formations would have been a result of the violent plate movement during that catastrophic event.

Once the land and rocks of the Grand Canyon were formed, catastrophists believe another catastrophe, involving large-scale water recession, cut out the canyon to expose the rocks and form the amazing structures we see today. Catastrophists also believe that some of the very top layers of rock (such as the igneous rock formed from volcanic activity) were made after the Flood by smaller catastrophes.

The catastrophism viewpoint can also explain why different fossils appear in different layers. There are few fossils below the Great Unconformity because those rocks were formed during the Creation week and shortly afterward. After the fall of man, death entered the world, but there was not much to fossilize as organisms were beginning to multiply and fill the Earth. Thus, there were a few strata with just a few types of small fossils. The strata above the Great Unconformity contain many more fossils because they were created at the time of the Flood when there were plenty of creatures that could be fossilized, particularly due to the flood actions. And because all land animals except for those on the Ark were killed, there were many dead organisms that could become trapped in the sedimentary layers.

As the floodwaters rose in different places from several sources (from beneath the Earth's surface and a deluge of rain), they caught different creatures at various flood stages. Sediments were laid down based on depth, direction, and speed of the floodwaters, so the creatures being fossilized in any given layer would have, most likely, been caught in the floodwaters in a given region.

So though a catastrophist viewpoint also suggests that the layers were laid down, one on top of another, they represent a much shorter time period. The deepest rocks are a result of the Creation week and some local catastrophes that occurred before the Flood. Most of the remaining rock strata are a result of the worldwide Flood. And the uppermost rocks are the result of recent local catastrophes and are very new in history.

However, the different fossils in each layer are not because the layers represent *different parts of Earth's history*. Rather, the earliest rocks are thought to have few fossils because of the nature of Creation and the short time period after the fall of man for organisms to have died. The different fossils above that are an indication that the Flood trapped and fossilized different creatures at different stages of the Flood, based on depth, direction, and speed of the floodwaters.

In the next section we will look at these 2 perspectives from another aspect of Earth's history.

THE GEOLOGICAL RECORD AND UNIFORMITARIANISM

Uniformitarians do not believe that sedimentary rock formed in all areas of the world during all time periods. So to relate layers from one area to another, they rely on **index fossils** to help them. Index fossils are fossils that are assumed to represent a certain period in Earth's past. They believe that fossils in any given layer are of organisms living in the time period during which the layer was deposited. And if you can find a fossil in one layer of rock that doesn't appear in higher or lower layers of rock, that fossil can be linked to *that* layer of rock and therefore that time in Earth's past—it is believed to be an index fossil of that specific time period. So *any* rock layer containing that particular kind of fossil is believed to be laid down at the same time as any other layer of rock containing that particular kind of fossil. Additionally, if an index fossil is found in a layer lower than a different index fossil and its layer, then they can hypothesize that the lower index fossil and its layer of rock were laid down before the other layer with its index fossil and are thus older in history. This leads uniformitarians to construct a geological record (see Figure 6.27).

This is often called a geological column, which is a theoretical picture in which layers of rock from around the world are meshed together into a single, unbroken record of Earth's past. Now, there is a *very* important point about the geological column you need to understand. *There is no place on Earth where all the layers of the geological column exist complete with their index fossils.* It is a theoretical picture, assuming each layer of rock represents a period in Earth's past and assuming the index fossils found in a given layer of rock are actually accurate indicators of which time period the rock was formed. Now, if either of these assumptions is wrong, the geological column is not accurate.

In the geological column, each layer has sub-layers within it, and each represents a past time period. These periods are given dates, and the suggested dates in the figure represent a major era of the geological column. Now if you haven't read the caption for Figure 6.27, please read it now.

You need to know that even though this suggested column of strata exists nowhere in the world in its completion and lots of fossil evidence shows parts of it to be incorrect, it is still presented as a factual diagram in most geology textbooks, even those written at the college level.

FIGURE 6.27
The Geological Record Reconstructed According to Uniformitarian Assumptions

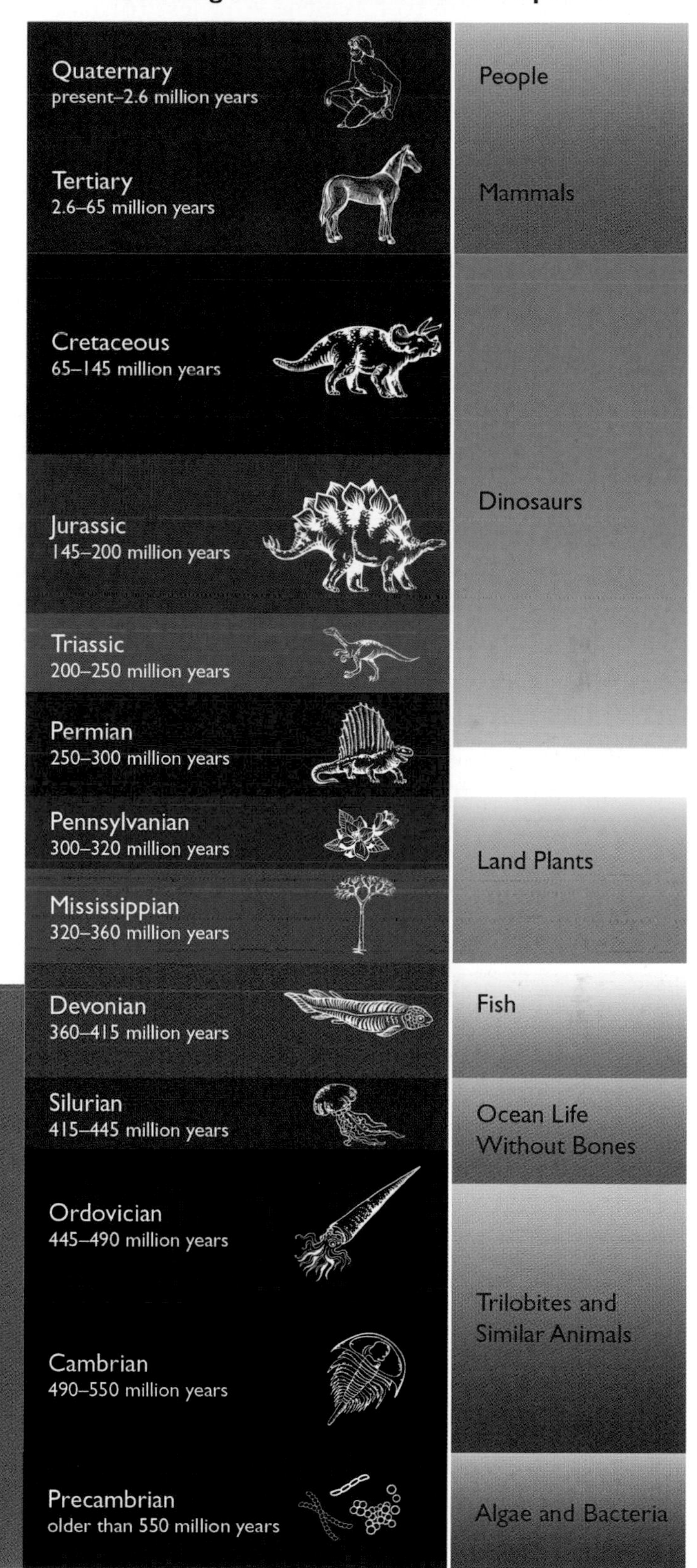

Fossils of algae and bacteria are in the lowest strata, then as you go through higher strata you find trilobites, ocean-dwelling creatures with no backbones, then fossils of fish, plants, dinosaurs, mammals and then human beings. Trilobites are shown only in Cambrian and Ordovician layers in the figure because they are most common there, even though they are actually found in rock layers all the way up to the Permian period. Most importantly, this figure is wrong to some extent. Fossil evidence has made it clear that the lower layers are not an accurate representation of Earth's history because fossils in Cambrian rock have been found that should not exist in rock older than Ordovician or Silurian rock. So though the science of geology has changed over time, the geological column as presented in most textbooks has not.

FIGURE 6.28
Marine Fossil-filled Strata in Argentina

Uniformitarians then take the geological column one step further by explaining that the oldest rocks seem to have the simplest forms of life as fossils, and as you move up the column, more and more complex forms of life are found. They believe this is evidence for the **theory of evolution** which states that all life on this Earth has one (or a few) common ancestor(s) that existed a long time ago. They believe the simplest life forms started to reproduce and the offspring had differences from the parents. If those differences helped them to better survive in the wild, then they were more likely to live long enough to reproduce and pass those better differences on to the next generation. After millions of years, the changes piled up, creating new species in greater complexity.

We'll talk more about the problems with this theory in another module, but for now, just be aware that evolutionists believe organisms can have enough changes in their bodies to eventually change into other types of organisms.

Uniformitarians believe the geological column seems to be a record of how this evolution occurred. It started with very simple life forms in the oldest rocks and then they evolved over time. They believe that the differences we see between fossils in upper rock layers is an indication of that. Remember, the geological column itself is a theoretical construct and doesn't exist in its entirety anywhere. So the whole idea that life appeared on Earth in that order is based on something that is an assumption itself!

And add to this the fact that the geological column in Figure 6.27 is made up of a tiny, tiny fraction of the fossil record. The vast majority of the fossil record is composed of hard-shelled creatures like clams, so you are looking at a small subset of what has been preserved in the form of fossils.

THE GEOLOGICAL RECORD AND CATASTROPHISM

Catastrophists interpret the geological record differently. Remember, catastrophists believe that most of the geological record we see today was formed as the result of one or more catastrophes. The worldwide Flood as described in the Bible (and confirmed by writings from many other cultures) is the biggest of these catastrophes and is responsible for a good portion of the geological record. In addition, other local catastrophes such as hurricanes or volcanic eruptions have produced some of the geological structures we see today.

There is compelling evidence to support this idea. The eruption of Mount St. Helens that I mentioned earlier is a good example. It was caused by an earthquake that created a landslide, ripping off the top of the mountain. That released magma within the previously inactive volcano, causing a major eruption, lasting for 5 months! At the height of the eruption, this local catastrophe was releasing energy equivalent to the rate of *one atomic bomb per second*, leveling forests and causing massive mudflows.

FIGURE 6.29
Catastrophic Erosion After Mount St. Helens Eruption

As a result of this, stratified sediments were rapidly laid down—much faster than years or millions of years. Regular strata of varied thicknesses were present, too. In the eruption, there were also many, many agents of erosion, including water, steam, and mud. They traveled very quickly over the landscape, cutting down through multiple layers of rock and creating a zigzag shaped main canyon. This Grand Canyon-like formation, one-fortieth the size of the original, was made in just 5 days, complete with a small stream of water flowing along the canyon bottom.

Therefore, we know by observation that these canyons were not formed by the small river flowing there. This teaches us that appearances can be very deceiving when it comes to canyon formation.

So let's think about all you have learned up to this point. The most historically accurate document of ancient history gives account of a worldwide Flood. Every major culture has a worldwide flood story, too, because there was indeed a worldwide Flood. Now think of the enormous geological implications of such a massive catastrophic event. Compared to a worldwide flood, the Mount St. Helens catastrophe would hardly be noticeable, yet it can build layers of stratified sediment several feet high. If the Mount St. Helens catastrophe can lay strata and carve out canyons that are one-fortieth the scale of the Grand Canyon, a massive post-Flood catastrophe could certainly lay strata and carve out the Grand Canyon itself.

Now looking at the fossil record from a catastrophist point of view, we can remember that there are 4 distinct rock groups: the rocks associated with God's creation of the world plus sedimentary rocks that are a result of the creative acts involving water; some local catastrophes such as volcanic eruption occurring after the Creation week but before the worldwide Flood; sedimentary rock that is a direct result of the Flood itself; and some sedimentary and igneous rock formations from local catastrophes occurring since the Flood (See Figure 6.30).

FIGURE 6.30
Fossil Record Rock and Fossil Groups

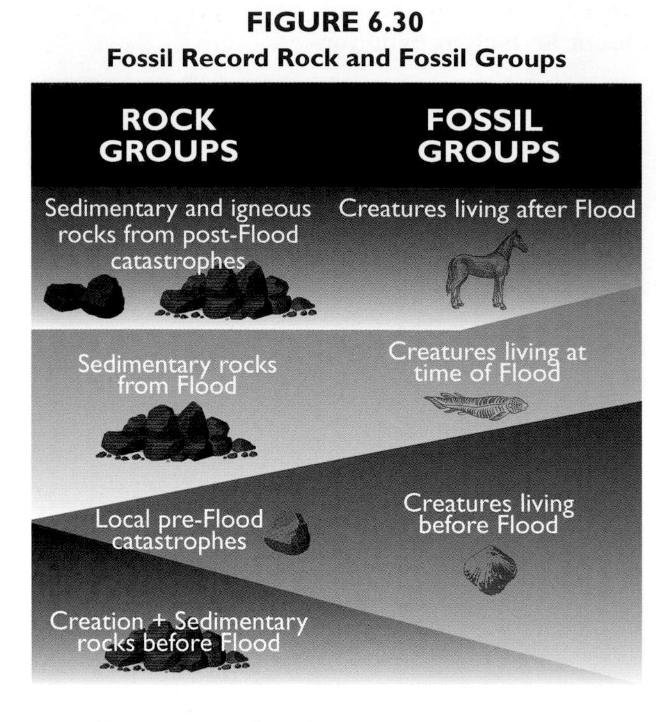

Fossils can really be split into 3 basic groups. Pre-Flood rocks have remains of creatures living before the Flood. Rocks that were laid down by the Flood have fossils of creatures living roughly at that time. And post-Flood rocks have fossils of creatures living after the Flood. So in a sense, this means the geological record does give us a glimpse into different periods of Earth's past, but it does it in 3 broad eras.

This assumption helps us to easily understand certain aspects of the fossil record. For example, paleontologists have found huge numbers of fossils concentrated in enormous deposits called **fossil graveyards.** That is not surprising with a catastrophism viewpoint. After all, the Flood probably forced these creatures to move in an effort to escape the scary conditions caused by the rapidly moving floodwaters. Huge amounts of moving sediment and mud overtook them and buried them quickly. With more and more sediments laid on top of them, the creatures became fossilized. Interestingly, some fossil graveyards contain fossils of many types of organisms representing several different climates. How could they all be found together in the same layer if there was not a worldwide Flood to move them to one location?

FIGURE 6.31
A Fish Fossilized in the Middle of a Meal and a Fossilized Man-made Hat

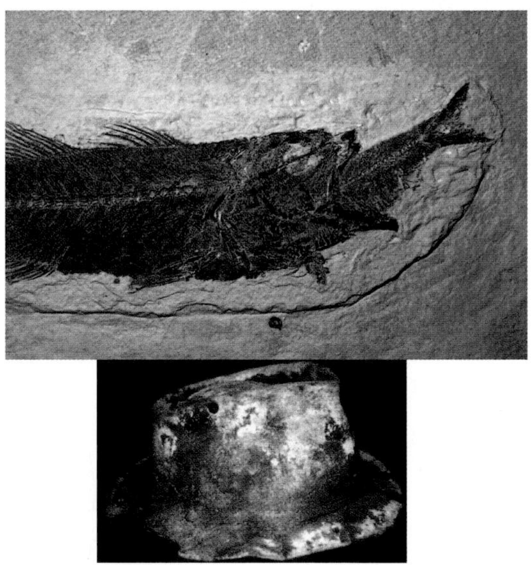

Other fossils indicate rapid preservation, such as the remains of a large fish *in the process of* eating a small fish. A fish doesn't die in the middle of a meal and then lie around while both it and its meal are encased in sediment. These fish were buried in an instant, without warning.

Moreover, the process of fossilization has been shown to occur rather rapidly, instead of requiring millions of years. For example, man-made objects have been fossilized within years or decades. As long as there are proper conditions, fossils can rapidly form. In fact, catastrophists think that this is the normal mode of fossilization, indicating that the fossils within the fossil record are not as old as uniformitarians think.

ONE MORE AGE ISSUE

Everything in creation is made up of atoms. Some atoms are heavier than others, and some of the heavier atoms are unstable. We call these **radioactive atoms.** Uranium is a type of atom that occurs in several forms, called **isotopes**. One of its isotopes—Uranium-238—breaks down, or decays, into an atom called thorium-234 which then further decays until the atom changes into lead-206. So we call uranium the parent atom and lead the daughter atom. This process is called **atomic decay**, and it is used in an attempt to determine how old an object is.

If we know the time it takes for a parent isotope to decay into its daughter, and we can measure how much of each is present in an object, in theory we can figure out how long it would take for that amount of parent isotope to change into that amount of daughter isotope.

Now, carbon-14 is another type of atom that can be used for this dating process, but it can only measure things that were once living—things with carbon atoms in them. One problem with carbon dating, though, is that carbon-14 decays rapidly. That means that it isn't very useful for dating things more than a few thousand years old.

The dating of igneous and metamorphic rock can be done by studying radioactive isotopes of uranium-238 to lead-206 via the process I just mentioned. However, scientists have used procedures that cause their decay rates to change. Well, that means that we cannot be sure of the accuracy of the dates given to these rocks. Add to this issue the fact that when the same rock is dated by more than one method, it often yields different ages. Even if it is dated with the same method, different results can be found.

FIGURE 6.32
Carbon Dating

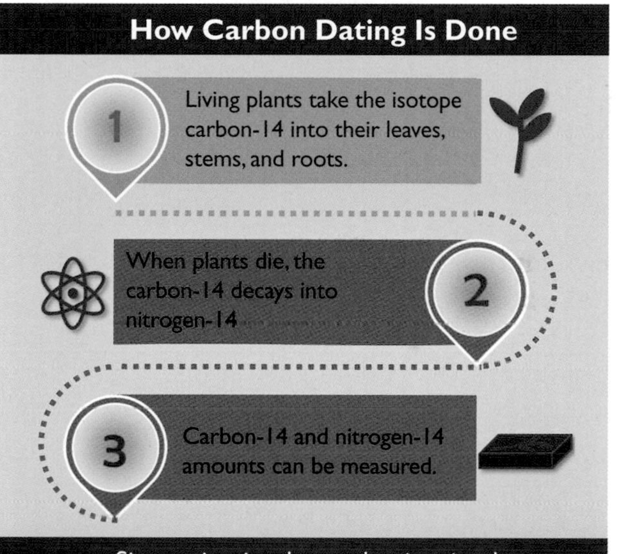

ON YOUR OWN

6.11 Create your own infographic titled Problems with Uniformitarianism using these points and the image:

1. There's no place on Earth where all layers of the geological column exist with their index fossils.
2. Index fossils are assumed to be accurate indicators of a certain time period—there is no evidence.
3. Evolutionary theory is based on these 2 major assumptions.
4. The geological column is based on a small fraction of actual fossils (most are clam-like).
5. Strata and canyon formation have been observed to be rapid.
6. Fossil graveyards can contain organisms from several climates.
7. There is evidence of rapid fossil preservation.
8. Dating techniques can be inconsistent.

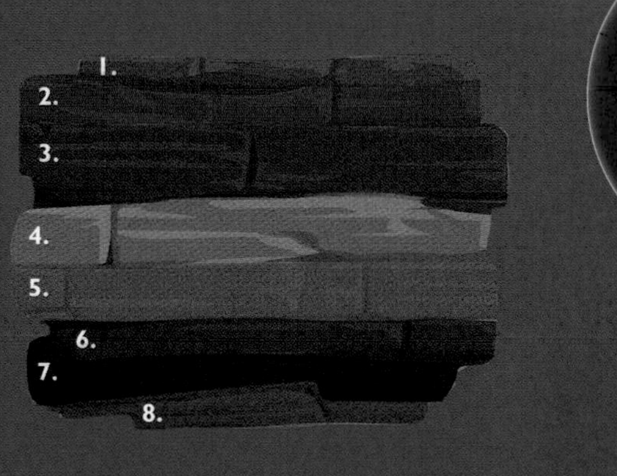

SUMMING UP

In this module, you learned more about Earth science, particularly focusing on geology and paleontology. It is an entire planet's worth of information that might leave your head spinning. But take a step back and think about how amazing this information is. We are still trying to better understand what our Earth is made of and how it works. This gives us clues to its marvelous creation and God's power and might when "In the beginning, God created the heavens and the Earth" (Genesis 1:1) and…BAM!…there it was in all its complexity!

ANSWERS TO THE "ON YOUR OWN" QUESTIONS

6.1

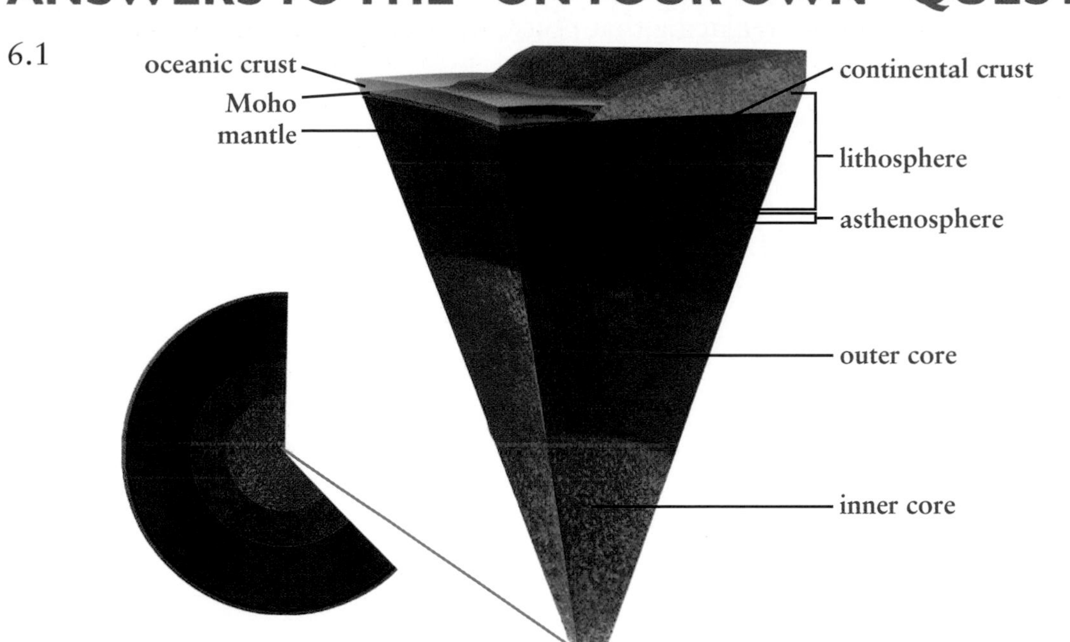

6.2 An indirect observation is **something you don't see directly happening but can reason from other observations.** For example, if you see 2 people walk by on the beach, you have directly observed 2 people. But if you see 2 sets of human footprints in the sand, that would be an indirect observation that 2 people walked by. You didn't actually see them, but you can reason that they walked by from other observations.

6.3 The 3 basic types of rock that make up Earth's crust are **sedimentary, igneous, and metamorphic** rock.

6.4 **The construction worker likely discovered a mineral, not a rock.** Minerals are crystalline and have many faces, or angled sides, giving them a crystalline shape.

6.5 **Erosion is a type of physical weathering** because the chemical material of the rock has not changed.

6.6 **Rusting iron in rocks is a type of chemical weathering** because the iron chemically reacts with oxygen in the air, changing its material makeup.

6.7 **Yes, it makes sense to think that the sedimentary rock in the Grand Canyon was laid down by water.** There is not a lot of water in Arizona now, but at some time in the past, there could have been water there. You have already learned that there **is a lot of evidence for the fact that a worldwide Flood occurred.** There certainly would have been water in Arizona then!

6.8 **A. Igneous and metamorphic rocks below the Great Unconformity; B. sedimentary (and one igneous) strata below the Great Unconformity; C. Sedimentary rocks above the Great Unconformity; D. Igneous rocks at surface.**

6.9 The fossil was formed by **petrifaction.** Petrifaction happens when mineral-rich water covers a dead object, replacing that object's materials with minerals and resulting in rock.

6.10 Four notable features of the fossil record are: **1. Most fossils are found in sedimentary rock. 2. The vast majority of all fossils on this planet are of hard-shelled organisms, like clams. 3. The fossil record contains the remains of some organisms still living today. 4. The fossils found in one layer of stratified rock can be considerably different from the fossils found in another layer of stratified rock.**

6.11 *Answers will vary.*

STUDY GUIDE FOR MODULE 6

1. Match the following words with their definitions.

a. Geology	A surface of erosion that separates one layer of rock from another
b. Humus	The preserved remains of a once-living organism
c. Minerals	Inorganic crystalline substances found naturally in the Earth
d. Erosion	The study of Earth's physical structure, its history, the processes acting on it, and the rocks of which it is composed
e. Unconformity	The decayed remains of once-living creatures
f. Fossil	The process of wearing or grinding something down by wind, water, or other natural agents

2. Match the major layers of Earth with their correct location. (*crust, inner core, outer core, mantle*)

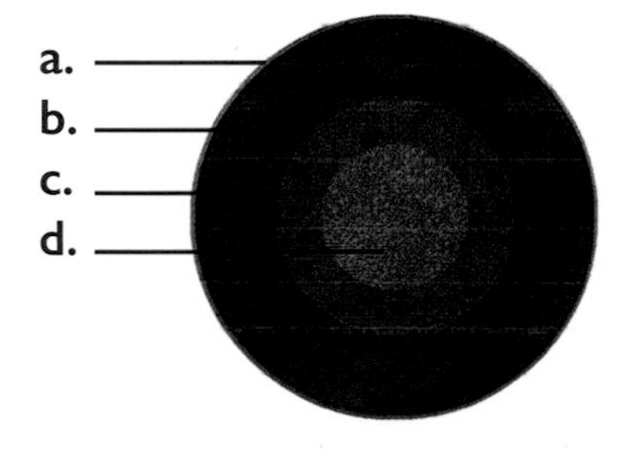

3. Choose the correct word for this statement. The (deeper, shallower) in the Earth, the higher the temperature and greater the pressure.

4. The idea of a broken sheet of Styrofoam floating on the surface of water, each piece moving, depending on how the water moves is an illustration of ____________________.

5. Choose the correct words for this statement: (Rocks, Minerals) often form crystalline shapes, and (rocks, minerals) do not.

6. Choose the correct words for this statement. Most of Earth's (sediments, mountains) are laid down by water, and most of Earth's (sediments, mountains) are created by actions of Earth's crust.

7. Scientists tested a pile of sand and rubble that was found below a large rock formation. They compared the rubble's makeup to the rock formation's makeup and discovered they were made of the same chemical composition. Was the sand and rubble a likely result of physical or chemical weathering?

8. What is the major carrier of sediments that makes them settle out in layers?

9. What rock type is the most common in the Grand Canyon?

10. A paleontologist discovers a fossil that is preserved 3-dimensionally and is completely made of rock. Which fossilization process formed it?

    a. mold and cast b. petrifaction c. carbonization d. amber formation

11. What are these 4 features describing?

    1. Most fossils are found in sedimentary rock.
    2. The vast majority of all fossils on this planet are of hard-shelled organisms, like clams.
    3. It contains the remains of some organisms still living today.
    4. Fossils found in one layer of stratified rock can be considerably different from the fossils found in another layer of stratified rock.

12. Choose the correct answer to complete these sentences. (Uniformitarians, Catastrophists) believe sedimentary rock formed through slow processes, much the same way we see it forming today, and (uniformitarians, catastrophists) believe much of the geology we see today is the result of processes that occurred once in Earth's past and will not be repeated.

EARTH SCIENCE— METEOROLOGY AND OCEANOGRAPHY

With a good understanding of the makeup of Earth, we can go further into our study of Earth science by learning about the forces acting on it. In this module, we will cover meteorology and oceanography.

METEOROLOGY

The term **meteorology** comes from the suffix *-logia,* which means "the study of," and *meteor,* which is Greek for "high in the sky." So meteorology is the study of weather.

Meteorology—The study of weather

This field of science includes the study of the atmosphere and how atmospheric processes determine the Earth's **weather** and **climate.** Why do we want to learn about this subject? Well, it is important to study weather and climate because they directly affect people. Let me first cover the difference between those 2 terms. Many people think weather and climate are the same thing, but they differ by a measure of time. You see, weather is a day-to-day state of the atmosphere, sometimes changing hourly. You may have rainy weather

Quaestio

Take a look outside your window right now. What do you see? Pay close attention to the landscape around you. Do you see mountains? Is it hot? Is it raining or snowing? Is your area often dry? Also, what kind of soil do you have? Is it sandy or made of clay? All these questions have to do with the features of the Earth where you live. And depending on your location on the planet, the conditions will be different. But there is a reason it is different. Just like there is an order to our universe, there is an order to both the physical features of the Earth and the weather you experience all year.

FIGURE 7.1
A Cloudy Sky over a Field

today and dry weather tomorrow. It may be snowy one morning and sunny that afternoon. On the other hand, climate has to do with conditions over relatively long periods of time. It is affected by how the atmosphere in a particular area behaves over years. Antarctica, for example, has a very cold climate while the Sahara in Africa has a very hot one. Thus, even though the overall temperatures might vary throughout the year, it is colder in Antarctica and hotter in the Sahara. Rainforests exhibit another type of climate—one that is humid (or wet) and is often warm.

FIGURE 7.2
The Dry Climate of the Sahara

FIGURE 7.3
A Panoramic Photo of Sunny and Rainy Weather

In Module 5, you learned that Earth has an atmosphere, a gaseous layer surrounding our planet. Our atmosphere is perfect for supporting life. It contains gases for living organisms to breathe, protects Earth from harmful radiation from the sun, behaves like a blanket to regulate surface temperatures, and helps to move fresh water to all parts of the world.

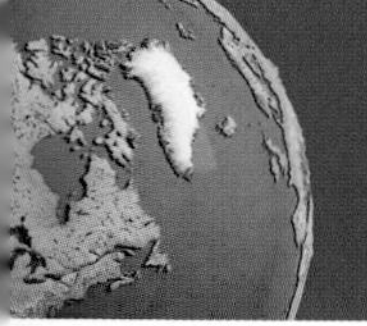

ON YOUR OWN

7.1 Explain the difference between climate and weather.

EARTH'S ATMOSPHERE

Our atmosphere is made of gases surrounding Earth. With just the right amounts of oxygen, carbon dioxide, and other gases for living organisms to use, our atmosphere works like a shield to protect Earth from harmful solar radiation and behaves like a blanket to keep temperatures from drastically changing. Even though it is about 480 km (300 mi) in thickness, most of the material in our atmosphere is concentrated within the first 10 miles from the surface. And the higher the altitude, the less material there is. That means there is less pressure from that material to "push down" on you.

The gases that fill our atmosphere are referred to as air. Now, air is made up of mostly nitrogen gas. That might surprise you because even though we need air to breathe, our bodies can't do anything with the nitrogen we inhale. Well, nitrogen *is* an important part of living organisms and is used by plants to produce proteins, which are critical to our nutritional needs; we just can't use it in a gaseous form. Oxygen is the second most abundant gas, which is a good thing because nearly all living things take in oxygen to survive. (Plants take in oxygen for their body processes and *release* oxygen, too.) Figure 7.4 shows the major composition of gases in air. Notice that water vapor is a minor component. Yet it is important to our Earth because water vapor helps to hold in the sun's heat as well as to produce rain and snow.

FIGURE 7.4

Gases in Earth's Atmosphere

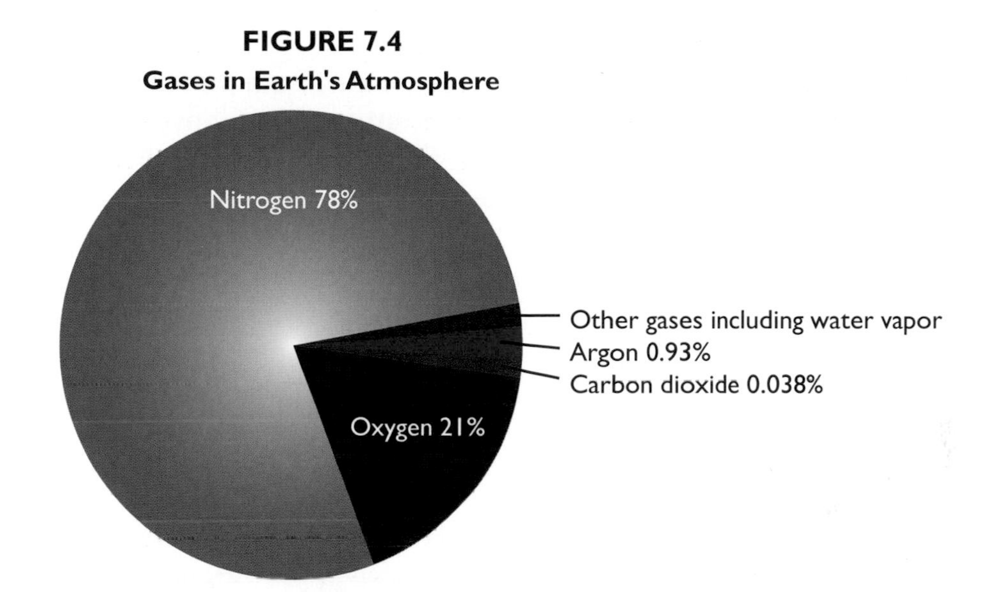

Argon is a gas that doesn't do anything when it comes to living organisms. It is nonreactive. However, people are able to use this gas in industry (welding, in light bulbs, and even lasers!).

To better understand the atmosphere, we can divide it into 2 major regions. The lower atmosphere begins at Earth's surface and extends up to an altitude of about 80 km (50 mi). It is called the **homosphere** because it is made up of a practically uniform mix of several gases.

think about this

Because oxygen is so important for living things, why isn't there a higher concentration of it in the atmosphere? Well, there is such a thing as *too much oxygen*. Higher oxygen levels can cause many non-flammable materials to be more likely to catch fire. Things that do burn would burn even hotter. And too much oxygen can cause our bodies to experience seizures and other physical problems. So, there is just the right amount of oxygen on Earth to support life without causing any harm!

In the upper part of the homosphere there is a thick layer of a gas called ozone. One molecule of ozone contains 3 atoms of oxygen, and the oxygen gas we breathe is made up of 2 atoms. That extra oxygen atom makes ozone a highly reactive molecule, so it is a good thing that there is not much here on the surface. But ozone is important because it helps to make a barrier, protecting Earth's surface from the sun's radiation.

The second, larger region of the atmosphere is called the **heterosphere**, and the 2 regions are divided by a boundary called the **turbopause.**

FIGURE 7.5
Major Regions of Earth's Atmosphere

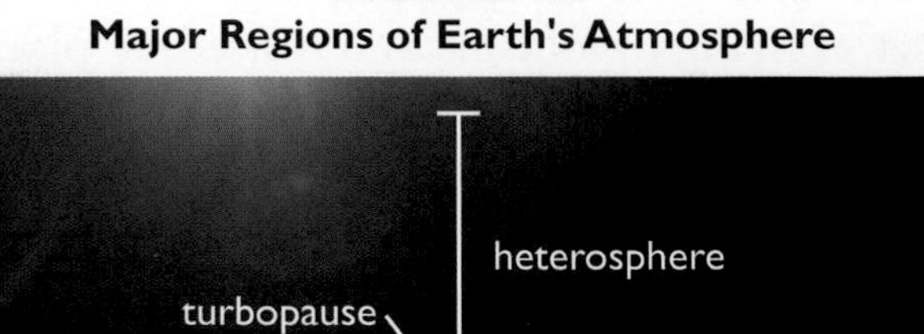

All of the atmospheric regions are given names as well as the boundaries between them. (Scientists like to give everything names!) But the boundaries are related in their terminology because they all end with "pause." I like to think of it as if you were traveling up in the atmosphere, you might pause a minute before entering each region! In reality, the turbopause is the level of the atmosphere above which turbulent mixing stops.

Unlike the well-mixed gases of the homosphere, the heterosphere is characterized by several layers of different gases. In fact, the prefix *homo-* means "same," and the prefix *hetero-* means "different." In other words, lighter gases are higher in the heterosphere and heavier gases are lower; they are not evenly distributed.

But that is not the only way we can divide Earth's atmosphere. We can also separate it into 5 main layers based on their density and temperature at different altitudes. You see, the atmosphere gets thinner and thinner as the altitude increases, with the gases eventually spreading out into space.

FIGURE 7.6
Layers of Earth's Atmosphere

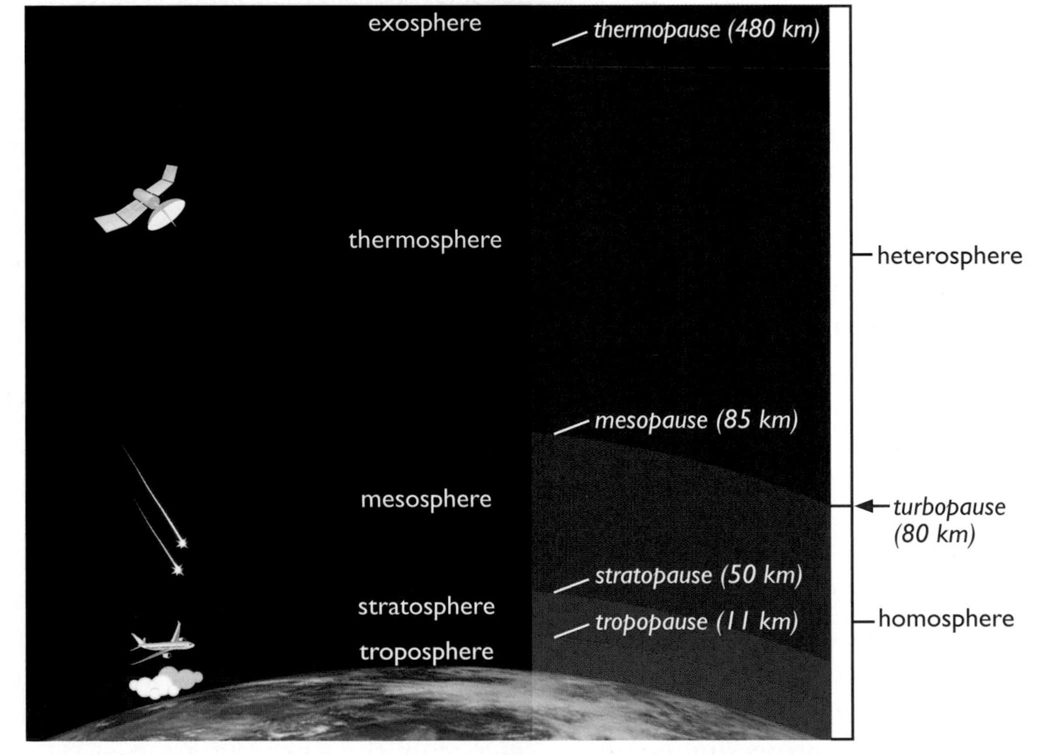

A good way to remember the order of the 5 atmospheric layers is to think of an astronaut asking directions to get to outer space: **Tr**aveling? **S**how **me the ex**it! (**Tr**oposphere, **S**tratosphere, **M**esosphere, **The**rmosphere, **Ex**osphere)

The **troposphere** is the closest layer to Earth's surface, beginning at the ground and going up to an average height of 11–13 km (7–8 mi). Practically all the water vapor and dust in the atmosphere is in the troposphere, which is why clouds are in this layer. That means that all of Earth's weather is in this layer, too. The air is warmer near the ground and gets colder as you move higher in altitude. At the upper end of the troposphere is the **tropopause.**

The **stratosphere** is the second layer, beginning above the tropopause and ending about 50 km (31 mi) above Earth. Ozone is abundant here and does its job absorbing the harmful radiation coming from the sun. Air in the stratosphere is dry (there is little water vapor), has strong and steady winds, and is about 1,000 times thinner compared to air at sea level. This is the layer where jet aircraft fly. Now, because ozone is in this layer, temperature actually *increases* a bit as you go higher in the stratosphere. That's because the ozone gas absorbs lots of light energy from the sun and releases it as heat energy. The upper end of the stratosphere is the **stratopause.**

The **mesosphere** begins at the stratopause and extends up to 85 km (53 mi) high. We know the least about this layer because it is too high for planes and weather balloons to fly and too low for satellites to remain in orbit. We do know that it is the coldest part of the atmosphere and this layer is where meteors generally burn up. The mesosphere is at the boundary between the homosphere and the heterosphere. The upper end of the mesosphere is the **mesopause.**

The **thermosphere** begins at the mesopause and extends to 480 km (300 mi) high. In this layer temperatures rise as you increase altitude. In fact, they can get up to 1,500 °C (2,700 °F)! Even though this layer is considered part of Earth's atmosphere there are very few gas molecules here. In fact, the atoms are so far apart that it is believed one atom can travel for a thousand miles before bumping into another one! This layer is where space shuttles once flew and where the International Space Station (ISS) now orbits Earth. But the reason the ISS does not burn up is that even though the gases in this region are very hot, not much heat transfer happens because the molecules are few and far between.

The thermosphere is also where **auroras** occur. You see, charged particles from space get trapped in Earth's magnetic field and get concentrated near the poles. While this is happening, they sometimes bump into molecules in the thermosphere and give energy to them. Those molecules don't like having so much energy, so they will shed it by releasing photons of light. Colorful light displays result. As you learned from Module 5, in the Northern Hemisphere the phenomenon is called the Aurora Borealis, and in the Southern Hemisphere it's called the Aurora Australis. Because there are so many excited molecules in this layer, there is a sub-layer within the thermosphere called the **ionosphere.** The ionosphere behaves like an electric mirror, bouncing radio waves back to Earth and helping them travel from one place to another.

FIGURE 7.7
Stunning Aurora Borealis over Iceland

(Sometimes you can catch an AM radio station far, far from its source due to atmospheric bouncing!) Now, you can probably guess that the upper end of the thermosphere is called the **thermopause**. Notice the naming pattern?

Well, the highest layer of our atmosphere is the **exosphere**. It is very thin and is where Earth's atmosphere merges into outer space. There is really no notable boundary at its uppermost point because the gas particles are so widely dispersed.

ON YOUR OWN

7.2 Using Figure 7.6 and the text following it as a guide, make an illustration of the layers of the atmosphere in your notebook. Be sure to include the 2 divisions of the homosphere and heterosphere (divided by how well the air is mixed) as well as the 5 atmospheric layers (divided by air density and temperature). In your illustration, include locations of clouds, jet planes, meteors, and the International Space Station. Then from the information in the paragraphs in this section, add the location of the excess ozone and where the auroras occur.

WHAT CAUSES WEATHER?

Remember, weather is a temporary condition of the air around us. It involves temperature, light, wind, how much water is in the air, air pressure, and air quality. Finally, it includes **precipitation**.

Precipitation—Moisture falling from the atmosphere as rain, snow, or hail

FIGURE 7.8
Stormy Weather

Weather is also affected by how close you are to the ocean and where on Earth you live. If I were to ask you to draw a picture of a polar bear in his natural environment, you would likely draw one in the snow. That is because you know they live near the North Pole where it is often snowy.

When it gets down to it, we can blame all weather on the sun. You see, because the Earth is curved and also tilted on its axis, the sun heats it with different intensities. You have to think about solar energy moving toward Earth the same way something like a ping-pong ball might move as it falls toward the ground—it will bounce at an angle if it hits something, and its direction can be changed by wind or if other factors affect it. When sunlight enters the atmosphere, some of its rays bounce off white clouds and back into space. Some rays are absorbed by the air molecules. The solar energy that hits the ground can be absorbed or reflected back into space, too. In fact, about 90% of sunlight that comes toward Earth does not reach the ground. That's how important the atmosphere is!

Solar energy that is absorbed by land, ocean, or air heats Earth and its atmosphere. At night, some of that warmth escapes back out to space, but much is held in by the blanket of air and clouds. The resulting temperature differences cause air pressure to change. Let me give you a definition for that.

Air pressure—A force exerted onto a surface by the weight of air molecules

To better understand air molecules, think of them as tiny little balls floating around. As they heat up, they move faster and bump into each other and things around them. Those molecules are pushing or pressing on things. That is how air pressure works. Very hot air molecules move faster and bump into each other more often. When a collection of hot air moves like this, it can push (or *press*, hence the word *pressure*) against other masses of air. This is one of the main things that creates weather.

EXPLORE MORE

Add ¾ cup of white vinegar to a clean, empty 2-liter bottle. Blow up a balloon and then let the air out again to stretch it out a bit. Add 2 tablespoons of baking soda into the empty balloon using a butter knife. Attach the balloon to the bottle by stretching the balloon's opening over the bottle's lip. Now lift the balloon and shake it a bit so the baking soda falls into the vinegar. You should notice the balloon expand with gas. The gas created from this reaction is carbon dioxide, which is one of the gases in our atmosphere. As more of it was made, the molecules were forced to bump into each other and push against the sides of the bottle and the balloon. Because the balloon is flexible, it stretched outward. The air pressure of the gas increased.

Because different areas of Earth receive different amounts of solar energy, the resulting air masses at different temperatures and pressures will move around. As Earth spins on its axis, this causes worldwide air rotation and massive air currents. Currents of air high in the troposphere called **jet streams** snake across the globe in both the Northern and Southern Hemispheres (see Figure 7.9) at places where masses of rising warm air and falling cool air intersect. If you think about it, the surface of Earth is directly facing the sun at the equator. As the air heats up there, it begins to rise, spreading both north and south. By about one-third of the distance toward the poles in both hemispheres, the air has had enough time to cool off, so it sinks back to Earth, eventually making its way back to the equator. At the poles, cold air sinks and travels down and away from the poles. When it reaches about one-third of the distance toward the equator, it warms up and rises, eventually making its way back to the poles. These 2 closed circulation patterns create a third one between themselves.

FIGURE 7.9
Jet Streams

As Earth rotates, these loops of air start to curve. This causes winds to move to the right in the Northern Hemisphere and to the left in the Southern Hemisphere, forming notable wind patterns (Figure 7.10). Those wind patterns have been very important historically, as sailors used them to travel around the world. In areas both north and south of the equator are predictable **trade winds** that ships used to cross the ocean for exploration and trade. However, there are locations (about 30° north and south of the equator) where winds are light and fickle, called the **doldrums.**

Now you don't have to completely understand how this all works, but just make sure you understand that these large-scale movements of air are actually what help to determine climate. Remember, climate deals with the overall conditions we would expect in a specific area, such as hot deserts, cold mountaintops, and rainy tropical forests.

FIGURE 7.10
Earth Wind Patterns

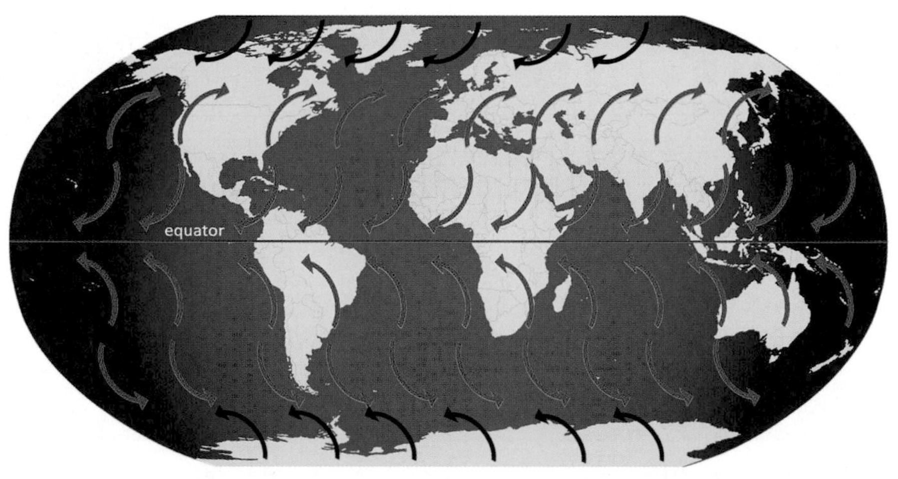

ON YOUR OWN

7.3 What is the one thing that drives all the weather on Earth?

ATMOSPHERIC WATER

Water is critically important when it comes to weather. Let's begin by first going over the **water cycle,** sometimes called the **hydrologic cycle.** Beginning in our oceans, lakes, and rivers, liquid water is exposed to heat by the sun, causing some of its individual molecules to gain enough energy to become gaseous water. We call that water vapor. You experience water vapor when you are heating a pot of water on the stove and see steam rise out of the pot, letting you know it's time to put the pasta in. This vaporization of water is called **evaporation.** See the root word *vapor* in it?

Once water evaporates, it tends to rise in the air because, believe it or not, it is lighter than the air molecules around it. Moving air currents carry the water vapor to places with a different temperature. When air cools, water tends to condense into clouds. You can see this if you spend time watching a thunderstorm forming. As the warm, moist air punches up into the cool, dry upper layers, it cools because (in the troposphere) the higher the altitude, the cooler the temperature is. When water vapor cools, it eventually wants to become liquid water again.

However, water vapor needs to do this on a surface. So when water molecules come across tiny dust particles in the air, they stick to them. The water molecules continue to pile on top of each other to form tiny liquid water droplets. This is the process of **condensation.** And condensation forms clouds. In fact, you could say that clouds are made of tiny bits of dusty-water droplets!

FIGURE 7.11
The Hydrologic Cycle

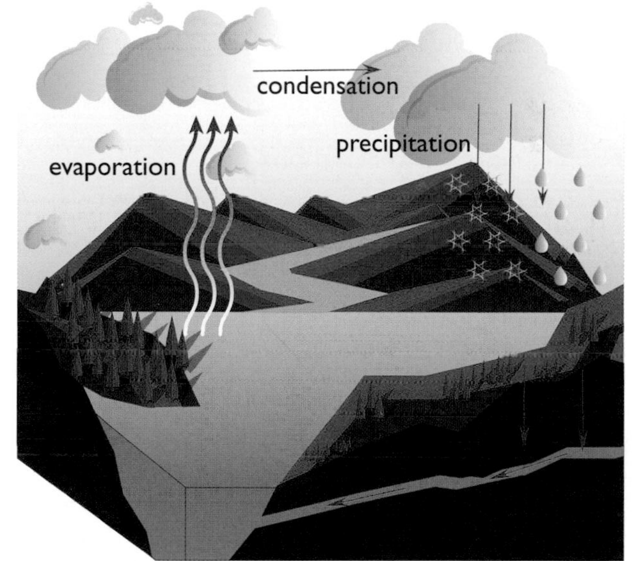

If enough molecules get together, the droplets of water become so large that they are too heavy to remain in the air. So, they begin to fall back to Earth. We call that rain or snow (or sleet, or hail, or freezing rain, depending on the temperature and air moisture in the area). This process is called **precipitation.**

If you think about it, water travels from Earth to the sky and back to Earth again: evaporation, condensation, and precipitation. As it does this, it moves around from the ocean or other bodies of water to land. The water on land eventually collects in rivers and streams and flows to bodies of open water again, where the cycle starts over.

creation connection

The first modern person to think of the water cycle was Bernard Palisy. Although he lived in the late 1500s, his ideas weren't accepted by the scientific community until the early 1800s. But here is something amazing: Job 36:27-28 says, "For He draws up the drops of water; they distill his mist in rain, which the skies pour down and drop on mankind abundantly." Think about that. "He draws up the drops of water." That is **evaporation.** "*They distill his mist...*" That is **condensation.** "*...in rain. The skies pour down and drop on mankind abundantly.*" That is **precipitation.** It's the hydrologic cycle! The book of Job is traditionally believed to have been written more than 2,000 years before Christ. Where did the writer get that scientific information? How did he know of the hydrologic cycle? Indeed, it is a testimony to God's omniscience and his speaking through the writer of Job.

Clouds

As you just learned, when the atmosphere holds too much water vapor, the water molecules begin to condense into small liquid drops that float in the air. When you take a hot shower, you might notice how the room fills with this fine mist of small droplets. Well, warm air is able to hold more moisture than cool air. This is why the relatively cold mirror in the bathroom usually fogs up when you take a hot shower. If warm, moist air is cooled, enough droplets will collect to form a cloud. Explore cloud formation further in Experiment 7.1.

EXPERIMENT 7.1

MAKE SOME CLOUDS

PURPOSE: To better understand what is necessary for cloud formation

MATERIALS:

- A large mason jar or other clear sturdy jar
- A saucepan or kettle to boil water
- 2 hot pads
- A 1-quart zippered plastic bag
- Ice
- A match and matchbox
- A dark sheet of construction paper

QUESTION: How do clouds form?

HYPOTHESIS: Write in your notebook what you think clouds need in order to form.

PROCEDURE:

1. Boil about 2 cups of water in the saucepan.
2. While the water is boiling, fill the zipper bag with ice, seal it, and set it aside.
3. Carefully pour the boiling water into the mason jar. Allow the water to sit for a minute to warm up the jar.
4. Using the hot pads, lift the jar and carefully pour out **all but about ½ cup water** into the sink.
5. Set the mason jar with the ½ cup of water on a counter.
6. Fold the construction paper in half width-wise to create a crease. Unfold the paper and open it up so it stands on its side behind the mason jar. This will help you to see what's going on inside.
7. Light a match and hold it at the mouth of the jar for a few seconds. Then drop it in the jar.
8. Quickly set the bag of ice on top of the jar and watch what happens inside. Write what you see in your notebook and include an illustration of your experimental setup.

CONCLUSION: Write what you learned about what clouds need in order to form.

In the experiment, you should have noticed almost immediately after setting the bag of ice on the jar that it began to become cloudy inside. The heated water released extra water vapor into the air above it. As it rose, it came in contact with the cooler area just below the ice. Now, you lit the match for 2 reasons. It first heated up the air inside the jar a bit before the flame went out. Then once it was dropped into the water, it released ash into the jar in the form of smoke. Well, that created tiny bits of material on which the water can condense. And you formed a cloud!

Clouds can form in 4 major ways, each as a result of warm air cooling off. If moist air cools down by the ground at night, it creates **fog,** which is basically a cloud formation at ground level. Alternatively, solar energy heats up the surface of the Earth, causing air to rise. When that warm air rises, it cools, and any water vapor it contains will condense and form **convection clouds.** When the wind blows warm, moist air on top of cooler, drier air masses, **frontal clouds** will form. Finally, as air moves along the ground and travels up the side of a mountain, it will cool and form **mountain clouds.**

FIGURE 7.12
Four Ways Clouds Can Form

The photos from left to right: Fog forms when moist air near the ground cools down at night. Convection clouds form when heated air rises. Frontal clouds form when warm, moist air blows into cooler air. Mountain clouds form when moist air blows higher in altitude up a mountain slope.

There are 3 major cloud *types*, based on their shape (see Figure 7.13). **Cumulus** (kyoom' you lus) clouds are white, puffy clouds with flattened bottoms. They form in air that is mixed by vertical currents. The flat bottom forms at the specific altitude where the air is cool enough to cause condensation. **Stratus** clouds are clouds that look a bit like layers of strata. This term comes from the Latin word *stratum*, which means "layer." **Cirrus** (sear-us) clouds form at high altitudes and are feathery in appearance (*cirrus* is the Latin word for "curl"). The feathery look comes from tiny ice crystals formed in the very cold temperatures of the higher atmosphere. Now, even though there are 3 basic cloud types, we can further differentiate them based on their height (*alto-*) and whether they are layered (*strato-*), tightly packed (*cumulo-*), or have excess moisture (*nimbo-*). Scientists who study the weather assign prefixes to these major cloud names and use them to describe all the types of clouds in the sky.

FIGURE 7.13
Cumulus, Stratus, and Cirrus Clouds

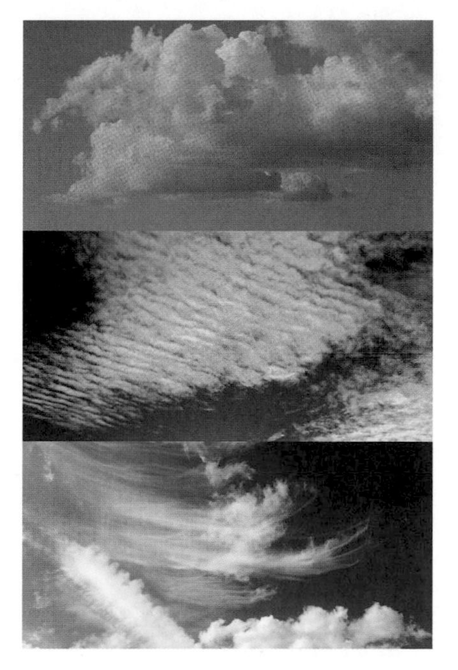

ON YOUR OWN

7.4 Which 3 of the following are necessary for any major cloud formation? Dry air; Warm air cooling; Cold air warming; Lightning; Dust or other particles in the air; Moist air; Mountains.

FRONTS

When a warm mass of air bumps into a cold mass of air, storms can result at their boundaries. This area is called a **front** because it is kind of like a battle line between the 2 air masses that are fighting for that space. When a warm air mass pushes against a cold air mass, the warm air tends to flow up and over the top of the cold air because colder air is generally denser than warm air. We call the warm, advancing air a **warm front.** As it moves over the cold air, the warm air climbs on top of it, rising and forming layers of clouds high in the air. The clouds build up until they create light rain or snow.

If a mass of cold air pushes against a warm air mass, the boundary where these 2 meet is called a **cold front.** Now, because the cold air is denser than the warm air, it wedges itself below and behaves like a plow of sorts, rapidly pushing the warm air upward. Like a warm front, the warm air in a cold front will rise and quickly cool, causing cloud formation and often violent storms.

FIGURE 7.14
Warm Front (left) and Cold Front (right)

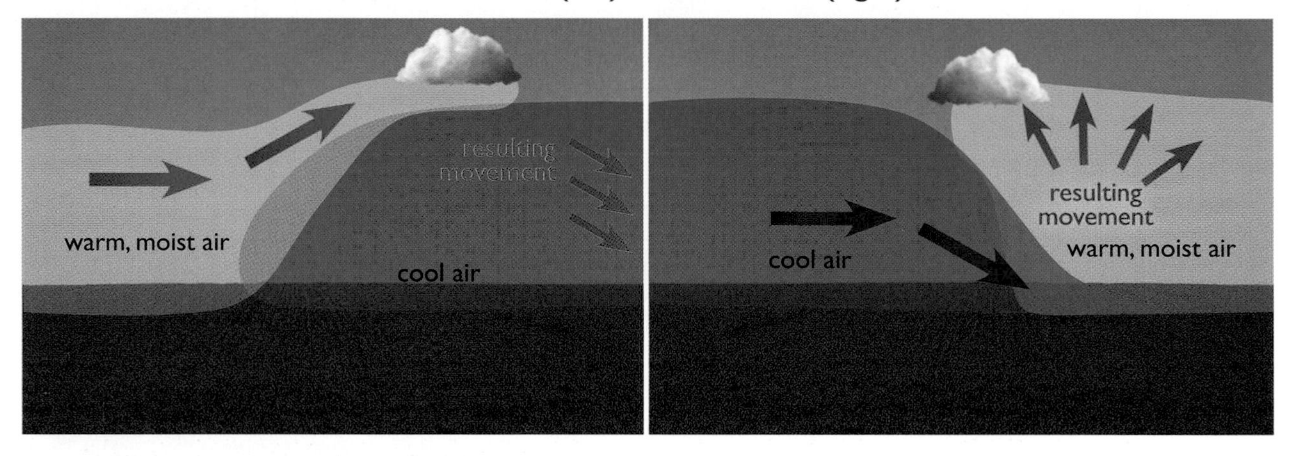

In some cases, 2 air masses push against each other but are unable to move one way or another. The front where they meet will not move. We call that a stationary front. Depending on the amount of moisture in the air, a **stationary front** can cause clear weather or stormy weather that may remain for quite a while.

Lastly, there are occasions when 3 air masses will meet. When a warm air mass is slowly moving over a cold air mass, there are situations where a second cold mass rapidly moves into the area and slides under the warm mass, lifting it upward. These

FIGURE 7.15
Types of Fronts and Their Symbols

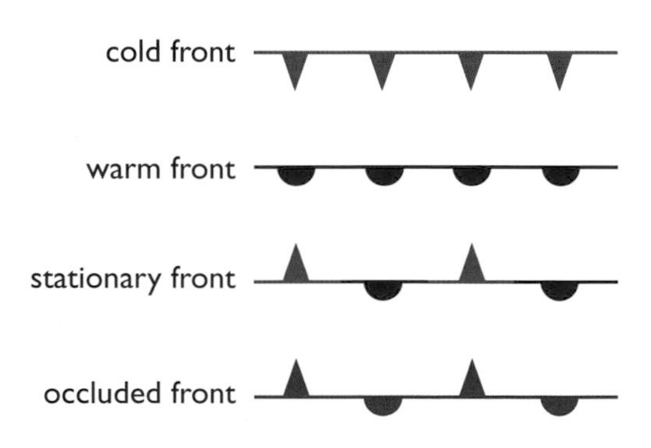

3 air masses create a Y-shaped front called an **occluded front.** The 3 air masses usually have different temperatures (warm, cold, and colder), and that can create cloudy skies, light rain, and eventually storms as the air masses push on each other.

Meteorologists (people who study weather) have symbols for each of these front types and will use them on a map to designate where air masses are located and how they are interacting (Figure 7.15). That helps them to forecast what kind of weather is coming.

ON YOUR OWN

7.5 Meteorologists measure air pressure at weather stations across the country. The readings use atmospheric pressure units called **millibars.** They can then connect identical pressure readings using lines called **isobars.** If there are closed isobar lines forming a circle, then that represents areas of high or low-pressure. High-pressure areas are often cool, clear, and fair, and low-pressure areas are warm, cloudy, and sometimes stormy. The image here can be found in your *Student Notebook.* Draw isobars (lines) to connect areas with the same atmospheric pressure number. Mark the high-pressure area with a large, capital H, and the low-pressure area with a large, capital L. According to your completed map and the information above, which area will experience cool, clear weather?

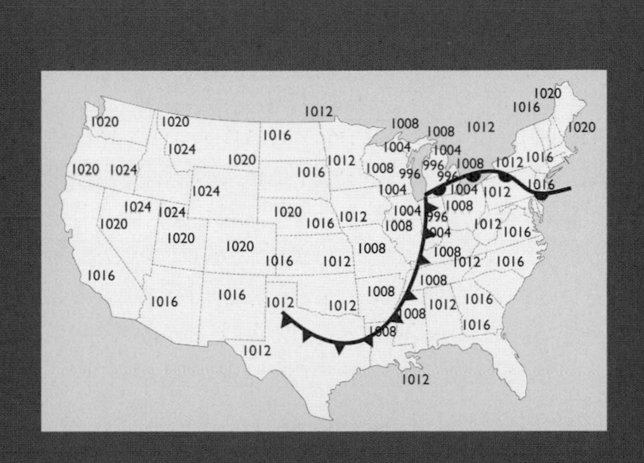

STORMS

If the right conditions exist, storms and other extreme weather can result. A thunderstorm, for example, starts with a strong upward movement of air. Normally, currents of rising air end up cooling before they get too high. But if the rising air is warm enough and moves fast enough, it can get high enough to form massive cumulus clouds. Eventually so much moisture is in the clouds and the droplets grow so large that the upward movement of air cannot keep them from falling. Thus, rainfall occurs.

Lightning

Huge amounts of electricity often build up in large cumulus clouds. This is thought to come from static electricity building up on ice particles as they collide into each other in the highest part of the clouds. As static electricity builds up in the cloud, a huge difference in charge can be found between the cloud and the ground, between one cloud and another,

FIGURE 7.16
Lightning Storm

Upward-moving, warm air (red arrows) cools as it rises, creating clouds. A buildup of moisture results, eventually creating precipitation and air moving downward (blue arrows). As the ice particles in the upper part of the storm cloud bump into each other, electrical charges build up, eventually releasing in the form of lightning.

or even between different parts of the same cloud. In the same way that you sometimes get a shock when reaching for a doorknob in the winter, static charges building up in a lightning storm can jump from one place to another. In a cloud-to-ground lightning strike, for example, the charges build up until they overcome the air's ability to separate them. Eventually, a stream of electrons (which are negatively charged particles) starts to zigzag its way down to the ground. It happens so quickly that it is difficult to see.

Lightning only lasts a few millionths of a second, but it has the power of about 2 trillion watts and can heat the air to over 30,000 °C (54,000 °F)! Well, that super-heated air rapidly expands, bumping into the air masses next to it. When the masses bump into each other, a huge shock wave of sound—called **thunder**—occurs.

EXPLORE MORE

The next time you experience a lightning storm, notice that you will see the lightning before you hear the thunder. That is because light travels faster than sound. Therefore, the flash of lightning will reach your eyes much more quickly than the sound of thunder. It turns out that light travels at a speed of 299,792,458 m/sec, and sound travels at 340 m/sec. So the farther away lightning strikes from you, the larger the difference between the time you see the light and the time you hear the thunder. Sound travels about 1 mile (1.6 km) in 5 seconds. Because light is practically instantaneous to your eye, try to count how many seconds elapse between the lightning and the thunder to figure out the distance of the lightning strike from you.

Tornadoes

Sometimes, during severe thunderstorms, a **tornado** will occur. This is a narrow funnel of rapidly swirling wind that begins in the clouds and stretches toward the ground. Tornadoes are believed to be formed in one of 2 ways. Smaller tornadoes are thought to form when a storm's downward moving air interacts with an upward moving air mass (called an **updraft**) that is forming a cloud in front of it. However, the most powerful tornadoes are thought to form from the rotating updrafts that are in large thunderstorms.

Why do they rotate so fast? Think back to our discussion about global wind patterns and how the path of moving air is affected by Earth as it spins. You usually can't see this effect on a small scale, but in a tornado enough air is moving fast enough that, suddenly, the rotating Earth causes a rotating cloud to form. A fascinating thing about tornadoes is that they (almost) always spin counterclockwise in the Northern Hemisphere and clockwise in the Southern Hemisphere. This is due to something called the **Coriolis effect** and also explains why our next major weather pattern, hurricanes, spin the same direction as tornadoes in their respective hemispheres.

Hurricanes

Hurricanes are large-scale storms. They can also be called cyclones or typhoons in other parts of the world. Most hurricanes form during warmer months after the ocean water reaches 27 °C (80 °F). Warm water will evaporate more easily than cool water so the air above the ocean during these months has large amounts of water vapor. Just like in a regular storm, this water vapor can condense to form clouds, releasing a bit of heat as it condenses. Well, all this released heat in the air adds to the already hot air temperatures. If the winds at the ocean's surface are moving the same direction as the winds up in the atmosphere where all this warm heat is growing, the warmth will not be dispersed and builds up over a few days. Then, with all this moisture and heat high in the air, bands of spiraling thunderstorms can form, blowing toward the center. All the updrafts of air around this system cause a central **downdraft** of air, called the storm's eye. As the storm moves across the water, more and more heat and moisture is whipped up into the system, further feeding its size. If conditions remain like this long enough, the heat, moisture, air pressure, and wind build each other up into a hurricane. The hurricane will travel across the spinning Earth, moving away from the equator and curving north in the Northern Hemisphere. If it moves over land, the strong winds and heavy rainfall can sometimes cause enormous devastation. Now, once a hurricane moves over land or cold water, there is less heat to feed it, so it begins to weaken and quickly falls apart.

FIGURE 7.17
Hurricane Katrina Viewed from the International Space Station

WEATHER PREDICTION

For the last 100 years, scientists have been able predict, or **forecast**, the weather using advanced technology. They typically monitor 5 major air properties to do this. With what you've learned so far, you might not be surprised to hear that because much of the discussion of weather has had to do with air and its properties. By measuring temperature, pressure, humidity, wind direction, and wind speed at various altitudes, meteorologists can determine fairly accurate predictions of what the weather will be like up to a week in advance.

Temperature

Air temperatures are measured with various types of thermometers, and the highest and lowest temperatures are noted each day at many levels of the atmosphere. Today, satellites are able to easily take these measurements.

Pressure

Remember when I talked about air molecules causing atmospheric pressure? They exert a push, or a force, on things. So, in denser air, there are more molecules in a given volume, and thus more pressure. Moving air also changes pressure. Thus, weather conditions are closely related to the pressure in the atmosphere. When pressure is falling, that usually means that bad weather is going to occur. When it is rising, that usually means good weather is coming. Pressure is measured with a device called a **barometer.** The simplest barometers consist of a column of liquid mercury in a glass tube with an air gap above it. As air pushes on that column, the change in height within the tube can be measured. In fact, the earliest air pressures were reported in inches of mercury. Perform Experiment 7.2.

EXPERIMENT 7.2
BUILD YOUR OWN BAROMETER

PURPOSE: To better understand how a barometer works

MATERIALS:
- A large mason jar or other clear sturdy jar
- A balloon
- Scissors
- A rubber band
- A drinking straw
- Cellophane tape
- A sheet of cardboard
- A fine-tipped marker

QUESTION: How does a barometer work?

HYPOTHESIS: Write in your notebook how you think air pressure might affect weather.

PROCEDURE:
1. With the scissors, cut all of the neck off the balloon.
2. Stretch the balloon over the mouth of the jar, pulling on the edges so the balloon's surface is tight.
3. Place the rubber band around the neck of the jar to hold the balloon tightly.
4. Cut off any bendy portion of the straw and make the cut slanted so the straw comes to a point (see diagram).
5. Tape the non-pointed end of the straw to the balloon surface.
6. Fold the card stock in half widthwise to create a crease and unfold so it will stand up.
7. Place the card stock right next to the pointed end of the straw and mark with a marker where the straw is pointing. Place a 1 next to that mark. You have just built your barometer.
8. Come back to the barometer throughout the day (or for several days) to see if the straw is pointing higher or lower and mark that spot with a 2, 3, and so on. Note in your notebook what the weather is like at each numbered spot.

CONCLUSION: Explain what you learned about how barometers work.

Barometers are instruments used to measure atmospheric pressure for the purpose of predicting weather changes. When the pressure is high, that means more air will be pushing down on the jar, so it will also push on the balloon's surface, bending it down and causing the arrow to point higher. When the pressure is low, less air is pressing on the jar, so the air inside expands, causing the balloon to rise up. That means the arrow will point lower. Remember, higher air pressure means the weather will be clearer and cooler, and low pressure indicates warm and changing weather.

Humidity

Humidity is a measure of how much water vapor is in the air. Moisture in the atmosphere is always evaporating and condensing, but if the moisture is evaporating faster than it can condense, then the air gets fuller and fuller until it can hold no more water molecules. This is known as **saturated** air. Meteorologists often compare the actual humidity to the humidity of the same air if it was saturated. This ratio is called relative humidity and is given as a percent. So, if the relative humidity is 50%, that means the air is holding half as much water vapor as it possibly can. Because warmer air can hold more water vapor as compared to cooler air, temperature affects relative humidity. Humidity is measured with a device called a **hygrometer** (high grah' mih ter).

FIGURE 7.18
Saturated Air (left) and Low Humidity (right)

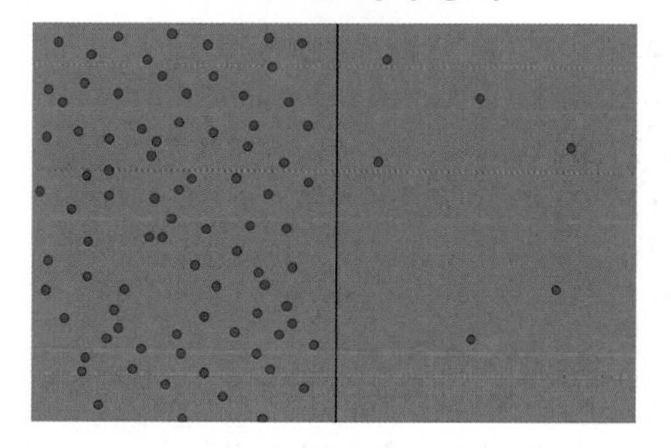

MOD 7

Wind Direction and Speed

Wind direction and speed are important to know so meteorologists can figure out which way a front is moving and when it might arrive in one place or another. Simple weather vanes can pivot to point in the direction wind is moving and **anemometers** (an ih mom' ih terz) are used to measure wind speed.

FIGURE 7.19
NASA Launching a Large Weather Balloon

Automated weather stations are able to monitor atmospheric conditions in various locations, sending recorded information to meteorologists. This technology enables meteorologists to gather data from many locations, particularly those difficult to travel to. Many have a thermometer, barometer, hygrometer, and anemometer as well as a rain gauge to measure rainfall.

FIGURE 7.20
NASA's Geostationary Operational Environmental Satellite 13 (GOES-13)

And these weather stations are not limited to land. High-altitude weather conditions are often measured by instruments attached to large weather balloons filled with helium or hydrogen. The data collected are then sent by radio to weather stations. Once the balloon goes too high, it expands until it pops, but the devices are safely parachuted back to Earth.

Another tool for meteorologists is **radar.** Radar stands for RAdio Detection And Ranging, and it uses radio waves to identify the size of objects and their distance. Radar can also identify airborne water, whether it is in the form of cloud droplets, ice crystals, rain, or snow. This helps meteorologists follow the development and movement of storms. Doppler radar is a newer technology, developed in the 1990s, and it can measure the speed and direction of various forms of water in the air.

Finally, meteorologists use satellites to track weather all over the Earth. Satellites orbiting the planet send information showing cloud locations, ground and ocean temperatures, high-altitude wind speeds, rain and other precipitation, humidity, and more. With all this data, scientists can more accurately plot weather conditions in an area and identify where—and even when—severe weather might occur.

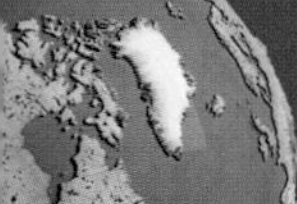

ON YOUR OWN

7.6 To predict weather, meteorologists measure 5 properties of what?

CLIMATE

We've spent a good amount of time covering weather, so now let's talk a bit about climate. Scientists have studied Earth's rocks and ocean sediments to learn more about our planet's past climate. By understanding how it has changed in the past, it might help us better predict future changes. Some of these discoveries include warm-climate fossils located at high latitudes, some even close to the poles. They have even found dinosaur fossils in Antarctica. Satellite radar images indicate that the desert area of the eastern Sahara was once filled with rivers and was lush with plants and other living organisms. Wooly mammoth fossils have been found in Siberia and Alaska, indicating that these areas once had different climates as well.

We covered much of the geological record and fossil evidence in the last module, so you should not be surprised to know that the uniformitarian model doesn't work when it comes to explaining these drastic climate changes. However, the catastrophism model with the Genesis Flood easily can explain what we are finding. The Flood resulted in a unique series of climate changes as well as producing a unique Ice Age climate after the Flood.

FIGURE 7.21
Pollen Grain Found in Antarctica Indicating Vegetation Once Grew in a Warmer Climate There

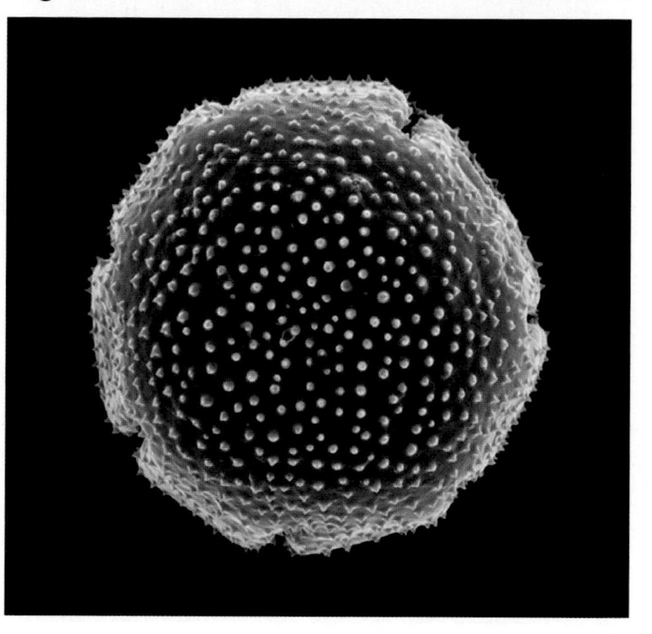

Although there has been evidence of climate change in the past, climate change has been relatively small since the melting of the large ice sheets at the end of the Ice Age. Today, we know that natural events can cause small climate changes. For example, extremely large volcanic eruptions can cause global temperatures to rise up to 0.6 °C (1 °F) cooler for many years. Even the number of sunspots on the sun may have an effect on our climate, causing overall temperatures to increase a bit when sunspot numbers are high and decrease when numbers are low.

ENSO

A major influence on year-to-year climate is the **El Niño-Southern Oscillation**, or ENSO for short. The temperature of the surface waters of the tropical East Pacific Ocean cycle up and down at regular intervals. This has a large effect on the climate of distant places, like North America. It is almost like a giant warm-water pool sloshing back and forth across the tropical Pacific Ocean. Besides the normal, annual warming and cooling of the ocean, every 2–7 years the surface waters on the eastern Pacific become warmer than normal during December, January, and February when this part of the world is experiencing summer. Fishermen first noticed this happening around Christmas (thus, the name El Niño, meaning "the Child"—Christ). In other years, the opposite pattern occurs, and the surface waters are cooler than average. We refer to this period as **La Niña**—the little girl. During El Niño conditions, the warmer waters change the weather in those areas, bringing heavy rains and flooding. These conditions are connected to areas all over the Pacific Ocean, too. During an El Niño season, droughts occur in India, southeast Africa, and the northern parts of South America. It also might cause the southern United States to have wetter weather. During a La Niña period, the conditions in these areas are (mostly) the opposite.

Scientists still do not know what controls ENSO, but lots of research indicates that it is a natural, global fluctuation. Additionally, there are several connected climate patterns throughout the world. The Pacific Decadal Oscillation (PDO) occurs in the North

Pacific Ocean and affects the weather across the Pacific Basin and beyond. The PDO oscillates on a 20- to 30-year cycle. Imagine having to know that in order to predict the weather!

The North Atlantic Oscillation (NAO) is a climate fluctuation in the North Atlantic Ocean, with pressure changes affecting Europe and North America. These natural fluctuations all over the globe mean that seasons of severe weather and seasons of calm weather are connected and cyclic!

FIGURE 7.22
The Seesaw ENSO Phenomenon

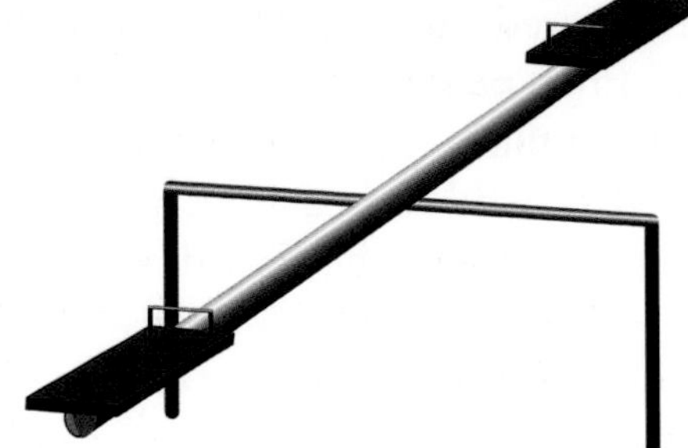

The ENSO Phenomenon involves a pattern of atmospheric pressure and ocean surface temperature changes across the tropical Pacific Ocean. This regular pattern behaves like a seesaw: when one area experiences high pressure, the other one experiences low pressure. This, of course, affects weather patterns and even alters climate in distant parts of the world for a few years.

Global Warming

The atmosphere holds heat from the sun, acting like a blanket and preventing it from easily escaping back into space. This keeps Earth nice and warm and allows living organisms to survive rather well. It behaves like a greenhouse, holding in warmth from the sun so that things can grow. Scientists call this effect of the atmosphere on global temperatures the **greenhouse effect.** The greenhouse effect is beneficial to Earth because it causes the planet to be about 33 °C (60 °F) warmer than it otherwise would be. And that is a good thing. Without it, much of our Earth's temperatures would be below freezing! And without the atmospheric blanket to smooth out the temperature changes, the Earth along the equator would bake during the daytime and freeze at night.

The greenhouse effect is primarily controlled by water vapor (with a small contribution from gases such as methane and carbon dioxide) in the atmosphere behaving like a blanket, keeping solar radiation from escaping the Earth. Now, some people think that the increase of carbon dioxide gas in our atmosphere is drastically changing *how much* heat is kept in our atmosphere. Well, we do know that carbon dioxide levels have been increasing since we started measuring them in the late 1800s. Some of this increase is due to burning fossil fuels, but this burning also produces materials that *reflect* solar energy, cancelling out the effect of holding in extra heat.

If the atmosphere absorbs more heat than it holds today, the overall climate could warm up, creating something called global warming. Scientists are trying to determine if global temperatures are indeed

FIGURE 7.23
The Greenhouse Effect

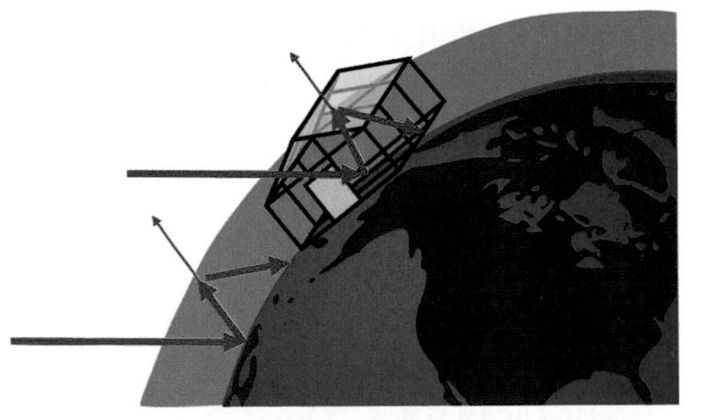

As sunlight enters Earth's atmosphere, much of it will bounce around, staying within the atmosphere in the same way that a greenhouse holds in warmth from the sun. All of that heat will eventually escape back into space, but the greenhouse effect slows down the process, meaning our days are much cooler and our nights are much warmer.

experiencing a warming trend and if this is a natural shift or if it is a result of people altering the planet. In other words, if global warming is occurring, is it a threat to life? However, even if there is a warming trend, it is hard to prove that man's efforts are causing it. Remember, global climates have changed before.

Now, we do have a responsibility to care for our planet, but there is much information on global warming that is incorrect or inflated. Until now, global warming has been slight and doesn't seem to be any different from what has naturally happened in the past. In fact, over half of the things that increase global temperatures are natural cycles of climate change. As scientists collect more data and do more research, hopefully we can focus on the facts and wisely approach this issue.

EXPLORE MORE

You can make a mini-greenhouse by taking a cereal bowl and covering it with plastic wrap. Place the covered bowl in a sunny window for about an hour. Measure your room's temperature with a thermometer and then carefully slip the thermometer under the plastic wrap without letting its tip touch the bottom of the bowl (use a piece of tape to secure it to the bowl's edge). After a few hours, you should notice the temperature in the bowl is higher because the plastic wrap behaved like a greenhouse, holding air in the bowl so that it held onto the sun's heat.

OCEANOGRAPHY

Oceanography is the study of the Earth's oceans and ocean floor, including what they are made of, how they move, and the organisms living there. The oceans cover almost ¾ of our planet and are important sources of food and other materials. You have already learned that the oceans have a major influence on the weather, and any changes in them can cause moderate climate change. It is important to study our oceans, then, in order to protect them as a resource and to preserve them for the future.

What Is Ocean Water?

Have you ever wondered what is in ocean water? Well, if you've ever tasted it, you know it has a good amount of salt. Now, most of the salt in the ocean (about 78%) is table salt, or sodium chloride, but there are other types of important salts as well. As a matter of fact, all the elements found in the Earth's crust are found in at least trace amounts in ocean water. The oceans contain dissolved oxygen, carbon dioxide, and nitrogen gas that is critical for sea life, too.

think about this

You might be surprised to know that gases can dissolve in water, just like solids can. But think about carbonated drinks. When you observe an undisturbed, sealed bottle of soda, you do not see any bubbles in it. Yet carbonated drinks have carbon dioxide gas dissolved inside. When you open the bottle, the pressure holding the carbon dioxide in the solution is released, and bubbles escape.

Because water is made from hydrogen and oxygen, some people mistakenly think that ocean animals break apart water molecules to breathe the oxygen in them. But that is not what happens. Ocean water contains dissolved oxygen just like carbonated drinks contain dissolved carbon dioxide gas. Ocean organisms take in that gas and use it in their bodies the same way you do.

OCEAN MOTION

Currents

The ocean is constantly moving. Large river-like streams of ocean water are created by winds, varying water densities, and even the rotation of Earth on its axis. Surface currents are large masses of water that flow along the ocean surface, usually as a result of consistent winds. The major global wind patterns (see Figure 7.10) influence these surface currents, causing them to move in a circular path, called a **gyre**. Unlike hurricanes and tornadoes, these ocean gyres rotate clockwise in the Northern Hemisphere and counterclockwise in the Southern Hemisphere due to the direction of the prevailing winds. As the currents flow from cold polar areas to warm equatorial areas and back again, they help to mix and disperse food, gases, and minerals. And when surface currents push away the surface water, masses of water from below move upward. This is called **upwelling**.

FIGURE 7.24
Major Ocean Gyres

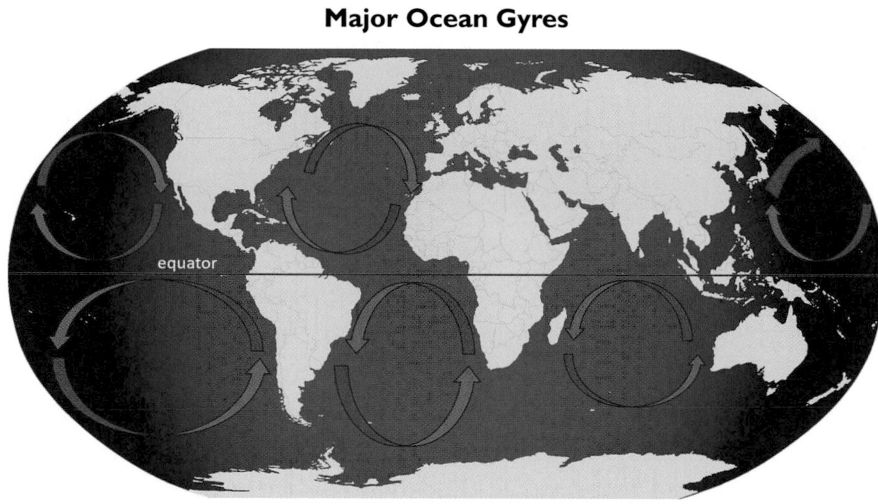

Ocean currents can also flow beneath the surface. Some currents move because water might have varying temperatures or different amounts of minerals dissolved in it. Denser water masses will sink, pulling water across the surface to replace what is sinking.

Waves and Tides

Waves are different from currents in that they are a rhythmic, back-and-forth motion of water that transfers energy without any overall change in direction of the water mass. Most waves are created by wind moving along the water's surface, causing them to travel for long distances. However, even though waves can travel for hundreds and thousands of miles, the individual molecules of water only travel a few feet. Think about a boat bobbing on the waves of the ocean. It actually just travels in a circle.

FIGURE 7.25
Waves Forming at the Shoreline

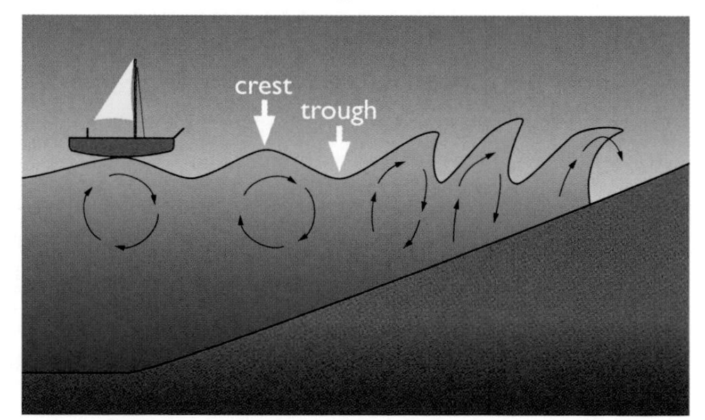

When a coral reef or a rise in the ocean floor interrupts the circular wave motion, the water molecules' motion is stopped, and other water molecules build up behind until the circle breaks apart, creating breaking waves. This is what we call **surf.**

Massive waves, called **tsunamis,** sometimes form as a result of an underwater earthquake or volcanic explosion. The rapid seafloor movement causes a sudden, large mass of water to change height. This forms a very deep, but not very high, wave that can travel for thousands of miles, eventually reaching the shore and rapidly mounting up as a wall of water. As the large wave grows, it may actually pull water away from the beach first, giving those near the shore a few minutes of warning to reach high ground.

Now, **tides** are another type of ocean water movement. They are regular and predictable as a result of the gravitational pull of the Moon and the sun. The Moon has the greater effect because of the combination of its mass and close position near Earth. Its pull causes a bulge of water on the nearer side. A second, opposite bulge results as Earth itself gets pulled a bit closer to the Moon, too.

FIGURE 7.26
The Ocean's Bulge Due to the Moon

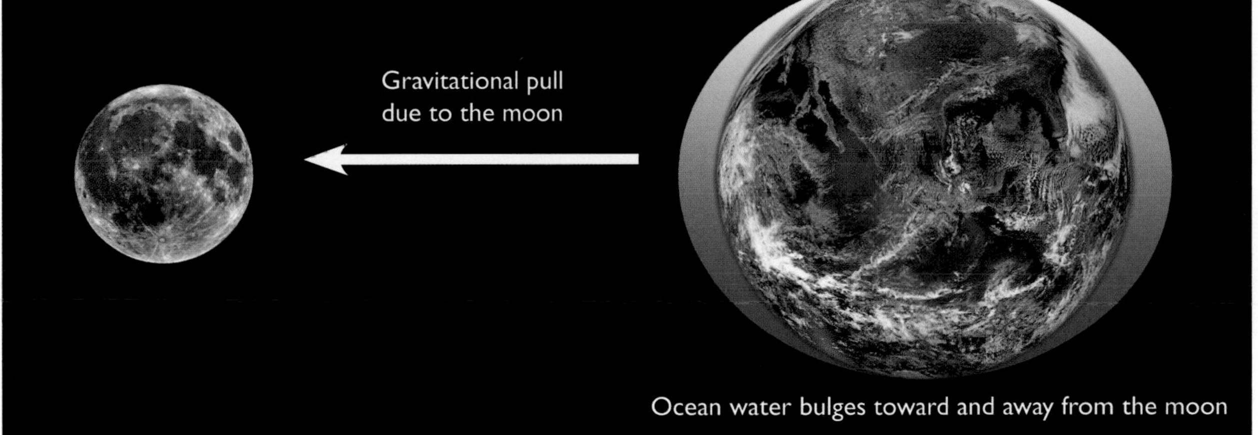

OCEAN GEOGRAPHY

Did you know that the ocean floor is not always flat? It is filled with massive mountains and deep gorges. In fact, even though Mount Everest is considered to be the tallest mountain at 8,850 m (29,035 ft) above sea level, the actual tallest mountain is Mauna Kea on the island of Hawaii in the Pacific Ocean. Measured from its base deep down in the ocean to its peak, is over 10,000 m (32,808 ft) tall! It is overlooked because much of it lies below the ocean's surface. Besides tall mountains, the ocean also has deep canyons and trenches, stretching down to 10,984 m (36,037 ft) underwater.

The coastlines of the continents are bordered by a gently sloping underwater plain called the **continental shelf.** The continental shelf is full of living organisms, including corals (sometimes forming large coral reefs), seaweed forests, and all kinds of diverse creatures. We'll study more about ocean organisms in a later module. At the outer end of the continental shelf is the **shelf break,** where the ocean floor becomes steeper. This marks the beginning of the **continental slope.** If you were to take a submarine down the continental slope, you would notice that eventually, light could not penetrate any deeper and the temperatures would become quite cold. Yet in this harsh environment, there are still massive amounts of living organisms, perfectly designed to live here. Many of them have larger eyes to capture what little light can penetrate. They also have large mouths and long teeth to eat whatever food they come upon. And many of them have mechanisms to create their own light! This is called **bioluminescence**, and it is a unique type of light creation, made by living organisms.

FIGURE 7.27
Diagram of the Ocean Bottom

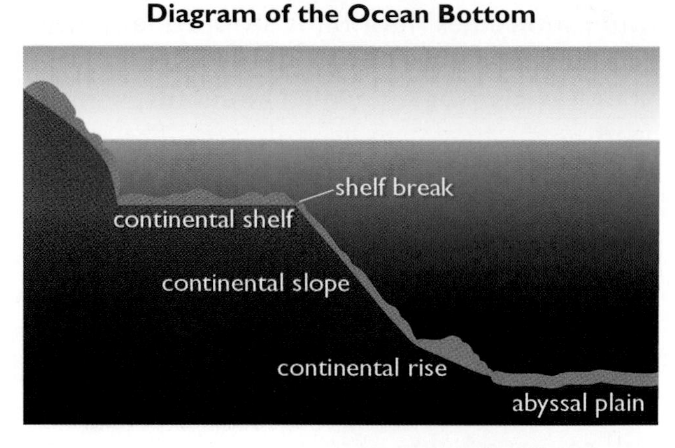

FIGURE 7.28
Bioluminescent Fish

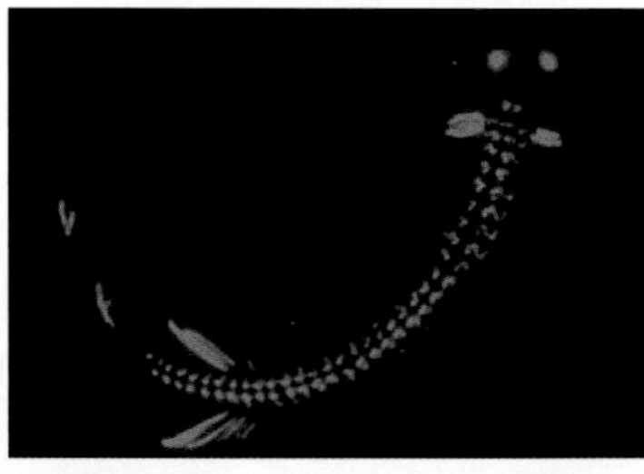

The continental shelf ends at the deep ocean floor which flattens out into the area called the abyssal plain. This is truly the ocean bottom. At an average depth of about 4.5 km (2.8 mi), the abyssal plain is more level than any plains found on land. Remember, though, that there are areas with deep canyons and mountainous volcanoes; however, many of these areas are found where the continental and oceanic plates of Earth's crust meet.

ON YOUR OWN

7.7 What is *really* the tallest known mountain in the world? Why is it often not considered to be the tallest?

OCEAN EXPLORATION AND STUDY

Man has always wanted to learn more about what is in our oceans. Some of the first studies involved using a diving suit that was connected to the surface by a hose that pumped air into it. That, of course, only allowed people to walk in these heavy suits at very shallow depths. With the advent of self-contained breathing devices, called **scuba gear**, divers can swim deeper in the ocean for longer periods. Scuba is an acronym for Self-Contained Underwater Breathing Apparatus, and modern scuba gear enables divers to stay underwater for about an hour at 60 ft in depth. This allows divers to study coral reefs and other ocean environments firsthand.

But the ocean is much deeper than what a diver can endure. Because of this, exploration ships are equipped with scientific instruments and laboratories to study more of the oceans. Many of these **ocean research vessels** are designed to collect large samples of ocean sediments or use radar to map the ocean floor. Deep-sea **submersibles** can take scientists to deeper parts of the ocean. Unmanned submersibles have even been able to reach the bottom of the deepest known ocean trench. Although we know much about the oceans and what is in them, you might be surprised to learn that we have only explored a

FIGURE 7.29
NOAA Ocean Research Ship the *Ronald H. Brown*

Ocean research vessels can be at sea for months at a time and many can deploy submersibles to observe and sample ocean depths. You can see a submersible being launched from this ship in the photo.

small percentage of our ocean floor. In fact, we know more about the surface of our Moon than what is in the deep sea!

Part of the problem is that the ocean is deep. And that creates a difficult environment. You see, the deeper you go, the more water is on top of you, pushing down on you. This can create great pressure. In fact, every 10 m (33 ft) of depth is like piling another atmosphere of pressure on your body. With an average depth of 4.5 km, or 4,500 m, that means there is an average of 450 of Earth's atmospheres pushing down on organisms living on the deep-sea floor! Humans certainly cannot survive that intense pressure, so we have to design special vehicles to take us there. Unmanned submersibles are able to more easily dive deeper, but they have to be remotely operated and still have to maneuver under high pressure, severe cold, and very salty conditions that are not good for metallic vehicles.

The more we learn about the amazing features of the oceans and the unique living environments, the better we are able to understand how our world works. Truly, there is much more to discover!

SUMMING UP

This module wraps up our study of Earth science. Hopefully, after covering the past few modules, you have a greater appreciation of our world and how it is made. Earth is perfectly positioned within its solar system, and its sun is precisely placed in the galaxy to be able to support life. The makeup of the Earth itself also enables living organisms to survive. From the cyclical nature of the weather to the regular flow of air and moisture around the planet, all of Earth's physical properties make it possible for us to live. No other known planet is like ours! This is a vivid testimony to God's great creation and His perfect design to uphold all living things.

ANSWERS TO THE "ON YOUR OWN" QUESTIONS

7.1 Weather is a daily or weekly status of the atmosphere while climate is the long-term overall physical conditions of a region.

7.2 Refer to Figure 7.6 as a guide. The excess ozone gases should be located in the stratosphere and the auroras would be in the thermosphere.

7.3 The sun heats up Earth, causing different air temperatures. This causes masses of air to move around, creating changes in the weather.

7.4 For clouds to form, warm air has to cool, the air has to be moist, and there needs to be dust or other particles in the air on which the water can condense. You could also say mountains, but that is only one possible cloud-forming situation where warm, moist air is pushed up the mountain and cools down as it reaches higher altitudes.

7.5 The area with the H will experience cool, clear weather.

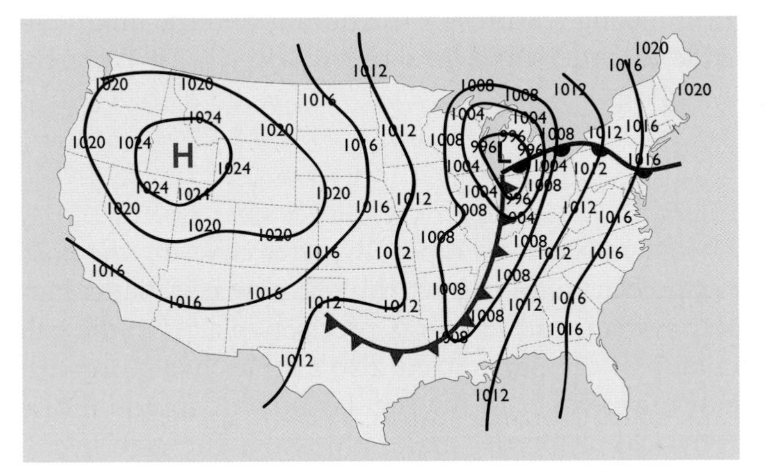

7.6 Meteorologists measure 5 properties of air to predict the weather. These properties include temperature, pressure, humidity, wind direction, and wind speed at various altitudes.

7.7 The tallest known mountain in the world is technically not Mount Everest. At over 10,000 m in height, Mauna Kea in the Pacific Ocean wins when measured from its base to its peak. It is overlooked because much of it is below the ocean's surface.

STUDY GUIDE FOR MODULE 7

1. Match the following words with their definitions.

a. Meteorology	A force exerted onto a surface by the weight of air molecules
b. Precipitation	The study of weather
c. Air pressure	Moisture falling from the atmosphere as rain, snow, or hail

2–3. Choose the correct words to complete the statements.

2. Rain, snow, hail, and sleet are all examples of (weather, climate).

3. The atmosphere can be divided into 2 major regions based on how well mixed the air is. The (homosphere, heterosphere) is the layer with well-mixed gases, and the (homosphere, heterosphere) is characterized by several layers of different gases.

4. The barrier at the upper edge of the mesosphere is called the

   a. thermopause b. turbopause c. tropopause d. mesopause

5. If you had a container of air and you were able to heat up the gases, what would happen to the air pressure inside the container; would it increase or decrease?

6. Which process is NOT a part of the hydrologic cycle?

   a. evaporation b. elevation c. precipitation d. condensation

7. Which type of cloud type has a white, puffy, flat-bottomed shape?

   a. cumulus b. cirrus c. stratus

8. Choose the correct words to complete the statement.
   Warm advancing air is called a (warm, cold) front and will move (over, under) a mass of cold air.

9. Place the steps to form cloud-to-ground lightning in the proper order.

   a. A difference in charge is created between the cloud and the ground.

   b. Static electricity builds up on ice particles in the cloud as they collide into each other.

   c. A stream of electrons (negatively charged particles) starts to zigzag its way down to the ground, forming the lightning strike.

   d. The charges eventually overcome the air's ability to separate them.

10. Which of the following is NOT one of the air properties that meteorologists use to help predict weather?

    a. temperature b. pressure c. humidity d. wind direction e. radiation

11. The El Niño-Southern Oscillation phenomenon as well as other climate oscillation patterns throughout the world help to support the idea that seasons of severe weather and seasons of calm weather might be ________________.

12. Which is NOT a regular movement of ocean water?

    a. tsunamis b. waves c. tides d. currents

13. True or False. Most of the ocean floor is very uneven, filled with mountains and trenches.

GENERAL CHEMISTRY

After a thorough understanding of Earth science, this module and the next one will be devoted to a different branch: that of physical science. Physical science includes chemistry and physics. The study of these sciences helps to describe how all of creation behaves and operates. This chemistry module will cover what makes up things in our universe. You will be amazed to know that everything in our world, our solar system, our galaxy, and our universe is made up of the same types of basic building blocks, put together in an orderly fashion and behaving according to elegant laws. Indeed, there is awesome order in creation, giving testimony to a wise Creator!

Quaestio

What makes up everything around you? For that matter, what makes up you? Well, everything is made up of material. This "stuff" and how it behaves is what you will learn about in this module. And although we know some information about this material, we don't know everything. But we *do* know where it came from. Colossians 1:16b-17 says, "...all things were created through Him and for Him. He is before all things and in Him all things hold together." At the beginning of creation, our Lord made everything there is and continues to uphold it to this day.

FIGURE 8.1
Earth, the Sun, and the Universe

MATTER

Let's start this module with a discussion of the "stuff" I mentioned. What is all this material? Well, we call it matter.

Matter—Anything that has mass and takes up space

So matter is a term for any type of material.

FIGURE 8.2
Balls with 2 Different Masses

The definition says that matter has mass. What do I mean by mass? Think about a bowling ball and a basketball. Both are the same shape and about the same size. But if you were to hold one in each hand while closing your eyes, you would easily be able to tell which is which. Why? One is much heavier than the other. The bowling ball has more matter packed into it. And if something has more matter, it has greater mass. Yet, mass is a bit different from weight. You see, if you weighed the bowling ball on a scale, it would weigh about 12 lb. But if you were able to fly to the Moon and then weigh the bowling ball there, it would weigh about 2 lb. But the bowling ball didn't lose any material during the flight; its *mass* remained the same, even though the weight changed. That's because weight has to do with the pull of gravity on something. The gravitational force pulling down on the ball on Earth is much stronger than that force on the Moon, so the ball weighs less on the Moon, even though it has the same mass. So matter has to have mass.

The definition says matter also takes up space. What do I mean by that? Well, when something takes up space, it has volume. So elephants, trees, and even bacteria take up space and thus have volume. Liquids and gases take up space, too.

EXPLORE MORE

To explore volume further, take a balloon and blow it up a little. Don't tie it off, but instead take a string and ask someone to use it to measure the distance around the balloon while you hold it. Hold that length of string up to a ruler to measure the distance around the balloon. Now add more air to the balloon and measure its size again. You should notice the balloon is measurably larger, meaning it takes up more space. Well, that means the added air increased its volume. Air takes up space!

States of Matter

Substances can be classified based on their physical condition. Think about water. When you pour it into an ice tray and stick the tray in a freezer, what happens to it? Well, it has changed from liquid water to solid water (ice). Is it still water? Of course, but it has changed its **state of matter**. You see, matter exists in 3 basic states: solid, liquid, or gas. The best way to remember this is to think again about that ice cube. It is a solid. When you take it out of the freezer, it begins to warm up. That means heat is being added to it. It then melts, or becomes liquid. If you then took that liquid water, put it in a pot on the stove, and heated it until it boiled, the water would start to leave the pot as steam. It is still water, though. But it is now a gas because even more heat was added to it.

FIGURE 8.3
States of Matter

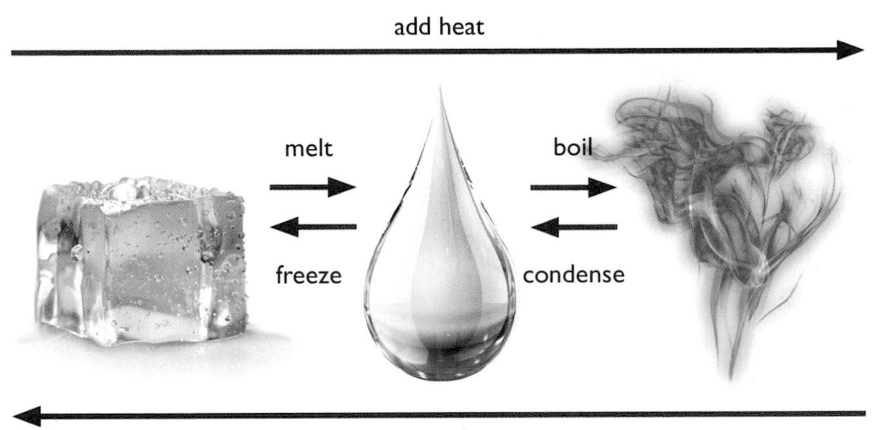

The pressure and temperature of a material will determine whether that material is a solid, liquid, or gas. Some solids, such as gold, for example, require a lot more additional heat to melt into a liquid. Others, like butter, require less. At a given amount of air pressure, the temperature where a solid becomes a liquid is called its melting point, and the temperature at which a liquid becomes a gas is called its boiling point. Of course, we can go the other way by saying the temperature a gas becomes a liquid is its condensation point, and the temperature a liquid becomes a solid is its freezing point. But it all has to do with the amount of heat a substance has (see Figure 8.3).

EXPLORE MORE

Take a bar of Ivory brand soap and place it in a bowl of water. Notice how it floats. That's because this brand of soap is filled with tiny pockets of air molecules. Carefully cut the soap into a few pieces to see them. Gaseous air is less dense than liquid water, so the soap floats. Now place the large soap pieces on a microwave-safe plate and put it in the microwave. Cook on high for 1 minute, watching continuously. Don't allow it to overcook. You should notice the soap growing into a large, puffy cloud. Let the soap cool and carefully touch it. It should be stiff, but the holes are much larger. That's because when you heat air molecules, they move around with more energy, expand, and take up more space. This is a demonstration of a physics principle called **Charles' law**. Charles' law states that when the temperature of a gas increases, its volume increases, too. Don't throw the soap away—it is still good to use!

ON YOUR OWN

8.1 Tell whether heat is added or removed when matter changes the following states: gas to liquid, solid to liquid, liquid to solid.

ATOMS

So what is matter made of? Practically everything you see around you right now is matter, and all of it is made up of **atoms.**

Atom— The smallest chemical unit of matter

You might remember that we learned a bit about atoms in Module 1 when we covered Leucippus and Democritus. Scientists have been studying atoms and how they behave ever since. Atoms are so small they cannot be seen even with the most powerful microscope! In fact, there are about 7.5 trillion atoms on the period at the end of this sentence. But if we can't see atoms, how do we know they exist? Well, it takes lots of experimentation. From the data collected, scientists have learned that the results they gathered can only be explained by *assuming* atoms exist. This means they have a great deal of indirect evidence for them. And there is such a large amount of evidence, scientists do believe that atoms are real.

What do atoms look like? Again, we've really never seen them, but through lots of indirect observations, scientists believe they understand an atom's basic structure. Atoms are created from 3 smaller components: **protons, neutrons,** and **electrons.** To explain what those particles are, you first have to understand something about electrical charges. You see, electricity is something we know exists. It is used to operate lights, ovens, motors, and more. Now, don't worry if you don't understand exactly what electricity is; scientists don't have a complete understanding of electrical charges, either. However, we *do* know that there are 2 types of electrical charges: **positive** and **negative.** We also know that most matter on Earth has an overall charge that is neither positive nor negative, or what we call **neutral.**

FIGURE 8.4
Nuclear Power Plant

Nuclear power plants use the properties of atoms to produce energy.

EXPLORE MORE

Blow up a balloon and tie it off. Now take an empty soda can and place it on its side on a flat surface. Rub the balloon back and forth in your hair very fast. Now hold the balloon as close to the can as possible without touching it. The can should start to roll around!

Negative charges attract positive charges. In the Explore More in this section, the balloon picked up negatively charged particles from your hair. When it came near the soda can, it attracted the positive charges in the can, causing the can to roll toward the balloon.

So we can say opposite charges (positive–negative) attract each other. And like charges (positive–positive or negative–negative) repel one another.

Atomic Structure

When you rub an inflated balloon in your hair, it picks up negatively charged particles from the atoms that make up your hair. These particles are called **electrons.** Positive components of atoms are called **protons,** and electrically neutral (no charge at all) components of atoms are **neutrons.** Additionally, the electrons are very tiny as compared to protons and neutrons. While protons and neutrons have about the same mass, an electron is about 2,000 times less massive. Interestingly, even though it is so comparatively tiny, these little powerhouses have exactly the same strength of charge as protons. It's not the same *kind* of charge, but it's the same *power*! Protons, neutrons, and electrons are called **subatomic particles** because they are smaller than atoms.

The arrangement of these particles is not random nor unordered. And that should make sense. God's creation is filled with an elegant order and intentional design. You will begin to see this as you learn more about atomic structure and how atoms interact. It is truly amazing!

A simplified model of the atom is called the **Bohr Model.** It is named for Neils Bohr who, in 1913, came up with it after studying the results of several experiments. He placed protons and neutrons together in the atom's center, called a **nucleus.** Normal atoms have the same number of protons and electrons, so we can say that the atom is neutrally charged or has an overall charge of zero.

FIGURE 8.5
Bohr Model of an Oxygen Atom

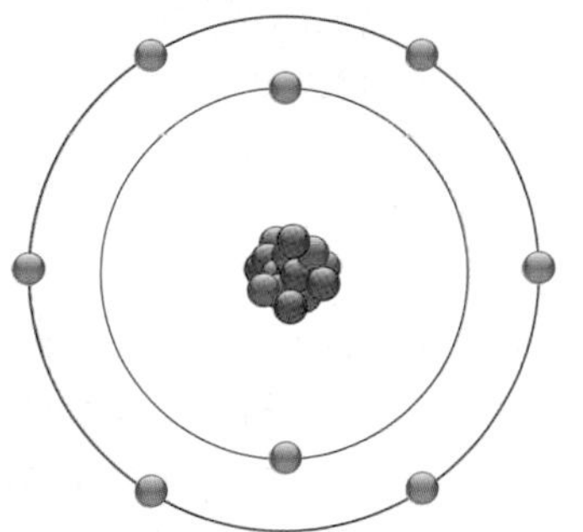

This oxygen atom model has 8 protons, 8 neutrons, and 8 electrons. The electrons orbit the nucleus in one of 2 possible orbitals. Because there are 8 positively charged protons and 8 negatively charged electrons, the overall charge of the atom is zero.

According to Bohr, electrons spin around the nucleus in orbits, called **orbitals,** much the same way a moon would orbit a planet. However, electrons can jump from one orbit to another, depending on how much energy each has. The farther away the orbital from the nucleus, the higher energy its electrons must have. So these orbitals are also called **energy levels.**

Since Bohr created his atomic model, more research has been conducted to better understand how atoms are arranged, and it turns out that they are a bit more complicated than Bohr's setup. Electrons indeed are at specific distances from the nucleus and can change those distances depending on their energy, but they don't travel in a fixed circle as if they were a train following rails. Instead, they orbit in clouds, meaning they can be at different distances from the nucleus at different times, but are within a specific "zone." And their orbit patterns can be spherical, dumbbell-shaped, and even more complex. It also turns out that atoms can only hold a certain number of electrons in these specific orbitals. The spherical orbitals can hold 2 electrons each, the dumbbell ones can hold 6 each, and so on.

think about this

The nucleus of an atom contains positively charge protons and neutral neutrons. However, if the protons are positively charged, shouldn't they repel *each other*? Why does the nucleus of an atom hold together? Well, there is another force acting here. It is referred to as the **strong force**, and although scientists aren't completely sure how it works, they know it is a massive force. In fact, if you break apart the protons within a nucleus, the nuclear energy released is huge. This is why nuclear reactions are so powerful!

Now although the electrons are a part of the atom, you need to understand that they are very far from the nucleus. In fact, they are so far away that if you think of the nucleus as a giraffe in the middle of a large sports stadium, the electrons would be teeny, tiny gnats circling far outside the stadium building! This means that atoms are more empty space than material. So, even though it is hard to believe, the chair you are sitting on is more space than stuff. In fact, *you* are made up of more space than *stuff*!

FIGURE 8.6
A Sports Stadium

Atoms are so full of empty space that if a giraffe representing an atom's nucleus were at the center of this stadium, the orbiting electrons would be gnats flying around outside the stadium.

You are probably wondering—if atoms are the building blocks of all matter, why are they made of smaller components, and wouldn't those smaller components be the building blocks? Well, even if you weren't wondering that, I am going to talk about it. You see, an atom is the chemically simplest substance. It cannot be broken down using *regular* chemical reactions. The only way to break up an atom is with nuclear power, which you might know involves massive energy! We'll discuss chemical reactions later on in the module, but you need to understand that atoms are considered the *LEGO bricks of the chemistry world*. And what makes atoms different from each other is how many protons, neutrons, and electrons they have.

ELEMENTS

Chemists have further studied atoms and figured out that atoms with the same number of protons in their nuclei (the plural of nucleus) have similar properties. Because of this we have a special name for them. They are called **elements.** All atoms of the same element behave in a similar way. This includes whether they conduct electricity or not, how shiny they are (called luster), the temperature at which they freeze or boil, their hardness, and even their color.

Think of gold. It's a solid at room temperature. It also is flexible and pliable, meaning it is easily shaped. Gold conducts heat and electricity pretty well and doesn't break down or rust if exposed to air. That's one reason why it is a good metal for jewelry. You wouldn't want your jewelry to rust! Each gold atom has 79 protons in its nucleus.

Oxygen, on the other hand, is a gas at room temperature. It is colorless, tasteless, and odorless. It easily combines with most other elements and is involved in processes that involve **combustion** (burning things). All atoms of oxygen have 8 protons in their nucleus. Explore more about the properties of elements in Experiment 8.1.

FIGURE 8.7
Solid Gold Bars

EXPERIMENT 8.1
EXPOSING ELEMENTS TO FIRE

PURPOSE: To better understand how different elements behave when exposed to fire

MATERIALS:
- A candle
- A match
- Cotton swabs
- 2 juice glasses
- Water
- 3 small plates
- 1 tablespoon of table salt
- 1 tablespoon of salt substitute (It should have potassium chloride as an ingredient.)
- Safety goggles
- OPTIONAL: A container of Damp Rid that you will carefully open to use 1 tablespoon of the material

QUESTION: What color flames result when different elements are exposed to fire?

HYPOTHESIS: Write in your notebook whether you think the color of the flame will be different with each substance tested.

PROCEDURE:
1. Fill both juice glasses with water.
2. Place about 1 tablespoon of the table salt into a small pile on one of the plates. Place the same amount of salt substitute in a pile on a second plate. If you are using it, place the Damp Rid material in a pile on the third plate.
3. Put on the safety goggles and light the candle. Record the color of the flame in your notebook.

4. Dip one end of a cotton swab into one of the glasses of water to moisten it. Now dip the wet end into the table salt completely covering it. Make sure a lot of salt is surrounding the cotton.
5. Hold the salt-covered swab in the candle's flame and note if the color of the flame changes. You will have to look carefully because the change may be slight. Repeat steps 4 and 5 again with another swab if you need to get a second look.
6. Place used cotton swabs in the second water-filled juice glass.
7. Record in your notebook what color the flame was when the table salt was burning.
8. Repeat steps 4–6 using the salt substitute. Record any color change in the flame.
9. If you are doing the optional sample, repeat steps 4–6 using the Damp Rid powder. Record any color change in the flame.
10. Clean everything up and put it away.

CONCLUSION: Write what you learned about the properties of the elements tested.

What did you see in the experiment? If everything worked out, you should have noticed that the candle flame originally burned with an orange-yellow color. When the table salt-covered swab was placed in the flame, it burned with a brighter yellow color. The salt substitute should have burned purple, and if you did the step using the Damp Rid, it burned with an orange color.

Why do you think the flames changed color? It has to do with the different properties of the elements. You see, as I mentioned earlier, atoms of the same element all have the same properties, and each element has its own unique properties. It should make sense that each element would burn differently. Table salt is sodium chloride, which is made up of sodium atoms and chlorine atoms. The salt substitute is mostly potassium chloride, which is made up of potassium and chlorine atoms. And the Damp Rid is mostly calcium chloride, which is made up of calcium and chlorine atoms. Because chlorine was in all 3 tests, the differences you noticed had to do primarily with the elements sodium, potassium, and calcium. They each have different properties that you could see when they burn.

think about this

Fireworks are known for their colorful explosions. And we can thank the unique colors produced by different elements for that. Inside each firework is gunpowder, some fuel, a burning agent, and a specific metal element. When the firework ignites, the atoms heat up and release a different amount of energy in the form of emitted light. Some of the colors are sodium-yellow, strontium-red, and copper-blue.

sodium strontium copper

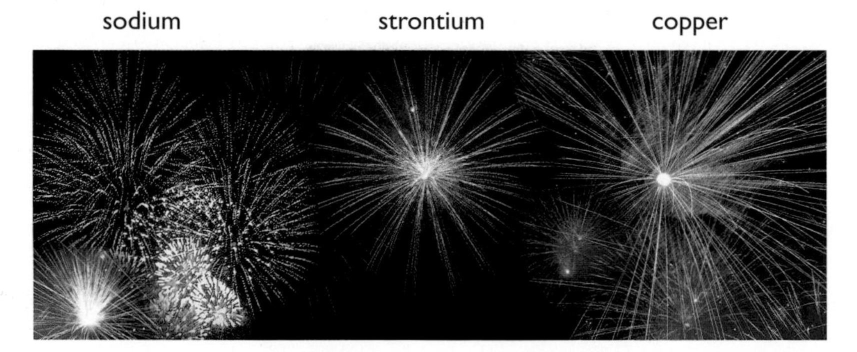

Now, at the time of the writing of this book, scientists have identified 118 basic elements in creation. However, you need to know that this number may change over time as new elements are discovered. It doesn't happen often, but it is a possibility.

As chemists learned more about the elements, they compiled the most important information concerning each element into a table called the **periodic table of the elements.**

ON YOUR OWN

8.2 Which of the following subatomic particles are found in the nucleus: protons, electrons, and neutrons? Where is the other one found?

8.3 Explain the difference between an atom and an element.

THE PERIODIC TABLE OF THE ELEMENTS

The periodic table of the elements (Figure 8.8) is a chemist's most important tool. It's more than just a listing of the elements. You see, as chemists learned more about the behavior and properties of elements, they discovered they could arrange them based on what they were made of and how they behaved. Before I get into that, notice on the table that each box has 1, 2, or 3 letters. Those are abbreviations for the elements' names. So element number one on the upper left of the table is the box for hydrogen and has a letter H. Element number 2 is helium and is abbreviated He. It couldn't be just H because that single letter was already used. Now look at element number 19. It has an abbreviation K. That element is potassium. Why isn't it P? Well, it is abbreviated by its Latin name, kalium. You see, chemists were working all over the world discovering elements, and some countries used Latin as a scientific language while others used English.

FIGURE 8.8

The Periodic Table of the Elements

1A	2A	3B	4B	5B	6B	7B	8B			1B	2B	3A	4A	5A	6A	7A	8A
1 **H** 1.01																	2 **He** 4.00
3 **Li** 6.94	4 **Be** 9.01											5 **B** 10.8	6 **C** 12.0	7 **N** 14.0	8 **O** 16.0	9 **F** 19.0	10 **Ne** 20.2
11 **Na** 23.0	12 **Mg** 24.3											13 **Al** 27.0	14 **Si** 28.1	15 **P** 31.0	16 **S** 32.1	17 **Cl** 35.5	18 **Ar** 39.9
19 **K** 39.1	20 **Ca** 40.1	21 **Sc** 45.0	22 **Ti** 47.9	23 **V** 50.9	24 **Cr** 52.0	25 **Mn** 54.9	26 **Fe** 55.8	27 **Co** 58.9	28 **Ni** 58.7	29 **Cu** 63.5	30 **Zn** 65.4	31 **Ga** 69.7	32 **Ge** 72.6	33 **As** 74.9	34 **Se** 79.0	35 **Br** 79.9	36 **Kr** 83.8
37 **Rb** 85.5	38 **Sr** 87.6	39 **Y** 88.9	40 **Zr** 91.2	41 **Nb** 92.9	42 **Mo** 96.0	43 **Tc** (98)	44 **Ru** 101.1	45 **Rh** 102.9	46 **Pd** 106.4	47 **Ag** 107.9	48 **Cd** 112.4	49 **In** 114.8	50 **Sn** 118.7	51 **Sb** 121.8	52 **Te** 127.6	53 **I** 126.9	54 **Xe** 131.3
55 **Cs** 132.9	56 **Ba** 137.3	57 **La** 138.9	72 **Hf** 178.5	73 **Ta** 181.0	74 **W** 183.8	75 **Re** 186.2	76 **Os** 190.2	77 **Ir** 192.2	78 **Pt** 195.1	79 **Au** 197.0	80 **Hg** 200.6	81 **Tl** 204.4	82 **Pb** 207.2	83 **Bi** 209.0	84 **Po** (209)	85 **At** (210)	86 **Rn** (222)
87 **Fr** (223)	88 **Ra** (226.0)	89 **Ac** (227)	104 **Rf** (265)	105 **Db** (268)	106 **Sg** (271)	107 **Bh** (270)	108 **Hs** (277)	109 **Mt** (276)	110 **Ds** (281)	111 **Rg** (280)	112 **Cn** (285)	113 **Nh** (284)	114 **Fl** (289)	115 **Mc** (288)	116 **Lv** (293)	117 **Ts** (294)	118 **Og** (294)

58 **Ce** 140.1	59 **Pr** 140.9	60 **Nd** 144.2	61 **Pm** (145)	62 **Sm** 150.4	63 **Eu** 152.0	64 **Gd** 157.2	65 **Tb** 158.9	66 **Dy** 162.5	67 **Ho** 164.9	68 **Er** 167.3	69 **Tm** 168.9	70 **Yb** 173.0	71 **Lu** 175.0
90 **Th** 232.0	91 **Pa** 231.0	92 **U** 238.0	93 **Np** (237)	94 **Pu** (244)	95 **Am** (243)	96 **Cm** (247)	97 **Bk** (247)	98 **Cf** (251)	99 **Es** (252)	100 **Fm** (257)	101 **Md** (258)	102 **No** (259)	103 **Lr** (262)

Nonmetals
Standard metals
Transition metals
Inner transition metals

The periodic table can tell us lots of information. For example, the numbers above the letters tell us how many protons an atom of that element has in its nucleus. So a hydrogen atom has one proton while a potassium atom has 19 protons. This is referred to as the atom's **atomic number.** Because most atoms are electrically neutral, they have the same number of electrons as protons. Thus, the atomic number also tells you how many electrons an atom of a specific element has. The number below the letters tells us the average mass of an atom of that element, or its **mass number.** Now, electrons are very small as compared to protons and neutrons, so the number of protons and neutrons are what play a part in an atom's mass. Within an element, there may be atoms with a different number of neutrons, even though they have the same number of protons. That affects the mass of the atom. We won't get into the details about that, but you can notice that with increasing atomic numbers on the periodic table, the mass number increases, too.

Why isn't the table more rectangle-shaped? Did you notice that? Other types of tables are. Well, there is an intentional placement of these elements. For example, elements within the same column behave in a similar manner. Isn't it interesting that the building blocks of the entire universe have an elegant order to them? Whenever we see order, it should make us realize that there is a Creator. The complex properties of every substance in our world (and beyond) are not just random in their makeup. Indeed, chemistry helps us to get a glimpse of the grand design by our God!

ON YOUR OWN

8.4 Using what you learned about atomic numbers and referring to the periodic table of the elements, list how many protons are in a single atom of sodium (abbreviated Na), krypton (Kr), and silver (Ag).

8.5 Write how many electrons are in each of the atoms from question 8.4.

If you look around you right now, you probably can find more than 118 kinds of materials surrounding you. (There are well over 12 substances just in the air!) But how can that be if there are only 118 elements? There must be more to the story. Well, atoms can combine to create other substances. So God created an order in the universe to produce a myriad of materials, efficiently doing it by having atoms link together into **molecules.**

Molecule—Two or more atoms linked together to make a substance with unique properties

I like to think that atoms are a bit like building blocks. For example, LEGO bricks are small, colorful, multi-sized blocks that can link together to create various shapes. In fact, if you had 10 different LEGO bricks, you could connect them together in many, many ways. You could connect a red and blue one. You could connect a black and brown one. You could take the red and blue and add 2 yellows to them. Each resulting structure would be a bit different, wouldn't it?

Remember how I said electrons orbited the nucleus? They spend their time whirling around it, always in motion. Even this solid book is filled with atoms that have electrons rapidly moving around. Well, that means they are the outermost part of an atom. It turns out that all atoms are the most stable when they have a complete set of electrons in the outermost position, called their **shell.** So atoms will interact with other atoms to try to reach that "happy" state of a full shell. And it is this interaction that creates molecules.

Each molecule has its own unique properties that are not necessarily the same as the properties of the individual atoms. For example, if you combine 2 atoms of hydrogen gas and 1 atom of oxygen gas, you end up with a molecule that is not a gas at all. You end up with water, which is a liquid at room temperature. To abbreviate the water molecule, we take the abbreviations of the atoms that make it up and can express it like this: H_2O. The subscript 2 means that there are 2 atoms of hydrogen in a single molecule of water. This is a **molecular formula.**

Oxygen gas exists as pairs of atoms, so its molecular formula is O_2. Ozone, on the other hand, is made up of 3 oxygen atoms, or O_3. Even though it is a gas like oxygen gas, ozone has different properties. You wouldn't be able to breathe it for one because even though you'd be surrounded by oxygen, it would be in a form that your lungs couldn't use!

FIGURE 8.9
Oxygen Atoms

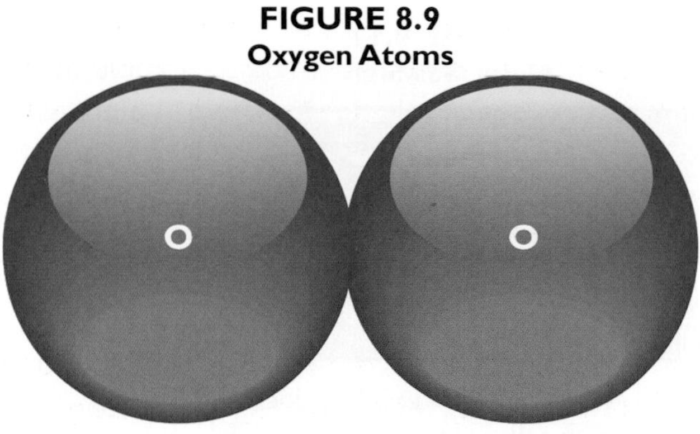

FIGURE 8.10
Water Molecule

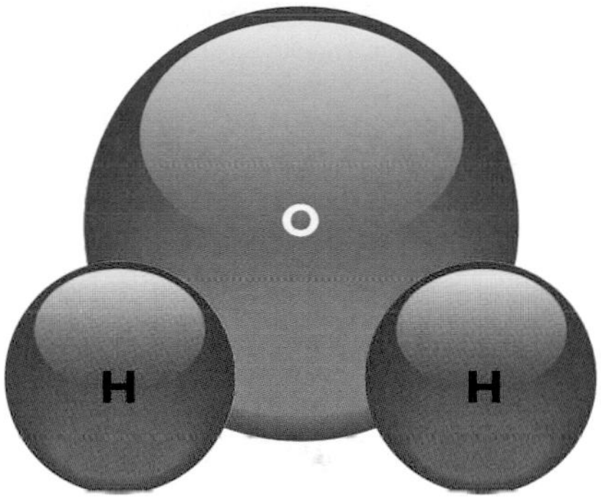

BONDS

Atoms can combine to form everything: apples, paper clips, horses, trees, cars, bacteria, clouds, planets, and even suns! And chemists understood that for a long time. But only recently did they figure out exactly *how* they combine and connect. Remember when I said that atoms want to fill their outer shell with electrons? Well, each energy level can hold a specific number of electrons. The first energy level can only hold 2 electrons. If an atom has more than 2 electrons, then those electrons have to orbit the nucleus in the second energy level. The second energy level can hold 8 electrons. Once it has 8, it is full, and any extra electrons have to orbit in the next energy level.

The outermost level of electrons is so important that the electrons in that level are given a special name: **valence** (vay' lence) **electrons.** If you know the outermost energy level and the number of valence electrons in an atom, you know something about how it will behave. Look again at the periodic table. The column on the far right contains elements known as the **noble gases.** That is because the atoms of these elements each contain enough electrons in the outer shell to completely fill it. Therefore they don't react or interact much with other elements. They're "happy" the way they are. Helium in this column has 2 electrons in its outer shell, but that fills the shell up because its outermost energy level is the first energy level, and the first energy level can only hold 2 electrons. The rest of the noble gases have 8 valence electrons, filling up their outer shells.

FIGURE 8.11
Neon Gas Sign

Although neon gas (Ne) doesn't react with other atoms, it can be useful. By running electricity across the gas, it causes the electrons to gain energy and then release that extra energy in the form of light.

The rest of the elements of the periodic table have atoms that are more reactive, wanting to fill their valence shells in one way or another. One way they can do this is by sharing electrons.

For example, an oxygen atom has an atomic number of 8. That means it has 8 protons. Well, it has to have the same number of electrons to be neutral, so oxygen atoms each have 8 electrons. The first 2 go in the first energy level, which can hold only 2. The next 6 are in the second energy level which can hold 8. That means oxygen atoms have 2 open spaces in their valence electron shell and are not very happy. They like a full electron shell.

Now look at hydrogen on the periodic table. It has an atomic number of 1, meaning it has 1 proton. That, of course means it has 1 electron, too. The first energy level for electrons can hold 2 electrons, so hydrogen atoms are not completely happy, either. They want 1 more.

Of course you know that atoms don't have emotions, but they really work to have full outer shells because that is a state where they are stable. So one way to get to that state is by sharing electrons with other atoms.

Think about a water molecule. Its formula is H_2O. That means it has 2 hydrogen atoms and 1 oxygen atom. Each hydrogen atom will *share* its only electron with the oxygen atom. The electron will spend some of its time orbiting the hydrogen and some of its time orbiting the oxygen. Oxygen atoms have 6 electrons in their outer shell that can hold up to 8 electrons. So if 2 hydrogen atoms are sharing their electrons with the oxygen atom, then the oxygen atom feels like it has a full outer shell... at least some of the time. In return, the oxygen atom will share one of its electrons with each hydrogen atom making it almost like they each have a full electron shell of 2. Look at Figure 8.12 to see what I mean.

FIGURE 8.12
Water Molecule with Covalent Bond

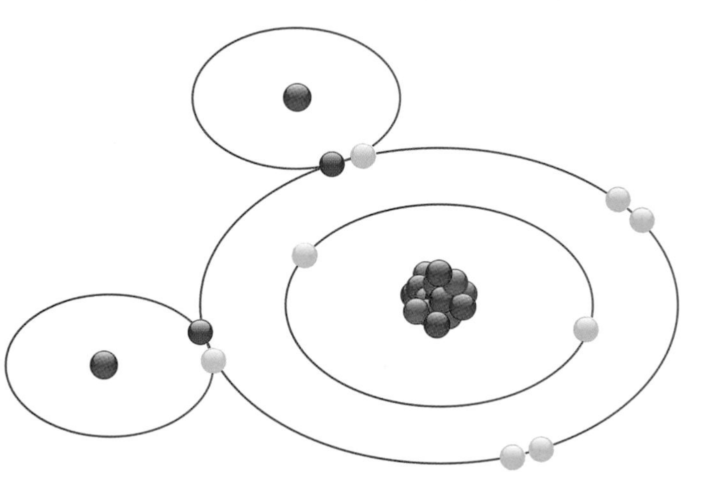

The oxygen atom has 6 valence electrons (shown as light blue in the diagram). Each hydrogen atom has 1 valence electron (dark blue). When they share electrons, the shared electron pair spends some of its time orbiting the hydrogen nucleus, making it feel like it has a full valence shell of 2 electrons. Some of the pair's time is spent orbiting the oxygen atom, and when both pairs do that, the oxygen feels like it has a full valence shell of 8 electrons. Can you see how the atoms are sharing their electrons by taking turns with the shared electron pair?

This is why water is so plentiful and is so stable as a substance. The oxygen and hydrogen atoms are quite happy. When atoms share electrons they create a bond, called a **covalent** (koh vay' lent) **bond.** They are *co*-operating with each other's *valence* electrons, so that is how you can think of that term.

Besides sharing electrons, some atoms will *give up* the electrons they have or *steal* electrons from another atom. When an atom steals an electron from another atom, it now has 1 more negatively charged particle than positively charged ones. So it has an overall charge of 1−. Atoms with an overall charge are called **ions** (eye' ons).

Sometimes atoms will give away their electrons, resulting in an overall positive charged ion (remember, they still have the same number of original protons). Chemists have special names for these ions. Positive ions are called **cations** (cat' eye ons) and negative ions are called **anions** (ann' eye ons). A good way to remember the difference is that the word *cation* has a letter "t" which looks like a plus sign, so cations are positive. Cations and anions have opposite charges, which means they are attracted to one another. Let me give you an example of this.

Sodium is a shiny, silver metal with only 1 valence electron in its third energy level. That means it either needs to take on 7 extra electrons to fill its outer shell or it needs to give away the single electron it has there. If it gives an electron away, that means it would have a full second energy level, and it would be happy. Well, it is much easier to give away 1 electron than take on 7. Now, chlorine has 7 valence electrons in its third energy level. So it can either take 1 electron from another atom or give its 7 away, and it is much easier to take a single electron. Can you see how sodium and chlorine would match up? Sodium can give its electron to chlorine (see Figure 8.13). If it does, then sodium will have 8 electrons in its second energy level and is happy. It also has one less negative charge, so it has an overall charge of 1+ and is a cation. Chlorine happily takes the electron from sodium, resulting in 8 total electrons in its third energy level, making it happy, too. Because it has an extra electron, it has an overall charge of 1− and is an anion. The positive sodium and the negative chlorine ions are attracted to each other because of their opposite charges. And this forms what is called an **ionic bond.** Ionic bonds form when ions are attracted to each other.

FIGURE 8.13
Sodium Chloride Molecule with Ionic Bond

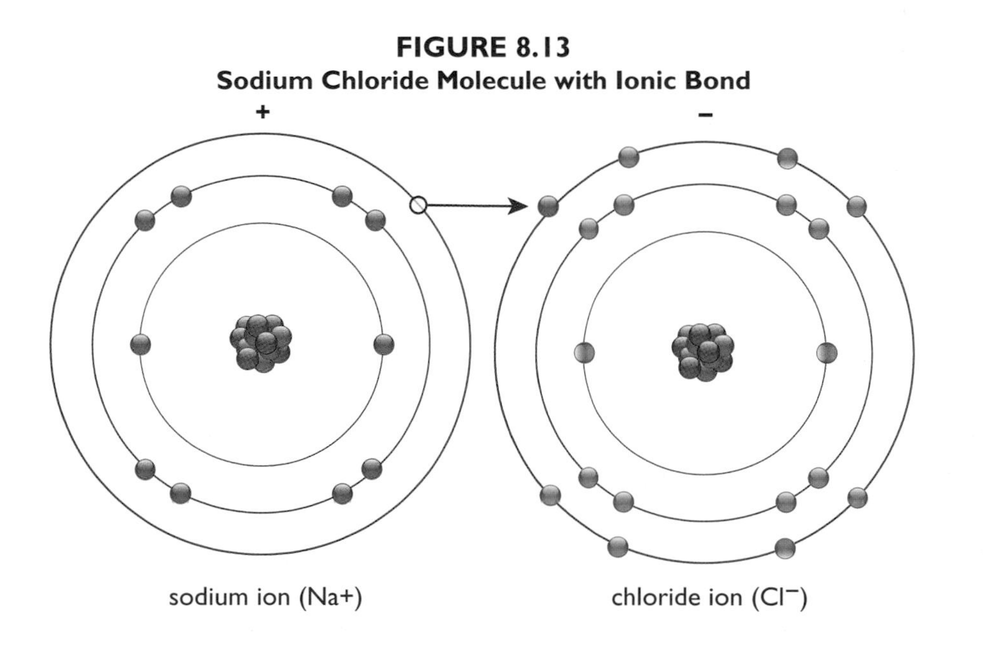

Sodium and chlorine *really* like to bond together. And they create a molecule called sodium chloride, which is common table salt.

All molecules are formed one of these 2 ways, either by sharing electrons to form covalent bonds or by taking/receiving electrons, which creates ions that form ionic bonds. It's all about the electrons and the desire to have that perfectly filled valence electron shell (or at least feel like it is filled!).

ON YOUR OWN

8.6 The 2 molecules below are hydrogen gas (on the left) and lithium fluoride. By looking at their molecular structure, determine if they are formed with a covalent bond or an ionic bond. If it is an ionic bond, which atom is the anion and which is the cation?

CHEMICAL REACTIONS

Before we go into the topic of chemical reactions, perform Experiment 8.2.

EXPERIMENT 8.2
SEPARATING A MIXTURE OF SAND AND SALT

PURPOSE: To explore the properties of a mixture

MATERIALS:

- 2 beakers—100 mL and 250 mL (or 2 glasses—one large and one small)
- Sand
- Table salt
- A funnel
- Water
- A measuring cup
- Filter paper (You can cut a circle out of the bottom of a coffee-maker filter.)
- Stirring rod (or small spoon)
- Measuring teaspoon
- Measuring tablespoon
- A stove
- A saucepan

QUESTION: What is a mixture?

HYPOTHESIS: Write in your notebook what you think will happen when the salt and sand mix together and whether it is possible to easily separate them again.

PROCEDURE:

1. Take a teaspoon of sand and a teaspoon of salt and pour them into the 100 mL beaker.
2. Use your stirring rod to mix them up well.
3. Add about $\frac{1}{8}$ cup of water to the mixture and use the stirring rod to mix. As the water mixes with the sand and salt, the salt will dissolve in the water and the sand will not.
4. Filter the mixture by first taking a circle of filter paper and folding it as shown below:

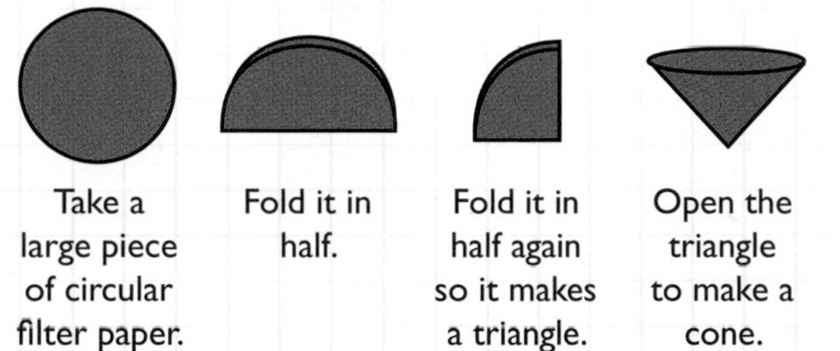

Take a large piece of circular filter paper.	Fold it in half.	Fold it in half again so it makes a triangle.	Open the triangle to make a cone.

5. Take the resulting cone of filter paper and place it in the funnel. In order to get the filter paper to retain its cone shape, wet it down with some water. This will cause the filter paper to stick to the funnel.
6. Hold the funnel above the empty 250 mL beaker so that anything falling through the funnel will land in it.
7. Now pour the mixture of water, salt, and sand into the filter paper. Make sure that the water level never rises above the top of the filter-paper cone. In addition, for best results try to pour off just the liquid first and leave the majority of the sand in your beaker until the very end. As the liquid filters through the paper, you will see it fall into the 250 mL beaker. As long as you do not allow the liquid level to rise above the top of the filter-paper cone, the liquid in the beaker will be clear. Continue this process until everything in the beaker (including the sand) has been poured into the funnel.
8. Once all of the liquid has filtered through the filter paper (This may take a while!), rinse the 100 mL beaker with 1 tablespoon of water and dump it all into the filter paper. Allow all of the liquid to drain through the filter paper.
9. Now what you have is pure sand on the filter paper and a mixture of salt and water in your beaker. To get rid of the water, pour the salt and water mixture into the saucepan and heat until it is boiling. Continue to heat it until all the water has boiled away.
10. Write in your notebook where the sand, salt, and water are now. Then clean everything up.

CONCLUSION: Explain what you learned about a mixture.

In Experiment 8.2, you took sand and salt and mixed them together. When you did this, you created a **mixture**.

Mixture—A substance that contains different compounds and/or elements

Now I need to define what a **compound** is as compared to an element. A compound is made up of one or more elements that are chemically bonded together. That means they can only be separated using chemical means. Table salt, for example, is a compound. It is made up of a bunch of sodium chloride molecules. So a mixture is when you have 2 substances that retain their individual properties, whether they are elements or compounds, even when they are mixed together. That is what happened when you mixed sand and salt.

FIGURE 8.14
Salt and Sand Mixture

When they were mixed together in the beaker, the molecules of sand (silicon dioxide) did not combine with the molecules of salt (sodium chloride) in any way. These 2 different types of molecules simply occupied the same general space. In the experiment, you eventually separated them.

Now, you *could* have done it by using a set of fine tweezers and a powerful magnifying glass. If you looked at the mixture through the magnifying glass, you would have seen little grains of salt and little grains of sand. You could then use the tweezers to slowly pick the salt out of the sand. With enough patience and time, you could separate the mixture that way. However, that method would have been very time-consuming. To speed up the procedure, we used a different method. You see, because the individual molecules still retain their own unique properties when they are in a mixture, we can use those properties to separate them. One property of salt is that it dissolves in water. Sand does not. We used the salt's property to help separate the two. You first dissolved the salt into the water and then filtered out the sand that didn't dissolve. Next, you removed the water from the salt by causing it to evaporate. Actually, the water and salt were a mixture at that point, too, and you used water's property of evaporating by heating the mixture until all you had left behind was the salt. In the end, the sand was in the filter paper, the salt was in the pot, and the water was in gaseous form in the air around you.

FIGURE 8.15
Classifying Matter

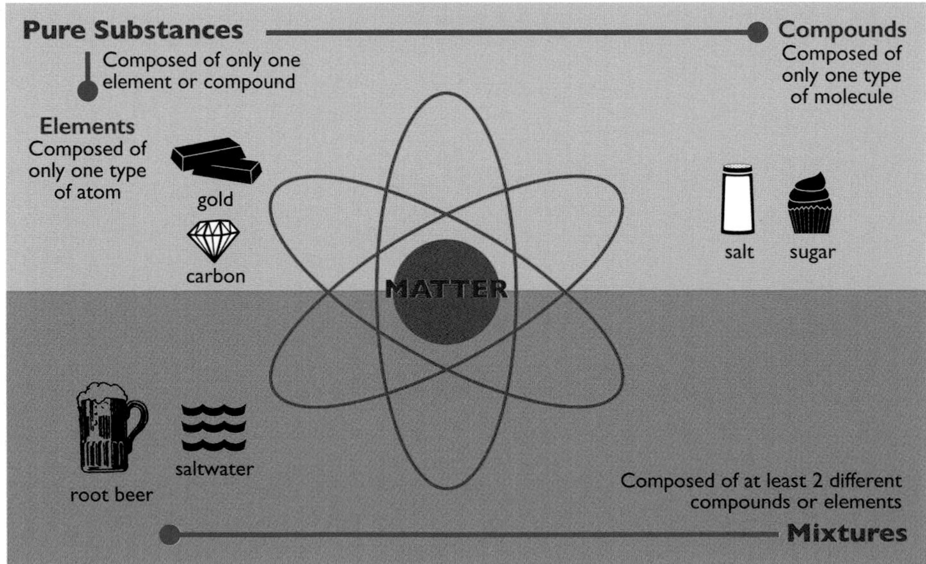

So mixtures can be separated because the individual components retain their unique properties; they are not chemically changed by being mixed together.

I want to stop here and do a little review so you can more easily remember some of the terminology that has been used. We've covered matter, atoms, elements, compounds, and mixtures. Figure 8.15 summarizes them for you. All matter can be divided into 2 groups: pure substances and mixtures. Pure substances can be further divided into elements (matter made up of one type of atom) or compounds (matter made up of one type of molecule).

CHEMICAL VERSUS PHYSICAL CHANGES

There is another feature of matter: it is able to change. And chemists classify the changes that matter undergoes into 2 large groups: a **physical change** and a **chemical change.**

Physical change—A change in which the atoms or molecules in a substance stay the same

Chemical change—A change that affects the type of molecules or atoms in a substance

One of the best ways to remember these changes is to think about the atoms or molecules involved. For example, if you take a sheet of paper and run it through a paper shredder, have you changed the molecules in the paper into different molecules? Of course not. It's just that now you have *tiny* pieces of paper molecules. They are still paper molecules. This is an example of a physical change. Whenever you change a substance without altering its molecules or atoms, you've made a physical change.

But what if you burned that sheet of paper? The molecules in the paper would eventually change into carbon dioxide, water vapor, and ash. This is an example of a chemical change; the types of atoms or molecules in the substance changed, so the substance has undergone a chemical change.

In Experiment 8.2, you added a salt and sand mixture into water, and the salt dissolved into the water. You could not see the salt, but it hadn't changed its chemical makeup. One way to know that would be to take a small sip of the saltwater mixture. It would have tasted salty, wouldn't it? The salt molecules are not changed, they're just very, very small. This is a physical change, then.

A good way to think about chemical and physical changes is to think about whether the changes can easily be reversed. When you dissolve salt into water, you can recover the salt. That is a physical change, then. But what about burning paper? Can you easily un-burn it? No, so that is a chemical change.

FIGURE 8.16
Lemonade and a Fried Egg

Lemonade represents a physical change with lemon juice and sugar dissolved in water. You can still taste that the sugar has its sweet property and the lemon juice is sour. A fried egg represents a chemical change because the molecules making it up have changed to *different* molecules.

EXPLORE MORE

Take a skillet and a raw egg. Break the egg into a bowl and examine it. Now heat the skillet on a stovetop and add the egg. Watch the egg as it changes. Once it is cooked, place the egg on a plate and study it. Do you think it would be easy to undo the change you just made? Can you un-cook an egg? No. So this represents a chemical change because chemical changes are not easily reversed. The egg's chemical makeup changed.

If you think about it, phase changes are a type of physical change, too. A substance remains the same molecules or atoms whether it is solid, liquid, or gas. Think of water. As a solid, it is ice, but the molecules are H_2O. Liquid water is also H_2O, and gaseous water is H_2O. No matter the state of matter, water does not change its chemical makeup.

Chemical Changes

Let's take a closer look at chemical changes now. Before we do, you need to know that there are some elements in nature that do not naturally exist as individual atoms. These are called **homonuclear** (hoh' moh new' klee er) **diatomics** (die uh tom' iks). Now those are some big words, but let me break them down so you will more easily understand and remember them. The prefix *homo-* means "same," and *nuclear* refers to individual atoms with their nuclei. So these molecules are made up of the *same* types of atoms. The prefix *di-* refers to the number 2, so there are 2 atoms connected together. Homonuclear diatomic molecules are molecules that are made up of 2 of the same type of atom. The atoms that exist this way are nitrogen, oxygen, chlorine, hydrogen and a few others. So the oxygen you are breathing right now does not travel into your lungs as a single oxygen atom, but as a molecule with 2 oxygen atoms. Therefore, its chemical formula is O_2. Now this is only when it exists as an element, not within another molecule. Water (H_2O) only has 1 atom of oxygen, right?

With this information, we can continue our discussion. Chemical reactions occur whenever there are bonds being formed or broken between atoms and/or molecules. Let's take a look at a basic chemical reaction:

$$2H_2 + O_2 \rightarrow 2H_2O$$

This is basically a chemical sentence, telling us what is happening. On the left side of the arrow are the **reactants.** These are the molecules that are going to react together. And then we have an arrow that moves us to the **product** on the right. So the reactants are made up of molecular hydrogen and molecular oxygen. Remember, hydrogen and oxygen are homonuclear diatomics, so when each element is by itself, it always exists as 2 atoms bonded together (thus the number 2 in the subscript below each reactant). This is why I called them *molecular* hydrogen and *molecular* oxygen. They exist as molecules, even though they are made up of the same atoms. Now notice the large number 2 before the molecule of hydrogen. That tells us that for this reaction to occur, you need to have 2 molecules of hydrogen for every 1 molecule of oxygen. That means you will have a total of 4 hydrogen *atoms* and 2 oxygen *atoms* involved in this reaction (see Figure 8.17). And when these homonuclear diatomic molecules react together, they produce 2 molecules of water. That's why there is a large 2 before the water molecule on the products' side of the arrow.

FIGURE 8.17
A Chemical Reaction

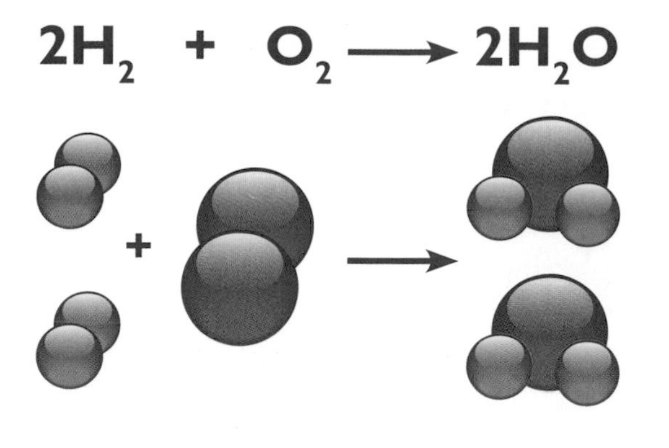

Notice in the diagram how there are 2 molecules of hydrogen. Each molecule is made up of 2 hydrogen atoms, meaning that on the reactants' side, there are 4 total hydrogen atoms (blue spheres). There is one molecule of oxygen, made up of 2 oxygen atoms, so there are 2 total oxygen atoms on the reactants' side of the equation (green spheres). Those molecules were broken up and rearranged into a completely different molecule: water. And there were enough "ingredients" to make 2 whole water molecules. Notice that there are still 4 total hydrogen atoms and 2 total oxygen atoms on the products' side of the equation. Every atom was reused to make new molecules.

It always takes a bit of energy to get a chemical reaction to start, kind of like using a match to get a fire blazing. There is actually one more *product* in this reaction, too. It may take a little energy to get the reaction to *start*, but this reaction produces a *lot* of energy as a product.

Well, chemical reactions represent chemical changes, not physical ones. The reaction in Figure 8.17 starts with 2 molecules that are both gaseous. They also have specific properties. Hydrogen gas is highly **combustible**, meaning it will easily burn or even explode! Oxygen gas is highly reactive. But water is a liquid and is neither combustible nor highly reactive. So this is a chemical change.

Chemical reactions are very important. Without them, you could not exist. That's because there are countless chemical reactions going on in your body right now, keeping you alive. In fact, without chemical reactions, there would be nothing in our universe. So it is very important to learn about them.

FIGURE 8.18
Separating Hydrogen and Oxygen from Water Molecules

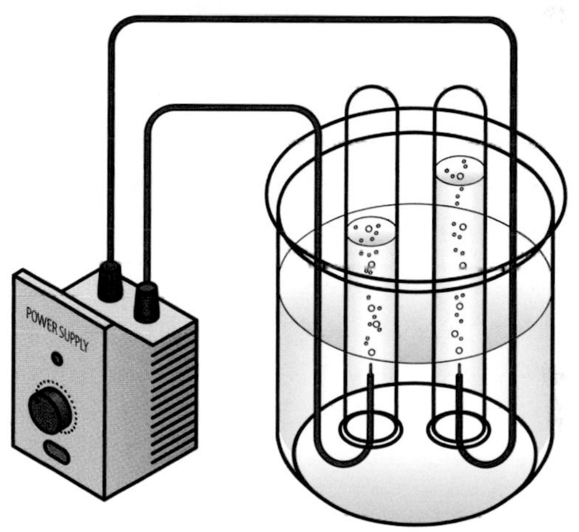

When an electric current is run through saltwater as in this setup, the water molecules can be broken up, separating the hydrogen and oxygen atoms. Those atoms will rapidly form homonuclear diatomic molecules and will collect as gas within the test tubes. Although water molecules can be created and broken up again, it takes lots of energy to do that. Thus, even though this reaction is reversible, it is not *easily* reversible like a physical change might be.

ON YOUR OWN

8.7 Classify the following changes as physical or chemical: a. Water freezing to become ice; b. Wood burning in a campfire; c. Melting butter; d. A rusting bicycle.

TYPES OF MOLECULES

In this last section, we'll go over some unique types of molecules.

Crystals

Many elements and compounds form solids that are crystalline in structure. That means they form **crystals**, having geometric sides. Elements such as carbon, silicon, and iron can form crystals. Compounds that form solid crystals include salt, sugar, and water.

FIGURE 8.19
Crystals of Quartz, Sugar, and Salt

EXPLORE MORE

Observe some common crystals with a magnifying glass or microscope. Use samples of salt, sugar, finely crushed ice, play sand, and (if you have a cooperating adult) a diamond. Except for the diamond, all these samples are *compounds* that are in crystalline form. The diamond is made up of the *element* carbon that has been exposed to massive heat and pressure to create a carbon crystal. Make illustrations in your notebook and describe their differences.

creation connection

Carbon is an element that is commonly found as a black, brittle substance. It is sometimes referred to as graphite and makes perfect pencil material. Carbon in graphite form is black because the carbon atoms are crystallized into a geometric shape that absorbs light. Very little light is reflected back by the carbon, and that is why it appears black. But after massive pressure and heat in the Earth, if carbon is able to quickly cool it forms a different crystalline structure with very different properties as compared to graphite. The resulting diamonds are still carbon atoms, but now *reflect* most light and are clear. They are also one of the hardest substances on Earth (graphite is very soft and brittle). Indeed, pressure and heat can produce great change. A poetically written, similar spiritual truth is found in the Bible. James 1:2-4 says, "Count it all joy, my brothers, when you meet trials of various kinds, for you know that the testing of your faith produces steadfastness. And let steadfastness have its full effect, that you may be perfect and complete, lacking in nothing." Trials and testing cause pressure in our lives that God uses to strengthen us and produce perseverance and steadfastness. Ever heard the expression "diamond in the rough?" It means that an experience will make you stronger and wiser.

Polymers and Plastics

What do you think balloons, DNA, wood, and rubber duckies have in common? Well, they are all **polymers** (pah' lih mers). You could say that right now you are completely surrounded by chemical polymers, and because DNA is a polymer you are made of polymers, too! So what is a polymer? Polymers are large molecules made up of smaller chemicals called **monomers** (mah' nuh mers), linked together in the same way that train cars are connected. The prefix *poly-* means "many" and *-mers* refers to parts, so a polymer is made up of many parts. *Mono-* refers to one, so it is a single part. Some polymers (like polyvinyl chloride or PVC pipe) are made by repeating the same small monomer over and over again, and others (like DNA) are made by 2 different monomers linked in a pattern.

In living organisms, carbohydrates are polymers made up of simple sugars, proteins are polymers made up of chemicals called amino acids, and nucleic acids (like DNA, which contains our genetic information) are polymers of nucleotides. Your hair is made up of a polymer called keratin. And the woody part of trees is made of the polymer called cellulose. Tree sap is made of a rubber polymer that has traditionally been used to make bouncy balls and even chewing gum! These are all **naturally existing polymers.**

FIGURE 8.20
Examples of Things Made from Polymers

Synthetic polymers are man-made polymers, and most are made from petroleum oil using chemical reactions. The first synthetic polymers were made by accident as an unexpected result of a chemical reaction. Most chemists threw them out because they thought they were useless. Eventually, chemists realized their great benefit to humans.

By creating polymers that could be permanently squished into shapes, the plastic industry was born. Containers, plates, medical materials, computers, and so many other materials are made with plastics. This material is lightweight and difficult to break. Plastics are long-lasting, too, and many can be recycled over and over again, creating new useful items.

Plastics can be formulated to be soft, hard, stretchy, or brittle, and they can be used almost everywhere. But because they do not break down very easily, man-made plastics can become a problem if they are thrown away. You see, natural materials easily are broken down by bacteria, fungi, and other methods. If you've ever seen a dead tree, you would have noticed it covered with mushrooms, mosses, and other things that help to break down the polymers in wood.

FIGURE 8.21
Tree Stump Broken Down by Mushrooms, Mosses, and Bacteria

But there are very few things that can break down plastics. There *are* a few natural processes, including sunlight and even a few living organisms, that are able to help break down these man-made polymers, but the process is very slow. This means plastic garbage piles can build up. And that's why it is very important for us to recycle our plastics so that these polymers can be refashioned into other useful items.

EXPLORE MORE

Recycle your own plastics into something new. Get a clean, clear, plastic food container that has a recycle logo with a number 6 in it (like in the diagram). Many brands of ridged cracker or packaged cookie trays are this type of plastic. Cut out some shapes about 1½–2 inches in size and color them how you would like, using permanent markers. Use a hole puncher to punch a hole at the top. Cover a cookie sheet with aluminum foil and place your shapes on the foil. Place in a preheated 350 °F oven and watch carefully. Within a minute or so, the shapes will shrink in size and curl up. Then after 2 minutes, they will quickly flatten out. As soon as that happens, remove them from the oven, using hot pads. Once cool, you can hang your creations from a keychain or make a necklace or bracelet! What's going on here is that the plastic is made of a polymer called polystyrene that has been stretched and molded into its original food container shape. When you warm up the material, all of the polymer chains move around and coil back up, making the sheet shrink. Polymers are amazing!

NOTE: You can use recycle #1 plastic, which is PET (polyethylene terephthalate), but it will remain curled up. However, this would make some colorful beads!

Acids and Bases

Have you ever bitten into a lemon? If you were to describe how it tastes, you would probably say it was sour. The chemicals making it taste that way are called **acids.** Acids are chemicals that have 3 basic properties. The first property is that they taste sour. You have likely eaten many foods that are acids, such as grapefruits and pickles. However, some acids are so strong they would damage your skin, so **you don't ever want to test whether a chemical is an acid by tasting it.** That could be dangerous! A second acid property is that it can conduct electricity when added to water. Acids can conduct electricity because it is easy for electrons to travel through them.

FIGURE 8.22
Properties of Acids

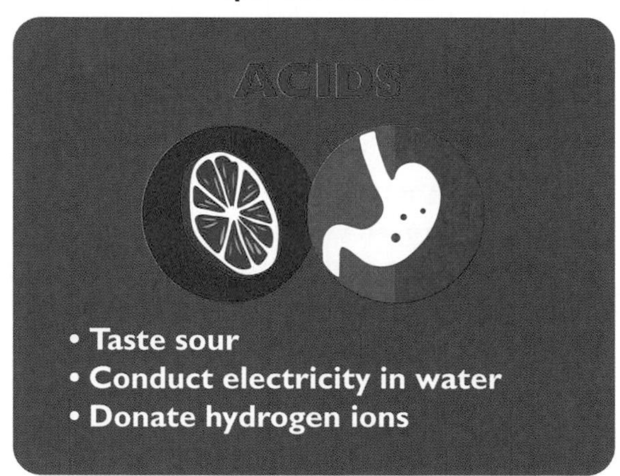

The third property is one I have to explain a bit more. Acids donate hydrogen ions. Remember that an ion is an atom that has either lost or gained electrons, resulting in an electrical charge. Well, a hydrogen ion is a hydrogen atom that has lost its one and only electron. What's left is its proton nucleus. All acids donate at least one hydrogen ion when they are mixed with other substances. That means there are lots of charged particles floating around, making the fluid able to conduct electricity.

Acids have different strengths. Some are very strong, such as hydrochloric acid, and others are weak, like lemon juice. Hydrochloric acid is the acid in your stomach that breaks down the food you eat. It doesn't eat up the inside of your stomach because of a thick, gooey, protective lining. Isn't it amazing how perfectly your body is designed? Chemically speaking, strong acids are made from molecules that easily give up their hydrogen ions. Weak acids are molecules that don't easily release them.

The chemical opposite of acids are **bases.** There are 3 major identifying properties of bases. The first is that they taste chalky and bitter. **Again, it is not a good idea to taste unknown chemicals**, but if you have ever had an upset stomach, you may have eaten Tums, which is an **antacid.** An antacid is a chalky base that works against the excess acid in your stomach. A second property is that bases feel slippery to the touch when they are dissolved in water. Soap and window cleaner are bases, and that soapy feel is a result of the basic chemicals in them.

Finally, a third property is that bases receive hydrogen ions. Now think about that. Acids donate hydrogen ions and bases receive them. That should make you think that acids and bases can work together. And, indeed, they do.

FIGURE 8.23
Properties of Bases

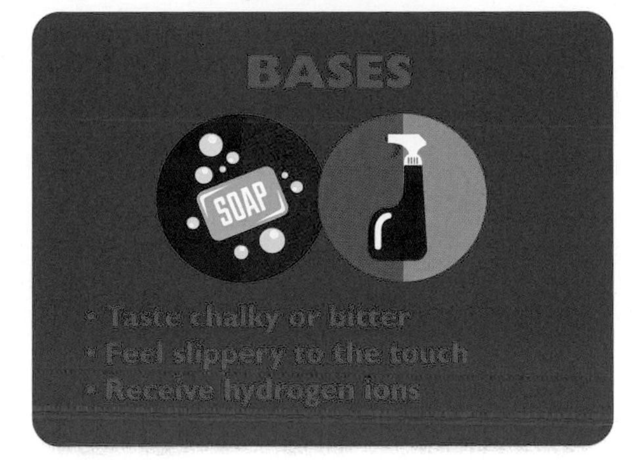

Let's talk a bit more about the antacid I just mentioned. Bases are often used to neutralize acids. Why is that? Well, they take away the acid's effect. Chemically, bases readily receive the hydrogen ions that acids donate in a chemical reaction. This results in neutral products.

Just like acids, bases can be strong or weak. Soap is a weak base, but drain cleaners are often strong bases. Bases are able to break down fats and oils, so this is why they are used as household cleaners.

Scientists measure the strength of an acid or a base on a scale called the **pH scale.** pH means the **potential for hydrogen.** Remember that acids contain hydrogen ions, so the pH scale is used to identify which substances are able to donate more hydrogen ions and are more acidic. The scale goes from 0 to 14, with 0 being the most acidic, 7 being neutral (neither acidic nor basic), and 14 being the most basic (sometimes referred to as **alkaline**). Pure water is a neutral material with a pH of 7. Lemon juice has a pH of 2, and battery acid has a pH of 0. You might think that means lemon juice and battery acid are pretty close together in their acidity, but this is a **logarithmic** scale. That means that each step increases by a factor of 10; so battery acid, which is 2 steps past lemon juice on the acidity scale, is 10 × 10 or 100 times more acidic than lemon juice.

FIGURE 8.24
pH Scale

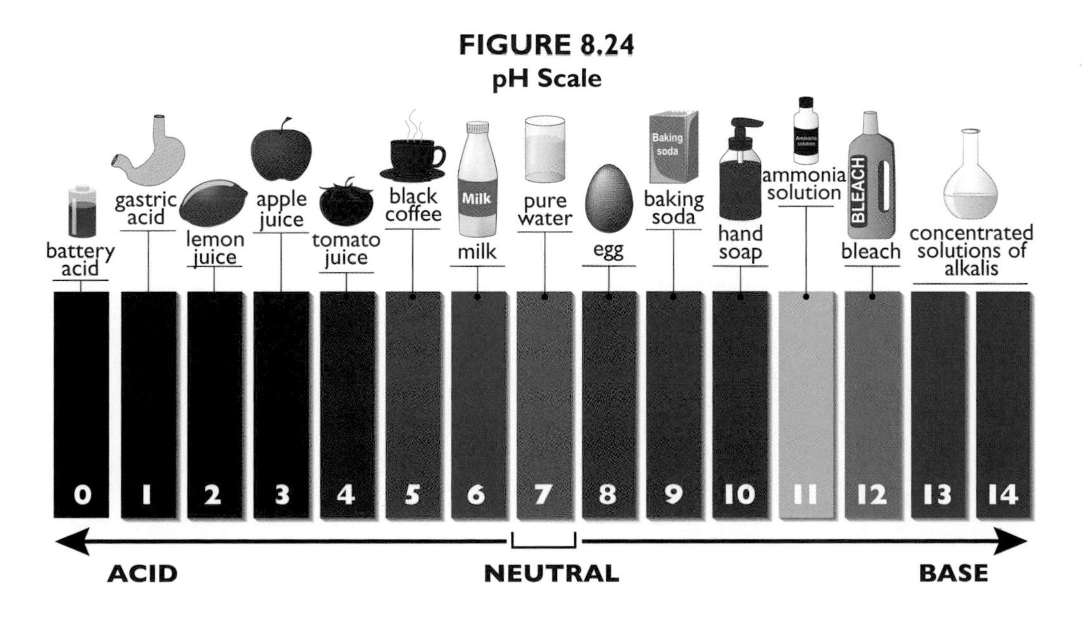

EXPLORE MORE

Indicators help to test whether a material is acidic or basic. One type of indicator is purple cabbage water. Take a few leaves of purple cabbage and boil them in distilled water for a few minutes. Allow the liquid to cool and carefully remove the leaves. The resulting liquid will turn pink in the presence of an acid and blue in the presence of a base. Pour some of the liquid into a few clear juice glasses. Now test some household liquids by adding a teaspoon of them to each cup and stirring them with a plastic spoon or wooden chopstick (Don't use silverware to stir it because some chemicals might affect the shiny finish). You can try lemon juice, milk, vinegar, water, dish soap, and (using gloves) some household cleaning supplies.

ON YOUR OWN

8.8 Give an example of a natural and a synthetic polymer.

8.9 What are the 3 main properties of an acid and the 3 main properties of a base?

SUMMING UP

We've only hit the tip of the iceberg when it comes to chemistry. That's because everything in creation is made up of chemicals. Their interactions with each other are why we are able to stay alive. And this is such a fascinating field; chemical reactions cause the stars to shine and make our hair grow. And as we learn more about the materials that make up all matter, we clearly see an order in their design. Indeed, the science of chemistry is one that helps us to see God's perfect order when He designed the universe!

ANSWERS TO THE "ON YOUR OWN" QUESTIONS

8.1 **Heat is removed when a gas becomes liquid. Heat is added when a solid becomes liquid, and heat is removed when a liquid becomes solid.**

8.2 **Protons and neutrons are found in the nucleus. Electrons orbit the nucleus in orbitals.**

8.3 **An atom is the smallest chemical unit of matter. Atoms with the same number of protons are the same element and have similar properties.**

8.4 **Sodium (Na) has 11 protons, krypton (Kr) has 36 protons, and silver (Ag) has 47 protons.** The number of protons is the same as the atomic number.

8.5 Because atoms are electrically neutral, there needs to be the same number of electrons in an atom as there are protons. So **there are 11 electrons in a sodium atom, 36 electrons in a krypton atom, and 47 protons in a silver atom.**

8.6 **Hydrogen gas is held together by a covalent bond.** You can see the 2 shared electrons in the model. **Lithium fluoride is held together by an ionic bond.** Lithium gave its electron to fluorine, giving lithium a 1+ charge and fluorine a 1− charge. They are now ions that are attracted to each other. **Because lithium has a positive charge it is a cation. Fluorine has a negative charge and therefore is an anion.**

8.7 Remember, a physical change does not change the actual molecules involved. **Examples (a.) and (c.) are physical changes, and (b.) and (d.) are chemical changes.**

8.8 **Some examples of natural polymers from the text include carbohydrates, proteins, DNA, hair, wood, and tree sap. Some examples of synthetic polymers include anything plastic, such as balloons, rubber duckies, or food containers.**

8.9 **Acids taste sour, conduct electricity when added to water, and donate hydrogen ions. Bases taste chalky or bitter, feel slippery, and receive hydrogen ions.**

STUDY GUIDE FOR MODULE 8

1. Match the following words with their definitions.

a. Matter	A substance that contains different compounds and/or elements
b. Atom	A change that affects the type of molecules or atoms in a substance
c. Molecule	Two or more atoms linked together to make a substance with unique properties
d. Mixture	A change in which the atoms or molecules in a substance stay the same
e. Physical change	Anything that has mass and takes up space
f. Chemical change	The smallest chemical unit of matter

2. If a scientist adds heat to a liquid material so that it becomes gas, what do we call the temperature at which this happens?
   a. freezing point   b. melting point   c. boiling point   d. condensation point

3. Atoms are made up of 3 basic types of particles. Which of these is NOT one of them?
   a. muons   b. neutrons   c. electrons   d. protons

4. True or false: Atoms of the same element behave in a similar way.

5. Refer back to the periodic table to find out how many protons are in a single atom of a. lithium (Li); b. chlorine (Cl); and c. gold (Au).

6. What type of bonding does this model of a sodium chloride molecule show?
   a. covalent bonding   b. ionic bonding

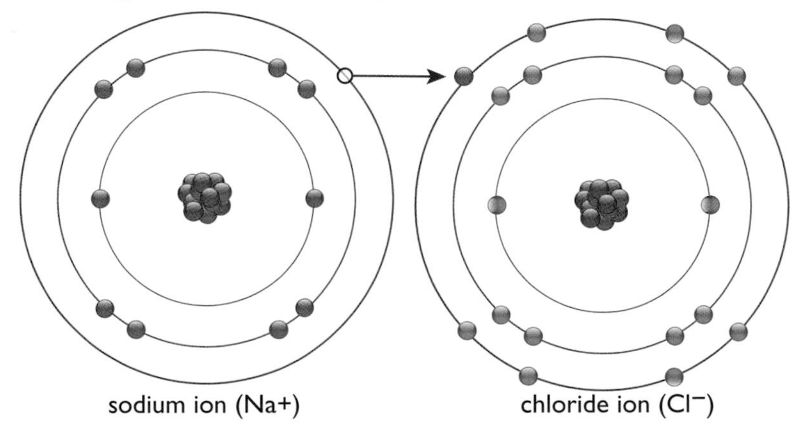

7. In the diagram in question 6, which ion is the anion: sodium or chloride?

8. Fill in the diagram with the correct words from the list (Matter, Elements)

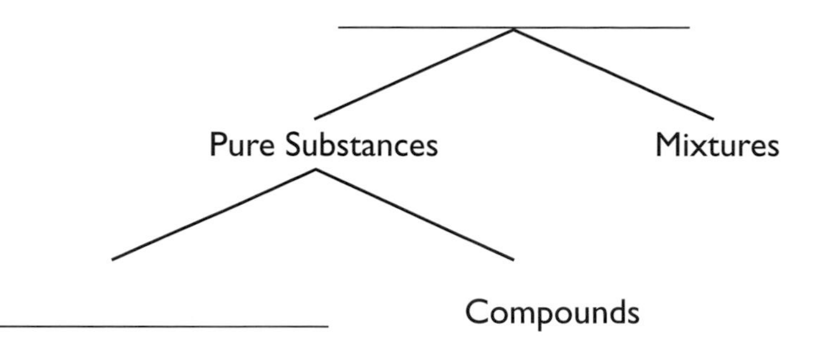

9. Identify each of the following as a physical change or a chemical change:

   a. shredding paper into small pieces

   b. burning paper in a campfire

   c. mixing a glass of lemonade

   d. cooking an egg

   e. freezing liquid water into ice

10. A dead tree is being broken down by mushrooms and bacteria. The wood material is made up of polymers. Nearby, a plastic milk container has been discarded, but it is NOT being broken down by mushrooms and bacteria. The plastic is also made up of polymers. Why is one polymer type readily broken down while the other type is not?

11. Identify which of the following properties belong to acids and which belong to bases: *Slippery to the touch, taste sour, receive hydrogen ions, taste chalky or bitter, conduct electricity in water, donate hydrogen ions*

GENERAL PHYSICS

This module will complete our discussion of physical science, focusing on physics. You may be surprised to know that you have already studied physics principles in this course. You see, physics is an underlying science that helps us understand many other scientific branches. For example, when you learned how water evaporates to water vapor (forming clouds), physics is the science that describes how that happens. Let's take a closer look at this fascinating subject!

FIGURE 9.1
A Rocket Operating under the Laws of Physics

Quaestio

In Genesis 1, we learn that God created the heavens and the Earth. He created light and water, forming seas and producing land. He made all living things and set Earth, the sun, Moon, and all the planetary bodies in motion. And He caused all these things to follow natural laws according to the order He set up within the universe. Indeed, it is the search for these natural laws that was the driving factor of scientific discovery for generations. Many of these involve physics principles regarding how things move and work. By studying these principles, we can get a better glimpse of the character of the One who set them up.

MOTION

If you look around, you will see lots of things in motion: animals scurrying, birds flying, leaves blowing in the wind, and trees swaying. You can see cars moving down the street, people riding bikes, and airplanes flying overhead. Even our Earth and solar system are in constant motion!

And all living things, even if they are not visibly moving, are moving inside. Animals have hearts that are constantly beating, and trees are transporting water up from their roots to their stems and leaves. Even nonliving things are moving as their atoms have electrons that are continuously whirling around their nuclei.

Auto mechanics study how cars work and fix them when they are broken. Well, the study of motion in physics is called **mechanics**. It has to do with exactly *how* things move. But movement is relative to another spot. Think about it. You probably are reading this while sitting on a chair or couch. Thus, you might not think you're moving. But you are on a planet that is orbiting a star (our sun) at 19 miles per second. And that star is orbiting the center of our galaxy at a rate of 155 miles per second. Our galaxy is moving through our universe at a rate of 373 miles per second. So, since you started reading this paragraph, you have *moved* almost 2,000 miles!

Yet, if you had a friend sitting on the couch next to you, that friend would not observe you moving at all. The only way to have observed you move that 2,000 miles would be if someone could view you from *outside our galaxy*! It all has to do with relative motion. For example, if you are riding on a train with a friend, you are not moving at all from your friend's perspective. We call that a **reference point**. However, if your friend is standing at a train station and you ride by in the train, then from your friend's perspective, you *are* moving. Can you see the importance of a reference point when it comes to motion? This means that **all motion is relative.** That's such an important point in physics that I placed those words in bold letters. Motion depends on the reference point that is used.

FIGURE 9.2
Moving Water Molecules

creation connection

Sir Isaac Newton was one of the most influential scientists of all time. Although some of his views were a bit unorthodox, Newton understood that God was critical to the existence of space. He said, "Gravity explains the motions of the planets, but it cannot explain who set the planets in motion. God governs all things and knows all that is or can be done." Indeed, he believed that scientific inquiry could not exist without a God to create all things and set them in motion.

Tiner, J. H. 1975. *Isaac Newton: Inventor, Scientist and Teacher.* Milford, MI: Mott Media.

FIGURE 9.3
A Train Station

The people on this train are not moving *in relation to each other*. However, *in relation to the people standing at the train station*, they are moving.

Speed, Velocity, and Acceleration

People driving on a highway must follow the rules of the road, one of which is the speed limit. This is the fastest rate they can safely travel on that road. Now think about the units for driving speed in the United States. Most interstate highways have a speed limit of 70 miles per hour. What are the units used for speed here? Miles per hour. That is actually a fraction with miles being divided by hour. So if people are traveling 70 miles per hour, that means they are going at a speed such that if they travel that same speed for an hour's time, they will move a distance of 70 miles. If they travel at a speed of 35 miles per hour, then after an hour of travel, they will have moved a distance of 35 miles. So the units for speed are distance (mile) over time (hour). We can measure speed in other units, too, as long as there is a distance unit over a time unit. Many other countries in the world use kilometers as their distance unit. So people traveling 70 miles per hour would also be traveling about 110 kilometers per hour.

FIGURE 9.4
Speed Limit Sign Understood as Miles per Hour

Speed—The rate at which an object moves

You already know that light travels very fast. Scientists measure the speed of light using the unit kilometers per second. They use a metric measurement because metrics are the units used in science. And they use seconds as a measure of time because light travels so rapidly that we get a smaller number if we can measure the distance traveled each second versus each hour. So the speed of light is 299,792 kilometers per second.

We can say that units are a very important part of reporting speed, can't we? In fact, you can find out the average speed an object traveled if you know the distance it went and the time it took for it to cover that distance.

Now, **velocity** is a slightly different term as compared to speed. Often these terms are used interchangeably, but there is indeed a significant difference. While speed tells you how quickly an object moves, velocity tells you how quickly it moves and in what direction.

Velocity—The speed of an object in a given direction

This may not seem like a big deal, but it really is. Say you had 2 trains riding on the same track in a city and both were going a speed of 50 miles per hour. Would that be a good thing? Well, it depends on their velocity. You see, if they were both coming into a city at 50 miles per hour in a western direction, then everything's fine. But what if one was traveling 50 miles per hour in a western direction and the other was traveling 50 miles per hour in an *eastern* direction? That could be terrible! So velocity gives us more information about the movement of an object than speed does.

Let's say that you were riding in a taxi going at 50 miles per hour north. A squirrel suddenly darts into the road, causing the taxi driver to slam on his brakes. The taxi begins to slow down until it comes to a stop. What happened to the taxi's velocity? Well the moment the driver put his foot on the brake, it caused the taxi to start to slow down. So the velocity began to decrease. It continued to decrease until the velocity was 0 miles per hour north, and you stopped.

FIGURE 9.5
Negative and Positive Acceleration

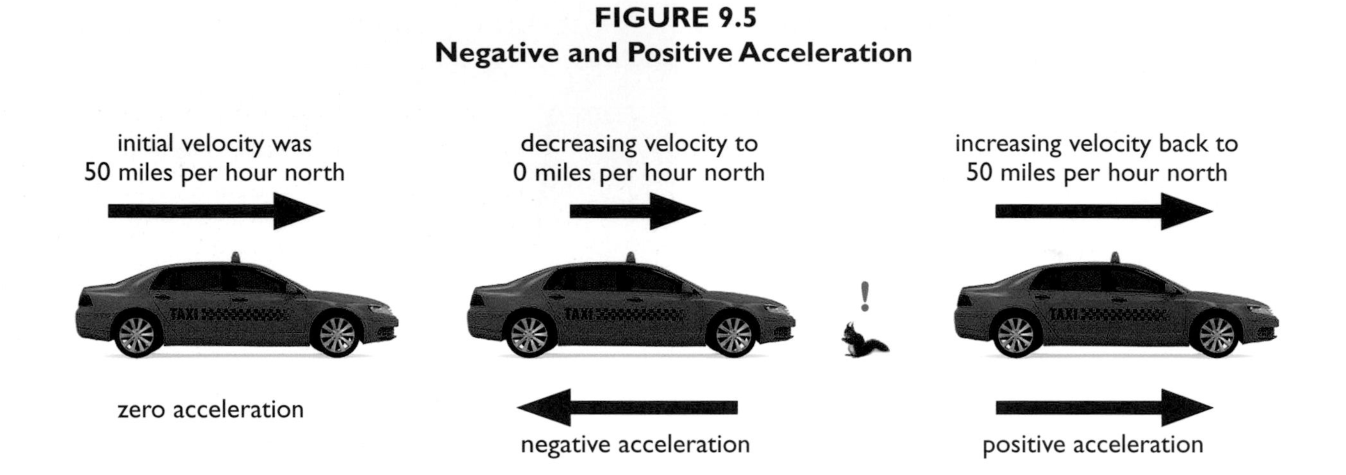

Once you and the driver caught your breath and the terrified (but safe) squirrel ran out of the way, the taxi driver began driving again. He began to increase velocity until the taxi reached 50 miles per hour in a northward direction again (see top arrows in Figure 9.5).

Because the velocity of the taxi has changed, we say the taxi has an **acceleration** (ak sel' er ay shun). Like velocity, acceleration is a term with a direction to it. When velocity increases, the direction of acceleration is in the *same direction* as the object's velocity. Acceleration is an increase in that object's velocity. In the taxi and squirrel example, after the taxi driver stopped, he began to accelerate to get the taxi going again. And he had a positive acceleration, which meant the direction of acceleration was the same as the original velocity. But earlier, when he was trying to stop to avoid hitting the squirrel, the taxi's acceleration was *negative*. That means the acceleration was in the opposite direction of the taxi's velocity. This all might make more sense if you look at Figure 9.5 again.

FIGURE 9.6
More Negative and Positive Acceleration

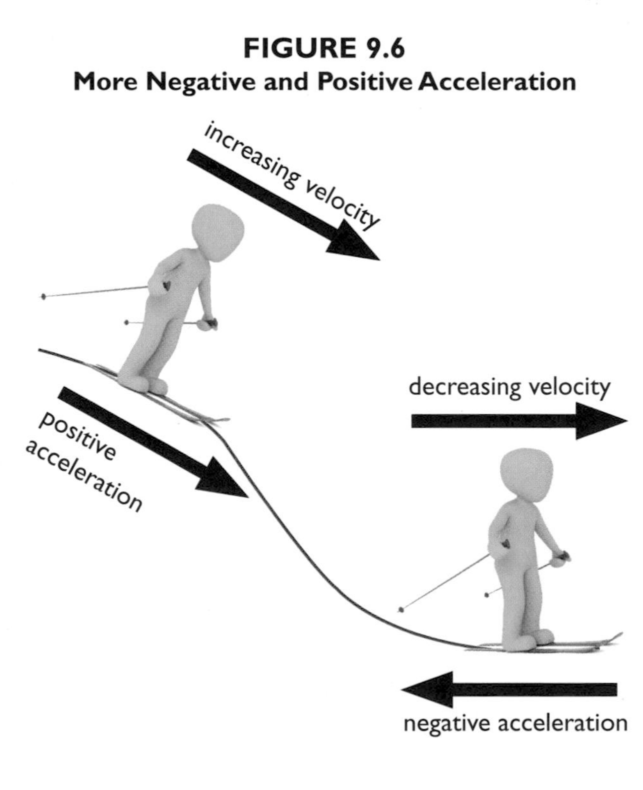

Sometimes, it is easier to think of negative acceleration as **deceleration**, at least for the scope of this course. They both mean an object is slowing down as compared to its original velocity, but it is more accurate to use the terms negative acceleration for slowing down and positive acceleration for speeding up.

When an object is accelerating, its velocity is constantly changing. The taxi in our example was initially traveling at a velocity of 50 miles per hour north. Before the driver hit his brakes, there was no acceleration, was there? The velocity remained constant. But once he hit the brakes, the velocity continually began to change, from 50 miles per hour north to 49 miles per hour north, and so on. Each moment the taxi was slowing down represented a different velocity—a slower one—which means that the acceleration was in a negative direction and the velocity was decreasing.

ON YOUR OWN

9.1 Which 2 of the following represent a velocity?

a. 50 miles per hour b. 20 feet per second north c. 16.2 meters d. 20 miles per hour west

9.2 When a car is slowing down, what happens to its speed and its velocity? Is its acceleration positive or negative?

FIGURE 9.7
Sir Isaac Newton

NEWTON'S 3 LAWS OF MOTION

You studied Isaac Newton in Module 1. In the first of his 3-volume set of writings, called *Principia*, Newton introduced and explained 3 laws of motion, making a direct link between math and science. Well, now it is time to learn about those laws.

Newton's First Law

Newton's first law is often called the law of inertia. It states that **an object will stay in motion with a constant velocity (or will stay at rest) until it is acted upon by an outside force.** Let me explain this idea further. Think about a soccer ball sitting on the ground. It is not moving, so we could say it is at rest. If no one kicks it, there is no strong wind, or nothing else bumps into it, what will it do? Of course, it will just keep on sitting there, won't it? As this first law states, if an object is at rest it will stay at rest until it is acted upon by an outside force. So when you kick the ball, you are the outside force causing it to no longer remain at rest.

Now what about the object-in-motion part of the definition? Suppose you are riding your bike and you stop pedaling. What happens? You *were* in motion but then you start to slow down until you come to a stop. That might make you think that the motion part of Newton's first law is incorrect. But there are other

FIGURE 9.8
A Bike Slowing Down Due to Gravity and Friction

things happening here. You see, once you stop pedaling, you might think that no other outside forces are acting on your bike. But there are! The bike is being affected by the pull of gravity, pulling it down toward Earth. And that increases its **friction.** Friction is a force resulting from surfaces rubbing against one another. Explore the action of friction in Experiment 9.1.

EXPERIMENT 9.1
EXPLORING FRICTION

PURPOSE: To learn how friction affects various objects

MATERIALS:

- A large book (The book does not have to be thick, but the larger the surface area of its cover, the better.)
- A paper clip
- A small pencil-topper eraser
- 2 lumps of clay each about the same size as the eraser
- A ruler

QUESTION: What happens when various objects are placed on an inclined surface?

HYPOTHESIS: Write what you think will happen to the paper clip, eraser, and clay when the book is raised on an incline.

PROCEDURE:

1. Lay the book flat on the table.
2. Roll one lump of clay into a smooth ball.
3. Line up the paper clip, eraser, and ball of clay along one short side of the book.
4. Slowly raise that side of the book so it forms an inclined surface.
5. Once the first item slides, stop raising the book and measure with the ruler how high you lifted the book. Write that height (and which item slid) in your notebook.
6. Very slowly, continue to tilt the book upward until the second item slides down the book. Now measure how high the book is from the table. Write that information in your notebook.
7. Keep raising the book until the last item slides down. Measure and record the book's height.
8. Now take the second lump of clay and flatten it into a small disc shape.
9. Repeat steps 1-6 using **only** the ball of clay and the flattened clay.
10. Write in your notebook which of the 2 pieces of clay falls first and how high you have to tilt the book to get each item to slide down the surface.

CONCLUSION: Write what you learned about friction based on the results of the experiment.

Let's talk about what happened in Experiment 9.1. When you lifted the book while the paper clip, eraser, and ball of clay were on it, you probably noticed that the ball of clay rolled down the book first. However, you may have seen the paper clip fall first if your clay was not completely rounded or had a sticky surface. The eraser should have slid last. What caused them to slide at different heights? It has to do with friction. You see, as soon as the book was tilted, gravity began affecting the objects, trying to force them to slide downward. But they did not move right away due to friction. However, the higher the book was tilted, the greater gravity's effect would be felt by the objects; and when gravity's force became stronger than the friction holding them in place, the objects slid down the book. So objects that slid down the book when the book was tilted only a little had just a small frictional force holding them in place. Objects that did not slide down the book until it was tilted very high had a large frictional force holding them in place.

FIGURE 9.9
An Asteroid Experiencing Little Friction in Space

The strength of the frictional force between the objects and the book has to do with the physical characteristics of each object. For example, the paper clip's smooth surface had less frictional force acting on it as compared to the rubbery surface of the eraser.

When you tilted the book with the clay ball and flattened clay, you should have seen the ball slide first. Even though both objects were made of the same material and were about the same mass, the shape affected the frictional force acting on them.

Let's return to the illustration of riding your bike. Your bike slows down due to the friction between the bike wheels and the road. In other words, the frictional force is an outside force acting on the moving object of your bike, thus causing it to slow down.

If you were to push your bike deep into interstellar space, the bike would continue to move indefinitely. That is because there would be little or no gravitational force or frictional force acting on it. (Remember, there is no atmosphere in space, so there are no gas molecules that bump into the bike.) So, the bike would stay in motion like Newton's first law states.

I keep using the word **force** in this discussion. I think it might be a good idea to explain what exactly a force is.

Force—A push or pull exerted on an object in an effort to change that object's velocity

So when you kick a soccer ball, your foot provides a *pushing* force on that ball to get it in motion. Gravity is a force that *pulls* objects toward Earth. And that's a good thing, or we would all float into space! We always can feel the force of gravity working on us. As we walk or run, we eventually become fatigued because gravity continually works against our movement.

I also want to further explain what **inertia** is. Inertia is basically a resistance to change. So in Newton's first law, a moving object will continue in motion, wanting to resist a change in that motion. Your body experiences inertia all the time. A good example is when you are riding in a car. Imagine yourself in the back of the car while your parent is driving, and the car suddenly has to take a sharp turn to the left. What happens to your body? It shifts to the right of the car. That's because your body was traveling in a straight line along with the car. Then when the car turned, your body wanted to continue going in that straight line. Your body's inertia caused it to keep moving forward until you bumped into the right side of the car.

FIGURE 9.10
Kicking Force

Newton's Second Law

The second law of motion Isaac Newton described builds on his first law. The first law involves objects in motion (or at rest) and how they will remain that way until a force acts on them. The second law has to do with *how much* force is needed to affect those objects. **Newton's second law** has to do with force. It states that **when an object is acted on by one or more outside forces, the total force is equal to the mass of the object times the resulting acceleration.** What does all that mean?

It basically says that a force is what causes an object to change its speed or direction. For example, would you need a greater force to push a piano or a chair across the floor? The piano would require a greater force because it has a larger mass, doesn't it? What about changing the direction of a soccer ball coming at you versus a soccer ball not moving at all? It would take a greater force to kick the soccer ball coming at you because it has acceleration in a direction that fights the direction of the force you will be kicking it with.

Here is where some of the math that Newton talked about comes in. We can easily explain this long law by converting it to a math sentence: total force = mass × acceleration (or $F = m \times a$).

EXPLORE MORE

Explore Newton's second law by having a friend sit on a swing. Gently push your friend, using a small force. How much acceleration does your friend have? Now push your friend with greater force. Notice the change in acceleration as compared to the gentle push. It should be greater. In the equation $F = m \times a$, your friend has not changed his or her mass, but when you increase force, you will see an increase of acceleration. That is mathematically necessary for both sides of the equation to be equal to one another. Can you see how this law can be explained and described mathematically? It's an elegant design of the physics of creation!

From this you could say that if you wanted to kick a ball into a soccer goal, a ball that is stationary will require less force than a ball that is coming toward you. In the math equation, the mass of the ball remains the same, but increasing the value of **a** means you have to increase the value of **F**. The greater the acceleration that is needed, the more force is necessary to give that acceleration (see Figure 9.11).

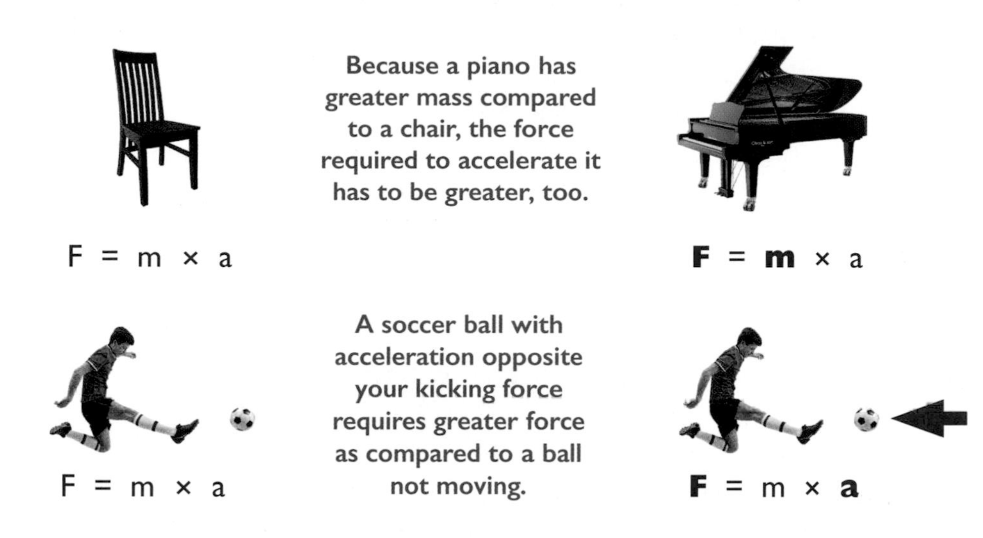

In the end, this law basically says that in order to have an effect on an object's motion, you must have a total push or a pull on that object (a force) that is the same as the object's mass times the amount of change in speed or direction.

Newton's Third Law

Let's talk about Newton's **third law** now. This law says that **for every action, there is an equal and opposite reaction.** The best way to explain this law is to think about 2 people on roller skates. They are facing each other and not moving. The first person pushes the second person with a rightward force. That makes the second person have a rightward acceleration. Newton's third law says there is an equal-sized force on the first person, coming from the second person, too. That will give the first person a *leftward* acceleration (Figure 9.12). Notice how the 2 forces are equal in size, but opposite in direction and involving 2 different objects (the 2 people)?

Now imagine a Civil War cannon firing. When a cannon fires a cannon ball, the cannon always jumps backward. What happens is that the cannon (and gunpowder and exploding gas) puts a force on the cannon ball; however, the *cannon ball* puts nearly an equal and opposite force on the cannon. Thus, the cannon ball moves forward, and the cannon itself moves backward.

This law is technically more accurate if you were to observe objects in space where there is no gravity or friction acting on them.

FIGURE 9.12
Newton's Third Law

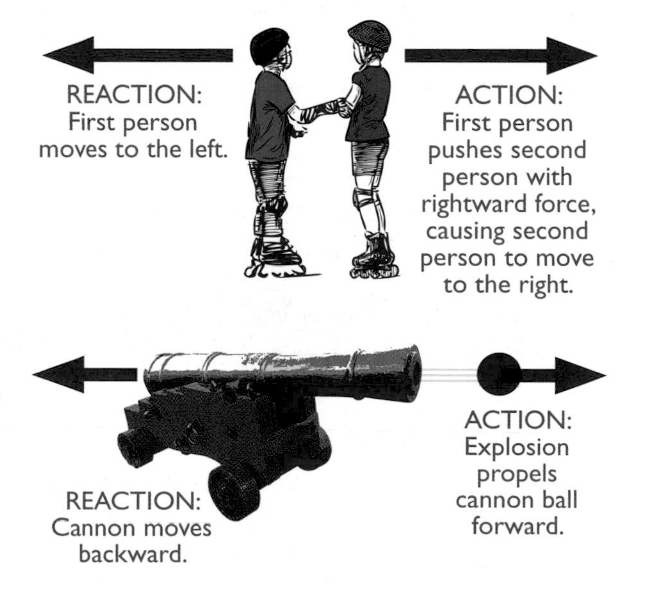

But Newton's third law still works on Earth; it is just more complicated to demonstrate because of other forces at work.

think about this

Newton's third law explains how rockets can fly. You see, when a rocket launches, it starts to burn fuel. This results in lots of hot gas that builds up pressure and pushes out of the rocket. In response, the gas that's being pushed out of the rocket pushes back on the rocket, causing the rocket to move in the opposite direction. This is called **thrust**, and it is the same basic principle as when you blow up a balloon and, instead of tying it off, release it. The pressure from the gas escaping pushes back on the balloon, and the balloon flies around the room.

ON YOUR OWN

9.3 Write Newton's 3 laws and make an illustration of an example in your notebook.

MORE ABOUT FORCES

I have already talked a bit about forces, but there are many ways that forces can be exerted in creation. Scientists don't fully understand how all these forces work, and they have come up with several theories. For the scope of this course, you should only be concerned with the types of forces introduced to you.

One force that exists in creation is the force that holds the center of an atom together. Last module, I briefly mentioned this strong force, and indeed it is believed to be the strongest natural force. Remember how the nuclei of atoms contain only positively charged protons and neutral neutrons? Well, the positive charges of the protons should repel one another, but they don't because the strong force is much greater.

FIGURE 9.13
Strong Force in a Nucleus

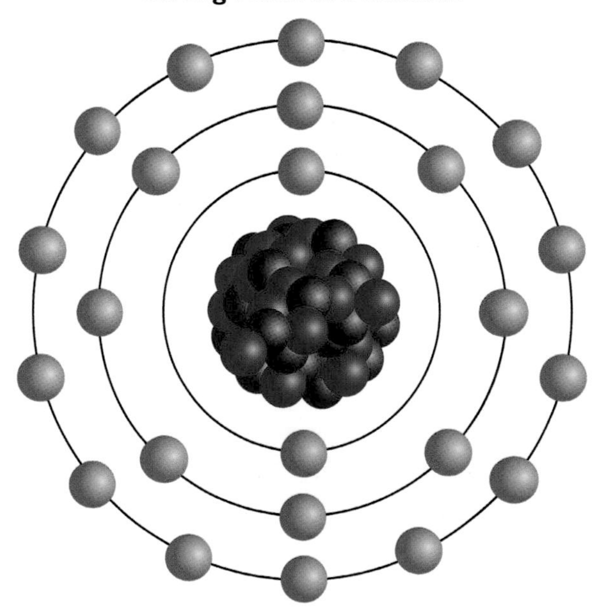

Gravitational Force

You are likely very familiar with a second force: gravitational force. In fact, you probably started experimenting with it when you were a toddler, dropping items from your high chair. When things fall, they move toward Earth because the gravitational force attracts them to Earth. We already talked about how Earth holds the Moon in orbit due to its gravitational force, but you might not realize that the *Moon* also has a gravitational force pulling Earth. They don't crash together because the movement of the Moon in its orbit around Earth keeps them apart.

As a matter of fact, any 2 objects that have mass are attracted to one another by their gravitational forces. But it is a relatively weak force as compared to the other forces, so an object has to be massive for its gravitational force to greatly affect anything else. When you jump up in the air, for example, the Earth pulls you down, but you also *pull the Earth up* toward you. It is just that your mass is so comparatively small that your gravitational force is extremely small, and you cannot perceive the Earth moving at all.

FIGURE 9.14
Gravitational Force

When you jump, both you and the Earth exert a gravitational force.

Electromagnetic Force

A third force that exists between particles is called the **electromagnetic force**. As its name suggests, it has to do with both electricity and magnetism. This force is attractive like the gravitational force, but it also can be a repulsive force. Think of what you learned in Module 8. Two positively charged objects repel each other, as do 2 negatively charged objects. But a positively charged object will attract a negatively charged one.

FIGURE 9.15
Electromagnetic Force

Electric force (lightning) and magnetic force (magnetic attraction).

This force is what makes electricity flow in an electrical circuit. It also is the force that holds electrons in an atom, and it makes lightning. But you might be surprised to learn that it is the same force that causes a compass needle to point to magnetic north on Earth and to cause magnets to attract or repel one another.

Last module, you learned that electrons can be taken by or given to atoms. Well, electrons are exchanged all the time, moving around and changing energy. In Module 8, one of the Explore More activities involved rubbing a balloon in your hair. When you did this, the balloon picked up several electrons from your hair's atoms. That means the balloon had an overall negative charge due to all those extra electrons you picked up. (Don't worry. Your body pulled extra electrons from the ground to make up for the lost ones.)

Every charged object has an invisible electric field around it, and anything that gets close to that field will be either attracted to or repelled by that charge. This electric field is an area of force that surrounds both electrically charged items as well as magnets.

FIGURE 9.16
Electrical Field around 2 Atoms of Opposite Charges (left) and a Magnetic Field around a Bar Magnet (right)

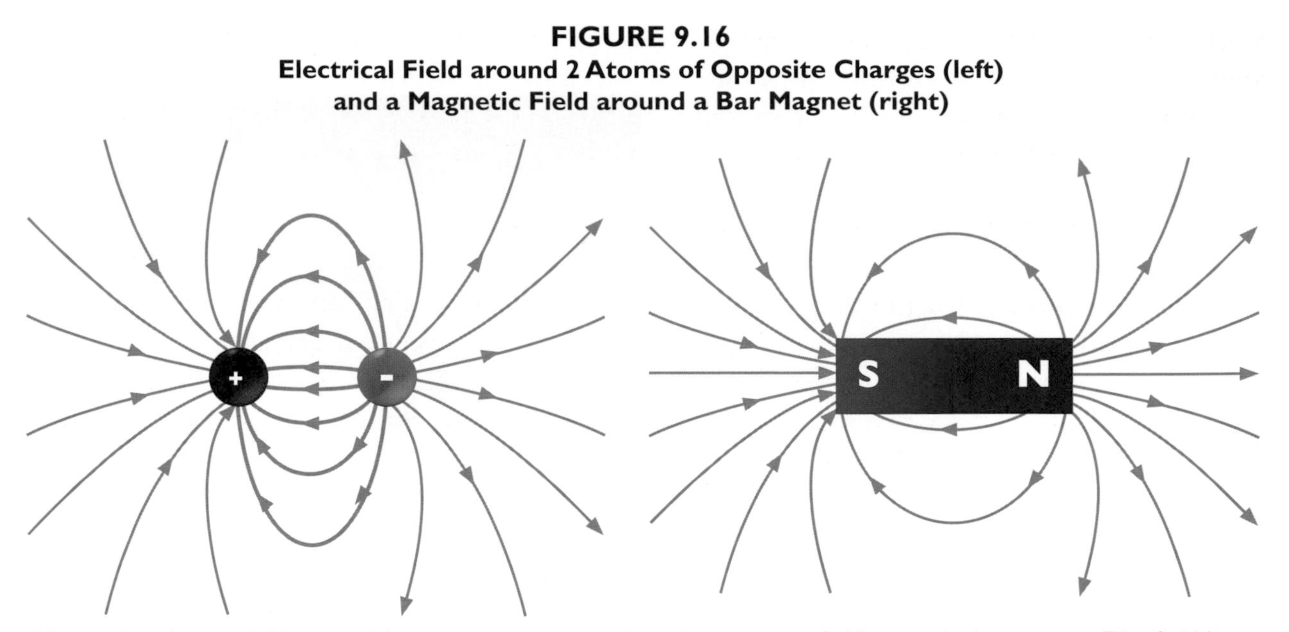

Notice the electric field around the atoms as compared to the magnetic field around a bar magnet. The field lines look similar. That's because the electromagnetic force is responsible for both.

Have you ever walked around your house wearing socks and then touched a doorknob or another person only to feel a shock? What happened was that you were picking up electrons with your feet as you were walking. The extra electrons piled up inside your body until you came close to something. All at once they jumped over to the other object (or person), and you felt a shock. The extra electrons in your body created something called **static electricity.** The electrons were static; they were not able to move away from you. Extra electrons are all negatively charged, and they want to move apart from one another. So, when you touch another object, they rapidly move to it as a flow of electricity. **Electricity is the motion of electrons from one place to another.**

We control the flow of electrons when we use materials, such as metal wires, that easily transport them. Some materials, like plastics, do not allow electrons to easily flow; we say they are poor conductors of electricity. Yet, metals such as copper conduct electricity very well. That is why the electrical wiring in your house is made up of metal wires, not plastic ones.

When electrons flow through a conductor like a metal wire, it is called an electric current. But electrons can flow through other materials besides wire. *People* can even conduct electricity. That is why it is not safe to stand out in a field during a lightning storm. Electrical charges build up in the clouds and the ground, and electrons will more easily move through a person than air! That is because people are filled

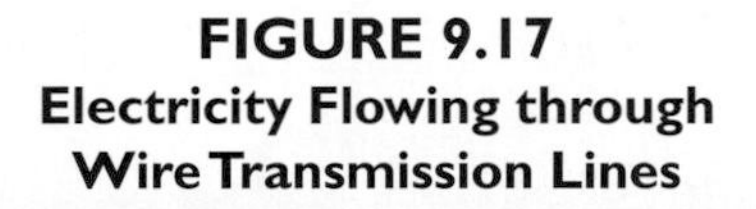
FIGURE 9.17
Electricity Flowing through Wire Transmission Lines

with ionic fluid that can produce ions (which, if you remember, are charged atoms and molecules).

Electricity in houses, cars, and appliances moves through **electric circuits.** Flowing electricity needs to move in a closed path.

Electric circuit—A closed path through which electric current flows

Electric circuits require a **power source.** From tiny button batteries to huge nuclear power plants, power sources can vary greatly. They also need an object to turn on, called a **load.** This could be a light bulb, a house air conditioner, or a computer. Loads will take away the energy from the electrons as they move through a circuit, so they are sometimes called **resistors.** They *resist* electric flow.

So what makes electrons want to move along a circuit? It is similar to what happens when lightning strikes. Electrons move from a place of higher electric energy to lower electric energy. Batteries, for example, have 2 sides with unequal electric energies, so when you connect the 2 sides, electrons will flow from the high-energy end to the low-energy end. Explore how circuits work by completing Experiment 9.2.

EXPERIMENT 9.2
BUILDING AN ELECTRIC CIRCUIT

PURPOSE: To better understand how electric current flows through a circuit

MATERIALS:
- 2 D batteries
- Electrical tape
- Insulated number 22 copper wire (about 18")
- Scissors
- 2 large metal paper clips
- A spring-tension wood or plastic clothespin
- A cork message board or a sheet of very thick cardboard, about 8" x 11"
- Masking tape
- 3 metal thumbtacks
- A non-LED, 3-volt flashlight bulb (You also can use a small car tail-light bulb from an auto supply store or the auto section of a large discount store.)

QUESTION: What are the major components of an electric circuit?

HYPOTHESIS: Write what you think is necessary for an electric current to flow through a circuit.

PROCEDURE:
1. First, you need to build a battery pack. Place the 2 batteries next to each other with the positive terminal of one battery facing up and the positive terminal of the other battery facing down.

2. Use electrical tape to secure the 2 batteries together. (Refer to Figure 9.18.)
3. Stand the batteries up on end and place a paper clip between the positive and negative contacts. Make sure it is touching both batteries and secure it with electrical tape.
4. Cut 2 pieces of wire about 6 inches in length and use the scissors to carefully cut through just the plastic insulation on each end of the wires, exposing about half an inch of metal. Once you cut the plastic, you can slide the plastic off of the metal wire. (A wire stripper tool will also work.)
5. Turn the battery pack so that the paper clip end is facing down. Place the stripped part of one of the wires on a battery contact and secure it with a strip of electrical tape. Do the same thing with the other battery contact and wire. (NOTE: Do not allow the unattached ends of the wires to touch each other, or you will create a complete electrical circuit and ruin the batteries.)
6. Wind one end of the exposed wire of the battery pack around a thumbtack. Hook a paper clip around the tack and press the tack into the cork board.
7. Cut a 5" strip of wire, strip both ends as you did in step 4, and wrap each end around 2 more thumbtacks. Place one thumbtack in the board so that when the paper clip spins around, it can touch it (see blue arrow in diagram).
8. Press the other thumbtack (the third one) where the light bulb will be placed.
9. Wrap the other wire from the battery pack around the metal part of the light bulb. You may need to secure it with electrical tape.
10. Clamp the clothespin around the metal part of the light bulb and orient it on the board so that it holds the bulb right on the third thumbtack. Tape the clothespin to the board with masking tape. Use several pieces to secure it.
11. Now complete your circuit by rotating the paper clip so it comes in contact with the second thumbtack. Observe what happens when the circuit is complete.
12. Rotate the paper clip so it is not in contact with the second thumbtack and again observe what happens. Record your observations in your notebook.
13. Clean everything up and put it away.

FIGURE 9.18
An Electric Circuit

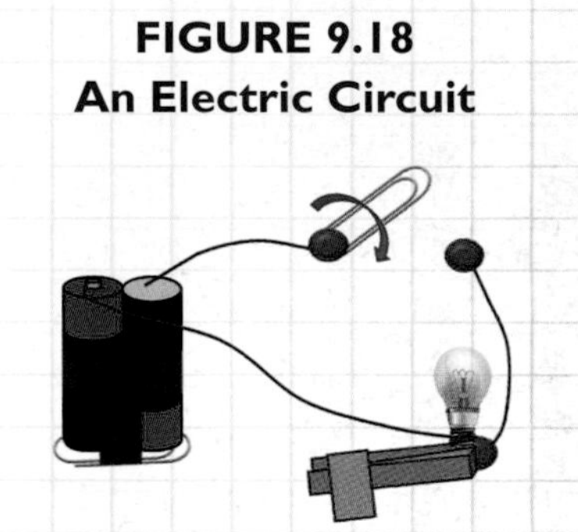

The paper clip can swivel around one thumbtack in order to touch the second one (blue arrow). This completes the circuit. Note that in this diagram, the tape securing the wires to the batteries is missing so you can see the circuit more easily.

CONCLUSION: Identify the power source, the load, and the switch in your circuit.

In the experiment, you should have seen the bulb light up when the paper clip touched the thumbtack. That paper clip behaved as a switch. When it touched the thumbtack, it created a complete circuit through which electrical current could pass. This is called a **closed circuit.** You see, when it is not touching the thumbtack, the electrons have no way of moving out of the battery pack all the way to its other side. It is an incomplete or **open circuit.** So in your circuit, the power source was the battery pack, the load was the light bulb, and the swiveling paper clip was the switch.

Magnetism

Remember that electricity and magnetism are closely related. Magnets exist in nature. In fact, the entire Earth is a magnet! So, what makes a magnet? Well, a magnet is any object that attracts and repels certain metals. Magnets also create magnetic fields. You can see in Figure 9.16 how magnetic fields are similar to electric fields.

EXPLORE MORE

There is a way to actually "see" the magnetic field of magnets. Take a white sheet of paper and set it on a tray or paper plate. Put a bar magnet under the tray. Now carefully sprinkle iron shavings around the area where the magnet is. You may need to gently shake the paper from side to side a bit to get the shavings to react to the magnet's force, but you should be able to see the iron shavings line up along the magnetic field. So you are not actually looking *at* the magnetic field, but you can indirectly see its shape by how the shavings behave around it.

FIGURE 9.19
Iron Shavings around a Magnet

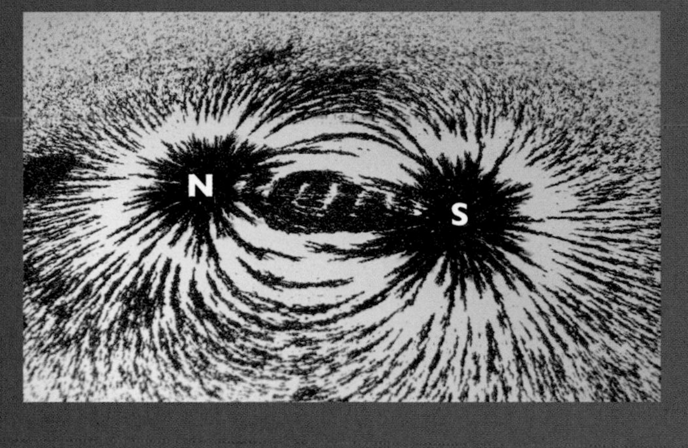

The same way that atoms can form positive or negative ions that can attract or repel one another, magnets have opposites that can do the same thing. You see, all magnets have a north and a south pole. The north pole of a magnet attracts the south pole of another magnet, and it will repel the north pole of another magnet.

You may have magnets on your refrigerator in your house. The refrigerator is made of metal and the magnets attract that metal. So when a magnetic object is placed near a magnetic field, it feels the force of that field by either being pulled toward the field or repelled by it.

Take a look at the top magnet in Figure 9.20. It's a bar magnet with a north pole on one side and a south pole on the other. If you took a very powerful saw and cut it in half, would you have one magnet with only a north pole and one with only a south pole? No, you would not. You would end up with 2 smaller magnets, each with a north and south pole. And you could cut them in half again and again, resulting in tinier and tinier complete magnets, each with a north and a south pole. That's because all magnets are made up of tiny magnets called **domains.** Magnetic domains are tiny regions in which the magnetic fields of atoms are grouped together and aligned. They are kind of like miniature magnets within a large magnet.

FIGURE 9.20
Bar Magnets

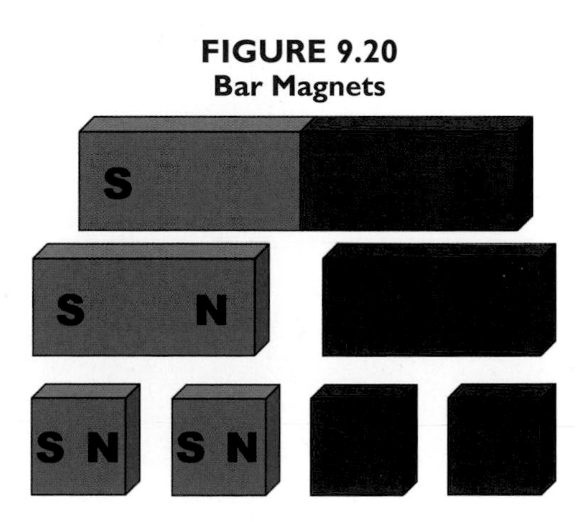

Now what do I mean when I say *aligned*? It simply means that the tiny domains have their north pole ends pointed in the same direction and their south pole ends pointed the opposite direction (Figure 9.21). Let's go even tinier in our description. When I said that the magnetic fields of atoms are grouped together and aligned, that means nearly anything with electrons can form a magnetic field. You see, whenever an electron is spinning around an atom's nucleus, it creates a little magnetic field around that atom. And electrons can spin in the same direction or in opposite directions to each other. If they spin in opposite directions, they are not aligned, and their magnetic fields cancel each other out. Substances that have electrons spinning in opposite directions have a weak response to magnets. Materials such as plastics have a weak response to magnets, and therefore magnets will not be attracted to them. This is why few things are magnetic. You see, most substances have electrons that spin in such a way that they are not aligned. However, if a substance has electrons that spin in the same direction, then the electrons are aligned, forming small magnetic domains. The more electrons that are aligned, the more magnetically attractive that material is.

FIGURE 9.21
Aligned Domains

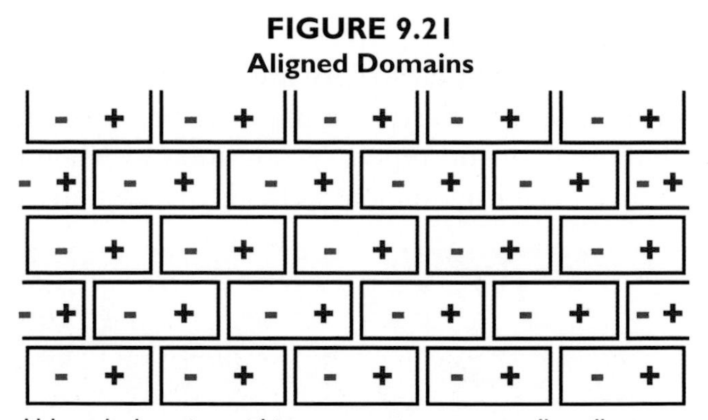

Although domains within a magnet are too small to illustrate, this figure can give you an idea how they are stacked and aligned so that all their positive sides are facing the same direction. Each brick here represents a single domain.

EXPLORE MORE

Some substances are made of atoms that can be *made* to align. Take a strong magnet and rub it along the length of a steel nail, moving along it in one direction only. Place the tip of the steel nail into a pile of steel paper clips. The nail should behave like a magnet and draw the paper clips to it. That's because when you rubbed the magnet along the nail, you were forcing the domains within the nail to align with each other. This made the nail behave like a magnet.

ON YOUR OWN

9.4 Explain how a switch works in an electric circuit.

9.5 In an earlier module, you learned how Earth had a magnetic field surrounding it. Now that you understand a bit more about the electromagnetic force, explain how this might be created from Earth's solid inner iron core and its liquid outer iron core that swirls around it as Earth turns on its axis.

SIMPLE MACHINES

Now that you have a better understanding of force, I can talk about how forces can be useful to people. Let's do this by discussing **simple machines**.

Simple machine—A device that either multiplies or redirects a force

A simple machine magnifies a force or changes its direction, particularly to make a task easier to complete. Most non-electronic machines are some combination of the 6 simple machines I will introduce in this section.

The Lever

The **lever** is a simple machine that magnifies either force or motion. It consists of a rigid **bar** that rotates around a fixed point called a **fulcrum.** If you think of a seesaw, you can think of the center as the fulcrum. Let's say there was a weight you wanted to move upward. So you placed it on one side of the seesaw. Then you pushed down on the other side. Your pushing is called the **effort,** and the weight you are causing to move upward is the **resistance.** The closer the fulcrum is to the resistance, the less effort you need to make the resistance move.

FIGURE 9.22
Parts of a Lever

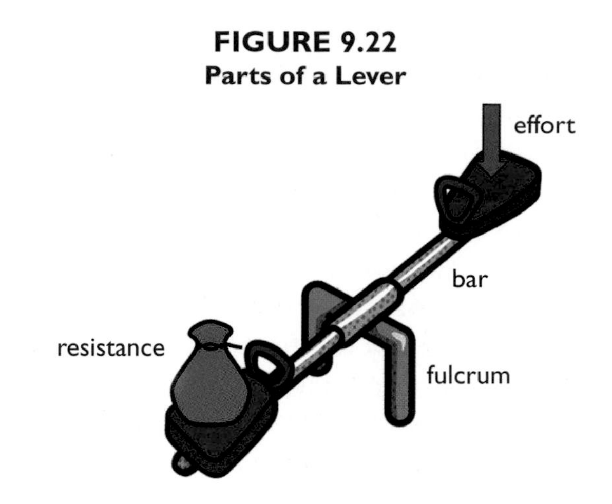

There are 3 classes of levers, based on where the fulcrum is located. The seesaw example is a **first-class lever.** It is when the fulcrum is located between the effort and the resistance (see Figure 9.23). A **second-class lever** is when the fulcrum is at one end of the bar and the resistance is between the fulcrum and the effort. A wheelbarrow is an example of a second-class lever. In a **third-class lever,** the fulcrum is at one end of the bar and the effort is between the fulcrum and resistance. A fishing pole is a third-class lever.

FIGURE 9.23
Classes of Levers

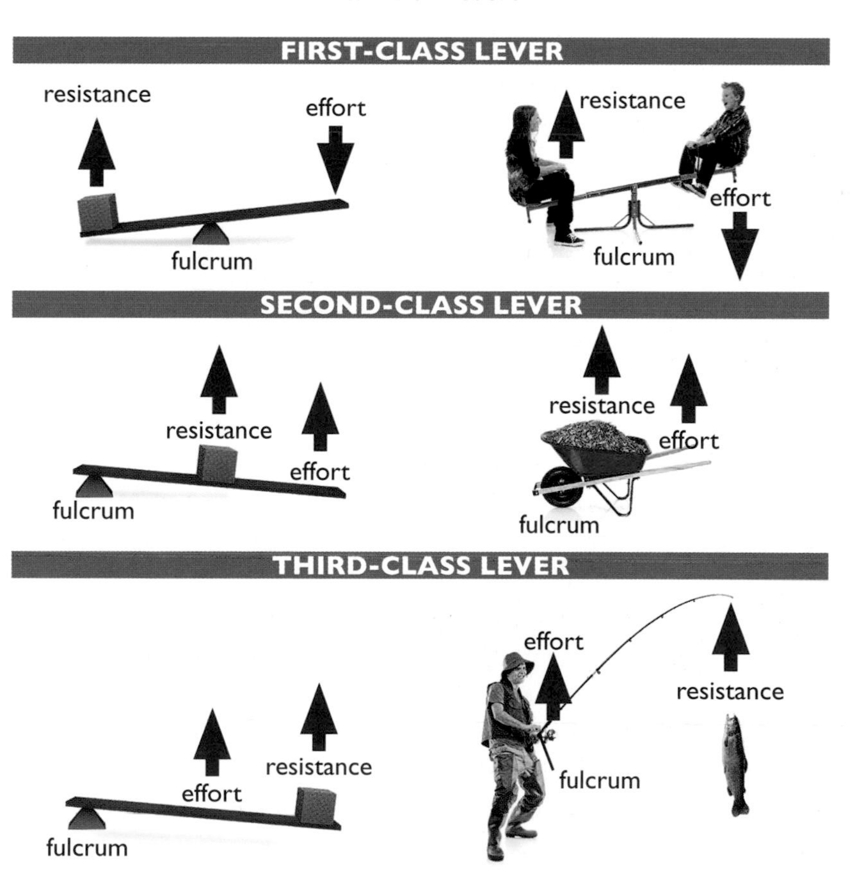

Notice that in the first-class lever, the direction of the effort and the resistance are opposite. If you push down, the resistance will go up. In a second-class lever, the effort and resistance move in the same direction. If you lift up, the resistance will also go up. And finally, a third-class lever has the effort and resistance both moving in the same direction. If you lift up, the resistance will go up.

Now, all simple machines create what is called a **mechanical advantage.** That is when a force or a motion is magnified to help a person do some kind of work. The first 2 lever classes magnify the force. If you give a little effort, greater force will result. The third one doesn't magnify the force, but it does increase the speed at which the resistance moves. So all of these machines can be helpful to get work done.

The Wheel and Axle

The **wheel and axle** is a simple machine that has a large circular wheel attached to a smaller cylinder (Figure 9.24, left). As the wheel turns, the axle turns, and as the axle turns, so does the wheel. In a car, an engine turns an axle that causes the tires to turn. So a force is applied to the axle and used to turn the tires. This creates a mechanical advantage in that the speed of the tires is magnified as compared to the speed of the axle. That makes the car go faster. Alternatively, a car's steering wheel is another application of this simple machine. You apply force to the *wheel* to get the axle to turn. Here, the mechanical advantage is that the force you apply is greatly magnified in the axle. Very large trucks, for example, have huge steering wheels because it requires a greater force to turn the post (which is the axle) as compared to a car.

The Pulley

A **pulley** consists of a grooved wheel that rotates freely on a frame. It is operated by laying a rope in the pulley's groove. When one end of the rope is pulled down, the wheel rotates and the other end of the rope is lifted up. In a pulley, the wheel is the only part that can rotate. Now, in order for a pulley to provide a mechanical advantage, more than one pulley needs to be used. A set of pulleys is called a **block and tackle.** You see, more pulleys working together will increase the force you are using. It becomes easier to lift an item. Looking at the block and tackle in Figure 9.24, let's say the resistance (weight) has a mass of 100 kg. That means that the effort to lift it would be 50 kg. The use of 2 pulleys together cuts the effort required to lift the resistance in half. But to take advantage of that, you have to pull more rope as compared to the amount of rope needed if using only one pulley. What I mean by that is in order to lift the resistance 1 m upward, the person would have to exert the effort by pulling 2 m of rope. You see, with any mechanical advantage offered by a simple machine, you have to "pay" for that advantage by having to use your force over a longer distance, such as with a series of pulleys. In a second-class lever, for example, the distance you have to lift the

FIGURE 9.24
Wheel and Axle and a Block and Tackle

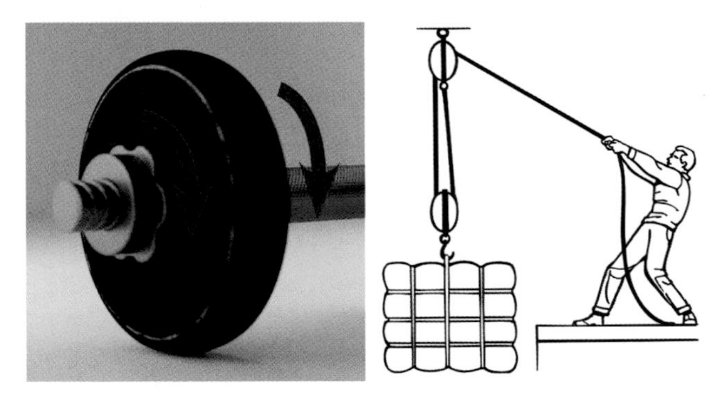

bar is much greater than the distance the resistance moves.

The Inclined Plane

Perhaps the simplest of the simple machines is the **inclined plane** (or ramp). It makes lifting a load easier because you can slide the load up the inclined plane rather than lifting it straight up. Of course, you pay for that mechanical advantage by having to push the load farther than just lifting the load directly upward.

FIGURE 9.25
An Inclined Plane Ramp

The Wedge

The **wedge** looks exactly the same as an inclined plane, but it is used differently. With an inclined plane, the force is applied parallel to the slope of the plane (Figure 9.26). But with a wedge, the force is applied to the plane's short edge. A wedge is generally used to separate things. By striking the vertical edge of a wedge, the pointed end applies a force to whatever it is in contact with. Wedges are used to split wood. The mechanical advantage here is that it takes less force to move 2 things apart (such as 2 sides of a log). However, you have to pay for that advantage in that you have to push the wedge in farther than the things you are separating will move apart.

FIGURE 9.26
Inclined Plane and Wedge

The Screw

The last simple machine I want to discuss is the **screw**, which is actually an inclined plane wrapped around the axle of a wheel and axle (Figure 9.27). The inclined plane of a screw is called **threads.** And the vertical distance between the threads is the **pitch** of the screw. A full turn of the screw will result in the screw traveling into an object by a distance equal to its pitch. Its mechanical advantage has to do with the circumference of the head of the screw and the pitch of the threads. Now, circumference has to do with the distance

FIGURE 9.27
A Screw
(An Inclined Plane and a Wheel and Axle)

around the screw, so screws with larger heads are easier to use. But it is very hard to get a screw into wood using your hands, isn't it? You have to use a screwdriver. Well, using a screwdriver is easier because you are basically building onto the screw machine. The screwdriver handle has a larger circumference, making it easier for you to turn around and thus increasing the force pushing the screw into the wood. The fatter the handle of the screwdriver, the greater its mechanical advantage and the easier it is to turn the screw into the wood.

ON YOUR OWN

9.6 List the 6 simple machines from this section and give a common example of each.

9.7 What 2 simple machines are combined to make a screw?

FIGURE 9.28
Ocean Waves at the Shore

WAVES AND SOUND

What is sound? In order to understand sound, we need to talk about waves. In fact, in this section and the next, we will talk about both sound *and* light in terms of waves. You probably can best think of waves as they move in water. Imagine you are standing on an ocean shore, ankle-deep in the water while waves hit your legs. That's very similar to what happens when sound travels.

But what does all this have to do with sound? Sound travels in waves. In fact, sound is a vibration that needs to travel through some kind of material. Like energy travels through water to produce waves, sound needs "stuff" in order to travel. That medium can be solid, liquid, and even gas. This means sound travels in air by bumping into some air molecules that then bump into the next molecules, and the next, and so on. Try the next Explore More to learn about that idea.

EXPLORE MORE

Take a stiff bowl and stretch some plastic wrap over it. (Tape it to the sides if it is not sticking well.) Scatter a little salt across the top of the plastic wrap. Now take a large metal pot and hold it so that the opening of the pot is facing the plastic wrap. With a metal spoon, hit the bottom of the pot and watch the salt jump. The salt is moving because the sound waves you made when you hit the pot traveled through the air, bumping into one air molecule after another until those molecules bumped into the plastic wrap. That caused the wrap to move, making the salt jump around. Experiment with this setup by hitting the pot with different forces.

Because sound needs a material to move through, it can also travel through liquid and solids. In fact, because the individual atoms or molecules of liquids are closer together, sound usually travels faster through liquids than through gas. And solids have atoms or molecules even *closer* together, so sound travels better through solids than through liquids (see Figure 9.29). The closer together the molecules are, the easier it is to move the sound vibration along. In fact, the speed at which sound travels is faster in solids than in liquids and faster in liquids than in gases.

FIGURE 9.29
Phases of Matter

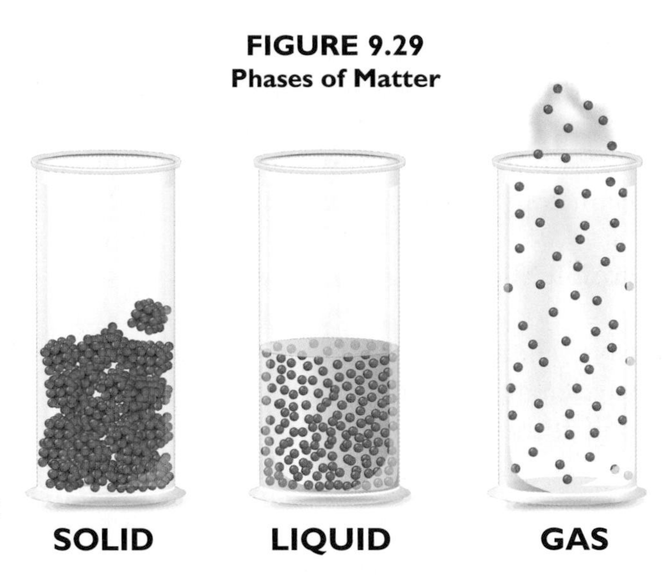

Speed of Sound

When people refer to the speed of sound, though, they are often referring to how fast sound travels in air. Using standard units, sound travels 760 miles per hour in air. We call this speed **Mach 1.** So if anything travels faster than 760 miles per hour, then it is moving faster than sound. We can say it is moving at **supersonic speed.** If an object travels twice the speed of sound, it is moving at Mach 2. If it is moving at 3 times the speed of sound, it's moving at Mach 3, and so on.

FIGURE 9.30
Mach 1 and Supersonic Speed

Each circle is a wave front, being produced by the plane engine. When the plane approaches Mach 1, it goes as fast as the forward part of the waves are moving, pushing them together. When the plane travels *faster* than the speed of sound, the plane moves faster than the forward waves are moving, causing the waves to bunch up and produce a sonic boom.

Some planes and rockets are able to fly at or beyond Mach 1. So if something is moving as fast or faster than sound can move, what do you think that object would sound like? Well, as a supersonic airplane flies in the air, its engines create sound. At slower speeds, that sound would travel outward in concentric circles as in Figure 9.30 (left). But if it is moving at Mach 1, the plane catches up to the forward sound waves as they are traveling. Those sound waves build up on each other. If the plane travels faster than Mach 1, it moves faster than the sound waves it created, causing many of the waves to overlap and crash into one another resulting in a louder-than-normal sound called a **sonic boom** (Figure 9.30, right). Lots of man-made items can move faster than the speed of sound. Bullets, rockets, cars, and even whips can create sonic booms. You might be surprised to learn that an object without a motor, such as a whip, can move faster than sound, but if the whip is swung just right, a loop travels along it that gains enough speed until it creates a sonic boom. In fact, if a person swings the whip just the right way, the whip's tip can reach speeds more than 30 times the initial speed of the whip! So the crack of a whip is technically a sonic boom!

Explaining Wave Anatomy

Take a look at Figure 9.31. This is a model of a wave. We can measure waves in several ways. The high spots on the wave are wave **crests,** and the low spots are **troughs.** A **wavelength** is the distance from one wave crest to another (or one trough to another). Now look at the height of the waves. From the center line, the height is called the **amplitude.**

FIGURE 9.31
A Transverse Wave

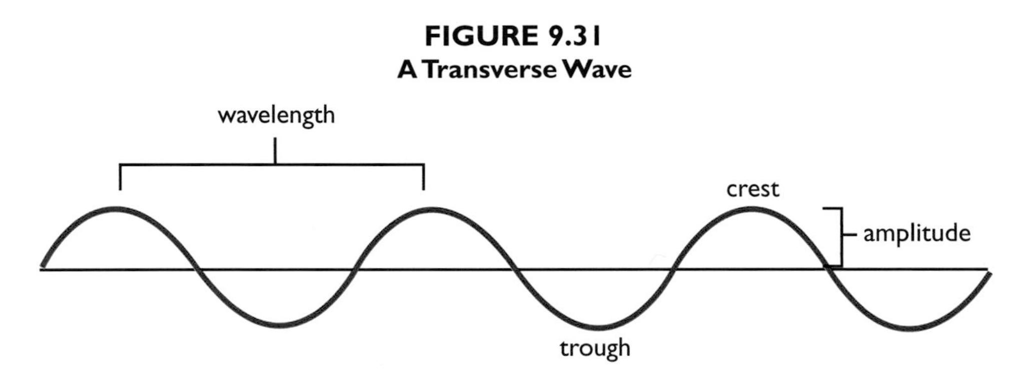

And there is one more feature of waves. Imagine again that you are standing on the ocean shore and waves are hitting your legs. If you were to time how many waves hit your legs each minute, that would be the **frequency** of the waves. It is a measure of how frequently you are getting hit by those wave crests. Now, if there was a storm to churn up the water, the waves might be moving faster in to shore and the number of crests hitting your legs might increase. Well, that is an increase of frequency.

How do all of these wave features affect sound? Just like waves at the beach, the bigger they are, the louder they sound. So tall sound waves are louder sounds, and short sound waves are softer sounds. Using proper scientific terminology, the higher the *amplitude* of a wave, the louder its sound. Think of an amplifier for a musical instrument. It amplifies the sound of the instrument, or makes the sound louder. So amplitude has to do with loudness.

FIGURE 9.32
Frequency

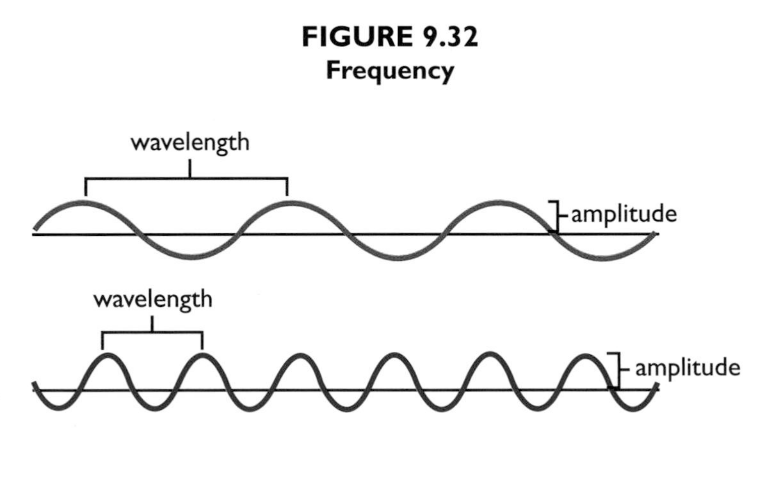

As I already said, frequency has to do with how close the wave crests (or wave troughs) are together. Can you see how wavelength and frequency are related? If a sound wave has a long wavelength (the distance from one crest to another), then it has a low frequency. The wave crests hit your eardrum at a slower rate. If a sound wave has a short wavelength, then it has a high frequency. The wave crests hit your eardrum at a faster rate. Look at the 2 waves in Figure 9.32. They both have the same amplitude, or loudness, but they have different frequencies, don't they? Frequency has to do with the **pitch** of a sound.

EXPERIMENT 9.3

WAVELENGTH, FREQUENCY, AND SOUND

PURPOSE: To understand how frequency affects sound

MATERIALS:

- 3 tall drinking glasses, all the same size and shape
- Water
- A metal spoon
- A rubber band (Use a thicker one for better results.)
- Scissors
- A large metal binder clip
- A block of wood thin enough for the binder clip to clamp onto (Several layers of cardboard will also work.)

QUESTION: What happens to sounds when wavelength (and thus, frequency) changes?

HYPOTHESIS: Write what you think will happen to the sound when you hit drinking glasses filled with various amounts of water.

PROCEDURE:

1. Fill the drinking glasses with water so that the first one is ¼ full, the second one is ½ full, and the third one is ¾ full. Line them up in order of increasing amounts of water.
2. Using the spoon, gently tap the side of each glass and notice the sound each one makes. Record any differences in your notebook.
3. Now take the rubber band and cut it so it is one long piece.
4. Using the binder clip, clamp one end of the rubber band onto the block of wood.
5. Hold the free end of the rubber band with one hand and stretch it so it is tight. Pluck the rubber band and listen to any sound it makes. Try plucking it again at different lengths and listen for how the sound changes. Write what you learned in your notebook.

CONCLUSION: Write what you discovered about wavelength and frequency and how they affect pitch.

What happened in the experiment? You actually performed 2 activities to explore how wavelength and frequency affect sound. In the first part of the experiment, you hit glasses filled with different amounts of water. The one with the least amount should have made a high sound; the one with the most amount should have made a low sound, and the one in the middle should have made a sound somewhere in between. If you hit each glass with an equal amount of force, the loudness, or volume of the sound, should have been the same for all 3 glasses. That has to do with amplitude, so the resulting sound waves you produced all had the same amplitude (height of waves). What changed was the pitch (high or low sounds). A different frequency will produce a different pitch. The high and low sounds have to do with a musical scale.

think about this

Because sound requires a medium in which to travel, it cannot travel in space. That's because there are no gases in space. So sound waves have nothing to bump into. Think about movies that are set in space. Whenever you see a spaceship traveling in space or an explosion in space, do you think there should be sound? After learning about sound waves and how they travel, you now know that there is no sound in space! So spaceship engines and explosions would be silent!

FIGURE 9.33
Instruments with Strings

Whether a person strums guitar strings, plucks harp strings, or hits piano keys that cause a mallet to hit the strings inside the instrument, all of these sounds are created by using strings of varied lengths and tensions to alter the resulting wavelength of sound produced. Music is physics!

When you hit the glass with the spoon, you caused the glass to vibrate. That, in turn, caused the air surrounding the glass to vibrate. The sounds you heard were these vibrations traveling through the air. Using different amounts of water inside the glass affects the sound because the water dampens the vibrations. This means that more water makes the glass vibrate slower, which produces a low-pitched sound like a bass singer. It also means that less water allows the glass to vibrate faster, which produces a high-pitched sound like a soprano singer. Don't confuse the scientific term *dampen* with getting something wet. To dampen something means to decrease its intensity. NASA engineers use dampening techniques during a liftoff to prevent the sound energy from destroying the launch vehicle; vibrations can be that powerful!

The same thing happened with the rubber band. When you pulled it very long, the sound produced by plucking it should have been a higher pitch as compared to the sound when you weren't pulling as hard. That's because when the rubber band was tight, it vibrated back and forth a short distance and at a fast rate. That made the sound waves close together, so the frequency with which the sound hit your ears was great. That made a high pitch. When the rubber band was looser, it vibrated back and forth a longer distance and at a slower rate, making the sound waves farther apart and reducing the frequency with which the sound hit your ears. That made a low pitch.

We can say that longer wavelengths are waves with lower frequencies and lower pitch while shorter wavelengths are waves with higher frequencies and higher pitch.

ON YOUR OWN

9.8 Remember that scientists use indirect observations to determine what makes up the inside of the Earth. If a scientist is studying how sound waves move through the Earth's core, which waves would move faster: those going through the inner core or those going through the outer core?

9.9 If the wavelength of a wave is increased, what happens to its frequency? (Hint: Look at Figure 9.32.)

LIGHT

We're going to end our study of physics by learning a bit about light. Think about a light bulb on a lamp. When it is on, light radiates outward from the bulb in all directions. If you stand near the light, you might notice your dark shadow on the wall behind you. That shadow is there because you are blocking the light. You see, light travels in a straight line. It cannot bend around corners on its own. Now, most lamps have lamp shades that allow some light to pass through. They are thin enough and made of the right material that allows some light to move through them. If you remove the lamp shade and hold a piece of glass near the light bulb, you would notice that all, or most, of the light passes through the glass. So we can say that materials (like glass) that allow most or all light to pass through them are **transparent.** Materials (like a lampshade) that allow some light to pass through them are **translucent.** And materials (like you!) that don't allow any light to pass through them are **opaque.** Opaque materials cast shadows because they prevent light from continuing past them.

FIGURE 9.34
Transparent, Translucent, and Opaque

Transparent Translucent Opaque

The straight lines, or beams, of light are made up of particles called **photons.** What are photons? Well, scientists are still learning more about them, but the short answer is that they are small amounts of electromagnetic energy. They are not made up of atoms, so they are not matter. But photons do sometimes *behave* like particles.

However, light also behaves like a wave. Remember how sound waves need a medium, or a material, through which to travel? Well, light and heat can travel through space. How is that true if light is a wave? We know that sound waves involve vibrations of atoms or molecules; light waves, however, vibrate *electric and magnetic fields.* And it is this electromagnetic field that creates electromagnetic energy. So light does *not* need matter to travel. And that is a good thing because light needs to travel from our sun to Earth. If it needed matter through which to travel, it could not get here, and nothing on Earth could live!

Radio waves, microwaves and all other radiated energy waves travel electromagnetically. These waves of light include all the colors in the world, too. In Module 5, you learned about the visible spectrum of light as well as light that we cannot perceive with our eyes, such as infrared and ultraviolet light.

Figure 9.35 shows the relative wavelengths of the spectrum of light. Notice how visible light is in the center and goes from shorter-wavelength violet light to the longer-wavelength red light. Infrared light has even longer wavelengths as compared to visible red light. As the prefix *infra-* suggests, it goes below (or further) than red. Ultraviolet light has much shorter wavelengths compared to visible violet light. The prefix *ultra-* means extreme.

FIGURE 9.35
Light Spectrum

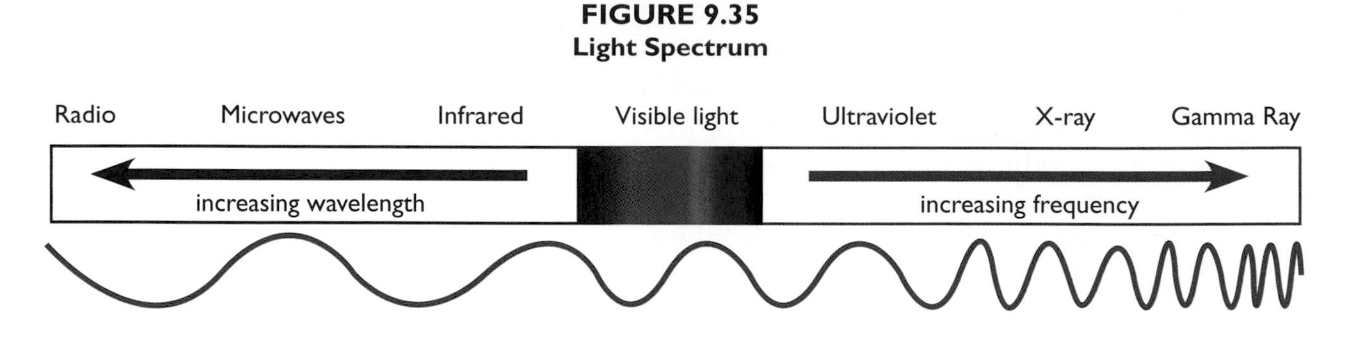

The human eye is able to identify light within a certain range of wavelengths. Those wavelengths make up white light, or visible light. Now, earlier, I said that light travels in straight lines. But because light also travels in waves, those light waves can be bent. If we shine white light into a clear **prism**, which is a triangular-shaped solid, it bends so much as it moves through the material that when it enters and exits the prism, each wavelength of light bends at a slightly different angle. This results in the various wavelengths spreading out, enabling you to see the individual wavelengths of color. This feature of light is also what produces a rainbow in the sky. After it has rained, tiny water droplets are still in the air. If your back is to the sun and you are looking above you at just the right angle above the ground, you can see a rainbow. It forms because each individual droplet of water acts as a tiny prism to bend, disperse, and reflect light back to your eye. And that creates a rainbow in the sky.

FIGURE 9.36
White Light Moving through a Prism

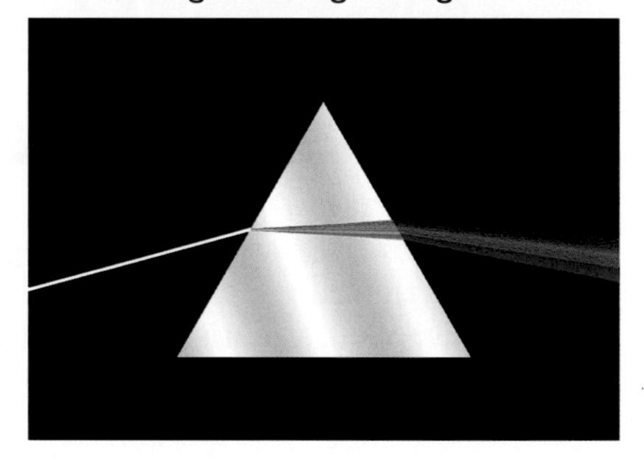

How We Perceive Color

So what happens, say, when you look at a red shirt? Well, white light, which is made up of all the colors of the visible spectrum, shines on the shirt. The red pigment of the shirt absorbs all colors of light except for the red wavelengths that bounce off the shirt and enter your eye. You might be surprised to learn that. The colors we see are a result of reflected light. When you look at a white shirt, you are seeing all the colors of the rainbow reflected back at you. So the white shirt does not absorb any color. On the other hand, a black shirt absorbs all the colors of the rainbow and doesn't reflect any. That means no visible light bounces back into our eyes. This is why black clothing often feels hotter when you are in the sunlight as compared to white clothing. The black clothes absorb all the visible light, and the white clothes reflect it.

EXPLORE MORE

On a sunny day, take a white piece of fabric and a black piece of fabric and go outside. Wrap the white fabric on one arm and the black fabric on the other arm and hold your arms out so they are both in the sun. Wait a few minutes and try to notice if your arms feel different. Does one feel warmer than the other? The black fabric should make your arm feel a bit warmer because it is absorbing the sunlight, and the white fabric is reflecting it.

Reflection and Refraction

Before we wrap up this module, I want to talk a bit more about how light moves. When light hits a mirror, it bounces off it, doesn't it? This is called **reflection.** Light will reflect off a shiny surface with the same angle as it came in when it hit that surface. To understand what I mean by that, think of a bouncy ball. If you take the ball and throw it straight at the ground, it bounces right back up to you. But if you throw it at the ground at an angle, what happens? The ball bounces up at an angle. In fact, if you were to measure the angle at which the ball approached the ground, you would find it equal to the angle of the ball's path after it bounced off the ground (see Figure 9.37). The same thing happens with light. On a reflective surface, the angle between the surface and the light's path as it approaches that surface is equal to the angle between the surface and the light's path after it bounces off that surface.

FIGURE 9.37
Reflecting Light

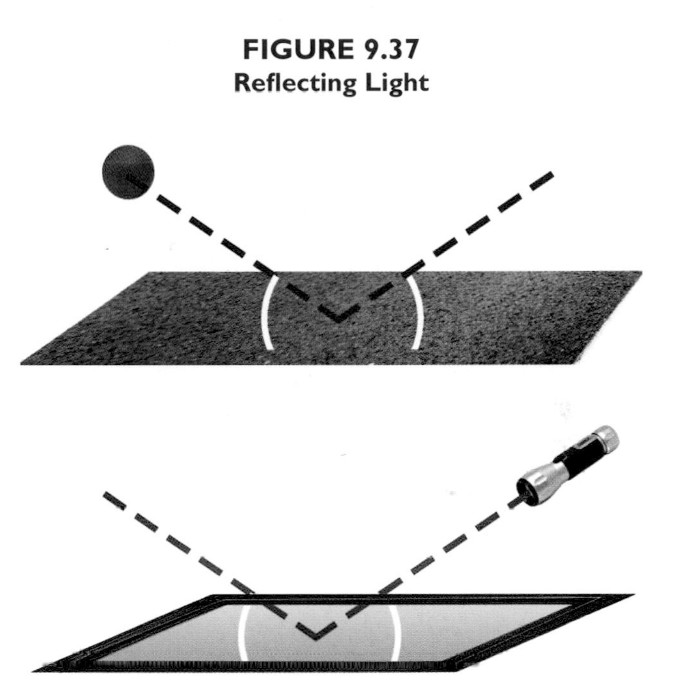

The angle between the beam of light and the mirror is the same as the light approaches the mirror and as the light bounces off it.

But light also can bend. This is what happens when it enters a prism or water. In fact, you can watch it bend when you stick a straw in a tall glass of water. The water causes light to bend such that when you look at the glass, the straw looks bent even though you know it is straight. This is called **refraction.**

ON YOUR OWN

9.10 Categorize each of these items as transparent, translucent, or opaque: clear drinking glass, book, waxed paper, water, ground glass, winter jacket.

9.11 Explain how a rainbow forms in the sky.

SUMMING UP

This brings us to the end of our study of physics as well as our study of physical science. I hope you have seen that things in creation move and behave according to specific principles. After studying the structure of Earth and its place in the solar system and universe, you now know more about the physical principles that are at work. Indeed, this universal order and organization reveals the hand of our God who not only created all things but also rules the way they behave. From the tiniest electrons within atoms to the burning and churning sun, all things work according to His commands!

ANSWERS TO THE "ON YOUR OWN" QUESTIONS

9.1 Velocity has to have a speed plus a direction, so the answers are (**b.**) **and** (**d.**). Option a. lists a speed without a direction, and option c. only lists a distance.

9.2 **When a car slows down, its speed and velocity both decrease.** A car going 50 miles per hour west, for example, might slow to 30 miles per hour west. It is still going in the same direction, but the speed changes value. **A car's acceleration will be in a negative direction** when it slows down. Positive acceleration would be increasing its velocity.

9.3. *Illustrations may vary.* **Newton's first law states that an object in motion (or at rest) will tend to stay in motion (or at rest) until it is acted upon by an outside force. Figure 9.10 is an example of this law. Newton's second law states that when an object is acted on by one or more outside forces, the total force is equal to the mass of the object times the resulting acceleration. Figure 9.11 is an example of this law. And Newton's third law states that for every action, there is an equal and opposite reaction. Figure 9.12 is an example of this law.**

9.4 A switch is a movable component of an electric circuit, set up so that it is in line with the circuit with an incoming wire and an outgoing wire. **When it moves so that its components are not touching both wires, the flow of electrons is interrupted and cannot pass through the circuit. When it moves so that its components are touching both wires, the flow of electrons is allowed to pass through.**

9.5 **The spiraling fluid iron layer causes the magnetic fields around the metal to roughly align in the same direction. This combined effect adds up to produce the magnetic field that surrounds Earth.**

9.6 The simple machines with examples are **the lever (wheelbarrow), wheel and axle (car steering wheel), pulley (block and tackle), inclined plane (ramp), wedge (log splitter), and screw (wood screw).** Other examples can be used.

9.7 **A screw is made from an inclined plane and a wheel and axle.** The inclined plane is wrapped around the axle, creating the spiraling threads of the screw.

9.8 The inner core is believed to be made of solid iron while the outer core is made of liquid. **Because sound waves travel faster through solids than they do through liquids, the scientist should expect sound waves to travel faster in the inner core than the outer core.**

9.9 **Increased, or longer, wavelengths result in lower frequency.** The wave crests will reach your eardrum at a slower rate.

9.10 **Transparent items are the clear drinking glass and water. Translucent items are waxed paper and ground glass. Opaque items are the book and the winter jacket.**

9.11 White light is made up of several different wavelengths of color. This feature of light is what produces a rainbow in the sky. After it has rained, tiny water droplets remain floating in the air. If the sun shines from behind you and hits those droplets at the right angle, the white light will bend within the droplets just like it has moved through tiny prisms. This causes the light to refract and then to reflect back to you so you see it as a rainbow.

STUDY GUIDE FOR MODULE 9

1. Match the following words with their definitions.

a. Speed	A push or pull exerted on an object in an effort to change that object's velocity
b. Velocity	A device that either multiplies or redirects a force
c. Force	The rate at which an object moves
d. Electric circuit	The speed of an object in a given direction
e. Simple machine	A closed path through which electric current flows

2. Two people are riding in a car and wave to a friend on the street as they drive by. From the car passenger's point of view, is the driver moving? From the friend's point of view, is the driver moving?

3. Which unit is not a possible unit for speed?

   a. feet per mile b. miles per hour c. kilometers per second d. inches per day

4. Which 2 of the following refer to a decrease in an object's velocity?

   a. negative acceleration b. acceleration c. deceleration

5. Which 2 of the following represent a velocity?

   a. 25 meters b. 50 feet per second north
   c. 20 kilometers per hour west d. 15 miles per hour

6. Match Newton's laws to their appropriate illustration.

1. An object in motion (or at rest) will tend to stay in motion (or at rest) until it is acted upon by an outside force.	a. Using stronger force to push a piano as compared to the force necessary to push a chair
2. When an object is acted on by one or more outside forces, the total force is equal to the mass of the object times the resulting acceleration.	b. A cannon moving backward when it shoots a cannon ball forward
3. For every action, there is an equal and opposite reaction.	c. A stationary soccer ball

7. A large flashlight is powered by a 9-volt battery and represents an electrical circuit. In this circuit, what is the load?

8. What letters should be in spaces a and b in the dipole diagram?

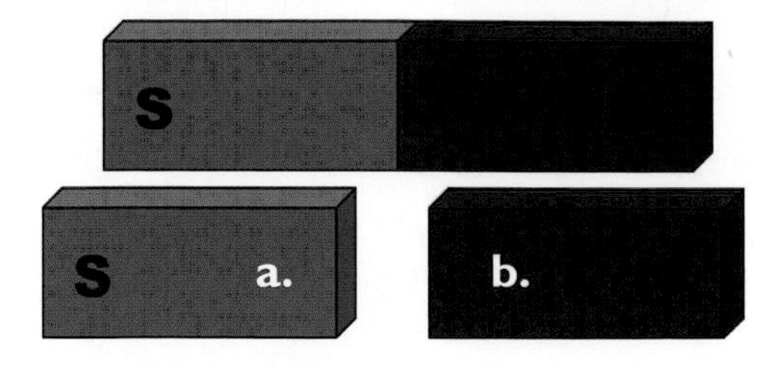

9. Match the simple machine to its example.

a. lever	block and tackle
b. wheel and axle	wood splitter
c. pulley	car steering wheel
d. inclined plane	wood screw
e. wedge	seesaw
f. screw	wheelchair ramp

10. You are watching an exciting movie set in outer space. There is a large explosion and a resounding boom, along with lots of fire and smoke. What is wrong with the science of this movie scene?

11. Which wave has a higher frequency? Which has a longer wavelength?

12. Which of the following is a translucent material?

a. shoe b. car windshield c. black construction paper d. lampshade

13. Which beam of reflected light is correct when the flashlight beam pictured is directed at a mirrored surface?

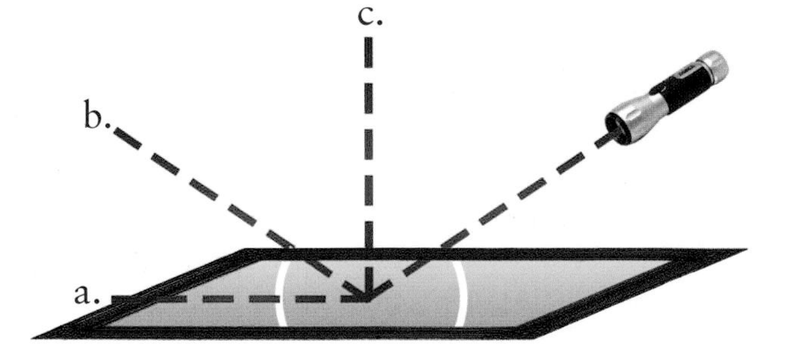

LIFE SCIENCE

You already have learned that the purpose of science includes carefully observing nature and discovering the laws in creation. I have covered many of those laws and how we can use those laws for the benefit of people, but it's time to discuss more about the "carefully observing nature" part. You see, as we study the natural world, we have to consider the living organisms within it. The study of living things is called **life science** or **biology**.

FIGURE 10.1
Living Plants

It might be easy to say that plants are living things, but trying to explain what makes them alive is a bit more difficult.

Before we talk about life science, we really need to understand what life is. You might already have a pretty good idea regarding what things are alive and what things aren't. For example, you know that a rock is not alive, right? And you know that a tree is alive. But scientists have to be a little more detailed to describe what it means to be alive. So they have come up with several criteria for life. For something to be alive, it has to meet every one of these criteria. If it fails to

Quaestio

Genesis 2:19-20a says, "Now out of the ground the Lord God had formed every beast of the field and every bird of the heavens and brought them to the man to see what he would call them. And whatever the man called every living creature, that was its name. The man gave names to all livestock and to the birds of the heavens and to every beast of the field."

From the beginning of creation, man has been naming, working with, and studying living things. In fact, in His Genesis command to Adam and Eve, God instructed them to subdue the Earth and use it for their benefit. As we delve into the study of life science in this module, you will explore more about living beings, just like Adam, Eve, and all of mankind have done.

meet even one, it is not a living being. So what are the criteria? Take a look at Figure 10.2.

When put together, these criteria describe what it means to be alive, at least from a scientific vantage point. Therefore, anything that meets all of these criteria is considered a living organism. Don't worry if you don't understand exactly what these mean. I will go over each one in the following sections.

FIGURE 10.2

DNA AND LIFE

The first criterion of life states that **all living things contain hereditary information in their DNA that enables life to continue through reproduction.** I'm going to address the first part of this criterion in this section and the next one. Then I will talk about reproduction and life after that.

You may have already heard about DNA, but why is it so special when it comes to life? First of all, DNA is an abbreviation for **deoxyribonucleic** (dee ahk' see ry boh noo klay' ic) **acid.** It is kind of like an instruction manual with information necessary to make the materials for a living being. Now, if we were to analyze an organism and determine every chemical that made up the organism, and if we were then to go into a laboratory and put those chemicals into a big pot, we would not have made something that is alive. In fact, we would just have a big mess in a pot. Why is that?

Well, there is more going on. Think about a model airplane kit. Let's say you take the kit, open it up and pile all the parts on the table. At that point, do you have a model airplane? Of course you don't. To make the model airplane, you have to assemble the pieces in just the right way, following the instructions. When you get done, all the parts are in just the right place and work together with the other parts. This produces a model airplane.

In the same way, DNA is the set of instructions that are a map for the chemicals that make up life to be arranged just the right way to produce a living system. Without this instruction set, the chemicals that make up a living organism would be nothing more than

FIGURE 10.3
A Model Airplane

It took a model-builder carefully following the instructions to assemble all the parts of this model airplane.

a pile of goo. But there is one more thing missing. The airplane needed a model-builder (you), and there is a model-builder for living organisms.

This builder is God. You see, there is a component of life that scientists cannot isolate. They can have all the chemicals necessary to produce a living being, but they cannot create a living organism from a nonliving bunch of material. For example, if you were to see a dead fish washed up on the seashore, you know that that fish has all the materials within its body to make a fish. It also has the instruction manual of DNA to help its body arrange those materials the right way. But something is missing. It is the hand of God that gives life. We need to always remember that. Never has a scientist been able to make a living organism from nonliving material. Life comes from the Creator!

DNA plays a *very* important role in that. It contains the information necessary to direct the chemicals in a living being to work together in just the right way to keep a living organism alive. Of course, the exact way in which DNA does this is a little complicated. When you take biology, you will learn a great deal about how DNA does its job. In this course, I want you to concentrate on what DNA looks like instead of the details of how it does its job. Understanding the structure of DNA now will make it easier for you to understand how DNA works later on.

So what does DNA look like? DNA is a molecule. In Module 8 you learned that a molecule is made up of more than one atom. DNA is a *very* large molecule. Most molecules in creation are made up of somewhere between 2 and 100 atoms linked together. DNA, however, is made of *millions* of atoms linked together! And that should make sense. To contain all the instructions for a living organism to remain alive, DNA must have a *lot* of information. In fact, it has been estimated that if we could translate into English all the information in a single human DNA molecule, it would fill up 1,000 books, each of which would be 500 pages long! And that is in just a *single* DNA molecule! You have 46 DNA molecules in each cell!

FIGURE 10.4
Volumes of Books Containing Lots of Information

Now even though DNA is large compared to other molecules, it is remarkably small when you consider all the information it stores. A DNA molecule, in fact, represents the most efficient means of storing data in all of creation. Many people today marvel at how much information can be stored in a small laptop computer. However, the best computer today cannot even come close to storing information as efficiently as does DNA. That shouldn't surprise you. The ultimate Designer created it.

creation connection

The efficient storage of information in DNA is massive. Suppose you were given a flash drive from a computer that had detailed drawings and instructions for assembling a bicycle. If you were told that the flash drive and all its contents were formed as the result of lightning striking a pile of garbage that contained plastic and metal, would you believe it? Of course not. That's because a complicated piece of technology like a flash drive does not result from an accident. Things like that are made as a result of careful design and manufacturing. Also, the *instructions* for assembling the bicycle (which are stored on the flash drive) could not form by accident, either. There's just too much information there. The instructions were clearly created by someone who knows how to make bicycles. Nevertheless, if you are a scientist and do not believe in God, you are *forced* to believe that a data-storage device *significantly more advanced* than humankind's best computer storage device and information *significantly more extensive* than the instructions for a bicycle—both came about as the result of an accident! Scientists who believe in God need not believe that. Just as computer storage devices and bicycle assembly instructions are designed and made by intelligent engineers, DNA and the information necessary to sustain life are designed and made by the most intelligent engineer of all: God!

ON YOUR OWN

10.1 Write the 6 criteria for life in your notebook and make an illustration next to each to help you remember them. Use Figure 10.2 as a guide.

THE STRUCTURE OF DNA

DNA stores an enormous amount of information, but how? Well, it has to do with the structure of DNA. Figure 10.5 illustrates a simplified portion of a DNA molecule. A DNA molecule is shaped like a **double helix.** If you don't know what that means, don't worry. You will be making a DNA model in a little while, and you'll see what it means then. The double helix is formed by 2 long strands of atoms linked together in just the right way, alternating between a sugar group and a phosphate group. These strands make up the backbone of the DNA. Each strand has units attached to it. And these units are called **nucleotide** (noo' klee oh tide) **bases.** There are 4 different nucleotide bases in a DNA molecule. Their names are **adenine** (ad' uh neen), **thymine** (thy' meen), **guanine** (gwah' neen), and **cytosine** (sy' tuh zeen).

FIGURE 10.5
A Simplified View of a Portion of DNA

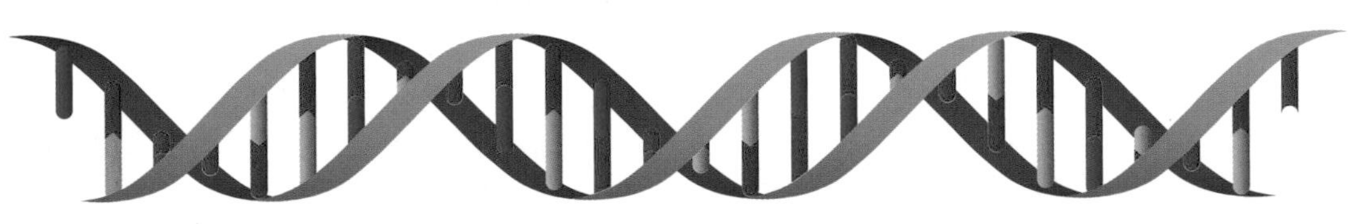

The best way to think of DNA's structure is to imagine a regular ladder that is twisted around. The side rails represent the backbones, which are illustrated by the purple ribbons in the diagram. Each rung (or step) is made up of 2 nucleotide bases. In the diagram, cytosine is represented by the blue bars and guanine is represented by the green bars.

They link together to attach the sides of the ladder. The chemical makeup of cytosine and guanine is such that they will always link together. They will never be able to link to an adenine or thymine molecule. However, adenine has just the perfect molecular structure to connect with thymine, so you will only see those 2 bases link. That's why the diagram shows blue and green (cytosine and guanine) always paired together and yellow and pink (adenine and thymine) always paired together.

FIGURE 10.6
A Slightly More Complicated DNA Model with Phosphate and Deoxyribose (sugar) Backbone

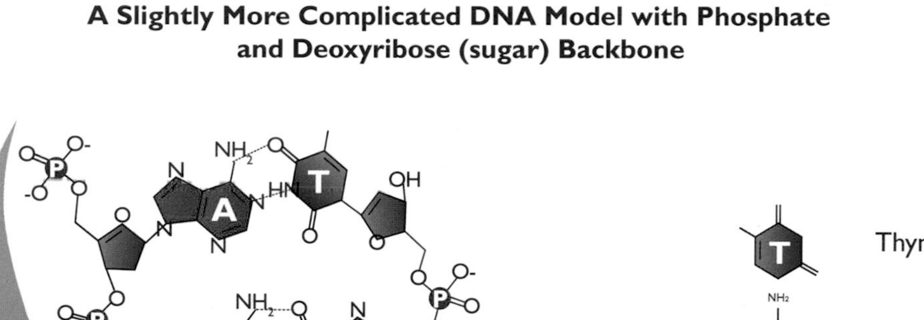

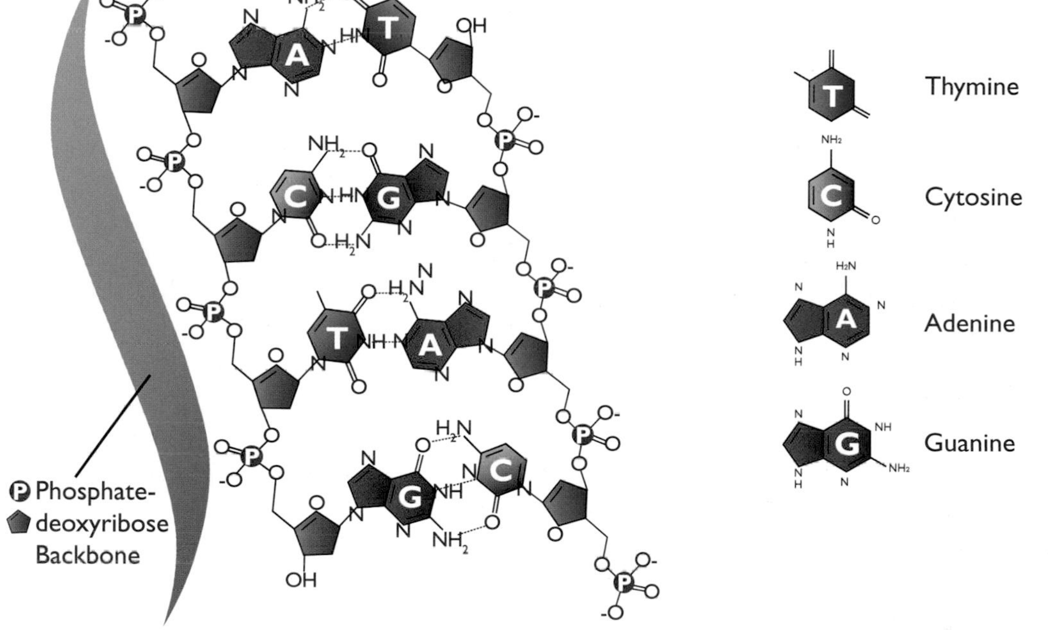

The information necessary to build and control the molecules of living organisms is stored in a coded series of these 4 nucleotide bases in DNA. I used the word *code* because it is indeed a coded amount of information. Think about the English alphabet. There are only 26 letters. However, when you arrange them into a specific order you get words. Some words are very small, and others are very large. Yet they are all information that means something to us. And that information changes depending on how the letters are arranged. Well, this is the same basic idea with how DNA works. The nucleotide pairs are arranged in a specific order. The order of nucleotides needs to be translated into something that a living organism can understand. And there are many chemical processes that occur in order to do just that. The details of these processes are way beyond the scope of this course, but you will learn some of them when you take biology. For now, just be sure you understand that DNA stores information as a series of the 4 nucleotide bases: adenine, thymine, cytosine, and guanine. And know that it requires proper chemical translation equipment for this information to be translated into something useful to a living organism. A good way to better understand DNA's structure is to build a model of it. Perform Experiment 10.1.

EXPERIMENT 10.1

BUILDING A CANDY MODEL OF DNA

PURPOSE: To better understand the structure of the DNA molecule

MATERIALS:

- 2 strands of black licorice that have hollow centers (Twizzlers brand works best for this.)
- 2 strands of red licorice that have hollow centers (Again, Twizzlers work well.)
- 4 different colors of gummy bears—several of each color (Colored marshmallows also work.)
- 2 long, stiff pipe cleaners (The ones with glitter cellophane fuzz work best.)
- 6 toothpicks (and a few to spare in case some break)
- Scissors

QUESTION: What are the main parts of a DNA molecule?

HYPOTHESIS: Write what you expect to learn by creating a 3-dimensional model of DNA.

PROCEDURE:

1. Cut the red licorice and black licorice into 1-inch lengths. You need 12 of each color.
2. Choose 4 different colors of gummy bears. Use one color for adenine, another color for thymine, another color for guanine, and another color for cytosine. Write the colors and which nucleotide base they represent in your notebook.
3. Pair your colored gummy bears so that the adenine and thymine colors are in one pile and the guanine and cytosine colors are in a second pile. You cannot mix colors in a pair. Remember, adenine (A) will only pair with thymine (T), and guanine (G) will only pair with cytosine (C). It doesn't matter if a pair is C and G or G and C as long as these 2 bases are always paired together.
4. Make your DNA backbone. Roll up one end of each pipe cleaner a bit so that the licorice won't slip off when it is threaded on. Now thread one pipe cleaner through the hollow centers of 12 licorice pieces, alternating between red and black. Do the same thing for the other pipe cleaner, beginning with the same color licorice piece as you used on the first strand. There should be 12 pieces on each pipe cleaner, 6 of each color.
5. The red licorice represents the sugar group and the black colored licorice represents the phosphate group. Make a note...the red and black colors linked together make up the backbone of DNA.
6. When you line up your 2 strands of licorice, they should have licorice colors in the same order. If not, restring one of them to match the other. Twist a knot on the other end of the wire for each backbone so the licorice stays in place.
7. Carefully pass a toothpick through 2 gummy bears from the same nucleotide pile so that you have a pair of A-T or C-G. Do this for 6 pairs. Make sure the 2 candies are in the center of the toothpick so that at least ¼ inch of the pointed ends are sticking out.
8. Stick the pointed ends of the toothpicks into the sugar groups (red licorice) of the DNA backbone so that you make a ladder.

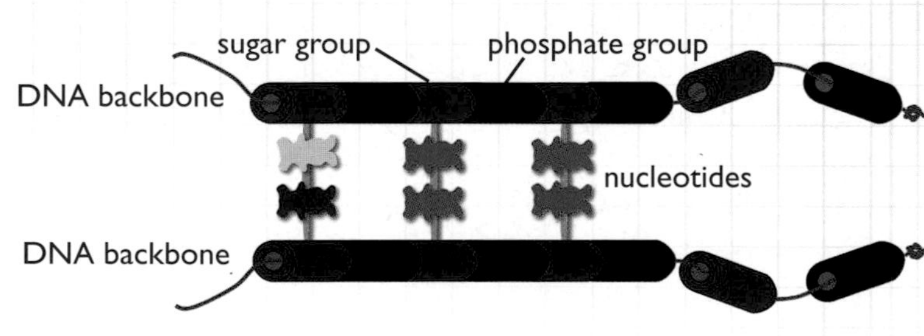

9. Now twist your ladder in a counterclockwise direction so that you create a double-helix spiral. Take a picture of your finished product so you have it for reference.
10. Clean everything up and put it away.

CONCLUSION: Write something you learned about DNA structure from this experiment.

Let me go over the components of your DNA model from Experiment 10.1. The 2 licorice strands represent the backbone of DNA. It is made up of sugar groups and phosphate groups. The double helix looks like a twisted ladder. The gummy bears represent the nucleotide bases, paired specifically as A-T, T-A, C-G, or G-C.

In living organisms, the sequence of nucleotide bases in the DNA (represented by the sequence of gummy bears in your model) is a code that can be translated into the information required for life's structure and maintenance.

It turns out that in order to figure out the sequence of nucleotide bases in DNA, you only need to know the sequence of nucleotide bases on one of the strands. Say, for example, someone takes your DNA model and eats the licorice and gummy bears from one whole strand of DNA, so that you are missing the other strand (see Figure 10.7).

FIGURE 10.7
Half of a DNA Molecule

If you knew, as in this case, that the red gummy bears (adenine) paired with white ones (thymine) while the green bears (cytosine) paired with yellow ones (guanine), then you could figure out the sequence of missing nucleotide bases on the DNA strand that the model-eater ate (see figure in Experiment 10.1 for comparison).

Thus, since the first bear on the half you have is white, you know the first bear on the half that was eaten must have been red because adenine (red) always links to thymine (white). Similarly, since green represents cytosine and yellow represents guanine, the second bear on the side of the DNA that was eaten must have been green because cytosine (green) only links to guanine (yellow). With this kind of reasoning, you can completely reconstruct the other half of the DNA, even though it is missing.

This is actually how DNA copies itself. The double helix ladder untwists and then unzips down the middle. Then new nucleotides come in to pair up with the unzipped strands, creating new double strands.

ON YOUR OWN

10.2 A scientist analyzes ½ of a portion of DNA. She determines the following nucleotide sequence: adenine, thymine, cytosine, adenine, guanine, cytosine, thymine. What is the sequence of nucleotide bases on the other half of this portion of DNA?

REPRODUCTION AND LIFE

Remember the first criterion of life states that **all living things contain hereditary information in their DNA that enables life to continue through reproduction.** We'll spend this section talking about the portion of that criterion that deals with reproduction and living things.

You see, all life forms reproduce. Dogs have puppies, cows have calves, and people have children. That's because if organisms do *not* reproduce, they will eventually become extinct. Reproduction is a means by which living organisms ensure that their kind will continue. So reproduction is God's way of continuing life. Now sometimes, just reproducing isn't enough to guarantee that. You already know that some organisms become extinct. That means for one reason or another, they died off faster than they could reproduce. As a result, there were eventually no more of those organisms left on Earth. But that is not what normally happens.

Since all living organisms reproduce, and since there are so many different kinds of organisms in creation, you should not be surprised to learn that there are many forms of reproduction. Some organisms, for example, need a partner for reproduction while others do not. A single bacterium will just make a copy of itself, creating a new bacterium-clone. Other organisms, such as some flatworms, can split themselves in half; then each half regenerates so it ends up with 2 complete flatworms. So they do not necessarily need a second organism to reproduce.

Among organisms that *do* need a partner for reproduction, there are many differences, too. Think about the difference between reproduction in sea turtles and reproduction in elephants. Sea turtles and elephants both need mates in order to reproduce, but their reproductive strategies are very different (Figure 10.8).

So why do sea turtles have so many offspring at a time while elephants usually produce one calf at a time? The answer is simple. God designed each living organism's reproduction strategy to meet that organism's survival needs. In the wild, young sea turtles die frequently because there are many organisms that eat them. Even before a sea turtle hatches out of its

FIGURE 10.8
Reproduction in Sea Turtles and Elephants

When sea turtles reproduce, the mother comes to shore to lay over 100 eggs at a time. The turtles hatch by themselves and have to make their own way to the ocean, fighting the perils of land predators as well as ocean ones.

When elephants reproduce, usually one calf is born at a time. Although the calf can walk almost immediately, it needs the protection and nourishment from its mother for a long time in order to survive.

nest, it is at risk of being eaten by crabs, shorebirds, and even raccoons. Once it reaches the ocean, it is still not safe. It is at risk of being eaten by all types of fish. A sea turtle's mother is long gone and doesn't provide any parenting. As a result, if sea turtles had few offspring, more would die each year than would hatch, so each year, there would be fewer and fewer sea turtles until there were no more left. Therefore, sea turtles must have several offspring in order to keep the population of sea turtles steady.

On the other hand, elephants live significantly less dangerous lives. There are fewer natural predators to attack them, and elephants live in very protective herds that help keep the young calves safe. As a result, the population of elephants will stay steady even though elephants have one or (rarely) 2 calves. The number of offspring that a living organism has, therefore, depends on how many offspring are necessary to keep the population level up.

Now, there are more differences in reproduction among the organisms in creation than just the number of offspring they have. Some animals lay eggs, and others are born live. Some animals when they are born (or hatch) are able to take care of themselves and don't require any parenting. Others need more parental care.

Horses, for example, have offspring that are born able to see, hear, move around, and regulate body temperature without a parent's help. Dogs, however, have puppies that are born unable to see. They are more helpless than foals and therefore require more parental attention.

think about this

When I mentioned that elephants have few natural predators, I was not referring to irresponsible human activity. You see, today there are many people who kill elephants not to eat them but in order to take their ivory tusks. This is not like a predator and prey situation where an organism is being hunted for food. This is excessive, unnecessary hunting which has drastically reduced elephant populations all over the world. Excessive hunting of elephants by humans has increased their death rates. But because they are only able to have one calf at a time, elephant populations have a hard time keeping up with the non-natural loss. The good news is that conservation efforts, education, and very strict laws are slowing this type of activity to keep elephants safe.

FIGURE 10.9
A Foal Running Alongside Its Mother

ON YOUR OWN

10.3 The bombardier (bom buh deer') beetle is a very interesting insect. It is a unique-looking beetle with a powerful chemical weapon that wards off any creature wanting to eat it. As a result, bombardier beetles live a very safe life. Would you expect bombardier beetles to produce a lot of offspring or only a few?

ENERGY AND LIFE

The second criterion of life states that **all living things use energy**. Let's discuss what that means. Basically, it says that all living organisms have to "eat" in some way or another. When you eat food, you're taking energy from the food and transferring it to your body. That means you are taking in energy from your surroundings (food) and converting it to energy that sustains you.

Now other organisms, such as plants, take in energy differently. They don't eat like we do, but rather produce their own food. Experiment 10.2 explores this.

EXPERIMENT 10.2

FINDING FOOD IN PLANTS

PURPOSE: To explore how plants produce and store their own food

MATERIALS:

- Eye protection such as goggles or safety glasses
- One slice of raw potato
- A pale green leaf (The paler the green, the better this experiment will work.)
- Rubbing alcohol (available at any drugstore)
- Iodine (available at any drugstore)
- A jar with a lid
- 2 shallow dishes
- A cookie sheet lined with parchment paper or waxed paper for protection (Don't use a cookie sheet you wouldn't want to risk getting stained by a drop or 2 of iodine.)
- Tweezers
- A small nonmetallic bowl

QUESTION: Can we see evidence of plants storing food?

HYPOTHESIS: Write what you think might happen if iodine is added to a slice of raw potato and to a leaf.

PROCEDURE:

1. Place the leaf in the jar and fill the jar with about 1 cup of rubbing alcohol.
2. Put the lid on the jar and let it sit overnight.
3. The next day, open the jar and dump out the rubbing alcohol. Keep the leaf.
4. Place the potato slice in one of the shallow dishes. Put the dish on the cookie sheet to protect your counter or table surface. Pour a bit of iodine on the white part of the slice. Be careful! Iodine can stain!
5. Place the leaf in the second shallow dish. Put the dish on the cookie sheet. Pour enough iodine into the dish just so the leaf is covered.
6. Fill the small nonmetallic bowl with water and place on the cookie sheet.
7. Wait for a few moments and then grab the potato slice with the tweezers. Rinse the potato by dipping it in the bowl of water. Try to avoid getting iodine on your hands or the table because it will stain them. Notice the color change that has occurred on

the white part of the potato. Rinse the potato's shallow dish in the sink, but be sure to use LOTS of water. Any iodine left in the sink will rust flatware and other metal objects placed in the sink, so you need to get rid of ALL the iodine.

8. Wait about 2 hours and then pull the leaf out of the iodine with the tweezers. Once again, rinse the leaf with water and look at it. Do you see a color change?
9. Clean everything up. Be sure to clean the sink with plenty of water!

CONCLUSION: Make a drawing of the potato slice and the leaf in the lab write-up section of your notebook. Color them as they appeared after you completed the experiment. After reading the next 2 paragraphs, explain why they changed color and write what you think the natural purpose of a potato is for a potato plant.

In the experiment, you should have noticed that when iodine was added to the white part of the potato slice, it turned a very dark blue. You might have even described it as black in color. That is because the potato contains **starch.** That's why we eat potatoes. Starch is a chemical we use as a source of food. It contains energy that our bodies can break down and use. Iodine is often used to test for the presence of starch because it turns a dark blue color in its presence.

When you put the leaf in the alcohol, the alcohol broke down the protective coating that covers the leaf. It also partially pulled out a chemical, **chlorophyll** (klor' uh fill), that gives the leaf its green color. That resulted in a pale leaf with no protective coating. So when you added iodine to the leaf, you should have seen all or part of it turn blue. That's because starch is also in the leaf. Leaves actually produce food in the form of a chemical called **glucose** (gloo' kohs). If the plant needs energy, it takes the energy from the glucose and converts it to energy for survival. Any extra glucose the plant didn't use is converted to starch or other chemicals to store for later.

FIGURE 10.10
Plants Taking in Sunlight for Photosynthesis

So plants produce their own food. That means they don't "eat" the same way you and I eat. But they DO convert energy from their surroundings into energy that sustains them. They take water from the ground and carbon dioxide gas from the air. Aided by the energy of sunlight, they chemically combine carbon dioxide and water to make glucose sugar in a process called **photosynthesis.**

Photosynthesis—The process by which green plants and some other organisms use the energy of sunlight and simple chemicals to produce their own food

EXPLORE MORE

You can use a plant's ability to make its own food from sunlight, water, and carbon dioxide to create your own self-sustaining living system. Take a small potted plant and place it in a jar with a lid that has just a bit of extra room for the plant to grow. Make sure the soil of the potted plant is very moist with water. Close the lid and use a marker to mark the height of the plant on the jar. Place the jar in indirect sunlight and check on it every few days for up to 4 weeks. You should notice the plant is making its own food (using the energy coming from the sunlight and the gases contained in the jar) as evidenced by its growth!

SENSING AND RESPONDING TO CHANGE

In our list of criteria for life, the third one says **all living things can sense changes in their surroundings and respond to those changes**. Think about that carefully. An organism's ability to *sense* changes is just as important as its ability to respond. For example, you know that a rock is not a living thing. But if that rock is perched on the edge of a cliff and the wind blows strongly enough, that rock might move according to the changing wind. It is being affected by the changing surroundings. But it is not *responding* to those changes because it doesn't have the capacity to "know" anything. However, something is definitely happening to it. We can say that it is not alive because it cannot sense the changing wind or *react* or knowingly respond to it.

FIGURE 10.11
Human Hands Using Touch Receptors

You see, living organisms have some method of receiving information about their surroundings. They have **receptors**, which are special structures that sense the conditions of their internal or external environment. Your skin, for example, has lots of receptors. They can identify touch, pain, and pressure. When you place your hand on the metal hood of a car on a sunny day, the pain receptors in your hand let you know you should move your hand away. The pain you *sense* from those receptors tells you that you need to do something about it: *respond*.

EXPLORE MORE

You can observe a living plant sense and. respond to change by taking a small potted plant and placing it in a sunny window for a week. (A small basil plant works well because of its soft, pliable stems.) Notice the direction of the leaves of the plant after that first week. They all should be oriented so they face the window. Now turn the plant around so the leaves face away from the window. In a few days or so, the plant should have adjusted the position of its stem and leaves. It has special light receptors to identify the direction of sunlight and uses internal water pressure to move its stems and leaves, orienting them to best receive the sunlight. It sensed and responded!

ON YOUR OWN

10.4 Name one way that plants can sense and respond to their surroundings.

THE CELL

The fourth criterion for life is **all living things are made up of** cells.

Cell—The smallest unit of life in creation

In order to explain what a cell is, let me use an illustration. Take a look at Figure 10.12. This is a basic illustration of a cell. Cells are surrounded by an outer covering called a **membrane.** The top of the cell has been cut away so you can see inside the membrane. A jellylike material called **cytoplasm** (sye' tuh plaz'uhm) fills the cell, and **organelles** (or guh nelz') are suspended in it. The organelles have specific jobs they have to do to keep the cell alive.

FIGURE 10.12
A Simplistic Representation of a Cell

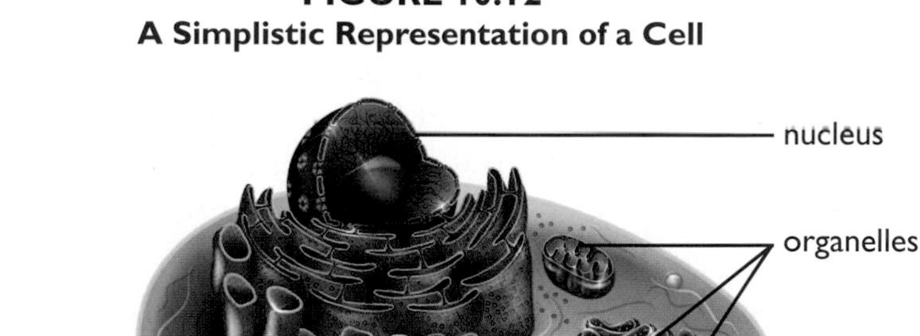

All living things are made up of at least one cell. Your body, for example, is made up of 30–40 trillion cells! They are designed to work together to make you the person you are. That's because every cell in your body has particular tasks it must accomplish. You have cells in your eye that detect light, sending signals to your brain so you can see. You have blood cells that transport oxygen to all the other cells in your body so those cells can burn food for energy. All the different cells in your body work with each other to accomplish the things that keep you alive.

What's interesting is that human cells have a similar structure to the cells in cats, dogs, and other animals. Of course, it takes many more cells to make you as compared to the number of cells to make a cat, and it takes even fewer to make a mouse. However, the tasks these cells perform and the ways they work together are different. That's a large part of why a human is different from a cat, and a cat is different from a mouse.

Now, cells are very small. The average cell in your body, for example, is about 2/10,000 of an inch (0.0002 in) across! Therefore, you cannot see most cells with your naked eye. You have to use a microscope.

However, it doesn't necessarily take a lot of cells to make a living organism. Many organisms, such as bacteria, are composed of only a single cell! And these single-celled organisms can perform all the functions of life: reproducing, eating, growing, responding, and more!

creation connection

In the past, most scientists believed that all cells were just small sacs filled with a jelly-like material. But since the mid-20th century they have learned (and are continuing to learn) that even the most basic unit of life is amazingly complicated. Cells are like small cities with complex machines carrying out intricate processes. That means that although a cell might be a basic structure, *it is not simple*. It is exceedingly complex. Even organisms made from one cell are super complex, able to undergo all the intricate processes of life. Indeed, life doesn't range from simple to complex, but *from complex to amazingly complex*!

FIGURE 10.13
Bacterial Cells

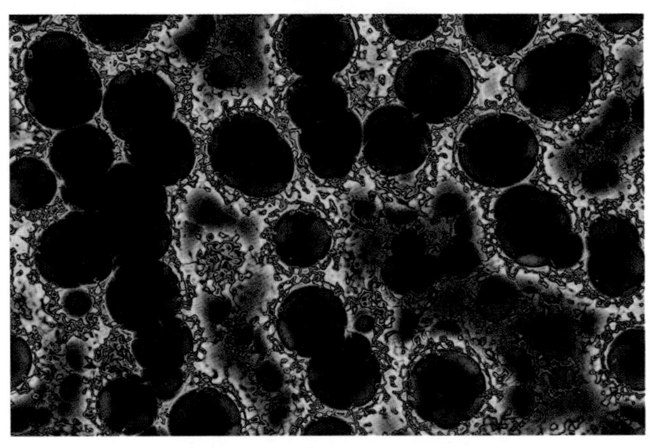

Cells are able to reproduce themselves. Whether they are a single-celled organism or part of a larger organism, they can reproduce. In fact, there are cells in your body that are reproducing *right now* as you read this text. After all, in order to grow, you need more cells. And those cells come from the reproduction of other cells. You also have cells dying in your body at all times, too. For example, millions of red blood cells in your body die every second! Thus, your cells are constantly reproducing in order to replace cells that have died and to make new ones so you can grow.

One part of the cell I want to mention is an organelle called the **nucleus** (see Figure 10.12). The nucleus is one of the most important organelles in the cell. It is where you will find most of an organism's DNA.

There are different kinds of cells in creation. The one illustrated in Figure 10.12 is an **animal cell**. Plants are made up of slightly different kinds of cells, appropriately called **plant cells**. And another kind of cell is typically found in the tiniest single-celled organisms. These organisms are called bacteria, and a **bacterial cell** does not have a nucleus. That's one reason the nucleus is considered an important organelle in the cell. The presence or absence of a nucleus in a cell can help identify what kind of cell it is.

ON YOUR OWN

10.5 Suppose a scientist is looking at cells from the following organisms under a microscope: bacterium (the singular form of bacteria), onion, mouse, grass, horse. Which cells would look very similar to each other under the microscope?

REGULATION AND LIFE

The fifth criterion of life states that **all living things chemically regulate their internal environment so it is stable.** What does it mean to chemically regulate an internal environment? Well, think about when you play a game of soccer or go jogging. Your normal body temperature stays around 37 °C (98.6 °F). But with excessive exercise, does your temperature go higher? Actually, no. You see, your body has a temperature regulation mechanism, much like a thermostat controls the temperature of your house. A region of your brain called the **hypothalamus** makes adjustments to your breathing rate, the level of sugar in your blood, and how quickly you burn up energy within your body. It signals your body to sweat so that as the sweat evaporates off your skin, you cool down a bit. These and other processes help to keep your body within the best temperature range for all of your body processes to work smoothly. The same mechanisms are in place to help control other conditions of your body, too.

Scientists call this process of regulation **homeostasis.** Homeostasis is a process in all living things to help maintain a stable internal environment by carefully controlling (regulating) all of the chemical processes occurring in them.

FIGURE 10.14
Playing Soccer

GROWTH AND LIFE

The sixth and final criterion of life is that **all living things grow.** This can be an increase in cell size or an increase in the number of cells within an organism. Most often, single-celled organisms will grow in size before they reproduce. The resulting new cells grow until they become a normal size for their kind. For multicellular organisms, growth also involves an increase in the number of cells. Once a multicellular organism stops growing in size (such as when a child becomes a full-grown adult), the cells of his or her body continue to grow and multiply to replace dying older cells.

FIGURE 10.15
Onion Cells Growing and Dividing

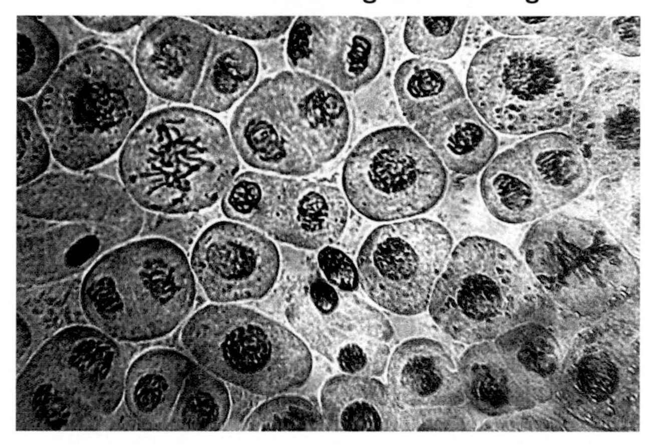

ON YOUR OWN

10.6 In the first "On Your Own" question of this module, you were instructed to write the 6 criteria for life and make an illustration. Now go back to that question and add at least one piece of information you learned for each criterion.

BIOLOGICAL CLASSIFICATION

Well, we've covered the 6 criteria of life. If something satisfies all 6 criteria, it is considered to be alive; however, if it fails to meet even one of them, it is not alive. Now, you need to know that depending on the source you are reading, some people group the requirements for life differently. For example, some people say there are 7 criteria, others say there are 4 criteria, but they all include the same requirements that we talked about.

As I mentioned earlier, the formal study of living things is called biology. Even with all the criteria that need to be met for something to be alive, God created a massive diversity of living things that biologists can investigate. In fact, there are branches within biology with a specific focus. The study of animals and how they live is called

zoology. Anatomy is the study of an organism's structures, and **physiology** is the study of the function of those structures. **Botany** is the study of plants, **microbiology** is the study of organisms too small to see without a microscope, and **ecology** is the study of how organisms interact with their surroundings and each other. Of course, there is some overlap between all these branches. For example, an ecologist might study a small area of a rain forest. In it are many plant types and animals, ranging from small ants and birds to monkeys and snakes. Plus, there is a whole host of microscopic organisms living there, playing a part in how all these creatures live together.

Classification

With over 1.5 million living organisms identified (so far) in creation, life scientists came up with a way to organize and categorize them. This method is called **classification.**

Classification—A method of sorting things according to shared qualities or characteristics

We use classification systems all the time. In fact, you probably use a classification system for the clothes in your room. Think about your shoes and your pajamas, for example. Of all the things you wear, you likely store all your shoes together in the same place. Why would you do that? Well, you know they are all worn on your feet and have a similar shape. How about your pajamas? I am pretty sure you won't store them in the same place as your shoes. Why is that? Well, your shoes come in contact with dirt on the ground as you walk; it is likely they are a bit dirty. So of course you wouldn't want them in the same place with clothes you sleep in!

FIGURE 10.16
Kitchen Classification and Organization

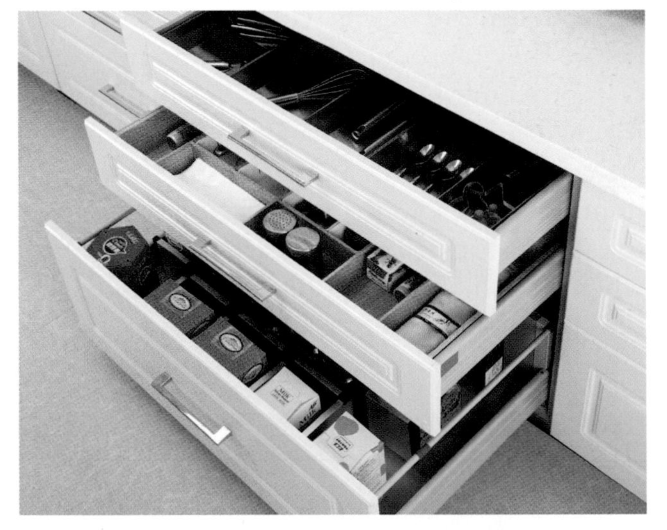

Unknowingly, you have come up with categories to *classify* your clothing. You look at their features (such as shoes with hard soles and dirt from outside) and group items with similar characteristics together.

Your kitchen is probably organized in a similar way. Utensils like spoons and forks are stored together, and pots and pans are in a different location. That is so they can be more easily found when you need something, but also because of their similar features and uses.

Living organisms are also classified based on their physical properties and characteristics. Some organisms have characteristics in common with other organisms, and some of their characteristics are unique. In the same way that you might categorize the clothes in your room in a different way than someone else would, biologists have different models that divide the living organisms in creation. We will go over the most current classification systems, but you should realize that as new information is discovered or as scientists discuss systems in more detail, these organizational systems may change in the future.

It is important for us to identify living organisms in a scientific manner. Up until the 1700s, scientists used common names to discuss living creatures, but that created problems. For example, if you wanted to talk about a red fish in the ocean, *you* might call it a red fish, but another person might refer to it as a fire fish. So to help that person understand the specific type of fish you're talking about, you could add a longer description of the fish. Perhaps you would say it is a red fish found in shallow ocean waters near coral reefs, and it typically grows to about 3 inches. However, having to do all that just to identify a fish can get difficult and confusing. To solve this problem, the Swedish botanist Carolus Linnaeus came up with a simple, practical method of classification. Between the years 1735 and 1758, this devout Christian man built his classification system on the principle that the created kinds of organisms never change into different kinds. He used his expertise in plant and animal studies to develop a system of naming organisms that we still use today. By using 2 Latin-based categories, his **genus** (jee' nus) and **species** system is called **binomial nomenclature** (noh' men clay tyure). That's just a fancy way of saying it's a 2-name (*bi*nomial) naming system (nomenclature).

Linnaeus took his 2-named organisms and then grouped them into 1 of 2 large categories—**kingdom Plantae** (plan' tee) for the plant kingdom and **kingdom Animalia** (an' ih mayl' ee uh) for the animal kingdom. Today scientists still group all living things into main categories called kingdoms, but they now know that many organisms cannot be classified into a plant kingdom or an animal kingdom. The use of a microscope, for example, revealed organisms that were neither plants nor animals. So, after further study of these tiny living beings called **microorganisms,** they looked for similar and different characteristics. Among them, biologists noticed that some organisms had cells with a nucleus, and other organisms had cells that didn't have a nucleus.

FIGURE 10.17
The Differences between Prokaryotic and Eukaryotic Cells

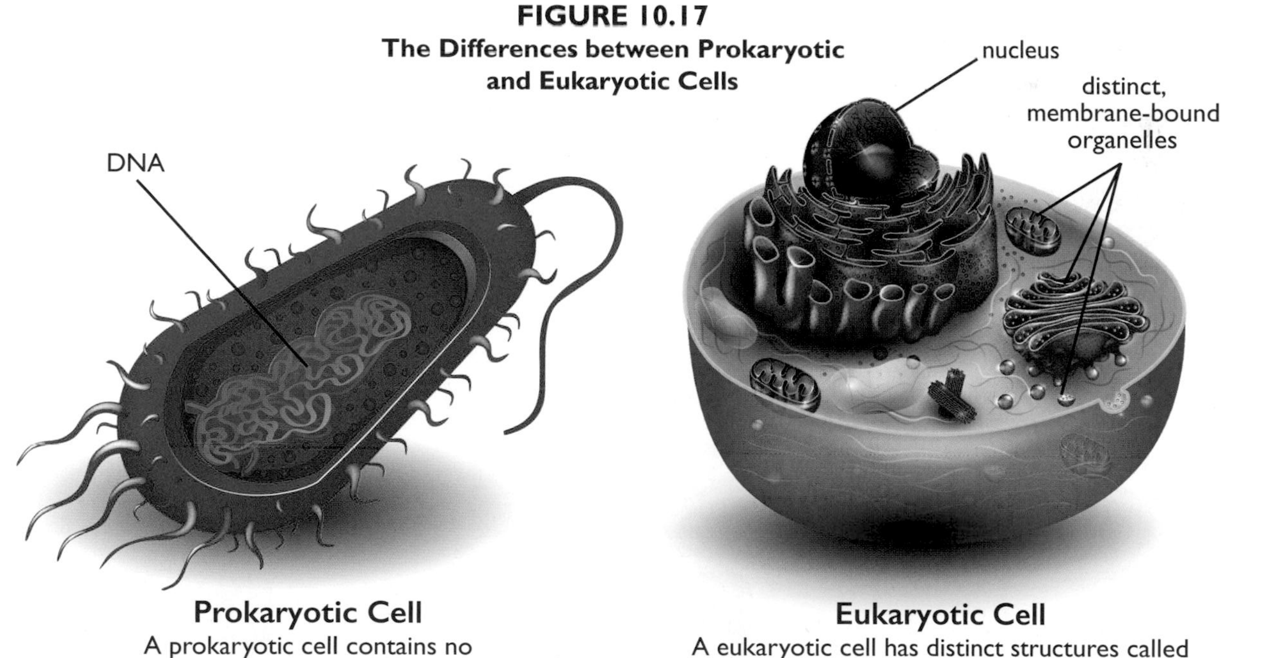

Prokaryotic Cell
A prokaryotic cell contains no membrane-bound organelles. The main feature of a prokaryotic cell is the DNA visible throughout the cell.

Eukaryotic Cell
A eukaryotic cell has distinct structures called organelles. They have their own tasks to perform in order to maintain the life of the cell.

What does that mean? Earlier in the module, you learned about plant cells, animal cells, and bacterial cells. The bacterial cells do not have a nucleus. Cells with a nucleus are called **eukaryotic** (yoo kehr ee aht' ik) cells, and cells without a nucleus and without distinct, membrane-bound organelles are called **prokaryotic** (pro kehr ee aht' ik) cells. Thus, we can define these 2 types of cells as follows:

Prokaryotic cell—A cell that has no distinct, membrane-bound organelles

Eukaryotic cell—A cell with distinct, membrane-bound organelles

So bacterial cells are prokaryotic cells, and plant and animal cells are eukaryotic cells. We call organisms with prokaryotic cells *prokaryotic organisms*. We call organisms with eukaryotic cells *eukaryotic organisms*. Thus, a bacterium is a prokaryotic organism, and a giraffe is a eukaryotic organism. Figure 10.17 has an illustration of both these cell types.

With a better understanding of these 2 cell types, I can now talk about how to split organisms into the different kingdoms. After the discovery of microscopic organisms and their cell structure, biologists added to Linnaeus' original 2 kingdoms to include **kingdom Monera** (moh neh' ruh), which contains mostly single-celled, prokaryotic microorganisms (bacteria), and **kingdom Protista** (pro tees' tuh), which contains mostly single-celled, eukaryotic microorganisms. Eventually a fifth kingdom was created, called **kingdom Fungi** (fun' jye), which includes mushroom-producing and other similar organisms.

FIGURE 10.18
Kingdom System Division Strategies Through History

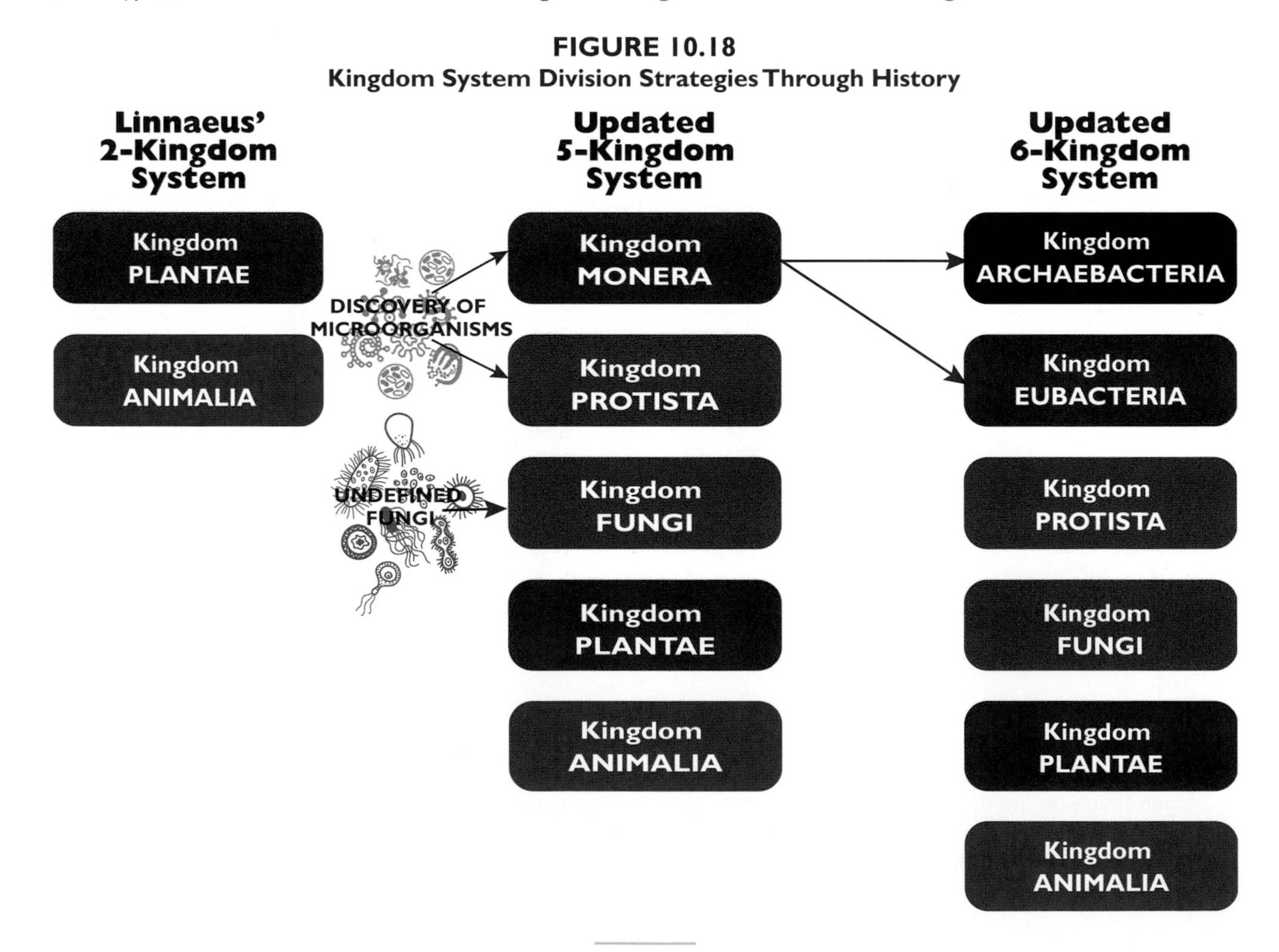

This brings us to the **5-kingdom system** (Monera, Protista, Fungi, Plantae, and Animalia), which has been in use since 1969. However, because of advances in the study of single-celled organisms in recent years, some biologists have suggested that kingdom Monera should be split into 2 groups because there are 2 main types of prokaryotic microorganisms. Thus, one group would be **kingdom Archaebacteria** (ar' kee bak tee ree uh), which contains single-celled organisms with a unique outer cell wall, an ability to withstand some antibiotic medicines, and a capability to live in extreme environments. The second new group would be called **kingdom Eubacteria** (yoo' bak tee ree uh), which contains the single-celled organisms that have a more common cell wall, are affected by most antibiotic medicines, and cannot live in extreme environments. This represents a **6-kingdom system** (see Figure 10.18).

FIGURE 10.19
A Culture of Bacteria

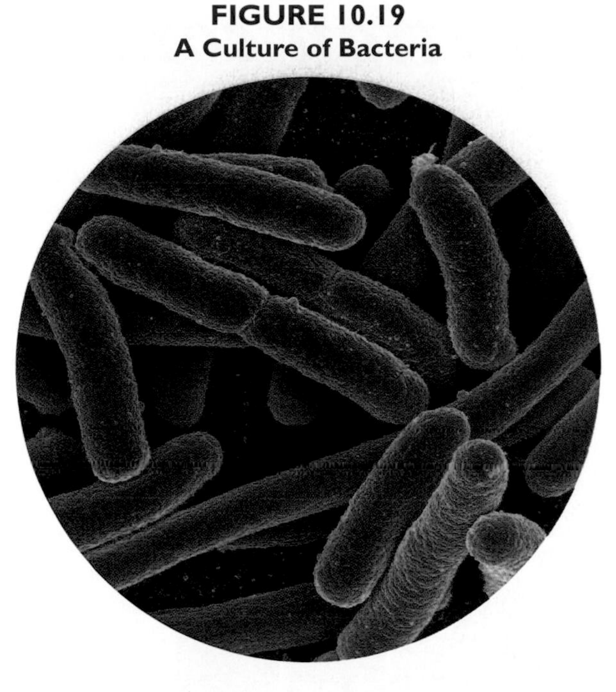

Why did I cover all this and not just tell you what the accepted kingdom groups are? It is important for you to understand that as we learn more about the organisms of our world, we need to sometimes change the models of science we have.

It turns out that even after splitting kingdom Monera into kingdom Archaebacteria and kingdom Eubacteria, some biologists felt that these 2 groups were very different as compared to organisms in the other kingdoms. So they wanted to add a higher rank, called a **domain,** that is broader than kingdom. In this model, all 6 kingdoms, then, could be split into 3 domains: **Archaea** (ar kay' uh), **Bacteria,** and **Eukarya** (yoo kay' ree uh). The domain Eukarya consists of 4 kingdoms, and by its title it shouldn't surprise you to know that the organisms in this domain are made up of eukaryotic cells. Kingdom Monera is split into 2 domains: domain Archaea and domain Bacteria. This additional information is summarized in Figure 10.20.

FIGURE 10.20
The 3-Domain System of Classification

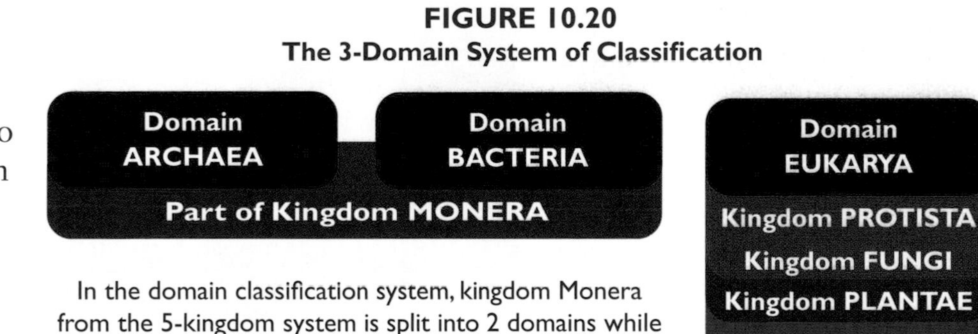

In the domain classification system, kingdom Monera from the 5-kingdom system is split into 2 domains while the other 4 kingdoms are under domain Eukarya.

Today, most biologists, particularly those in the United States, use the 3-domain classification system and don't use kingdom Monera. However, biologists in other countries continue to use the 5-kingdom system. That is why it is important for you to understand all systems. For this course, we will use the 3-domain system.

creation connection

Because I am talking about different systems of classifying life, you should know about another classification system used by those who believe all living things were created by God. Genesis 1:25 says, "And God made the beasts of the earth *according to their kinds* and the livestock *according to their kinds*, and everything that creeps on the ground *according to its kind*. And God saw that it was good" (my emphasis added). This alternative system, called **baraminology** (bear' uh min ol' uh jee), makes an effort to figure out the *kinds* of creatures God specifically created on Earth. God built variation within each kind. That's why dogs can look different, but they are still dogs and have similar characteristics that all dogs share. Imagine a mutt dog, for example. It has characteristics of lots of types of dogs, and if you breed it with another mutt, you would get a litter filled with puppies of various sizes, colors, and temperaments. They are all within a dog kind that might include domestic dogs, wild dogs, wolves, and other similar animals, each having changed a bit over time to better survive. With each litter of puppies, those that had slightly thicker fur in a cold climate would be more likely to survive long enough to pass those thick-fur features on to their puppies, and those with thinner fur were less likely to survive and reproduce. Eventually there would be only thick-furred dogs in an area, yet they would still be of the same dog kind. As all organisms changed—or **adapted**—to better survive in their environment, it resulted in a huge diversity of life. So baraminologists came up with groupings called **baramins**, which are various kinds of organisms created by God. There is actually a lot of evidence to support this classification scheme.

FIGURE 10.21
Various Dogs of the Same Species

ON YOUR OWN

10.7 Explain the difference between a prokaryotic cell and a eukaryotic cell.

THE 3 DOMAINS IN CREATION

Domain Archaea

Let's go over the characteristics of organisms in each of the 3 domains. Domain Archaea (Figure 10.22) is made up of mostly single-celled prokaryotic microorganisms. They often live in extreme environments, such as hot springs, high altitudes, and deep oceans. Scientists refer to them as **extremophiles**, which means they "love extreme" living. That's because they do well in locations that would kill many other living organisms on Earth. Some have been found living on dust particles floating almost 4 miles above Earth's surface, and others have been discovered living in a nuclear reactor even while it was running!

FIGURE 10.22
Domain Archaea

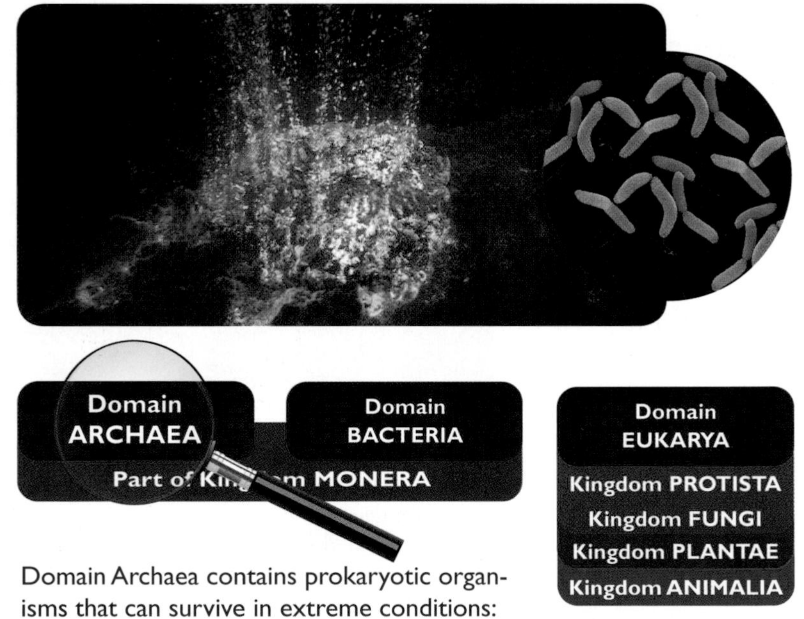

Domain Archaea contains prokaryotic organisms that can survive in extreme conditions: the extremophiles. The left image is a deep ocean vent where thriving sulfur bacteria (on the right) can withstand high temperatures.

Domain Bacteria

Domain Bacteria (Figure 10.23) is the second domain and it contains all the prokaryotic microorganisms that, for the most part, *do not* live in extreme environments. Most of them live as single-celled organisms and are sensitive to traditional antibiotics. Bacteria are all around us. Some of them are helpful to humans, and others can make us sick. For example, there are about 150 different types of helpful bacteria living on or in your body right now. They are in such large populations that their number is equal to the number of cells in your entire body! And a majority of them play an important role in your body, helping you to live better. For example, some that live in your intestines produce vitamin K, a substance your body needs. Some types of bacteria help us make cheese, and others help make Earth hospitable to life by photosynthesizing, creating life-sustaining oxygen as a product of that process.

FIGURE 10.23
Domain Bacteria

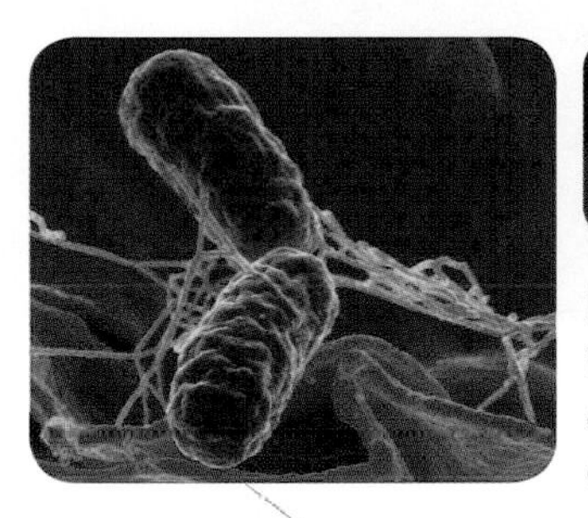

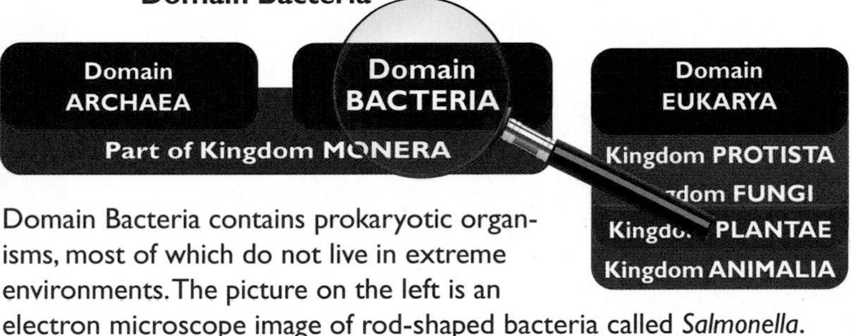

Domain Bacteria contains prokaryotic organisms, most of which do not live in extreme environments. The picture on the left is an electron microscope image of rod-shaped bacteria called *Salmonella*.

Now, there are also many bacteria on Earth that can cause disease. Some, such as the bacterium *Clostridium* (claw strid' ee um) *botulinum* (bot' yool in uhm), can cause food poisoning. That is why we are careful to prepare certain foods by cooking or washing them. It helps to remove potential harmful bacteria.

Domain Eukarya

The third domain— domain Eukarya—consists of all organisms with eukaryotic cells (Figure 10.24). And there are 4 kingdoms within this domain.

The first kingdom in domain Eukarya is **kingdom Protista.** It includes some organisms that are composed

FIGURE 10.24
Domain Eukarya

Domain Eukarya contains all the organisms with eukaryotic cells. It is divided into 4 kingdoms (from left to right, top to bottom in the images): Protista (like the *Paramecium*), Fungi (like mushroom-producing organisms), Plantae (plants), and Animalia (animals like the zebra).

of only one eukaryotic cell. It also contains organisms referred to as **algae** (al' jee). Some types of algae exist as single cells, but others are made up of many cells and look like water plants. However, they are not plants. Plants have specialized components like roots, leaves, and stems. Algae, such as seaweeds, do not. Algae are very important organisms; their ability to photosynthesize is critical to the health of our planet. Why is that? Well, the sheer number of algae on the planet make them the largest group of photosynthesizers, even more than all the plants of the world. Thus, algae are responsible for most of Earth's oxygen supply!

FIGURE 10.25
Dinoflagellate (left) and Kelp Algae

Like bacteria, organisms in kingdom Protista include those that are beneficial to life and others that are harmful. For example, one protozoan, *Entamoeba* (ent' uh mee' buh) *histolytica* (his' toh lih' tih kuh), causes dysentery, which includes severe diarrhea, intestinal cramping, fever, and, in severe cases, death. It is found in contaminated water, which is why it is important to make sure our water supplies are clean.

The next kingdom in domain Eukarya is **kingdom Fungi.** Like kingdom Protista, it is made up of microscopic and macroscopic organisms (those we can see with the naked eye) with eukaryotic cells. Two common examples of fungi are mushrooms and yeast.

This kingdom mostly contains organisms that feed on dead organisms. Please understand what I mean when I say that an organism "feeds on dead organisms." Lions, for example, kill their food before they eat it, but they do not feed on dead organisms. They kill live organisms and eat them. An organism that feeds on dead organisms finds something that is *already* dead (and usually has been dead for a while) and then feeds on it. An organism that feeds on dead material is called a **decomposer.**

Decomposer—An organism that breaks down the dead remains of other organisms

Decomposers are critical to our world. Think about that. God created a built-in recycling system! Decomposers prevent a massive buildup of once-living material. In a single autumn, for example, the average elm tree will drop as much as 400 lb of leaves on the ground. Imagine what a forest of elms would do! Without decomposers, this material would pile up until the trees choked on their own dead leaves in just a few seasons. However, the decomposers break down the leaves into fertilizer that can then be reused by the trees.

EXPLORE MORE

To observe the decomposing process, take a peeled banana and cut 2 similar slices from it, each about one cm thick. Wet each slice with just a little water to wet the surface. Sprinkle some yeast granules (from the baking section of the grocery store) onto one of the 2 slices and place each slice in a separate zippered plastic bag. Use a marker to label the yeast bag. Seal both bags, place each bag on a separate paper plate, and then put them on a counter or shelf out of the way for about a week. Notice the decomposing power of the yeast cells on their banana slice.

The next kingdom in domain Eukarya is **kingdom Plantae.** It includes multicellular organisms that are made of many eukaryotic cells and produce their own food. These are the plants in creation. Trees, grasses, and bushes are all members of kingdom Plantae. Remember when I said that there are organisms in kingdom Protista (the algae) that can make their own food? Well, algae don't have specialized parts like roots, stems, and leaves, so they are not in this kingdom.

EXPLORE MORE

Study how plants differentiate into leaves, stems, and roots by observing dried bean seeds sprouting. Take a clear plastic cup and a paper towel. Fold the paper towel so that it is the same height as the cup. Roll up the paper towel and place it in the cup so it covers the insides of the cup as much as you can. You can add a second paper towel to fill the cup's center if you need to. Thoroughly wet the paper towel and make sure it is sticking to the insides of the cup. Dump out any standing water in the cup. Place 4 dried beans evenly spaced around the cup, between the paper towel and the side of the cup so you can see them when you look through the side of the clear plastic cup (see diagram). Cover the cup with plastic wrap to keep everything moist and let it sit for a few days. Check the cup regularly to make sure the paper towel remains moist; add a little water if necessary. Watch the beans sprout to form roots, a stem, and eventually small green leaves. Each of these structures has specific jobs to keep the plant healthy.

I already mentioned that plant cells are different from animal cells. Let me quickly discuss why. Plant cells have a nucleus and organelles, just like animal cells, but there are some important differences. First, most plant cells are a bit squarer than animal cells. Second, while both plant and animal cells have a cell membrane, only plant cells have a **cell wall.** Animal cells do not have cell walls. The cell wall is a rigid structure that has holes in it to allow nutrients and other chemicals to pass through. It helps provide structure to the plant. The third major difference is that a plant cell has a large organelle called a **central vacuole.** This structure is like a water balloon. It fills with water, increasing its size. This pushes the organelles and cytoplasm in the cell toward the cell wall. The cell wall is stiff, so it pushes back toward the force created by the expanding vacuole. This results in a rigid cell that helps plants to stand upright.

FIGURE 10.26
Plant Cell (left) and Animal Cell (right)

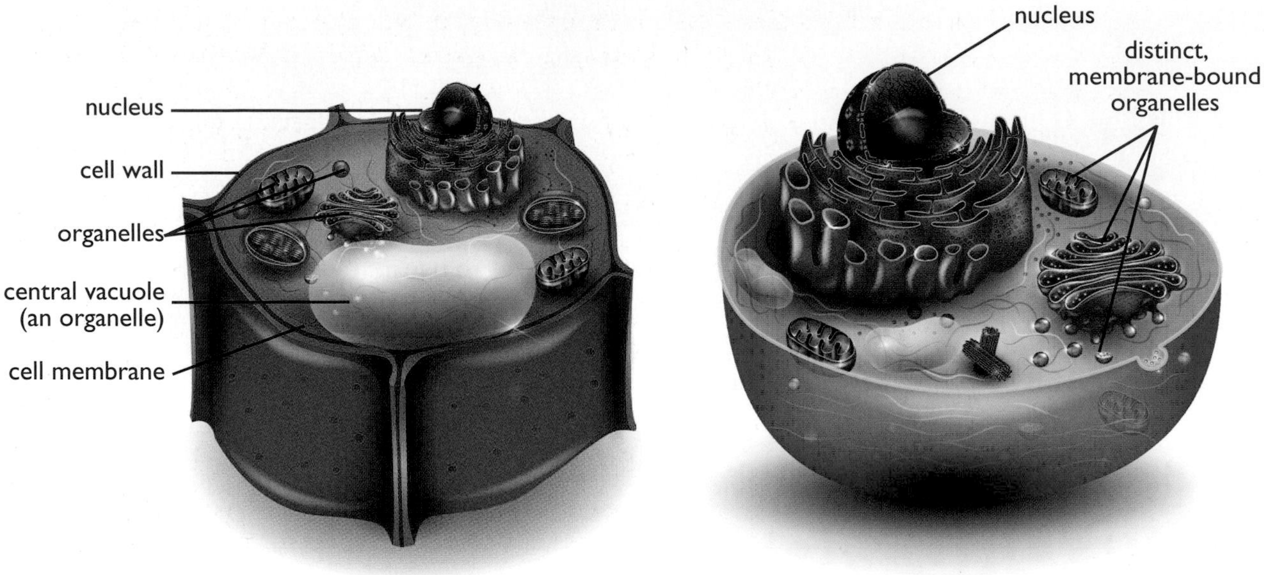

nucleus
cell wall
organelles
central vacuole (an organelle)
cell membrane
nucleus
distinct, membrane-bound organelles

What happens when you stop watering a potted plant? It starts to wilt, doesn't it? Wilting occurs because the cells are not getting enough water to fill their central vacuoles. Thus, the vacuoles don't push against the cell walls to provide the rigidity needed to hold up the plant. This pressure is called **turgor pressure**, and it plays an important role in plant cell biology. Indeed, plants need water!

The last kingdom in domain Eukarya is kingdom Animalia. This group includes multicellular organisms made of many eukaryotic cells like the plants, but members of this kingdom eat other (usually living) organisms rather than making their own food. Members in this group are called animals and they include butterflies, birds, elephants, fish, and alligators. Humans are also placed into this group. Now, don't worry. I am not saying that humans are animals. Clearly, humans are not animals. Humans are made in the very image of God. Animals are not. Thus, there is a huge difference between people and animals. However, from a biological point of view, scientists group humans in the same kingdom as animals. We are made up of the same basic kinds of cells that the animals are made of. But we are very special!

ON YOUR OWN

10.8 Make an illustration of the diagram portion of Figure 10.20 in your notebook. Add a drawing or picture and a few words to each domain and kingdom to help you remember them.

TAXONOMY

At this point, we've divided up all the living things in creation into 3 domains, and one of those domains was further divided into 4 kingdoms. But you know that life is very diverse. So within those domains and kingdoms, there are subcategories to further differentiate the organisms placed there. For example, kingdom Animalia has a wide range of organisms including centipedes, elephants, ducks, and snakes. Those are very different creatures, aren't they?

Thus, Linnaeus further divided organisms into smaller groups. Each level is called a **taxon.** The term **taxonomy** is a method of classifying organisms into their various taxa (the plural of taxon). I already mentioned how Linnaeus gave organisms a genus and species name. Within a genus there are various species. For example, both lions and tigers belong to the same genus, *Panthera*; however a lion is given the genus and species name *Panthera leo*, and a tiger is given the genus and species name *Panthera tigris*. Both are big cats and have several similar physical structures and behaviors. Therefore they are placed in the same genus. However, they are different enough from one another that they are differentiated into 2 separate species. One thing about genus and species names—there is a grammar to how they are written. Both are always either italicized or underlined, and the genus name is always capitalized, and the species name is not (see Figure 10.27).

FIGURE 10.27
Panthera leo **(lion) and** ***Panthera tigris*** **(tiger)**

There are many species within a genus grouping. Every genus belongs to a **family,** and families can be grouped together in an **order.** Orders are grouped into a **class,** and classes are grouped into a **phylum** (fye' lum). Finally, phyla (the plural of phylum) are grouped into a kingdom.

Figure 10.28 has the complete taxonomic classification of a tiger and a mule deer. You can see that they are both in the same kingdom, phylum, and class, but they differ from that point on. Yet they are both in kingdom Animalia, aren't they?

FIGURE 10.28
Taxonomic Classification of a Tiger and a Mule Deer

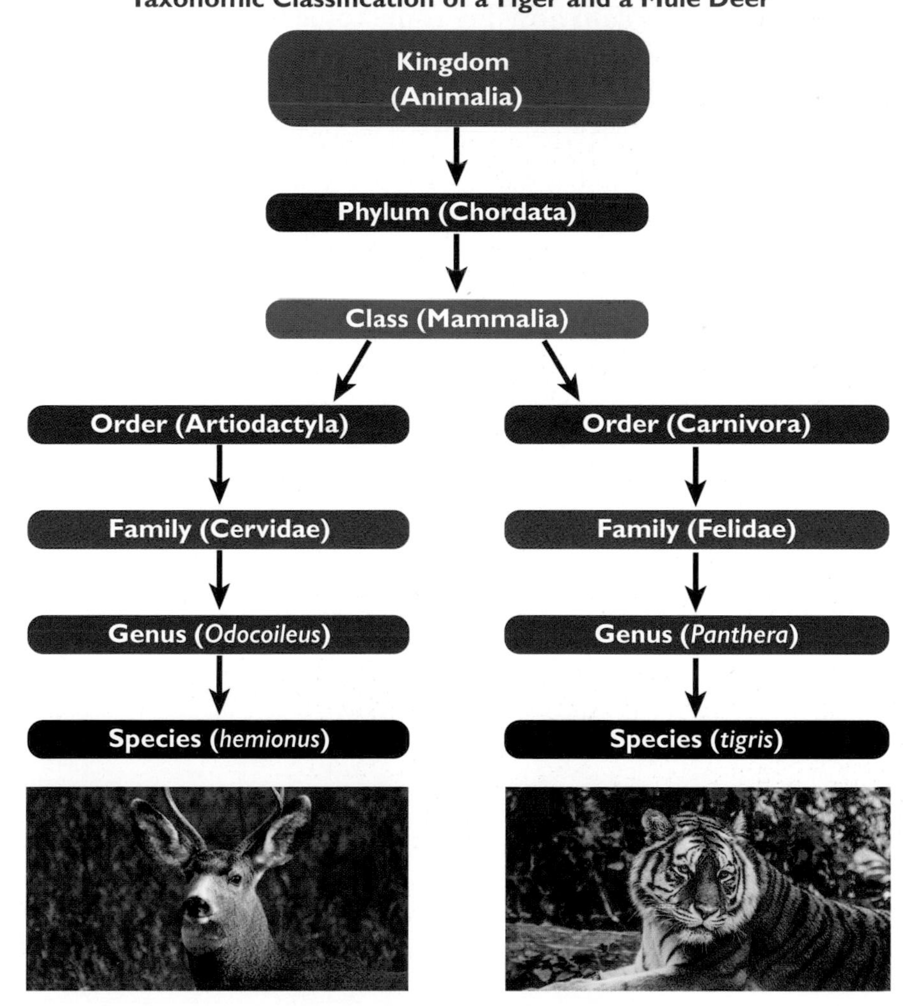

A good way to remember the order of these divisions is to think of the first letters of each category type. Kingdom,

Phylum, Class, Order, Family, Genus, and Species can be more easily remembered by this mnemonic: King Philip's Class Ordered Frozen Grape Sodas.

ON YOUR OWN

10.9 You compare several organisms from different orders within a given class. You then compare organisms from different classes. In which case would you expect the differences to be greater?

SUMMING UP

In this module, we covered how to determine what makes something alive. You might not have expected that question to be such a complicated one to answer. Once you learned the criteria for life, you then learned how to categorize all the organisms in creation. I hope you have a greater appreciation for the vastness of life science and how broad this field is. Perhaps the most significant point in this entire module (at least for me!) is that *there is no simple organism in creation*. Even the "simplest" organisms, such as those in domains Bacteria and Archaea, are very complex cells that undergo practically all the same jobs as larger organisms. Because of this, and with the growing information that biologists discover about them, it is increasingly more difficult for those who believe in the theory of evolution to explain how life came to be without the hand of a Creator. Indeed, *life does not range from simple to complex, but from complex to amazingly complex*! What a testimony to God's creative hand!

ANSWERS TO THE "ON YOUR OWN" QUESTIONS

10.1 *Answers will vary.* Use Figure 10.2 as a guide.

10.2 You know that adenine will always pair with thymine, and thymine will always pair with adenine. Similarly, cytosine will always pair with guanine and guanine will always pair with cytosine. If the sequence given is adenine, thymine, cytosine, adenine, guanine, cytosine, thymine, then the sequence of nucleotide bases on the other half of this DNA would be **thymine, adenine, guanine, thymine, cytosine, guanine, adenine.** To make it easier for you to see, let's abbreviate the nucleotide bases to read ATCAGCT. A good way to remember which pairs with which is that AT is always a pair. It is the only pair that makes a word. Thus, you always know that TA will be a pair, too. And that, of course, leaves C and G to pair up. So your answer would be TAGTCGA.

10.3 Since the bombardier beetle leads a pretty safe life, there will not be a lot that die before having babies. Thus, they do not need a lot of extra "replacements." Therefore, you would think that **bombardier beetles have few offspring.**

10.4 There are many ways that plants sense and respond to change. **They can sense where the greatest amount of light is, and they grow toward that light; they can sense when they touch a structure, and if the structure is right, they will wind themselves around the structure for support; they can sense when it is night and respond, many closing their flowers at night and opening them in the morning.** Though I have only talked about one of these in the module, you might know about the other ones or may have come up with another.

10.5 **The onion and grass cells would look similar because they are both plant cells. The mouse and horse cells would look similar because they are both animal cells.** The bacterium cell would not look like any of the others, as it lacks a nucleus and other membrane-bound organelles.

10.6 *Answers will vary.* Any information from the corresponding sections is acceptable.

10.7 **A prokaryotic cell is a cell with no distinct membrane-bound organelles, and a eukaryotic cell is a cell with distinct membrane-bound organelles.**

10.8 *Answers will vary*, **but for Domain Archaea, you can draw a bacterium like the one in Figure 10.22, plus write that many of these organisms are prokaryotic extremophiles. Domain Bacteria can have a drawing of a bacterium like in Figure 10.23 plus information stating that they are bacteria we encounter the most and many of them are non-extremophiles. Domain Eukarya can have a description of organisms with eukaryotic cells. And you can make an illustration like the ones in Figure 10.24 for each kingdom.**

10.9 Because an order is a smaller group of organisms within the same class, **you should expect the organisms from different classes to have the greater differences**

as compared to organisms of different orders within the *same* class. For example, mammals and insects are 2 different classes in kingdom Animalia. A butterfly (insect) is very different from a bear (mammal). But within the mammals, a bear and a dog (from different orders within the same mammal class) are more similar to each other than the bear and butterfly.

STUDY GUIDE FOR MODULE 10

1. Match the following words with their definitions.

a. Photosynthesis	A method of sorting things according to shared qualities or characteristics
b. Cell	An organism that breaks down the dead remains of other organisms
c. Classification	The process by which green plants and some other organisms use the energy of sunlight and simple chemicals to produce their own food
d. Decomposer	The smallest unit of life in creation

2. The first criterion of life is that all living things contain hereditary information in their ___________ that enables life to continue through reproduction.

3. Which nucleotide pairs up with cytosine?
   a. guanine b. adenine c. thymine d. chlorine

4. A female bluefin tuna can produce up to 10 million eggs a year. With this information, would you expect that young bluefin tuna live a dangerous or a safe life?

5. The second criterion of life is that all living things have a method by which they extract ___________ from their surroundings and convert it into energy that sustains them.

6. The third criterion of life is that all living things can _________ changes in their surroundings and ___________ to those changes.

7. Which cell type does NOT have a nucleus?
   a. animal cell b. plant cell c. bacterial cell

8. Which of these is NOT a way the body regulates itself?
   a. sweating b. adjusting breathing rate
   c. adjusting heart rate d. fingernail growth

9. A scientist is looking at a slide of microorganisms and identifies a living cell that has no nucleus or other distinct, membrane-bound organelles. Is it a prokaryotic or a eukaryotic cell?

10. In the 3-domain system of classification, only one of the domains has kingdoms to further divide it. Which domain is it?

    a. Domain Archaea b. Domain Bacteria c. Domain Eukarya

11. Fill in the missing words in the classification divisions of living organisms:

    K________, Phylum, C______, Order, Family, Genus, and S______

GENERAL BIOLOGY

With a better understanding of what makes something alive, we can now talk more about the study of living things. Last module, you learned about the criteria of life as well as how scientists classify organisms into groups. In this module, we will go further into the several branches of science within biology. First, let me give you a formal definition of **biology**.

Biology—The study of living organisms

FIGURE 11.1
Red-Eyed Tree Frog, *Agalychnis callidryas*

Quaestio

Isn't it amazing how God created such a diverse array of organisms? Think about a sunflower and a frog, for example. Both are living things. But one makes its own food while the other one needs to get food by eating other things. One reproduces using seeds while the other one lays eggs. One is planted in the ground while the other one moves around. However, both interact with their environment and have unique requirements in order to live. They have specific requirements for water and can only survive within a certain temperature range. When we consider these characteristics of frogs, sunflowers, and even other living organisms, it is clear that there is much to study in the field of biology. Thus, studying living things requires us to focus on specific areas within this field.

Now, that is a pretty simple definition; however, there really is much more to it. Biology is the study of living organisms through lots of specialized fields that focus on their body structure, body functions, behavior, and where they live. Thus, there are many branches of biology. In this module, you will learn about some of the major ones. However, you need to understand that this is just a small list within a global-sized field of study!

MOLECULAR BIOLOGY AND BIOCHEMISTRY

Molecular biology is the branch of biology that deals with the structure and function of the chemicals of living things. **Biochemistry** is similar. It has to do with the study of the chemical processes that happen within living organisms. Why is it important to know what's going on chemically in living things? Think about the last time you had a muscle cramp. They can be pretty painful. Muscle cramps happen as a result of many things, but a common cause is a potential lack of potassium in your diet. You see, potassium is an element that our bodies need for our muscles to contract. Without enough in our bodies, things start to work improperly, and we feel symptoms such as a painful cramp in our leg. Don't worry if you get one. Perhaps just eating a banana that is rich in potassium might be the perfect solution to your problem.

FIGURE 11.2
Potassium-Rich Bananas

With that example, I hope you can better understand the importance of studying the chemicals within living organisms. It is important for us to know how these processes work because that helps us to treat people who are ill. It also helps us better understand what other living organisms need to survive.

The Chemicals of Life

Cells are responsible for carrying out the processes of life. They make and transport critical materials for an organism to survive. Even though cells are extremely intricate structures, composed of complex molecules, and lots of elements are involved, it turns out that they are primarily made from just a few basic types of atoms. All cells contain 4 major elements: carbon, hydrogen, oxygen, and nitrogen. These elements combine in various ways to make lots of compounds. The major compounds in cells are **carbohydrates, lipids, proteins,** and **nucleic acids.** Many of these may seem familiar to you. But let me go into a little detail about each.

Carbohydrates are molecules made from carbon, hydrogen, and oxygen only. They are one of the main sources of food energy for most animals. Carbohydrate molecules include sugars and **starches.** Interestingly, a starch molecule is a very large molecule made up of simple sugar molecules bonded together. When an organism eats starches, its body first breaks them down into their individual sugar components. Then, it can utilize the energy stored within the sugar molecules.

Lipids, also known as fats, are complex molecules. One of the unique properties of lipids is that they do not dissolve well in water. You may have seen how oil (which is a lipid) and water do not mix. Well, that is because the structure of oil molecules is such

FIGURE 11.3
The Chemicals of Life

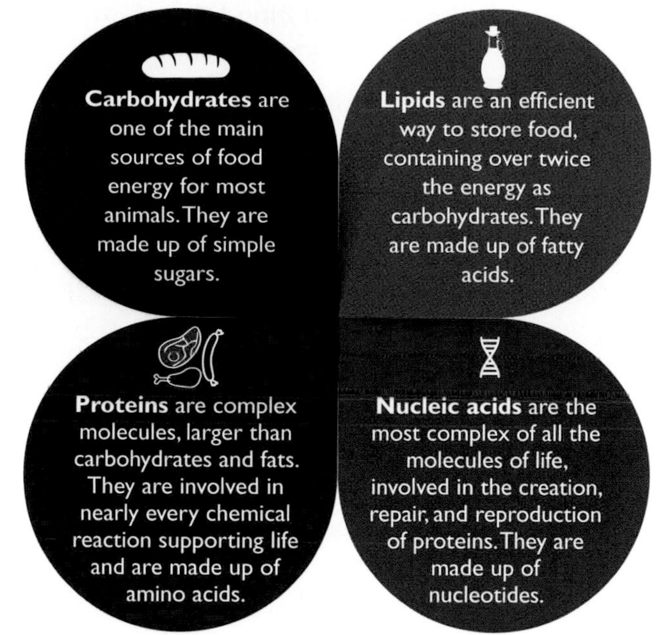

that they do not "like" to be near water molecules. Biologically speaking, most organisms store much of their extra food as lipids. That's because more than twice as much energy can be stored in an ounce of fat or oil as compared to an ounce of carbohydrates. It is more efficient.

Proteins are also complex molecules but are much larger than either carbohydrates or fats. They are involved in nearly every chemical reaction that supports life. Second only to water, protein is the most plentiful substance in the body. In humans, that means that our muscles and organs are mostly made up of protein. Proteins are necessary to carry out lots of chemical processes including growth, maintenance, and cell replacement.

Finally, nucleic acids are the most complex of all the molecules of life. They include DNA, which stores all the information for making the structures of living things. **RNA,** or **ribonucleic** (rye boh new clay' ic) **acid,** is also an important nucleic acid. Like DNA, RNA is involved in the creation, repair, and reproduction of proteins. It differs in structure in that it is typically made up of a single strand of nucleotides, and DNA is made from 2 strands bonded together.

As scientists better understand the chemistry that helps make life possible, they get a greater appreciation of life's diversity and what organisms need to survive.

ON YOUR OWN

11.1 Using Figure 11.3 as a guide, list the 4 chemicals of life and the smaller molecules that they are made from.

CELL BIOLOGY

Cell biology is the study of cells and **cytology** is a branch of cell biology that focuses on cell structures and how they function. Last module, you learned that the cell is the fundamental unit of life. All living things are made up of at least one cell. In fact, after cells were thoroughly studied, scientists came up with the cell theory stating that not only are things made up of at least one cell, but *all cells come from pre-existing cells.*

Cell Structures

With a better understanding of the molecules involved in cells, I can now go over the 3 main parts of a eukaryotic cell: the **cell membrane,** the **cytoplasm** (sy' toh plaz uhm) with all its structures, and the **nucleus.** The cell membrane is a flexible **semipermeable** membrane with the job of surrounding and protecting the inside of the cell. What does semipermeable mean? When something is permeable, it allows materials through it. So a semipermeable membrane only allows some things through. Think of a tennis net. It has holes in it that allow air to pass through. Small flying insects and other tiny objects can go through it as well. But it will not allow a tennis ball to pass. For that matter, a basketball, a bicycle, or even a human could not pass through a tennis net! This feature is an important one because it means the cell membrane is highly selective, allowing only certain substances to enter or leave the cell. So oxygen gas can be moved into the cell through the membrane, and wastes are transported out. Additionally, helpful materials like nutrients are allowed to enter while important internal structures are kept from leaving.

FIGURE 11.4
Semipermeable Membrane (Yellow) Keeping Red Blood Cells from Passing Through

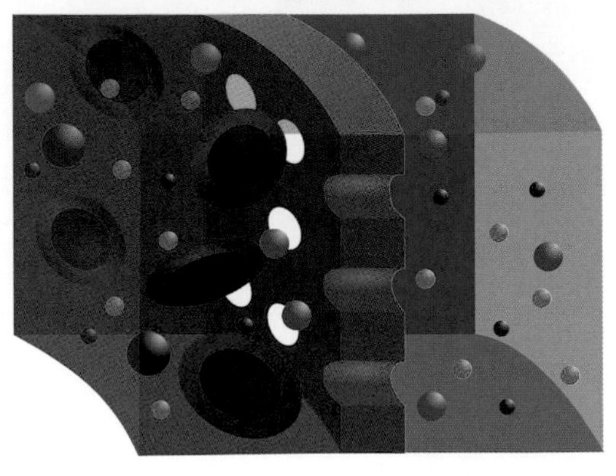

Inside the cell membrane is a jellylike material called cytoplasm. It contains several important structures, called organelles, that do specific jobs for the cell to properly function. I introduced organelles in the last module, but I want to talk about some of the major ones now. Because you will study these structures in more depth in a future biology course, I will highlight a few here. Refer to Figure 11.5 as I introduce them.

FIGURE 11.5
Major Eukaryotic Cell Organelles

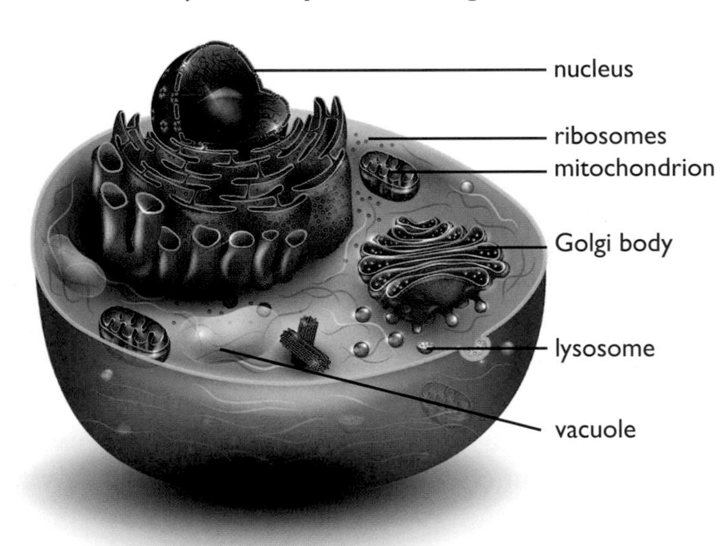

Ribosomes are non-membrane-bound structures that are responsible for making proteins. Because they are not bound by a membrane, ribosomes are found in both eukaryotic and prokaryotic cells. The rest of the organelles I will discuss are membrane-bound organelles, so they are only found in eukaryotic cells. **Mitochondria** are considered the powerhouses of the cell. They are the organelles that provide energy for the cell to use. **Vacuoles** are membrane sacs that contain various substances for different jobs. Waste vacuoles, for example, carry the waste products of cell digestion to the edge of the cell for elimination. Food vacuoles contain nutrients, fluids, and minerals. **Golgi bodies** are organelles where proteins and lipids are stored and then altered to suit the needs of the cell. They look like stacks of pancakes. **Lysosomes** are membrane-enclosed containers that hold chemicals called enzymes. These chemicals are for breaking down materials in the cell. They can digest food or break down the cell when it dies.

The nucleus is another organelle and behaves as the cell's control center. It holds the cell's main DNA and is surrounded by a semipermeable **nuclear membrane** to separate the nucleus from the surrounding cytoplasm.

There are a couple special structures I want to mention, too. Eukaryotic cells that photosynthesize have organelles called **chloroplasts.** These organelles are the location where the process of photosynthesis occurs. Additionally, you learned in Module 10 that plant cells have an outer, rigid cell wall that provides structure. Bacterial cells have cell walls, too.

Cell Anatomy

I haven't covered all of the organelles in a cell, but if you consider those that I did cover, you might be able to understand that cells are very complex. As you learned last module, even prokaryotic cells have intricate structural design. And all cells undergo complex processes to take in energy, process energy, reproduce, create and take in specific materials, and even communicate!

You can think of a prokaryotic cell as if you were living in a one-room cabin. There would be areas in the cabin for cooking, sleeping, storage, and even recreation (Figure 11.6). Each area would have specific items, such as pots and pans in the kitchen, to help you perform the activities you need to do. Prokaryotic cells are kind of like that. They don't have internal membranes to separate structures, but there are *areas* within the cell where processes such as DNA replication or protein production occur.

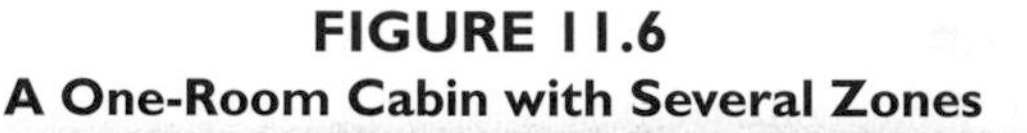

FIGURE 11.6
A One-Room Cabin with Several Zones

Using a similar analogy, eukaryotic cells are like a multi-roomed house. A bedroom would be contained within walls, and a door would allow you to go in and out of it. A kitchen would be where all the cooking occurs. Well, each organelle in a eukaryotic cell represents a location where cell processes occur. Each organelle has specialized functions for processing food, removing wastes, transporting chemicals around, or other critical actions. The benefit of having separate "rooms" allows each organelle to maintain its own conditions in order to best do a specific job. A good example of this is the lysosome I mentioned in the last section (see Figure 11.5). Lysosomes have the job of recycling materials in the cell. To do this, they have to keep an acidic pH environment. That is *not* a good environment for other organelles. However, because the lysosome is surrounded by a membrane, other areas of the cell are protected. Therefore, because different environments can be created within a single cell, eukaryotic cells can carry out some complex chemical processes that prokaryotic cells cannot. And that enables eukaryotic cells to grow much larger than prokaryotic cells. Now, that doesn't mean that prokaryotic cells aren't complex. Eukaryotic cells are just *much more* complex!

To give you a good idea of the complexity of the chemical processes within a cell, I want to go over one of them. This is a process that occurs in both prokaryotic and eukaryotic cells. The cell membrane is made up of a unique double layer of molecules called **phospholipids.** These molecules have a water-soluble end and a non-water-soluble end. So they line up in 2 layers with the non-water-soluble sides facing inward. The water-soluble sides of the molecules are facing either outside the cell or inside the cell (see Figure 11.7). When a large hydrophilic molecule needs to enter the cell, it moves to a pump located in the wall of the membrane. *Hydrophilic* technically means "water-loving" referring to something easily dissolved in water. So this molecule needs help moving through the non-water-soluble center of the membrane. You see, it takes energy to move big materials into the cell, so there is a cellular "machine" that is necessary. This **protein pump** moves the hydrophilic molecule through the protective membrane via a series of chemical-binding processes. The cell is designed so that it only moves certain substances like that into the cell. Additionally, the membrane's structure is such that it behaves as a protective wall, keeping out other large, unwanted chemicals and keeping in necessary ones. Of course, water and other small molecules can pass through the cell membrane. Yet even then, there are processes that help to control how much of these are allowed through. And that is just *one* process involving *one* job (moving materials in and out of the cell) that *one* structure (the cell membrane) can do. Indeed, the cell is like a small city with internal highways, power plants, trash vehicles, and more, working together to run a microscopic city.

FIGURE 11.7
A Portion of a Cell Membrane

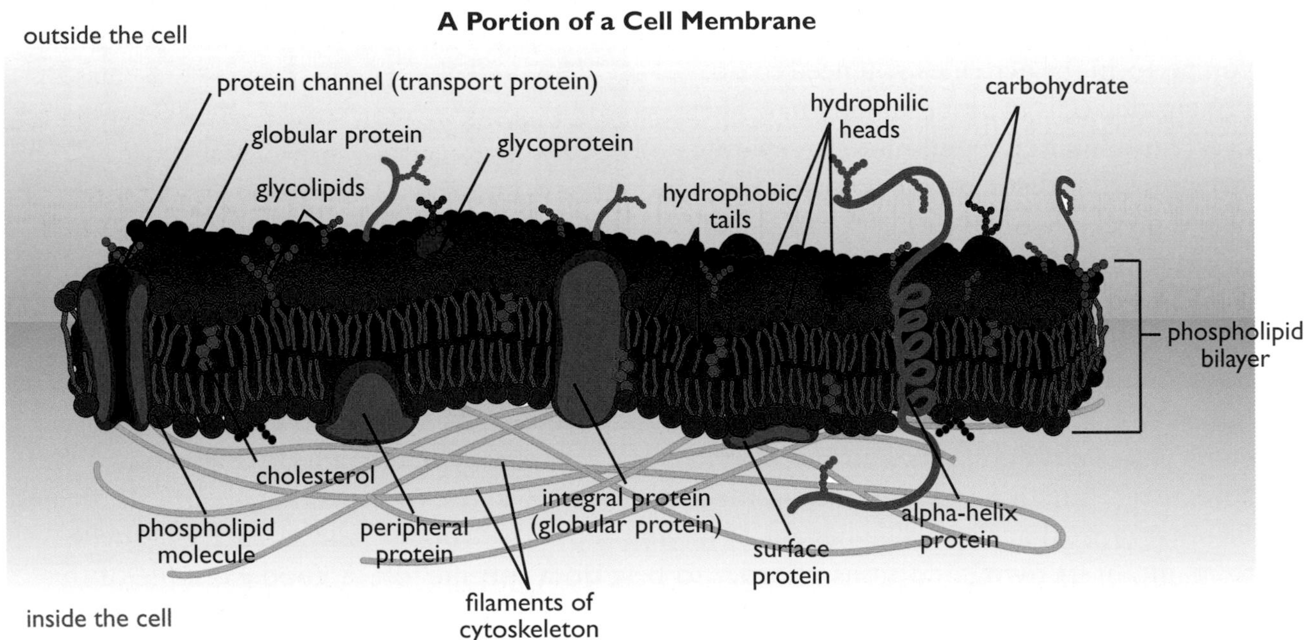

This portion of a cell membrane shows the phospholipid double layer (the bilayer) with the water-loving red circles facing either outside the cell or inside the cell. Notice that there is a lot more going on here. There are large proteins that are embedded in the membrane, used for transporting larger molecules through. Carbohydrates extend outside the membrane so that other molecules can be identified. The whole membrane is internally supported by a cytoskeleton (literally a cell-skeleton), made from strong filaments. And this is just some of what we know that one structure of all cells can do!

ON YOUR OWN

11.2 Why is a semipermeable membrane helpful to a cell?

11.3 Explain the analogy of a one-room cabin and a prokaryotic cell.

MICROBIOLOGY

Microbiology is the study of microscopic organisms. Many of these little creatures are single-celled organisms, but some are composed of many cells. When we refer to a single-celled organism, we call it a **unicellular** organism; and if an organism has more than one cell, it is **multicellular.**

Unicellular—Consisting of a single cell

Multicellular—Consisting of more than one cell

The prefix *uni-* means "one," and the prefix *multi-* means "many," so those words should be easy for you to remember.

Some microscopic organisms are prokaryotic, with no membrane-bound organelles. As I explained last module, these are the bacteria. Bacteria live everywhere. Some are beneficial to humans, others are neither harmful nor helpful, and still others can kill us. This hidden world of organisms can affect our health, help to make our food, and even influence our environment.

The study of microbiology extends beyond the bacteria, though. It includes members of the fungi and even **viruses.** You may have heard of viruses before. But why didn't I mention them last module when I talked about living organisms? Well, by definition, viruses are not living things. They do not meet all the criteria for life. Basically, a virus is made up of a protein shell surrounding instructional information such as DNA. One criterion a virus does not meet is that it cannot reproduce itself. It has to attack an existing cell and then inject its instructional information inside. The virus instructions then take over the reproductive mechanisms within the cell to produce more viruses until the cell exhausts its resources and bursts. The newly made viruses within the cell then move on to find another healthy cell to take over.

That might sound pretty gruesome, but if you've ever been infected by a virus, you know that it doesn't take long for you to start feeling sick. For something so tiny, taking down a gigantic being like a human is no small task!

Microbiologists use special tools to study microorganisms. Of course, a microscope is very helpful due to their tiny size. In Figure 11.8, an **electron microscope** is used to view viruses. This device helps microbiologists to see things smaller than bacteria. An electron microscope uses beams of electrons instead of beams of light, receiving the images with special lenses.

FIGURE 11.8
Electron Micrograph Image of a Bacteriophage Virus

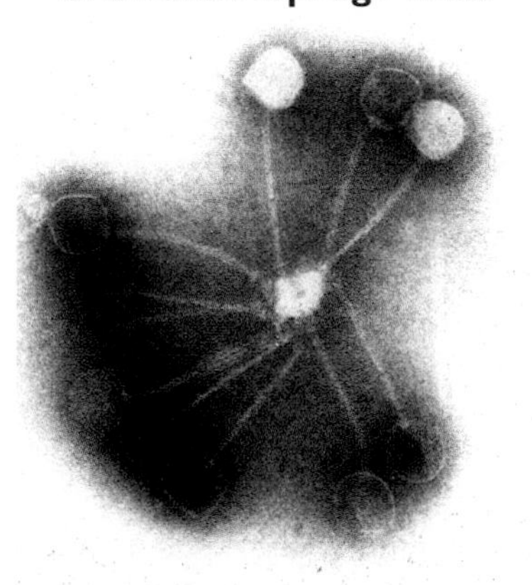

FIGURE 11.9
Two Bacterial Cultures

Another way to study microorganisms is to grow them in **cultures.** Culturing is a term used to describe growing microorganisms in a controlled environment. Conditions such as temperature, food source, and the presence of specific chemicals can be managed to determine in what environments the organisms are able to best live (Figure 11.9). Perform Experiment 11.1 to see this firsthand.

EXPERIMENT 11.1
GROWING A YEAST CULTURE

PURPOSE: To better understand the process of growing cultures

MATERIALS:
- Warm and cold tap water
- A liquid measuring cup
- A drinking glass
- A permanent marker
- 2 empty 20-oz. soda bottles (Most water bottles are too flimsy for this experiment.)
- A packet of activated baker's yeast
- A teaspoon
- Sugar
- 2 balloons

QUESTION: Under what temperature conditions does yeast grow best?

HYPOTHESIS: Write if you think yeast will grow better in a warm or cold environment.

PROCEDURE:
1. Measure ½ cup tap water, pour it into the glass, and put it in the refrigerator until it is cold.
2. Using the permanent marker, write the words "warm water" on one soda bottle and "cold water" on the other one.
3. Add 1 teaspoon of yeast into each bottle.
4. Add 1 teaspoon of sugar to each bottle.
5. Add ½ cup cold water you chilled in the refrigerator to the bottle marked "cold water."
6. Add ½ cup of warm water to the bottle marked "warm water." To get the warm water, turn on the tap water so that the water coming out of it feels like a warm bath, but not a hot one. The temperature should be about 110 °F.
7. Gently swirl the bottles to make sure the contents are mixed.
8. Stretch a balloon over the mouth of each bottle.

9. Place the cold water bottle in the refrigerator and the warm water bottle in a warm area like a sunny window pane or on top of a running dryer.
10. After about 30 minutes, notice if anything happens to the balloons. Write what you observe in your notebook.

CONCLUSION: Write which temperature (warm or cold) is the better condition to culture yeast.

What happened in the experiment? If everything went well, you should have noticed that the balloon on the warm water bottle was filled with more gas than the balloon on the cold water bottle. Remember that yeast is a single-celled fungus. Before you added it to the water, it was in a dormant state. That means that its physical functions had slowed until conditions became good for growth. When you added it to the sugar and water, the yeast began to feed on the sugar, using it as food energy so it could grow and multiply. That process also produced carbon dioxide gas. The yeast in the warm water should have produced more carbon dioxide gas, which filled up the balloon. The yeast in the cold water did not grow as well and produced less gas. Thus, in order to best grow this type of yeast, you need to provide it with a warm environment.

The field of microbiology is important to people because it helps us better understand those organisms that help us live better as well as those organisms that can harm us. We call the harmful organisms **parasites.**

Parasitology

Parasitology is a sub-branch of microbiology that is concerned with the study of organisms that live on or inside other organisms, harming them. Although there are some parasites that are not microscopic, most of them are. They include viruses, certain bacteria, and some fungi.

Although there are many helpful microorganisms, the study of the ones that harm us has helped scientists come up with ways to fight infections. The use of **vaccinations** (vax in ay' shunz), antibiotics, and even clean water has lowered the rate of infectious organisms harming people. A **vaccine** (vax een') is a special injection of material containing whole (or parts of) harmful microorganisms that have been killed or weakened so that they don't cause disease. When they are injected into your body, the body's systems immediately work to attack these foreign materials. And because they are dead or weakened, it is much easier to fight them. When your body does that, it remembers what to do the next time you get infected with the same harmful organisms. And the next time, even though the "bad guys" are strong, your body is able to react much faster before the infection has time to spread.

think about this

An interesting inclusion in the study of microbiology is **prions**. These are not considered microorganisms because they are not living entities. Rather, prions are long protein molecules folded into an abnormal shape. You see, because proteins are such large molecules, they have to be folded up into specific shapes in order to do their jobs. Improperly folded prions can cause infectious disease, such as mad cow disease.

If your body *does* get an infection it has trouble fighting, it is often helpful to take an antibiotic medicine that works to kill the organisms infecting you. Now, notice the word *antibiotic*. *Anti-* means "against," and *biotic* refers to a living organism. Thus, antibiotics are medicines that only work on living organisms such as bacteria. They do not fight off viruses.

The fields of microbiology and parasitology are fascinating, and there is much more to learn. Not only can microorganisms cause disease, but they also can be used to develop drugs or fight other microorganisms. Indeed, we should respect these tiny creatures that can pack a powerful punch!

FIGURE 11.10
Bread Mold of the Genus *Penicillium*

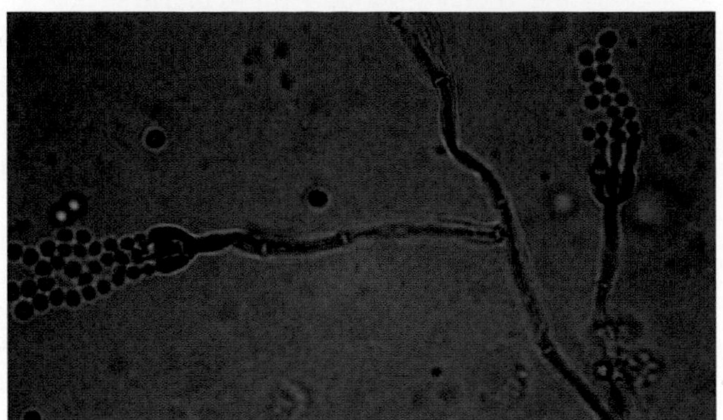

Penicillium is a genus of fungi known as bread molds. Some species produce a chemical called **penicillin**, which is a molecule used as an antibiotic. It is naturally produced by the mold to kill off harmful bacteria. Humans take advantage of this natural antibiotic to help people fight off bacteria, too!

EXPLORE MORE

You can grow and examine your own bread mold by moistening a piece of bread with tap water and placing it on a small paper plate. (NOTE: The fewer preservatives in the bread, the faster this activity will work.) Next, take some dust from a windowsill and sprinkle it onto the bread, loosely covering the plate with plastic wrap. Set the plate in a warm, dark area where it won't be disturbed. Check the bread each day to make sure it hasn't dried out. Add a few drops of water if it does. In a few days, you should notice dark spots and fuzzy material growing on the bread. Don't completely uncover the bread but examine it through the wrap so you don't inhale any of the spores. The fuzzy portions are the body of the fungus, called the **mycelium.** (See the section on Mycology in this module.) The dark spots contain the mold spores. Once you're done observing it, carefully dispose of the bread in the trash.

IMMUNOLOGY

After talking about microbiology and parasitology, I think it is a good idea to highlight **immunology,** too. Immunology is a branch of biology that is concerned with immunity. Well, that only helps if you know what immunity is. Immunity has to do with the systems of living organisms that protect from infection. The human immune system, for example, is made up of organs, molecules, and cells that are distributed throughout the body. Their job is to patrol the body, looking for foreign materials and attacking them. It is kind of like a tiny internal police force, ready and waiting to capture invaders. The immune system also works to repair or remove damaged material in the body. By recognizing and responding to foreign things and repairing injuries, our immune system works to keep us healthy.

Immunologists try to understand how our body systems work and what happens to us when the systems don't work correctly. They have learned that the human immune system has a long-lived memory to help prevent or minimize repeat infections. Have you ever had chicken pox or know someone who has had it? It is a very contagious infection caused by the varicella zoster virus. People who get this virus often develop a rash of very itchy spots all over their bodies. However, those who have gotten the chicken pox virus are then immune to it later on. You see, when their body first sees the virus, it identifies it as a foreign object and starts to fight it off. However, it takes some time to build up the fighting mechanisms to attack this virus. In most cases, people recover from the chicken pox and are fine. But their bodies don't forget what happened. You see, our bodies have something called adaptive immunity. What happens is, when the body gets an infection, it creates memory cells that can produce a process "short cut." That way, if the body ever sees the same virus again, it can respond much more quickly and overcome the attack. Therefore, once you have had the chicken pox, you can be around someone else with the infection, and you are not at risk of getting sick.

FIGURE 11.11
Healthful Foods to Fuel Your Immune System

ON YOUR OWN

11.4 Explain one criterion of life that a virus does not meet.

11.5 Many infectious diseases caused by viruses and bacteria are spread through one of 3 ways: infected people, animals carrying the disease, and contaminated food or water. Ways to prevent this spread is to wash your hands well, wear protective clothing or bug spray, and make sure your food is well cooked and the water is fresh (boiled water kills most disease-spreading organisms). Make a short infographic titled "Three Ways Infectious Disease Can Spread" and also include something you can do to help prevent each one.

MYCOLOGY

Mycology is the scientific study of fungi. You already learned that these are living things within kingdom Fungi and include mushrooms. Most fungi are **saprophytes.**

Saprophytes—Organisms that obtain their nourishment from dead organisms

So they feed on things that are already dead. That's why you'll see mushrooms growing on dead logs. They are breaking down the food material stored in the tree. To get their nutrients, the fungi **decompose**—or take apart—the chemicals bound up there. If you think of a composer as a person who *puts together* music, to *de*compose means to break down something. So we can say that fungi are decomposers, breaking down the complex molecules of dead plants and animals into simpler ones they can use as food. Mycologists (scientists who study mycology) look at both harmful and helpful fungi. An example of those that are harmful are the fungi that can cause athlete's foot in people. Beneficial fungi include *Penicillium roqueforti* that makes cheese.

The fungi you are likely most familiar with are the **club fungi,** which are macroscopic (able to be seen without a microscope). They produce spores when they

FIGURE 11.12
A Mushroom Fruiting Body

reproduce. Some club fungi are edible, and others are poisonous. Common club fungi include the mushrooms and toadstools. Now, many people mistakenly think of the mushroom shape as the complete organism, but you might be surprised to know that it is just a small portion. You see, most fungi are made of thread-like structures called **hyphae** (high' fee). These threads grow in a tangled mass called the **mycelium** (my see' lee um). The mycelium is the main body of the fungus, but it is rarely visible. It is found growing in the ground, in a decaying tree, or wherever there is dead material that the fungus can feed on. When the fungus is ready to reproduce, it sends up a stalk of tightly bound hyphae with an umbrella-shaped cap that forms spores. These **fruiting bodies** can often pop up overnight, ready to release hundreds of reproductive spores.

When people see mushrooms in their yard, they sometimes will kick, step on, or mow over them in an effort to remove them. But they actually are *spreading* the spores, potentially increasing mushroom growth! If you know what a fruiting body is, then you will carefully cover them with a bag, gently pulling them out of the ground for removal. That way you don't spread the spores.

Another type of fungi are the molds. You have likely seen them growing on old cheese, fruit, or bread. Mold spores are so small that they can be carried in the air for miles. If you leave bread uncovered, bread mold spores will eventually land on it and within a few days start to grow. Now, don't worry. Most molds that grow on bread won't hurt you if they are eaten in small amounts. But it is still good to keep bread covered for this reason.

Mycologists have much more to learn about the wide variety of organisms in this kingdom. It is an important group to study because of their saprophytic contribution to the environment. Many fungi are useful to humans, too, producing food and medicine. And they are fascinating!

ON YOUR OWN

11.6 Explain what happens if you kick the mushrooms in your yard.

BOTANY AND PLANT PHYSIOLOGY

Botany is the scientific study of plants, and it includes learning about their structure and how they live and interact in the environment. **Plant physiology** is a subcategory of botany that focuses on the function of plant parts. One of the most notable features about most plants is their ability to make their own food through the process of photosynthesis. This is critical for animals and humans, too, because our diet comes either directly from plants or from eating animals that eat plants.

The major location where photosynthesis occurs is in the leaves of a plant. As sunlight enters the cells of the leaf, some of its energy is absorbed by the chloroplast organelles. The green-colored pigment, called **chlorophyll** (klor' oh fill), absorbs light energy so the plant can make its food. Using carbon dioxide gas, water, and solar energy, the chloroplast produces a sugar (called glucose) as well as oxygen. Most often, glucose is not used by the plant right away. Rather, it is combined into long chains of sugar molecules, called **starches.** These are stored up for the plant to use later.

FIGURE 11.13
Amazon Water Lily Leaf 3 Meters (6 Feet!) Wide

When it is time for a plant to utilize its food, it undergoes a process called **cellular respiration.** Cellular respiration combines glucose with oxygen to produce energy. It also produces carbon dioxide and water. If you look at the 2 processes of photosynthesis and cellular respiration, you will notice that the reactants and products are exactly opposite (Figure 11.14). However, the chemical *steps* in the process of these reactions are different. There also is one notable difference between these 2 processes. While cellular respiration can occur any time of the day or night, photosynthesis is limited to daytime only, when sunlight is available. Yet, both photosynthesis and cellular respiration are designed to work together. Photosynthesis uses light energy to make glucose, and cellular respiration uses glucose to provide energy for the plant. And the oxygen that is made during photosynthesis is used during cellular respiration, and the carbon dioxide and water made during cellular respiration are necessary for photosynthesis. What a perfect design!

FIGURE 11.14
Photosynthesis and Respiration

PHOTOSYNTHESIS

solar energy + carbon dioxide + water ⟶ glucose sugar + oxygen

CELLULAR RESPIRATION

glucose sugar + oxygen ⟶ energy + carbon dioxide + water

Additionally, animals that breathe air (humans, too!) are a perfect match for plants. While plants produce oxygen, animals need oxygen to breathe. And while animals exhale carbon dioxide, plants need that gas to produce their food. You see, although plants use some of the oxygen they make from photosynthesis for their own cellular respiration, they don't use much. That way they release more oxygen into the atmosphere than they take in.

One way botanists study plants is to identify them as **woody** or **herbaceous** (her bay' shus). As a rule, plants with woody parts, such as trunks or woody stems, tend to grow every year. These are **perennial** (per en' ee al) plants. Plants without woody parts are called herbaceous, and as a rule, these plants live for only about a year. We call these **annual** plants. So when you look at an old oak tree, you know it has a large woody trunk, so you can call it a woody plant. It also lives for many years, some oaks attaining several hundred years in age!

FIGURE 11.15
Bristlecone Pine Trees Live Thousands of Years

creation connection

Photosynthesis is one of the most important chemical reactions on the planet. In fact, if it could be duplicated in man-made containers, we likely could solve all the world's food-energy problems. However, the complex machinery within plants is one that scientists cannot come close to duplicating. It is difficult to come up with the energy necessary to break up water molecules into hydrogen and oxygen so the plant can make sugar. So much energy is needed that it would cause living tissue to break down. However, we don't see plants disintegrating everywhere. That's because they have a unique and complex system to enhance the energy's effects. And there is evidence of oxygen in the supposedly oldest rocks on Earth. Thus, photosynthesizing life must have been around from the beginning of time and could not have evolved.

Plant Structures

I already mentioned in this course that plants are living organisms with leaves, stems, and roots. Let's talk a bit about each of these structures. You might think of a leaf as having a flattened football shape; however, leaves come in all shapes and sizes. The large, main portion of the leaf is the blade. It is attached to the stem with a small stalk called a **petiole** (peh' tee ole). There are 2 basic kinds of leaves: **simple leaves** and **compound leaves.** A simple leaf is a single leaf attached to the stem by a single petiole. A compound leaf has several leaflets attached to a single petiole (Figure 11.16).

FIGURE 11.16
Simple and Compound Leaves and 3 Leaf Mosaic Types

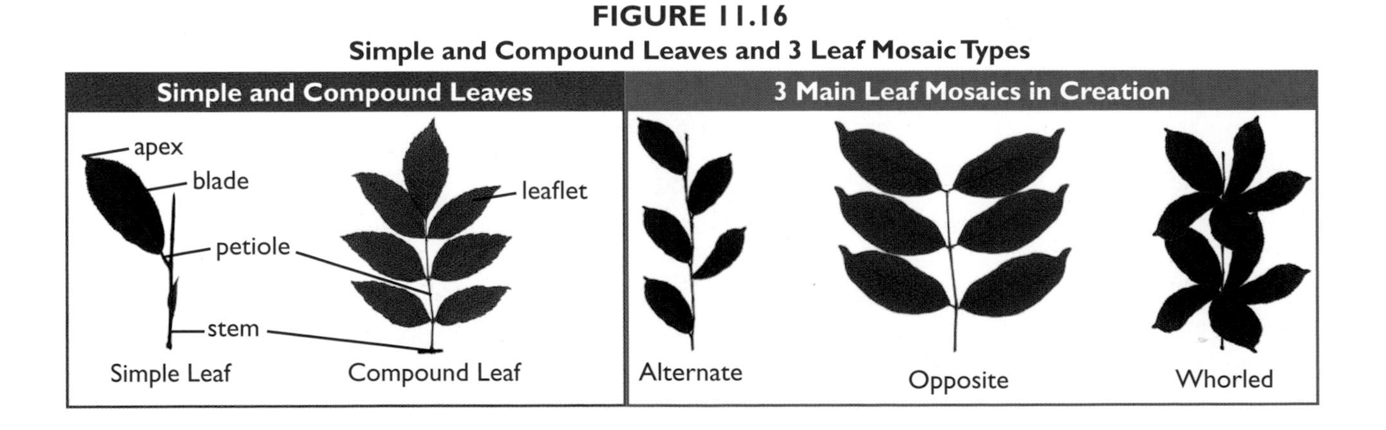

To gather the most sunlight for photosynthesis, leaves are arranged in a way that the largest amount of their surface area is exposed to the sun. The arrangement of leaves on a plant's stem is called the **leaf mosaic** (moh zay' ik). Three major types of leaf mosaics are **alternate** (the petioles attach to the stem in a staggered manner), **opposite** (the petioles attach at the same point on opposite sides), and **whorled** (the leaves spiral around or surround the stem).

There are actually 3 more leaf characteristics botanists use to help classify plants: **leaf shape, leaf margin,** and **vein arrangement.**

Common leaf shapes are seen in Figure 11.17. **Linear** leaves are like blades of grass, having the same width from the top to the bottom. Long and tapered leaves are **elliptical.** Egg-shaped leaves are **oval.** A leaf that is triangular in shape is called a **deltoid** (del' toyd) leaf. Spade-shaped leaves are called **cordate** (kor' dayt), and circular leaves are **orbicular** (or bik' yoo ler). **Lobed** leaves have deep indentations. If those indentations are very deep and sharp, then the leaf has a **cleft** shape. **Needlelike** leaves are what you find on pine trees. There are other leaf shapes in creation, but these are the most common.

FIGURE 11.17
Common Leaf Shapes in Creation

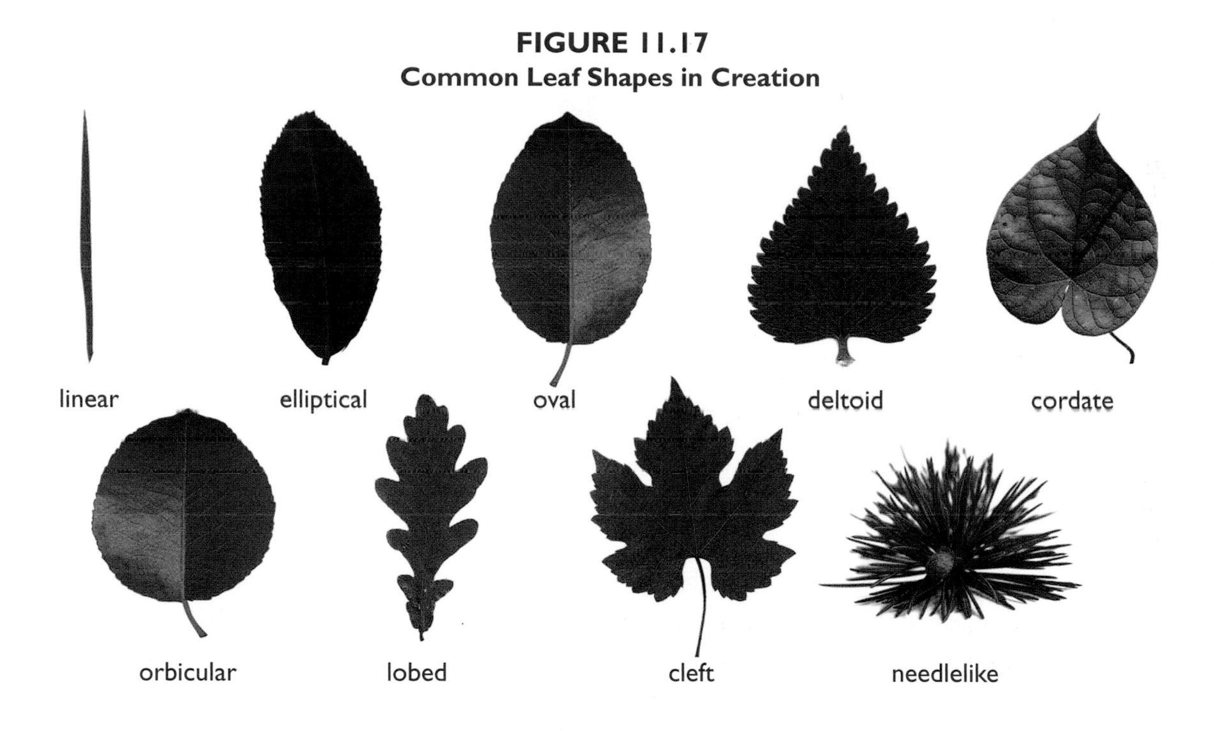

Leaf margins have to do with the edges of the leaf. Figure 11.18 illustrates these.

FIGURE 11.18
Common Leaf Margins

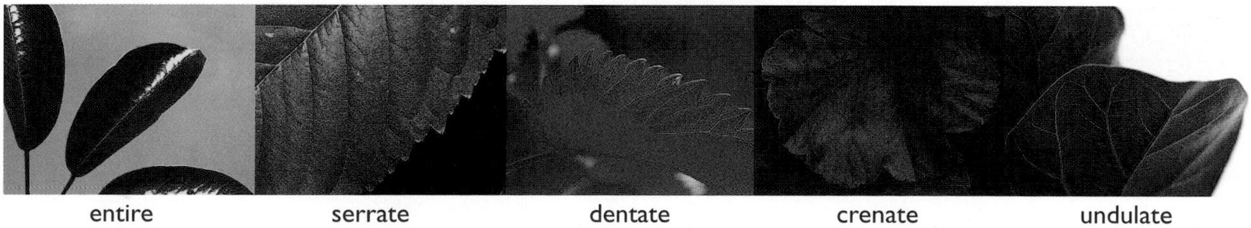

entire serrate dentate crenate undulate

Finally, the veins of a leaf are arranged in unique ways from one type of plant to another. Veins are made from the vessels that transport nutrients and water around the plant. If there is a large, central vein that extends from the petiole, it is a **midrib.** When a leaf's veins run parallel to the midrib, that leaf has **parallel venation.** When they all branch out from the midrib, the leaf has **pinnate venation.** And when a leaf's veins not only branch out from the midrib, but those branches also have branches on them, the leaf has **palmate venation** (see Figure 11.19).

FIGURE 11.19
Leaf Venations

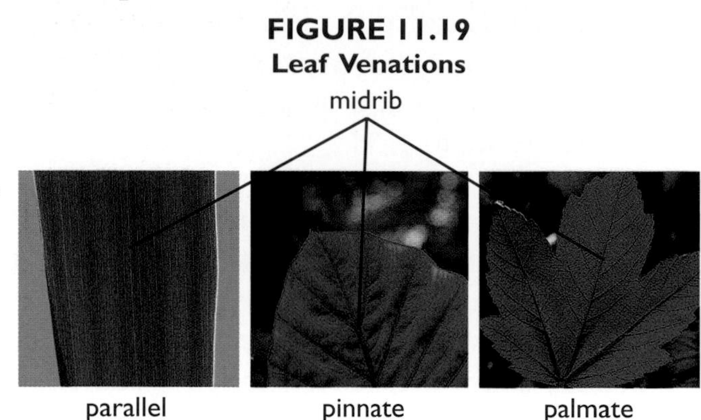

EXPERIMENT 11.2
LEAF COLLECTION AND IDENTIFICATION

PURPOSE: To better understand the external structure of leaves

MATERIALS:
- Leaf press or old books and waxed paper
- Lab notebook
- Tree identification book (from the library or online sources)

QUESTION: What types of trees and other plants are in my area?

HYPOTHESIS: Write how many different types of leaves you think you will discover.

PROCEDURE:
1. Begin collecting leaf specimens from trees and other plants in your area. Try to find about 20 different types of leaves. Make a note in your notebook about each tree or bush from which you collect a leaf.
2. Allow sufficient time for the leaves to dry. Leaves that are damp will mold later.
3. Press your dried leaves in a leaf press or between the pages of old books. You can use waxed paper to protect the book pages.
4. If you are using thin books, add weight to the book stack to help press the leaves.
5. Alternately, you can quickly press leaves between 2 layers of waxed paper with a low-temperature iron. Put a paper towel between the ironing board and the waxed paper as well as between the iron and the waxed paper to avoid getting wax on your iron or ironing board. Trim the waxed paper a short distance from the leaf before mounting.
6. Attach the leaves carefully to the pages of your laboratory notebook or mount them on poster board for display.
7. Include the following information for each leaf (use Figures 11.16-19 for reference), along with the identification of the plant if you know it:

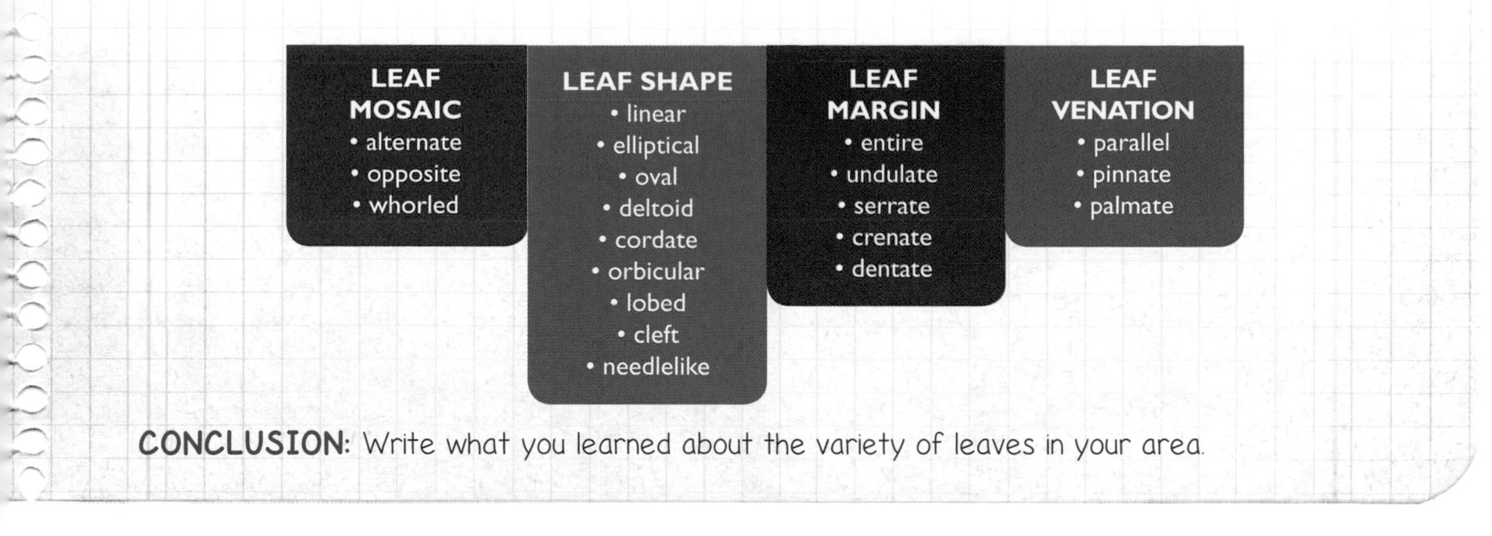

LEAF MOSAIC	LEAF SHAPE	LEAF MARGIN	LEAF VENATION
• alternate • opposite • whorled	• linear • elliptical • oval • deltoid • cordate • orbicular • lobed • cleft • needlelike	• entire • undulate • serrate • crenate • dentate	• parallel • pinnate • palmate

CONCLUSION: Write what you learned about the variety of leaves in your area.

Leaf Color

If I were to give you a coloring page with a picture of a tree, along with a pack of crayons, what color would you make the leaves? Most likely, you would color them green, right? That's because most trees have green leaves. However, many leaves regularly display other colors. And some lose their green color in the fall. Where do all these colors come from? Well, the green color is due to chlorophyll. That's the photosynthetic pigment that absorbs sunlight for photosynthesis. But many plant leaves have other pigments that create yellow, orange, red, and even purple coloring.

EXPLORE MORE

Find the hidden chlorophyll in purple cabbage leaves by taking a few leaves and placing them in a pot with one cup boiling, *distilled* water for several minutes. Using tongs, carefully remove the leaves and observe them. You should notice that much of the purple pigment has come out of the leaves, turning the water purple. Additionally, you should be able to see some green in the leaves now. That is because chlorophyll is in the leaves, but was masked by the purple pigment. Store the purple water in a container in the refrigerator for the Explore More activity later in this module.

The trees that lose their leaves in the fall are called **deciduous** (dee sid' you us) trees. Before they drop from the tree, the leaves can turn gorgeous reds, oranges, and yellows. What happens is that at the base of each leaf's petiole is a thin layer of cells that are able to identify the shortening daylight hours in the fall months. They then block off the water and mineral flow to the leaves. This prevents the leaves from being able to produce chlorophyll, and their green color fades away, leaving behind the other color pigments that

FIGURE 11.20
Glorious Fall Leaf Colors

already existed in the leaf. Eventually the cells in the leaves die, and the leaves fall off the tree, but not before producing glorious fire-like displays for us to enjoy!

Roots and Stems

The roots of a plant have 3 major functions. They absorb water and nutrients from a plant's surroundings and then transport them to the rest of the plant. They also behave as an anchor to hold the plant in place, and they are often used as a location for food storage. Carrots, for example, are actually the root of the carrot plant, filled with nutrients that the plant stored for later use.

Plant stems come in many forms. Some are stiff and straight like trees and tall flowers. Others are winding and soft like vines. Still others grow along (watermelon plants) or under (potato plants) the ground. Like roots, stems have 3 major functions. They support and produce the plant's leaves. They behave like a highway, conducting water and nutrients to and from the leaves and roots. And they undergo photosynthesis. Now some plants, such as large trees, have stems that photosynthesize only when the plant is young, but others do it throughout the plant's life.

Stems can be either soft and herbaceous or hard and woody. The major difference between them is that woody stems have bark. This allows a woody stem to continue to grow larger and larger. If an herbaceous stem grows too much, its outer protective layer would crack, exposing the inner parts of the stem to the environment. But in a woody stem, when the outer part of the bark cracks, the inner part produces new outer bark to protect the stem. This is why large trees, such as oak trees, have cracked and rough bark. These trunks are just the main, woody stem of the oak plant.

FIGURE 11.21
Several Types of Tree Bark

Plant Classification

We aren't going to spend a great deal of time classifying all the types of plants, but it is helpful to understand some of the major "branches" that separate this kingdom so you know more about this interesting field of botany. Plants can be divided into 2 groups: those with **vascular** (vas' kyoo lar) **tissue** and those without. Of course, it helps to know what vascular tissue is to better understand this separation. First, when a group of similar cells have a specific function, they form **tissue**. For example, muscle tissue in the human body is made up of uniquely designed cells with the specific function of contracting when they receive a signal. That helps you to move your body around. Vascular tissue in plants is used to carry water and dissolved material throughout them. It is kind of like the blood vessels in animals, moving water and nutrients around instead of blood.

So plants that *do not* have vascular tissue do not have a means of transporting water and nutrients around. Thus, they have to be small so their cells can directly absorb materials. Mosses are an example of nonvascular plants. Vascular plants can grow much larger because they have a means of transporting materials all over their bodies. Sequoia trees, for example, can grow over 250 ft in height and have trunks that are up to 85 ft in circumference!

Among the vascular plants are those that produce seeds and those that do not. An example of seedless vascular plants are those in phylum **Pterophyta** (ter' uh fye tuh). Plants in this group are commonly called ferns. Ferns produce spores through a complicated life cycle. These spores often are stored in small vessels beneath the fern leaf (Figure 11.22).

FIGURE 11.22
Underside of a Fern Leaf Showing Spore Vessels

There are several phyla of seed-making vascular plants (see Figure 11.23). Two of the more common ones are phylum **Coniferophyta** (con uh' fur oh fye tuh) and phylum **Anthophyta** (an' thoh fye tuh). Members of Coniferophyta are called the conifers and are known for producing cones. Pine trees, for example, produce 2 types of cones. One type is a seed cone, and the other is a **pollen** cone. Pollen are microscopic grains from the male reproductive part of plants. Both cone types are necessary for the tree to produce seeds for reproduction. Members of phylum Anthophyta are known as the flowering plants. They grow flowers to produce seeds for reproduction. Many of these seeds form within a fruit of some sort that helps to protect and disperse them.

FIGURE 11.23
A General Plant Classification

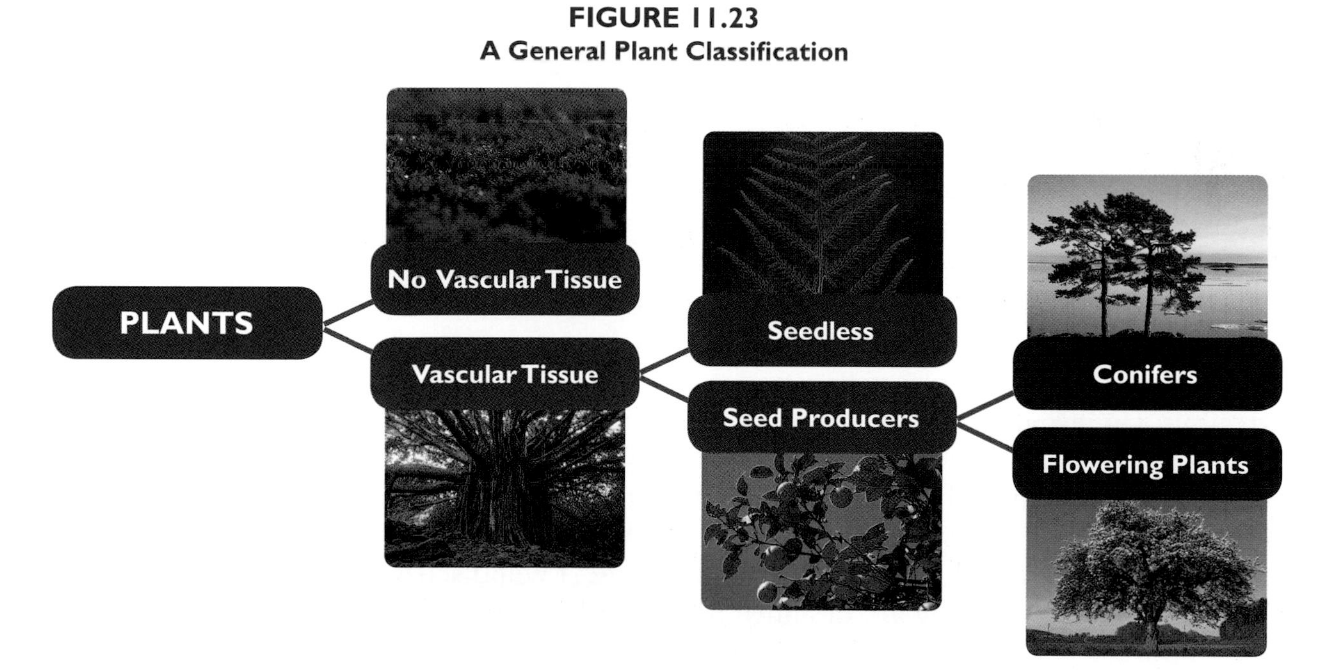

Of course, both nonvascular plants and vascular plants (both seedless and seed-making) are further divided into smaller groups, but this gives you an idea of the vast diversity of organisms that botanists can study.

ON YOUR OWN

11.7 List the 3 major functions of roots and the 3 major functions of stems.

ANATOMY AND PHYSIOLOGY

Anatomy and **physiology** are 2 branches of biology that are often studied together. That's because while anatomy deals with all the parts and structures of organisms, physiology looks at how they operate and work together. These 2 branches can be applied to any living organism because all creatures have unique structures with intricate ways they work together. For this section, I will discuss basic anatomy and physiology in the human body, but you need to know that each living being has structures to do the same types of processes. For example, you probably know that the human body has a skeleton as a supportive structure. Other animals, such as horses, birds, and fish, have internal skeletons, too. Clams, on the other hand, have the external support structure of a shell. Crabs also have an external skeleton. Trees have trunks and stems for supportive structures. And even bacteria have the external supportive structure of a cell wall, along with internal supportive fibrous cellular material.

You already learned much about the cell and its complex processes. But within multicellular organisms, there is even more complexity. You see, individual cells do all the work within the body, including growth, manufacture, and transport of critical substances. With so many types of jobs a cell can do, they come in a vast range of sizes and shapes, each designed for a specific group of tasks to work together. Cells can be rounded, flattened, or spindle-shaped and can even have projections (Figure 11.24).

FIGURE 11.24
Common Human Body Cell Types

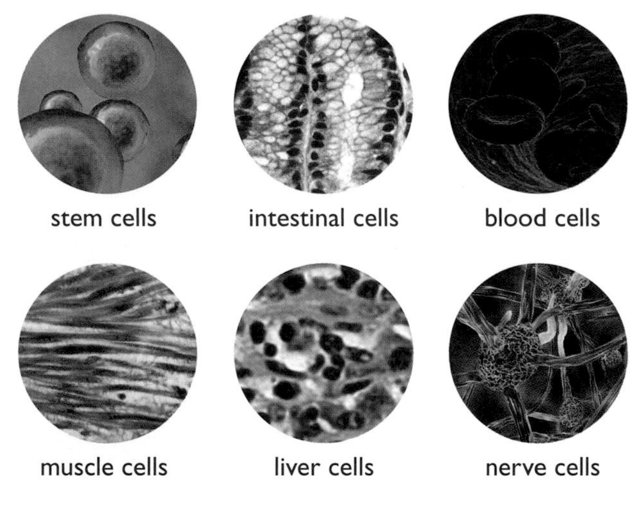

For example, nerve cells have several short and one very long extension. They are designed to carry nerve impulses throughout the body. Muscle cells are long and fibrous, designed to contract in unison. Because of this, they use up lots of energy, so they have extra mitochondria, which are the powerhouses of the cell.

Cells that are grouped together with a common function form tissue. There are 4 types of tissues in the human body: **epithelial** (ep uh thee' lee uhl), **muscle**, **connective**, and **nerve.** For example, the cells of epithelial tissue work together to form protective barriers. So they are found in skin and areas around **organs.** (I will discuss organs in just a bit.) The cells of epithelial tissue are designed to rapidly multiply as cells become worn out or are injured. You can imagine that would be a good thing if you cut your skin! Muscle tissue provides movement. Some of that movement is consciously controllable, such as the muscles you use to move your arms and legs. Other movement goes on without you having to think about it. And that is a good thing. Can you imagine having to consciously make your heart (which is mostly muscle) beat every moment of every day, even while you sleep? Connective tissue is perhaps the most diverse tissue in the body. As its name suggests, it is designed to link parts of the body together. Connective tissue in the human body includes bone and blood. This tissue type also connects bones to other bones (**ligaments**) and bones to muscle (**tendons**). Finally, nerve tissue is designed to conduct signals to and from all the parts of the body. It is coordinated in the brain in most animals, and others have just a grouping of nerve cells that behave as a management center to direct the body's functions.

So how do cells "know" what type of cells they will be? That is really a good question. You see, although each cell has the complete information within its DNA to perform practically any job, some information is active and other information is not. Scientists still do not know exactly what causes a cell to differentiate to perform specific jobs. There is much that goes on within cells as they develop and grow that we just do not know yet!

Now, just like each cell has its own specific structure, each tissue type has a unique structure, too, which allows it to do a particular job. The various types of tissues work together to make up **organs** in the body. Organs are specialized structures (such as a heart or lung) made up of cells and tissues that perform a specific function in an organism.

And these organs work within **organ systems.** There are several organ systems within the human body. Let's talk about some key organ systems along with their key roles. The **cardiovascular system,** for example, is an organ system that transports nutrients, gases, wastes, and other materials throughout the body. Driven by the continuous pumping of a muscular heart, the superhighway of blood vessels is filled with blood that acts as a transportation medium. The **respiratory system** is responsible for providing oxygen to the blood and removing carbon dioxide gas from it. Remember that in order to break down nutrients for energy, cells need oxygen. As a by-product of that process, they produce carbon dioxide gas that needs to be removed from the body. The lungs work with a muscular **diaphragm** that contracts to fill the lungs with air. Air moves in through the **trachea,** which is a large tube leading to each of your 2 lungs. It continues to branch into smaller and smaller passages, ending in small air sacs called **alveoli** (al vee' oh lye). This is where the exchange of oxygen and carbon dioxide occurs between your blood and the air.

FIGURE 11.25
The Human Digestive System

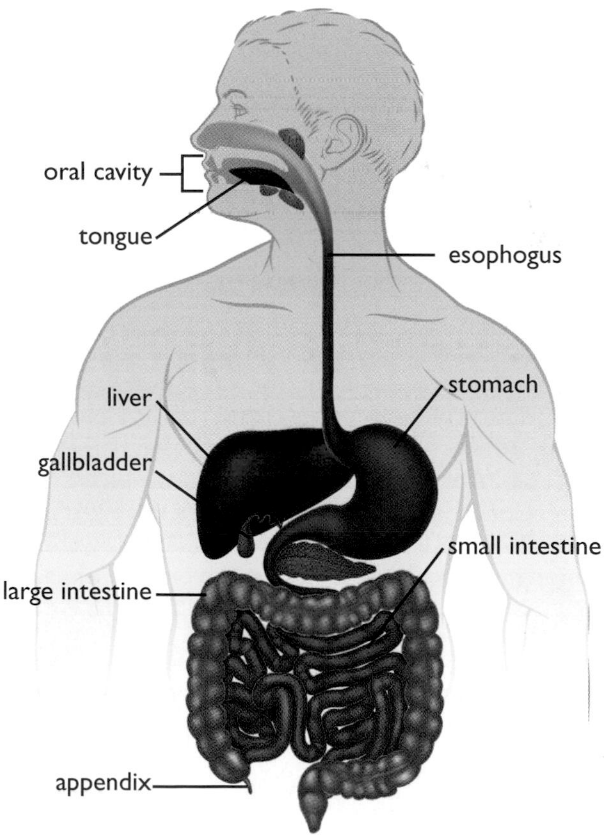

EXPLORE MORE

A fun way to see how you exhale carbon dioxide is to take some purple cabbage and boil a few leaves in a saucepan with one cup of distilled water. (You can use the purple water from the previous Explore More activity if you performed it.) Allow them to boil for a few minutes so that their purple pigment colors the water. Remove the saucepan from the heat and carefully discard the leaves. Once the liquid cools, pour some of it into a clean, small, clear glass. With a straw, blow into the solution to create bubbles. After a while you should notice that the solution's color changes. That's because the pigment from the cabbage leaves turns pink if it is mixed with an acid (and green if it is mixed with a base). Your solution should have turned pink because the carbon dioxide you exhaled mixed with the water to form a weak acid, called carbonic acid.

The **digestive system** works to break down and absorb nutrients. Utilizing organs such as the stomach, pancreas, liver, and small and large intestines, this long pathway works to mechanically and chemically break down your food into molecules that can be absorbed into your blood. The **skeletal system** is designed to provide support and attachment locations for muscles. It also protects critical parts of the body. For example, your rib cage protects your heart and lungs.

There are several more systems within the human body. The **muscular system** supports and moves the parts of the body. The **nervous system** is responsible for receiving input from the senses, processing that input, and then sending out impulses to respond to what was sensed. It also has control over many of the body's functions and activities. The **urinary system** removes liquid wastes from the body. The **endocrine system** controls functions within the body using specific chemicals called hormones. The **reproductive system**, of course, forms reproductive cells. And the **lymphatic system** works to return fluid in and around tissues back to the bloodstream and transport infection-fighting blood cells around.

Biologists studying anatomy and physiology look very closely at the structures within these systems and how they all work together. The more they learn, the more they are understanding that there is no part of the body that can exist independently. Every body part works to benefit the whole body.

creation connection

Indeed, all parts of the body are created by God and serve a perfect purpose. As it says in I Corinthians 12:14-21, "For the body does not consist of one member but of many. If the foot should say, 'Because I am not a hand, I do not belong to the body,' that would not make it any less a part of the body. And if the ear should say, 'Because I am not an eye, I do not belong to the body,' that would not make it any less a part of the body. If the whole body were an eye, where would be the sense of hearing? If the whole body were an ear, where would be the sense of smell? But as it is, God arranged the members in the body, each one of them, as he chose. If all were a single member, where would the body be? As it is, there are many parts, yet one body. The eye cannot say to the hand, 'I have no need of you,' nor again the head to the feet, 'I have no need of you.'"

ON YOUR OWN

11.8 List the 4 tissue types of the human body and write one job they perform.

ZOOLOGY

Zoology is the study of the anatomy, physiology, behavior, and classification of the animals in creation. We already have talked a bit about anatomy and physiology as well as classification of organisms by phylum. But because the animals of the world are some of the most familiar ones to you, let's spend a little time talking more about the kingdom Animalia to better understand what zoologists study. Now, according to their body structure, animals can be grouped into 2 main divisions. These are not classifications, but they are just general groupings. Animals that have a backbone are called **vertebrates,** and animals without a backbone are **invertebrates.** Vertebrates include familiar animals such as fish, amphibians, reptiles, birds, and mammals. These animals all have a support structure made up of small bones called **vertebrae** that extend in a line from the skull to the hind legs. A backbone, then, is another word for the spine.

FIGURE 11.26
Human Backbone Composed of Vertebrae

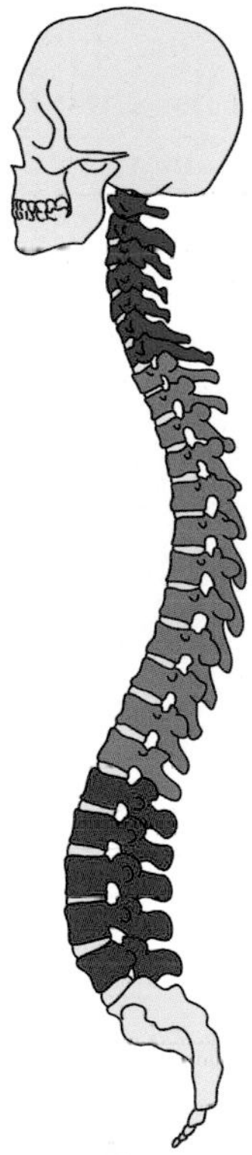

Animals without backbones—or invertebrates—include sponges and sea stars as well as shelled animals like clams, oysters, and snails. Insects and other joint-footed organisms like crabs and lobsters are invertebrates as well. These animals vary in size and shape, based on where they live and how they move. Because they do not have a supportive backbone structure, they have other means of support. Sponges, for example, have an elastic protein called **spongin,** plus small, sharp, structural spines made from calcium or silica. Clams, oysters, and snails have an external supportive shell.

Now, insects and other joint-footed invertebrates are in phylum **Arthropoda.** The word *arthropoda* literally means "joint-footed." One notable feature of these organisms is that they have a skeleton on the outside of their bodies. Called an **exoskeleton,** it is made from a stiff material called **chitin** (Figure 11.27). The exoskeleton provides support the same way that a suit of armor protected a medieval knight. However, when the animal grows, its armor cannot grow with it. So when an arthropod needs to grow, it first has to crawl out of its old exoskeleton. It then grows a new larger one that has extra space for it to live in for a while. This process is called **molting,** and during the time the organism sheds its old exoskeleton and grows and hardens a new one, it is very vulnerable to attack. Exoskeletons limit the size arthropods can reach. You see, the larger the organism, the bigger and heavier its exoskeleton needs to be. And this makes it difficult to carry it around. Needless to say, the arthropods that can grow largest are those that live in the ocean. With the support of the

FIGURE 11.27
Inflexible Crab Exoskeleton

surrounding water, arthropods can grow much larger than their terrestrial counterparts. For example, the largest living known arthropod is the Japanese spider crab with an extended leg span of 3.8 m (12 ft) and a weight of 19 kg (42 lbs)!

GENETICS

You probably already know that an organism's offspring have similar features as their parents. This means they inherited these features, sometimes called **traits.** Well, **heredity** is the passing down of characteristics from parents to offspring by means of **genes** within cells' **chromosomes.** I just introduced a lot of new terms here. Let's go over them. Heredity has to do with characteristics being passed down from parent to offspring. If someone tells you that you have your mother's eyes, they mean you received some of her characteristics by heredity. You inherited them.

These features are passed down through genes inside the chromosomes of cells. You see, your DNA is tightly coiled up into chromosomes that are in the nuclei of cells. This is the way all that information can be compactly stored in your cells' nuclei. So your chromosomes have all the information to tell your cells how to build your body and maintain it. That includes the chemicals needed to make your hair the color it is, your overall height, and even what age you might lose your first teeth. Nucleotides are arranged in a specific order in the DNA, and groups of those nucleotides code for specific characteristics, or traits. Those groups are your genes, or your genetic material.

All living creatures have genetic information. It is the basis by which they pass down their traits. Each species has a different amount of coded information. The **human genome** (all the genes a human has), for example, has approximately 6 billion base pairs. Remember that a base pair within a strand of DNA is either adenine and thymine or cytosine and guanine. This massive amount of information is spread out over 46 chromosomes in humans. Now, all humans have genetic material in common with each other, even if it is slightly different. Those slight differences make you unique. Isn't it amazing that from the beginning of time, with the billions of people who have lived, no two people are exactly the same?

FIGURE 11.28
Genes Code for Skin Color, Creating a Wide Range of Hues

This branch of biology, commonly called **genetics,** is the study of genes, how they are different, and how organisms inherit characteristics.

Throughout history, people noticed that children look like their parents, inheriting certain traits. They also realized that some traits dominated other ones. For example, when a blue-eyed woman married a brown-eyed man, most, if not all, of their children had brown eyes. And this passing down of traits was studied for centuries, even before the mid-20th century when scientists realized that DNA was the mechanism for coding for an organism's characteristics.

As you learned in Module 1, the father of the study of heredity is Gregor Mendel. He worked in the mid-19th century to study how organisms inherit their characteristics. Through Mendel's studies as well as others, scientists learned that some traits follow an all-or-nothing pattern, and others do not. For example, Mendel worked with pea plants, and he learned that the species he was growing would produce either purple or white flowers. No matter how many times he bred the plants together, he would only get plants with purple or white flowers, and not light purple or some other color. This is an all-or-nothing type of heredity.

FIGURE 11.29
Pea Plants with Purple Flowers

Now, other gene combinations have a *range* of expressions. Think about the height that people can grow. Some people are tall, and others are short. If 2 tall people have a child, that child is likely to be tall, too, but he or she may be shorter or much taller than the parents. In many cases, 2 shorter-than-average parents will have a child that grows to a taller-than-average height. That is because there are several genes that control a person's height. A child will inherit some of the height information from one parent and some of it from the other, so depending on the information that all those genes contain (plus other factors, too), that child could grow within a range of heights.

The field of genetics is certainly an interesting one. And there is still so much to be discovered about it. You will learn much more about this fascinating branch of biology in your high school biology course, too. But it is important to note that there is significantly more to what makes an organism's characteristics than just its DNA. The characteristics of all organisms are determined by genetic and environmental factors. For example, a plant located in an environment that does not have the appropriate minerals in the soil will not grow as well as the same kind of plant located in a better location. They both might have similar genetic characteristics, but their environment affects what they look like and how strong they are.

EXPLORE MORE

Inherited traits are characteristics that are passed down from your parents. Some traits are noticeable while others are not as easy to see. Some examples of these are the ability to roll your tongue (Figure 11.30), attached or unattached earlobes, and being left- or right-handed. It turns out that about 80% of people have what are called high-frequency traits when it comes to these characteristics. This means most people have free-hanging earlobes, the ability to roll their tongues, and right-handedness. Take a poll of as many people as you can to find out if they have these traits and to see how many are in that 80%. Create a table with your results.

FIGURE 11.30

EVOLUTIONARY BIOLOGY

Evolutionary biology has to do with the theory of evolution. Now **evolution** is the concept that different kinds of living organisms are thought to have developed and changed from earlier life forms in Earth's history. It is sometimes called **Darwinism,** named after the first man who came up with this idea: Charles Darwin. I discussed Charles Darwin in Module 1, but it is important for you to know that this field of biology is one that many scientists today are studying in order to identify possible processes that could explain how complex life came to be without the hand of a Creator.

However, the more we are learning, particularly in the fields of molecular biology and microbiology, the more we are discovering *that there is no simple life form*. I have said this several times already in this course, but it is worth repeating. The more you learn about living organisms, the more you should understand this important fact. But this fact makes it harder for evolutionists to explain how a complex living organism came from nonliving material.

OTHER BRANCHES OF BIOLOGY

Although you might think we have covered every area of biology, you need to know that I have only talked about the major ones. In this scientific field is **radiobiology,** which involves the study of radiation on living things. Learning how solar radiation affects a person's skin is one important area of study in this scientific branch. **Biophysics** studies the application of the laws of physics to biological activities. For example, think of the difficulty of blood circulation in a giraffe. The giraffe's heart has to work pretty hard to pump blood all the way to its head, fighting the pull of gravity the whole way. **Biotechnology** is the study of biological processes so that scientists can produce better antibiotics, hormones, and helpful medicines. Hopefully you already understand the importance of that field!

There are other branches I don't have the space to discuss, although we *will* go into greater detail in future modules that cover 3 more branches of biological study. In the next module, you'll learn about **marine biology,** which is the study of organisms living in and around the ocean. You will also learn more about marine algae, a biological branch called **phycology.**

With a better understanding of living organisms, we will then delve into the subject of **ecology** in Module 13. This is a branch of biology that has to do with the relations organisms have with one another and their surrounding environment.

SUMMING UP

Well, after this module, hopefully you can see that when I talk about biology, I am referring to a very broad field of study. And that should make sense. Because there is such great diversity among living things, you should expect that there would be a great variety of sciences in order to study them.

ANSWERS TO THE "ON YOUR OWN" QUESTIONS

11.1 The 4 major chemicals of life (along with the molecules they are made from) are **carbohydrates (simple sugars), lipids (fatty acids), proteins (amino acids), and nucleic acids (nucleotides).**

11.2 A semipermeable membrane allows only certain substances through. Ideally, **necessary substances are allowed in while unwanted substances are not.** If cells had a non-permeable membrane, nothing could get in or out, which would prevent the cell from taking in water and nutrients and from getting rid of wastes. If cells had fully permeable membranes, then all substances could come in, including harmful ones. Additionally, good materials in the cell could escape.

11.3 **A one-room cabin has no internal walls to separate rooms like the kitchen and bedroom. Instead, there are designated areas within the cabin for cooking, sleeping, storage, and more. In each area are specific items (like pots and pans in the kitchen) to perform the activities in that area. Prokaryotic cells do not have internal membranes to separate structures but rather have specific areas within the cell where processes such as DNA replication occur.**

11.4 One criterion of life that a virus does not meet is that **it cannot reproduce itself.** It must rely on the reproductive mechanisms of a cell by attacking the cell, injecting its viral instructional information into it, and then using the cell's reproductive machinery to make more viruses.

11.5 (*Answers may vary.*)

Three Ways Infectious Disease May Spread

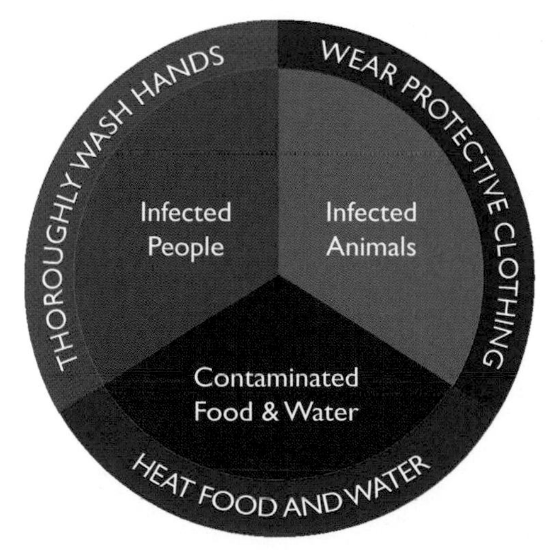

11.6 **Mushrooms are actually the fruiting body of the entire organism, most of which grows underground or inside decomposing plants. When you kick a mushroom, you are spreading the reproductive spores, potentially causing *more* fungi to grow in your yard.**

11.7 The 3 major functions of roots are (1) to absorb water and nutrients from the plant's surroundings and transport them to the rest of the plant; (2) behave as an anchor to hold the plant in place; (3) act as a location for food storage. The 3 major functions of stems are (1) to support and produce the plant's leaves; (2) to conduct water and nutrients to and from the leaves and roots; (3) to undergo photosynthesis.

11.8 The 4 types of tissue in the human body, along with what they do, are as follows: (1) Epithelial tissue rapidly multiplies to replace cells. It forms protective barriers within the body, too. (2) Muscle tissue provides either consciously or unconsciously controlled movement. (3) Connective tissue connects parts of the body together, whether it is bone to bone (ligaments) or bone to muscle (tendons) or a superhighway of delivery material (blood). (4) Nerve tissue conducts signals to and from all the parts of the body.

STUDY GUIDE FOR MODULE 11

1. Match the following words with their definitions.

a. Biology	Organisms that obtain their nourishment from dead organisms
b. Unicellular	Consisting of more than one cell
c. Multicellular	Consisting of a single cell
d. Saprophytes	The study of living organisms

2–5. Fill in the blank with one of the following: carbohydrates, lipids, proteins, nucleic acids.

2. __________________ are complex molecules that are involved in nearly every reaction that supports life and primarily make up muscles and other organs of the body. They are made up of amino acids.

3. __________________ are one of the main sources of food energy for most animals and are made up of simple sugars.

4. __________________ are the most complex molecules of life, involved in the creation, repair, and reproduction of proteins. They are made up of nucleotides.

5. __________________ are an efficient way to store food energy and are made up of fatty acids.

6. The semipermeable cell membrane is similar to which of these?
   a. concrete wall b. curtain c. door d. tennis net

7. Which type of cell has membrane-surrounded "rooms" so that each spot is able to maintain specific conditions to do designated jobs: a prokaryotic cell or a eukaryotic cell?

8. Which criterion of life does a virus not meet?
   a. able to reproduce b. able to sense and respond to stimuli
   c. able to grow d. contain hereditary information, like DNA

9. A person sees several mushrooms growing in his yard. He picks them out of the grass and throws them away. Has he prevented more mushrooms from growing in his yard?

10. Which of the following is NOT a major plant root function?
    a. produce plant leaves
    b. absorb water and nutrients
    c. anchor for the plant
    d. food storage

11. Which of the following is a responsibility of nerve tissue?
    a. rapidly multiply to replace cells
    b. controlled movement
    c. connects parts of the body together
    d. conducts signals to and from all the parts of the body

12. Choose the correct word:
    Animals that have a backbone are called (invertebrates, vertebrates).

MARINE SCIENCE

Marine biology is a branch of biology that explores organisms living in or around the ocean. **Marine science** includes the environments in which these organisms live; however, often these 2 terms are used interchangeably. Because the oceans cover about ¾ of the planet, you can imagine that this is a vast subject to cover. To get a good understanding of marine science, let's first discuss the oceans themselves so that you better understand the conditions marine organisms require in order to live. Then we can do an overview of ocean creatures based on their classification. And finally, we will explore some of the living environments that are unique to the ocean.

Next module, we will do a more thorough study of the branch of biology called **ecology,** which involves a study of the **ecosystems** of the *world*. However, you need to understand what ecosystem means now, so I will give you a definition.

Quaestio

If you were to look out over the ocean, what would you see? Water, of course. But that water is special. If you tasted it, you would know instantly that it isn't pure H_2O, right? And that ocean you're looking at is a vast one, connecting to other oceans all around the Earth. Now think about what those oceans contain: a vast variety of organisms ranging from the smallest bacterium to the largest animal to have ever existed (the blue whale)! The oceans are perfectly designed to support a boundless diversity of creatures we only have begun to discover. We truly can join the Psalmist when he says, "O Lord, how many are your works…There is the sea, great and broad, in which are swarms without number; animals both small and great" (Psalm 104:24–25)

FIGURE 12.1
The Vast Ocean Horizon

Ecosystem—A community of organisms that interact with each other and their physical environment

You see, an organism in the wild has to have a place to live, whether it is underwater, buried in the ground, or up in a tree. Each organism has different needs, too. For example, some like warm temperatures while others cannot survive well unless it is cold. I will talk much more about this in the next module, but it is good to have a general understanding of this idea now.

THE OCEANS OF THE EARTH

In an earlier module, you were introduced to some of the ocean's physical features, including its salinity and its depth. Well, there are 4 large ocean basins in the world. You can think of them like large bowls. These 4 basins are the **Pacific Ocean basin,** the **Atlantic Ocean basin,** the **Indian Ocean basin,** and the **Arctic Ocean basin** (see Figure 12.2).

FIGURE 12.2
The Earth and Its Ocean Basins

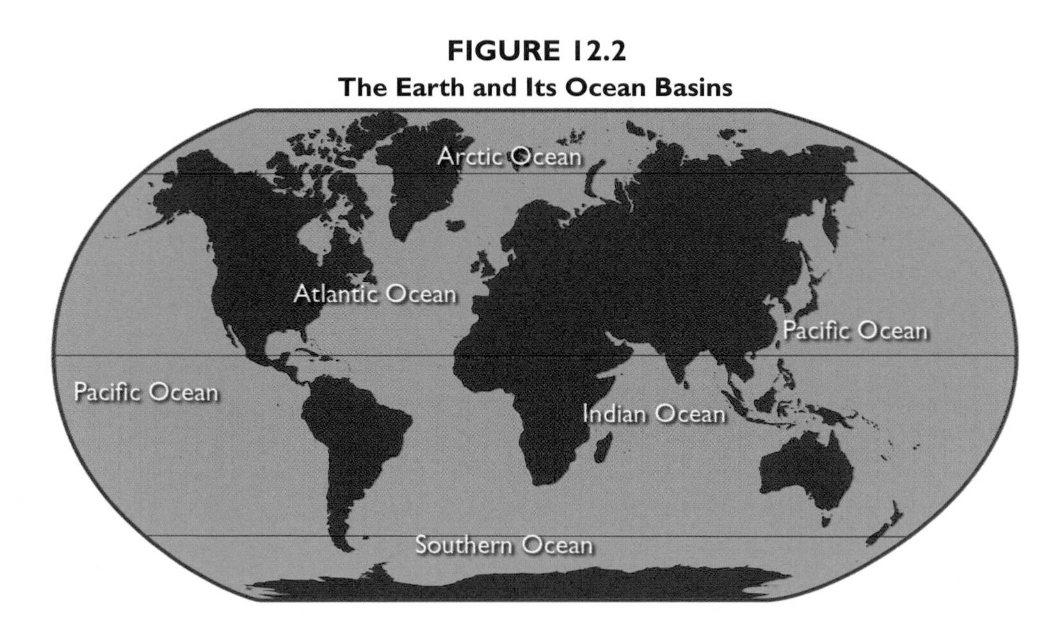

The Pacific Ocean basin is the largest, covering about 166,000,000 km^2. Now there is a fifth major ocean that is not really a basin. It is the **Southern Ocean,** and it circles the Earth along the coast of Antarctica. All of these oceans are connected to one another. That means that, in theory, an organism could swim from ocean to ocean, moving around the planet. However, most creatures don't do this. Why not? Well, most organisms are not able to withstand the differences in temperature, pressure, and even salinity from one part of the world to another.

Many of the differences in the water have to do with how deep it is. Sunlight, for example, can only penetrate to about 200 m (656 ft). However, the ocean is an average of 3,000 m deep. That means sunlight cannot reach much of the ocean below the surface waters. Thus, no organisms can photosynthesize there. No sunlight also means the temperature is colder the deeper you go. With more and more water overhead, there is greater pressure pushing on animals as well. Because of these differences, scientists have divided the ocean depths into layers.

There are 5 basic ocean layers. The **sunlight** layer (also called the **epipelagic** [ep ih pill aj' ik]) is the surface layer of the ocean extending down to 200 m. There is plenty of light and warmth in this layer, although both decrease the deeper you go. Most oceanic life exists in the sunlight layer. And, of course, this is the layer where photosynthesis can happen. The **twilight** layer (also called the **mesopelagic**) goes from 200 m to 1,000 m. A small amount of sunlight can reach this layer but not enough to allow for photosynthesis. This layer is much colder than the sunlight layer and there is more pressure here, too.

The **midnight** layer (also called the **bathypelagic**) is from 1,000 m to 4,000 m. It is called the midnight layer because no sunlight can reach it. However, as you will learn later in this module, there is light made *by the sea creatures* living in this layer. Below the midnight layer is the **abyss** (uh biss') layer. Also called the **abyssopelagic** layer, it extends from 4,000 m to 6,000 m, receives no sunlight, and is very, very cold. In fact, temperatures in the abyss layer are near water's freezing point. Much of the ocean floor is at this layer's depth.

FIGURE 12.3
Divisions of the Ocean Depths

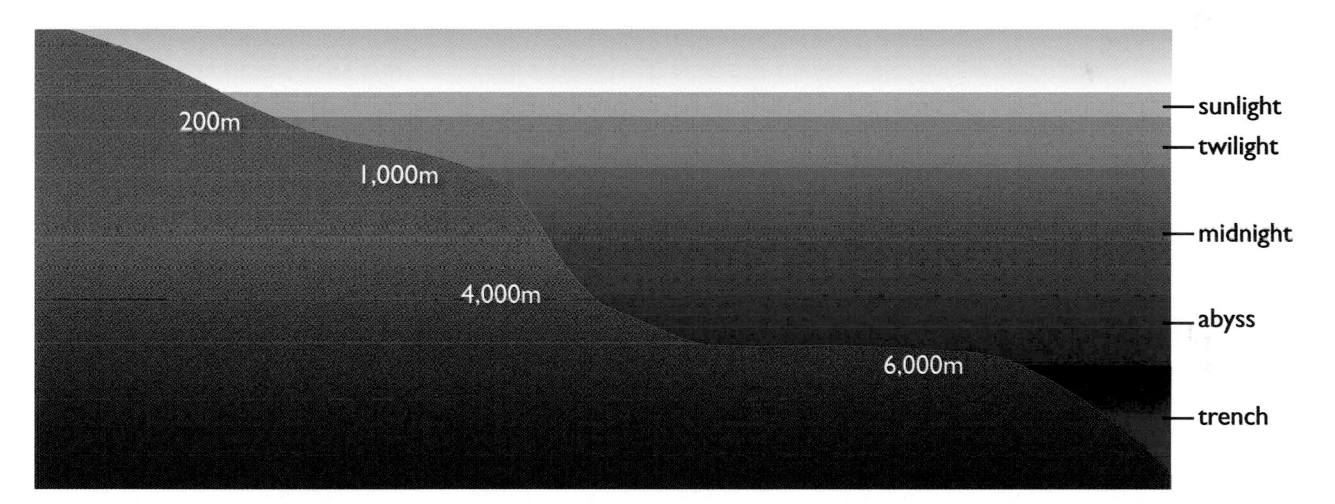

The deepest layer is called the **trench** layer (or the **hadalpelagic** layer). It starts at 6,000 m and extends to the deepest parts of the ocean trenches. Even though it is very dark, has cold temperatures, and experiences extreme pressure, many ocean creatures are perfectly designed to live in this layer. To better remember these layers of the ocean, perform Experiment 12.1.

EXPERIMENT 12.1
AN EDIBLE OCEAN LAYER MODEL

PURPOSE: To better understand the layers of the ocean

MATERIALS:
- 8 Oreo cookies
- A butter knife
- 2 zippered storage bags
- Chocolate pudding (Milk chocolate looks better than dark chocolate.)
- 4 graham crackers
- Vanilla, banana, or butterscotch pudding (You choose, based on which flavor you like!)
- Whipped cream
- A tall, transparent glass
- A serving spoon

QUESTION: What are the layers of the ocean and how do they differ?

HYPOTHESIS: Write how you think the physical features change in each ocean layer.

PROCEDURE:
1. In this experiment/activity, you will be creating an edible model of the 5 ocean layers and then illustrating the layers along with writing their physical features in your notebook.
2. Twist open the Oreo cookies and use a butter knife to scrape the frosting from the middle. Discard the frosting or save it for later.
3. Place the cookies into a zippered bag, zip it closed, and crush the cookies into crumbs.
4. Place about ½ cup of the cookie crumbs into the glass. This represents the trench layer.
5. Layer ½ cup of the chocolate pudding over the cookie crumbs. This represents the abyss layer.
6. Place the graham crackers in the second zippered bag, crush them into crumbs, and add ½ cup to the glass. This represents the midnight layer.
7. For the twilight layer, place about ½ cup of the vanilla pudding over the graham crackers.
8. Add a final layer of whipped cream over the pudding to represent the sunlight layer.
9. Using the information in the paragraphs before this experiment, make an illustration of your model in your notebook and label the 5 ocean layers. Add the layers' depths and a few facts about each one. Indicate what happens to pressure as depth is increased by drawing an arrow from the top of the glass to the bottom. Write "Increasing Pressure" along this arrow.
10. Now enjoy eating your Ocean Layer parfait!

CONCLUSION: Write one interesting fact you learned about the ocean layers.

ON YOUR OWN

12.1 Even though the ocean basins are connected to one another, why don't most ocean organisms move around the Earth?

TINY OCEAN ORGANISMS

Marine bacteria are found throughout the oceans. They play important roles in the ocean, some undergoing photosynthesis and others breaking down dead organisms. Remember that those decomposers are critical to the rest of the environment. If they didn't help to break down dead material, it would pile up. Then all the nutritional material bound up in the dead organisms would not be usable to the rest of the organisms in creation. Not to mention, we'd have whole, dead fishes and other creatures piling up on the ocean floor!

An important group of marine bacteria consists of the **cyanobacteria.** These guys are often called blue-green algae because they are bluish-green in color and look like mats of algae when they grow in large groups. However, they are not algae at all. They are bacteria. So cyanobacteria is a better name for them. These bacteria are able to photosynthesize at great rates. They also do something very important for all other living things. They take nitrogen gas from the atmosphere and transform it into a molecule that other living things can use. You see, all organisms need nitrogen-containing molecules to make their proteins, but they are not able to utilize nitrogen gas. So the cyanobacteria convert nitrogen gas to make it usable, an amazing and important feat for one of the smallest creatures in the ocean.

FIGURE 12.4
Image of the Cyanobacteria *Tolypothrix*

ON YOUR OWN

12.2 Nitrogen is an element that is present in all proteins. Proteins are used to build and repair bones, muscles, cartilage, blood, and more. They also make up important body chemicals. Why, then, are cyanobacteria so important to all other living organisms?

think about this

Photosynthetic marine algae are extremely plentiful and cover much of the Earth. Because of this, they produce so much oxygen that even if all the rainforests in the world were no longer able to photosynthesize, there would still be enough oxygen from marine algae to support life on the planet! Of course, removing the rainforests would create lots of other problems.

MARINE ALGAE

There are 2 groups of marine algae that are important for me to talk about. The first group is made up of single-celled eukaryotic algae. These little living organisms include the greatest producers of oxygen on the planet. Why is that? Well, the oceans cover almost ¾ of the Earth, so they represent a majority of its surface area. That means there is more opportunity for photosynthesizing ocean organisms to utilize the sunlight there. And they do.

The second group of marine algae are multicellular algae. These organisms are often called seaweeds because they look like weeds growing in the ocean. There are many types of seaweeds—ranging in colors from red to brown to green—and varying in size from a few centimeters to over 90 m in height! These organisms are *not* plants. They do not have true leaves, stems, or roots. That's because they do not need materials to be transported around their body. Why? Well, they are immersed in seawater that provides the nutrients and water they need. All the cells of these organisms are able to directly take in nutrients as well as remove any wastes. However, multicellular algae do have similarly *shaped* parts as compared to plants. In order to have greater surface area to receive sunlight for photosynthesis, they have **blades.** Blades are leaf-shaped, but do not have the veins and specialized structures for gas exchange. Many seaweeds have **pneumatocysts** (new mat' oh sists), which are gas-filled floats that help to hold the algae upright in the water. The blades and pneumatocysts are connected together by a stem-like **stipe.** And to keep from floating away, many seaweeds have **holdfasts** that attach to a hard surface. All of these parts can be seen in Figure 12.6.

FIGURE 12.5
Leafy Dragon Fish Blending In with Multicellular Algae

FIGURE 12.6
Body Parts of Multicellular Algae

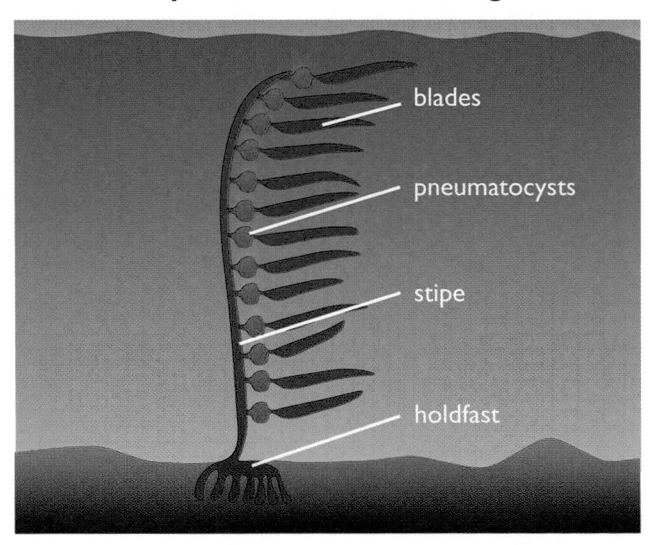

Some seaweeds incorporate calcium into their bodies, making them rigid. That helps to provide hard structures on which other organisms can live. Other seaweeds, like kelp, can grow so large that they create underwater forests—whole environments for a host of creatures to make their home.

The Plankton

We can't leave this section without talking about **plankton.** A planktonic organism is one that either cannot swim at all or cannot swim strongly enough to move against the ocean current. Thus, it is forced to float along with the water. Most plankton consist of bacteria, single-celled algae (called **phytoplankton**), and small animal-like creatures called **zooplankton.** Juvenile fishes, invertebrates, and other young organisms are also planktonic for at least a part of their lives. Plankton provide a great food source for many ocean organisms.

ON YOUR OWN

12.3 Match the seaweed structure with the job it does:

a. holdfast	1. provides more surface area to collect sunlight
b. blade	2. attaches to a hard surface
c. pneumatocyst	3. connects other parts of the seaweed together
d. stipe	4. provides flotation to hold the algae upright in the water

MARINE PLANTS

Marine plants live in or around the ocean. The **seagrasses** are the only plant group that is completely marine. These plants look very much like the grass growing in a park; their horizontal stems grow buried in the soil and their roots reach down in the sediment. The leaves extend upward, creating an underwater "lawn." Like land grasses, seagrasses have roots that take in nutrients and transport it to the rest of the plant.

FIGURE 12.7
Sea Turtle Eating Seagrass

Other marine plants are technically land plants that are able to tolerate salty conditions. They are important because they provide places for marine organisms to live. They also can hold sands and sediments among their roots to minimize erosion during storms and severe wave action.

OCEAN INVERTEBRATES

Sponges

In our tour of organisms of the ocean, I hope you are learning that just about every category of organism in the world exists in the ocean, too. In fact, there are many more types of organisms that live in the oceans that do *not* have counterparts on land—like the **sponges.**

Sponges are a group of marine invertebrates. Remember, invertebrates are organisms that do not have a backbone for structural support. You are probably very familiar with

FIGURE 12.8
Shrimp Living inside a Sea Sponge

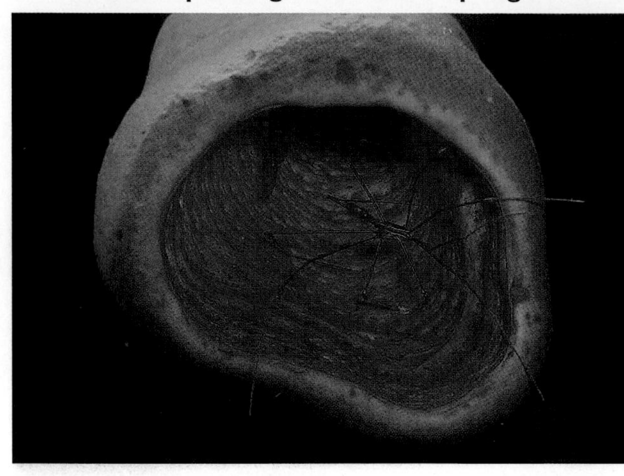

sponges, but it's likely that the ones you have used are man-made. Real sponge animals are not the rectangular-shaped scrubbing tools you find packaged in a store. Indeed, sponges are made up of complex groups of special cells that work together to do specific jobs. They do not form actual tissue, but the cells work together in a superbly organized way.

Sponges grow in a wide variety of shapes, sizes, and colors. Species range from less than a few centimeters to several meters high. Now, sponges do not move around. They are attached to a bottom surface called a substrate.

This phylum, **Porifera,** is composed of animals filled with many pores or holes in their body. They take in water through the smaller holes, run it through a series of canals, and then direct it out of a large hole in the top. As the water passes by, each cell is able to take in nutrients and remove wastes. That is why a sponge does not need whole organ systems to perform its functions. Each cell can take care of itself. But these cells *do* work together. Some are designed to perform digestion or repair cell damage. Other cells work to move the water in and out of the sponge. And others are designed for support. In the larger sponges, there is a web-like skeleton made of elastic protein fibers called **spongin.** These fibers are flexible and give a sponge its elastic "sponginess." Other large sponges have an additional network of spiny **spicules** that add extra support. If you have ever used a natural sponge to wash your dishes or your car, it is one that does not have spicules because they would scratch the surface you are cleaning.

Jellyfish

Another phylum of ocean invertebrates is phylum **Cnidaria.** This group of creatures includes jellyfish, sea anemones, and corals. There are many more types of cnidarians, but we will just focus on these 3 to give you a good understanding of the organisms in this phylum. Unlike the sponges, cnidarians have specialized *tissues* that perform specific functions. Remember that the sponges have specialized cells, but not specialized tissues. Additionally, cnidarians can move in a more intricate way than the sponges. They can even move to capture prey.

Now, cnidarians have one of 2 basic body forms as adults. They can be a **polyp** (pah' lip), which looks like a barrel with tentacles extending upward from its top. Or they can be a **medusa** (med oo' sah), which looks like an umbrella on top with tentacles extending downward. In both forms, their mouth is in the center of the tentacles. You can think of these 2 body forms as basically the same, but one is the upside-down version of the other. Just know that they are not really *exactly* the same shape because a polyp lives most of its life attached to a surface, and a medusa is free-swimming and can pulse to move around a bit.

But the real reason you can think of them as opposites has to do with where their mouth is. You see, they don't really have a front and back or a top and bottom to their body. Instead, they have a mouth—or **oral**—side and a side opposite the mouth—or **aboral**—side (see Figure 12.9).

FIGURE 12.9
Medusa (Left) and Polyp (Right) Cnidarian Body Forms Showing Oral Side

Another common feature of the cnidarians is that their tentacles are covered with special stinging structures, called **nematocysts** (nee mat' uh sists). A nematocyst is like a loaded, poisonous harpoon that is ready to shoot when it is triggered. This harpoon releases poisons into prey so the cnidarian can surround it with its tentacles and bring it to its central mouth. Some cnidarians have nematocysts that are not long enough to penetrate a human's skin, so they are not harmful to people. However, others can cause a painful sting.

EXPLORE MORE

You can make your own model of a nematocyst by gathering a ping-pong ball, a 12-inch piece of string, a balloon, cellophane tape, and electrical tape. Attach one end of the string to the ball using a piece of cellophane tape. Using electrical tape, attach the other side of the ball to the rounded end of an unfilled balloon. Use a couple pieces of tape to make it stick well. The string represents the stinging harpoon, and the ball represents the sack filled with poison. To "load" your nematocyst, wrap the string around the ball and then blow the balloon up a bit. Push the wrapped ball into the rounded edge of the blown-up balloon, allowing the balloon to deflate as you push the ball. You may need a helper to hold the ball as you do this. Now the ball and string *should be surrounded* by the unfilled balloon. Gently hold the nematocyst in place. To trigger the nematocyst, forcefully blow into the balloon and watch the mechanism release from your gentle grip!

To load nematocyst, push string-wrapped ball into the rounded end of the balloon as you let out the air.

Jellyfish are cnidarians that exist for most of their lives as a large medusa form (Figure 12.9, left). That means they have an umbrella-shaped top, called a **bell**, and they have tentacles extending downward. Their mouth is located in the center of their tentacles. Once they capture their prey, they move the food to the central mouth so it can be digested. They have no hard skeleton and thus will swim in the water by contracting their bell in rhythmic movements. However, jellyfish cannot swim strongly enough to avoid the movement of the currents in the water so they technically are considered planktonic organisms, even though they can be very large in size. Some jellyfish have a bell that can grow to 3 m (almost 10 ft) across! The bell of a jellyfish is filled with a jelly-like material, and that is what gives this group of organisms its name.

Now, one organism that is commonly mistaken for a jellyfish is a Portuguese man-of-war (Figure 12.10). Although this is a cnidarian like a jellyfish, it is actually made up of a *colony* of small polyps that are specialized to form different parts of the man-o-war. So one polyp forms a gas-filled float, another polyp will be a tentacle, and so on. Portuguese man-of-wars are not able to pulse as they move because they have no bell like a jellyfish does. They do, however, have nematocysts that cause a terribly painful sting if they touch human skin. In fact, if a man-of-war tentacle breaks off and comes in contact with your skin while you are swimming in the ocean, it can still sting you!

FIGURE 12.10
Portuguese Man-of-war

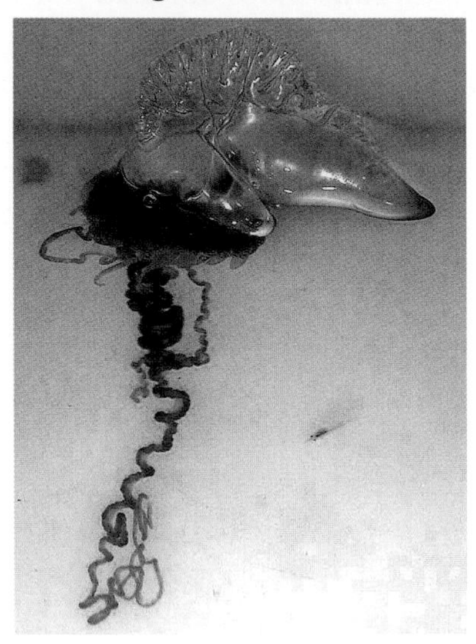

Anemones

Sea anemones and corals are cnidarians that are grouped into a different class than the jellyfish. This group contains organisms that spend most of their lives in the polyp stage (Figure 12.9, right). Many anemones exist as large single polyps, attached to a hard surface. They use their tentacles to capture plankton or other organisms and then move the prey to their central mouth for digestion. Like jellyfish, anemones do not have a hard skeleton. Some anemones live in a relationship with specific species of fish. This relationship is called **symbiosis.**

Symbiosis—A close living situation between 2 species where at least one of the species benefits

FIGURE 12.11
Symbiosis Between Clownfish and a Sea Anemone

A common example of symbiosis is between a clownfish and a sea anemone. You see, clownfish have a slimy covering, part of which comes from the anemone. This makes the fish immune to the anemone's stings; the coating will not cause the nematocysts to release. Thus, the fish swim inside the anemone's tentacles, protected by them. They get a safe place to live because other fish will not venture into the anemone's tentacles to try to eat the clownfish. But the anemone gets a benefit, too. The clownfish's waste products actually feed the anemone, increasing its food supply. So in this symbiotic relationship, both organisms benefit!

Corals

Coral individuals look similar to sea anemones, however they often divide their body up to produce multiple mouths! They remain connected by a thin layer of tissue (Figure 12.12). What makes corals unique among the cnidarians is that they produce cup-shaped walls around each polyp and they remain attached together when they reproduce another new polyp. The walls are made of hard, chalky calcium carbonate for protection. When a polyp is threatened, it can retreat into its calcium carbonate cup to avoid being eaten.
You have probably heard of coral reefs before. Reefs are important places where lots of ocean organisms can live. They are mostly made from the calcium carbonate skeletons of dead coral polyps, calcified algae, and even calcified sponges, all covered over by a thin layer of living coral polyps. When a polyp dies, a new generation grows on top of the old skeletons, allowing the reef to continue growing.

FIGURE 12.12
Tiny Coral Polyps

ON YOUR OWN

12.4 Illustrate the difference between a polyp and a medusa, showing which way the tentacles are oriented. Include the location of the mouth in each illustration.

ARMORED OCEAN INVERTEBRATES

Some ocean invertebrates have hard external skeletons for protection. Named for their armor, they are collectively called **shellfish.**

Mollusks

Mollusks are organisms within the phylum **Mollusca.** They include snails, clams, squid, and octopuses. (Octopi is *not* scientifically correct!) What makes all these organisms similar? Well, most mollusks have a soft body protected by a shell made from calcium carbonate. The shell provides protection and also helps to support the body. The soft body is covered by a **mantle,** which is a layer of tissue that makes the shell and other important body parts. All mollusks have a mantle.

Some mollusks crawl around on a muscular foot. Snails have a protective shell into which they can pull their fleshy foot for protection. Other mollusks are protected by 2 shells that are hinged together. Clams are like this. They don't crawl around but instead use a fleshy, muscular portion of their body to dig down into the sand. Oysters also have a hinged set of shells. They don't live buried in the sand or mud but attach to a hard surface such as a rock and filter small food particles from the water.

Squid and octopuses do not have a protective outer shell. Octopuses do not have any hard parts with the exception of a small, hard beak used to bite into their prey. Octopuses also have a muscular foot that is divided into 8 sucker-covered arms. Because they have no shell, they can squeeze through very tiny crevices and hide in irregularly shaped shelters.

FIGURE 12.13
Examples of Mollusks: Conch, Giant Clam, Octopus, and Squid

Squid have a thin, flexible internal shell called a **pen** that provides support and a bit of structure. The muscular foot of squid is divided into 8 sucker-covered arms and 2 tentacles that surround their mouth. The 2 tentacles only have suckers on the tips and can extend out to capture prey. Squid can range in size from just a few centimeters in length to the size of sea monsters. That's right. The deep sea colossal squid—genus *Mesonychoteuthis*—can grow to 10 m, or 33 ft! The eyes of a squid that size would be as large as dinner plates!

Both octopuses and squid have a unique ability to change color. That's because they have special pigment-filled cells that can expand or contract to help the animals match their surroundings. Octopuses are the masters of camouflage, able to mimic most background colors and even *change the texture of their skin* to hide!

Arthropods

Ocean arthropods are those joint-footed organisms like shrimp, lobsters, and crabs. They have a rigid, but flexible, exoskeleton that protects their body. As you learned in an earlier module, when an arthropod needs to grow, it has to shed its external skeleton and grow a new larger one. This process is called molting, and it is a vulnerable time for the animals. Most marine arthropods are in class **Crustacea** (crust ay' sha). They are well suited for marine living, having **gills** to collect dissolved oxygen gas out of the water. (I will define gills in the next section.) Many crustaceans also have special structures for swimming.

FIGURE 12.14
Body Division of a Shrimp

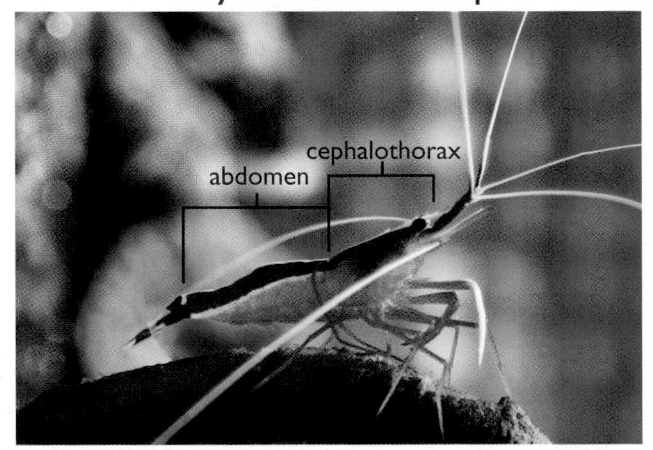

Shrimp, lobsters, and crabs have 5 pairs of legs for walking. In most creatures, the first pair is larger and has claws for defense and obtaining food. Their body is divided into 2 major parts. The head and thorax are fused together to form a **cephalothorax** (sef uh low thor' axe). They also have an **abdomen**, which is often mistaken for their tail (Figure 12.14).

Shrimp and lobsters have a long abdomen. Many species live on the ocean bottom, scavenging for leftover bits of food. Crabs have a small abdomen that is folded under their larger, usually rounded cephalothorax. Male crabs have a small, narrow abdomen, but female crabs have a wider, flattened abdomen that is perfectly designed for carrying eggs. Like shrimp and lobsters, most crabs scavenge for food.

creation connection

Some shrimp species feed on the parasites of fish. They set up cleaning stations where a fish will allow the shrimp to crawl all over its body—even inside its mouth. The shrimp will pick off and eat any parasites it finds. This is an example of symbiosis, where both organisms benefit. The shrimp gets plenty of food to eat and the fish gets all its parasites removed. This is yet another example of the incredible design we see in creation. Fish need to be cleaned of parasites, and shrimp need to eat. God has solved both problems by creating fish with the instincts to seek out cleaner shrimp, while at the same time creating shrimp that are not afraid of the fish and are happy to clean them of parasites.

Echinoderms

The organisms in phylum **Echinodermata** (ee ky' noh der mah' tah) are exclusively marine. They include sea stars, sea urchins, and sand dollars. One of the things that is similar about these organisms is that their bodies are designed with a base of 5 radiating parts. Think of a sea star. (Marine biologists like to call them sea stars instead of starfish because they are not fish.) Most sea stars have 5 arms coming out of a central disk. They don't have a head or sides. Instead, like cnidarians they have a mouth—or oral—side and a side opposite the mouth—or aboral side.

These organisms have a fascinating body design to help them move. It is called a **water vascular system,** and it is made up of a series of water-filled canals. You have probably played with water balloons before. Imagine you are holding a long, skinny water balloon. If you were to squeeze it on one end, what would happen to the other end? It would get stiff and probably swell a bit as it fills with water. Well, that is similar to how a water vascular system

FIGURE 12.15
Examples of Echinoderms: A Sea Star, Sea Urchin, and Sand Dollars

behaves in echinoderms. The canals are filled with water and extend outward to help the organism move and do other jobs. Many of the canals have hundreds of extensions that end in little suction cups called **tube feet**. These help the organism move around, transport food to the mouth, or carry wastes away from it.

This hydraulic system is so strong that sea stars can use it to open up a clam. They use force from all parts of their hydraulic system to allow the tube feet to pull it apart!

Echinoderms are known for their amazing ability to regenerate lost body parts. If a sea star, for example, loses one of its arms, it can readily grow a new one. In fact, if an arm is broken off and has enough of the central body still attached, that arm can grow an entirely new sea star, too!

FIGURE 12.16
A Sea Star Regenerating 2 Legs

Sea urchins look like round, spiny pin cushions. Like sea stars, their bodies are divided into 5 portions, they have a central mouth on the underside of their body, and their aboral side faces upward. Their spines help to protect them from predators as well as providing some movement.

Sand dollars are basically flattened sea urchins. Their bodies also are divided into 5 portions, and they have an oral and aboral side. Many people hunt for sand dollars on the seashore. When they find them, the sand dollars are often white and hard. But this is actually the internal skeleton of a *dead* sand dollar. The skeleton of living sand dollars is surrounded by tissue with hundreds of small spines along their bodies and rows of tube feet to help them move about. They bury themselves partially in the sand, slightly upright with their central mouth located at the level of the seafloor (see Figure 12.15). That way they can feed on any material they find there.

ON YOUR OWN

12.5 Write one interesting fact you learned about a mollusk and one interesting fact you learned about an arthropod.

12.6 Echinoderms' bodies are designed with a base of how many radiating parts?

NON-BONY FISHES

There are 2 basic groups of fishes. Before I go any further, I need to explain why I am using the word *fishes* as a plural word instead of *fish*. You need to understand that there is a unique grammar in scientific fields, and it serves a purpose. For example, when a scientist refers to a single organism, he will use the word fish. When he refers to a *group* of organisms of the same species, he will also use the word fish. But when he is referring to a group of organisms of *many* species, he will use the word fishes. That way, the information he conveys will be in greater detail.

Thus, non-bony *fishes* are grouped into class **Chondrichthyes** (kahn drik' thih eez) or the cartilaginous fishes. These fishes have a body support composed of only **cartilage**, not bone. How can a fish survive without bones? First, cartilage is different from bone because it has no bone cells. But it is a fibrous material that is flexible, yet sturdy. You can get an idea of how flexible these skeletons are by playing with the upper part of your ear, which is supported by cartilage. If you bend cartilage, it will flex but hold its shape. The thicker the cartilage, the less flexible it will be. This gives you some idea of the flexibility a cartilaginous skeleton gives these creatures.

FIGURE 12.17
Leopard Shark and a Southern Stingray

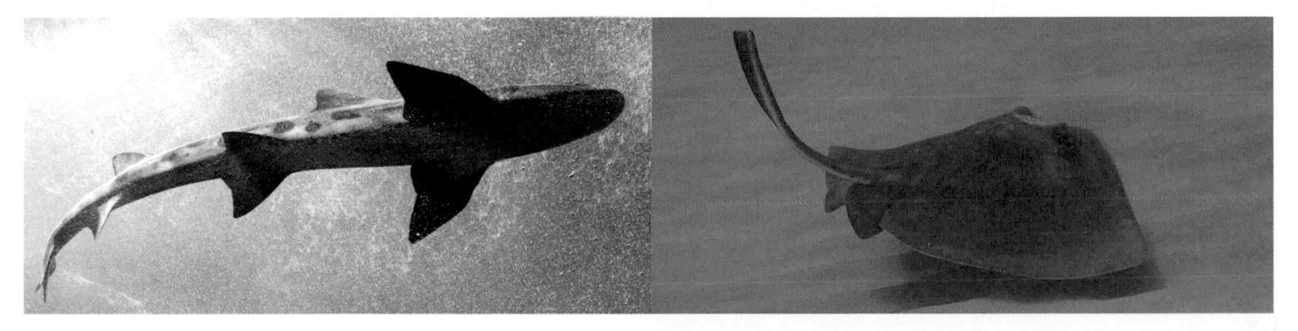

Cartilaginous fishes include sharks and rays. Some of these fishes *do* have some pretty hard parts in their skeletons. You see, some of their cartilage (specifically the jaws) has become hardened with calcium salts and is quite strong. You can imagine that a large shark needs to have a sturdy jaw to capture its food!

Sharks

Sharks are a good example of members of this class. Most species have a mouth located on their underside. It is curved downward on the ends so they can open it wide enough to bite into prey. But that makes it look like they are frowning. To add to their threatening appearance, they have several rows of razor-sharp teeth. What happens is that when one tooth is lost, another from the row behind it advances forward like it's on a conveyor belt in order to take the lost one's place. This happens quite often. Some shark species can replace an entire row of teeth every 10 days! But this is a perfect design that enables them to always have fresh, sharp tools for feeding.

Sharks are beautifully designed for fast swimming and maneuverability. They are torpedo-shaped, which helps them easily glide through the water. Their fins help maintain balance and steer as they swim.

FIGURE 12.18
Sand Tiger Shark

This sand tiger shark looks like it is ready to attack, with its down-turned mouth and rows of bared teeth. Its mouth is open so water can move past its gills. Thus, that menacing look is just a fish swimming and breathing!

Now, sharks need to breathe, but they are under the water. In order to get oxygen they have gills.

Gills—Organs for taking oxygen from water

All fishes and most other larger water creatures breathe through gills. Gills remove the oxygen gas that is dissolved in water. As I mentioned in an earlier module, many people mistakenly think that gills break up water molecules into hydrogen and oxygen, using that oxygen to breathe. But that is not what happens. The same way that sugar easily dissolves into water, oxygen gas can dissolve in it, too. And that is what fishes use to breathe. In fact, in some lakes or shallow ocean inlets, if the water is not moving and sits for a long time, the oxygen gas will get used up by the living things there. If that happens, the organisms will suffocate because there is no dissolved oxygen to breathe!

FIGURE 12.19
Whale Shark and Diver

The size of sharks varies greatly. The smallest known species is the spiny pygmy shark (genus *Squaliolus*), whose full-grown size is about 25 cm (10 in). The largest sharks (in fact the largest of all fishes) are the basking shark (genus *Cetorhinus*—up to 15 m [50 ft] long) and the whale shark (genus *Rhinocodon*—up to 18 m [60 ft] long). These big sharks feed on the tiniest of organisms, filtering small plankton out of the water.

creation connection

Some people want to prevent the threat of shark attacks by removing the shark populations from the coastlines, but this actually can have a negative effect. In one example, large sharks were netted off the coast of South Africa. As a result, the number of small sharks—which were being eaten by the large sharks—increased! The small sharks then began to feed on the bluefish population, which was a commercially important resource in that area. It is evident from this incident that sharks play a significant role in the delicate balance of God's creation.

Rays

Rays have a different body shape as compared to sharks. Their bodies are flat with a thin tail. They *do* have fins like sharks, but the fins are very large and wing-like, allowing many rays to appear to fly through the water. Most rays live on the ocean floor and feed on creatures like clams and crabs that are buried there. Because of where they live, their mouths are on the underside of their body and their eyes are on top. That makes sense since they feed on what is buried below while watching for predators coming from above. Those that live on the ocean floor have a set of plates instead of teeth. The plates are large and flat and are made of calcified material to crush the hard shells of their prey.

Stingrays have a whip-like tail that has stinging spines at its base. In many species, the spines have barbs oriented in a reverse direction, like the barbs at the end of a fishhook. That way, when the spine goes into flesh, it will not easily come out because of the barbs. To make this defense mechanism more powerful, many spines have a groove to inject poisonous venom.

Even though that sounds alarming, stingrays do not use their spines for aggression, but strictly for defense. Occasionally, an unsuspecting person might accidentally step on a stingray lying on the sandy bottom of the ocean and receive a terrible surprise. To avoid such a nasty encounter, you can simply scuff your feet as you walk in shallow water. The commotion your feet make as they scuff along the floor will scare away any stingrays before you have a chance to step on them.

FIGURE 12.20
Manta Ray

Some rays do not live on the ocean floor. Manta rays (genus *Manta*), for example, have fins that look like wings for "soaring" in the water. Mantas feed on tiny plankton as they swim, filtering it out of the water. The 2 horns on each side of their mouth help to corral food into it. Isn't it amazing how each organism has perfect features for where it lives? Mantas can grow to be pretty large: up to 7 m (23 ft) from wing tip to wing tip.

ON YOUR OWN

12.7 Why do sharks benefit from having rows and rows of teeth?

BONY FISHES

Most of the fishes in creation are in class **Osteichthyes** (ah' stee ik' thih eez). They are the bony fishes, or fishes that have an internal skeleton made mostly of bones. There are so many types of fishes in the world that they make up nearly half of the world's vertebrates. And because we still have not explored all of the world's oceans, there are likely more species we haven't yet discovered.

FIGURE 12.21
Blue Tang Showing Membranous Fins and Terminal Mouth

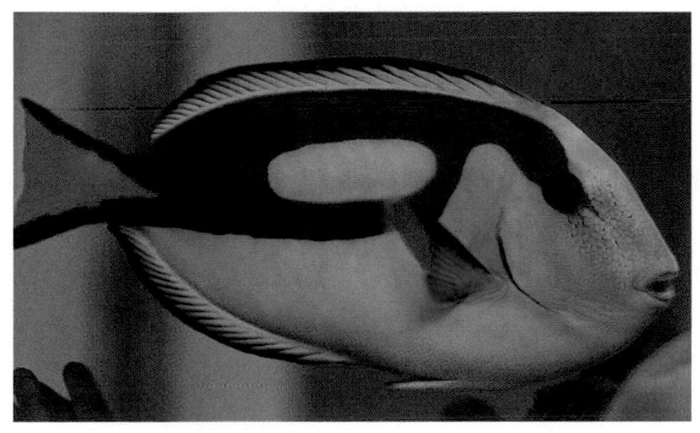

In contrast to the cartilaginous fishes, bony fishes have fins that are made up of a thin membrane of tissue, supported by bony spines, or rays. Cartilaginous fishes have fleshy fins. As I mentioned earlier, the mouths of most cartilaginous fishes are located on the underside, but most bony fishes have mouths located at the front tip of their bodies (Figure 12.21). This lets them move their jaws more easily. Bony fishes have teeth that are attached to a jawbone, but unlike cartilaginous fishes, they do not move forward in rows when they are lost. However, lost teeth are often replaced.

One more amazing feature of most bony fishes deserves mention. When sharks and other cartilaginous fishes stop swimming, they usually start to sink. That's because their bodies are denser than the water around them. Now, sharks *do* have a fairly large liver that stores less dense fats and oils, but that is not enough to help them remain at a certain depth without moving. On the other hand, most bony fishes have a special gas-filled sac called an **air bladder.** It behaves much like a balloon; and, depending on how much gas is inside, it allows a fish to sink or rise in the water column. The fish can control the amount of gas so that it can even remain at a specific depth without having to use any energy by flapping its fins. Perform Experiment 12.2 to learn more about buoyancy.

EXPERIMENT 12.2

SHARK AND FISH BUOYANCY

PURPOSE: To explore how sharks and bony fishes maintain their buoyancy in the water

MATERIALS:

- 2 empty toilet paper rolls
- 3 balloons
- Water
- A large mixing bowl
- Vegetable oil
- A funnel
- Markers (optional)

QUESTION: How do sharks and bony fishes stay buoyant in the water?

HYPOTHESIS: Write how you think both types of fishes stay up in the water column.

PROCEDURE:

1. If you want, draw an illustration of a shark on one toilet paper roll with a marker. Draw a picture of a bony fish on the other roll. These will be your model swimmers.
2. Fill the mixing bowl with water.
3. Fill the 3 balloons so that they are still able to fit inside the toilet paper rolls. Using a funnel, fill the first balloon with water and tie it off. The balloon need not stretch to hold the water; just fill it loosely. Do the same thing with oil to fill the second balloon and tie it off. Finally, fill the third one with air and tie it off.
4. Stuff the water-filled balloon in the shark roll and place it in the bowl. Write what happens.
5. Remove the water balloon and repeat with the oil-filled balloon. Write in your notebook what happens.
6. Stuff the air-filled balloon in the fish roll and place it in the bowl. Write what happens.
7. Clean everything up and put it away.

CONCLUSION: Which creates more buoyancy in water: oil or air?

What happened in the experiment? If everything worked out, you should have noticed that the toilet paper roll sank with the water-filled balloon inside it. That's because the mass of the toilet paper roll and water-filled balloon was greater than the mass of water it displaced.

When you added the oil-filled balloon, the roll should have floated, just below the water's surface. That is because oil is less dense than water, so it caused the roll to float. The air-filled balloon should have done the same thing, but it might have floated even higher in the water than the oil-filled balloon.

Now, the oil-filled balloon helped to illustrate how a shark keeps its buoyancy in the water. Its large, oily liver isn't as dense as the surrounding water, so it helps the fish to stay up more easily. Sharks still need to keep swimming so they don't completely sink, but the oil definitely helps. Bony fishes, on the other hand, have an air-filled bladder. The air-filled balloon illustrated how they can easily stay up in the water column by controlling how much air is in the bladder.

FIGURE 12.22
Moray Eel Displaying Elongated Shape and Spotted Coloring

Bony fishes have various body shapes depending on where and how they live. Fast swimmers are torpedo-shaped like sharks. Those that slowly move around surfaces looking for bits of food have more rounded or even boxed-shaped bodies. Some are elongated to blend in with their surroundings or to wiggle into narrow crevices.

Their colors also vary based on where they live. Those that swim in the open ocean tend to be silvery or blue to blend in to the water. Fishes that live among colorful corals are usually brightly colored or patterned. Those living in the very deep ocean where no light can reach are either black or red. You might be surprised to hear that they would be red because nothing can see them. However, as you learned in the physics module, black is a pigment made up of all the colors in the rainbow. That means it takes *less energy to produce a red pigment than a black pigment*. For fishes that live in the deep ocean, conserving energy is a very important thing!

OTHER MARINE VERTEBRATES

The rest of the ocean creatures I will talk about are all air breathers. That means they breathe using lungs instead of gills. Because air breathers cannot take in oxygen from the water, they have to come to the surface at least once in a while. Thus, a majority of these organisms live on or near the surface. Some, however, are uniquely designed to live much deeper (at least until they need to grab a breath!).

Reptiles and Birds

Marine reptiles have to be able to endure losing water in a saltwater environment. So their scales help them prevent water loss. Most species of reptiles lay eggs on land. That means that not only do they have to come to the surface regularly to breathe, but they also have to leave the ocean to reproduce.

Sea turtles are reptiles similar in design to land turtles. The major difference is that their head and legs are not able to be drawn into their shell. Additionally, their legs are flipper-shaped to aid in swimming. That is great for being in the ocean, but is not great when it is time to lay eggs. Now, only the females will come to shore to dig a nest and lay eggs. They have a challenging time crawling out of the ocean beyond the high tide level so they can dig. Once laying up to 150 eggs, the female will bury the nest and crawl back to the sea. When the young turtles hatch, they must dig themselves up out of the sandy nest and make their way to the ocean. This may sound fairly easy, but they face a great deal of peril before they even reach the water. If their nests don't get scavenged by crabs or other predators, they are in danger of being eaten during the long trek across the beach to the surf. And once they reach the water, they are still easy prey for fishes and seabirds.

FIGURE 12.23
Green Sea Turtle

A sea turtle's nostrils are located on the upper part of its snout, which is the perfect design for an aquatic air breather. They come up to the surface intermittently to grab a breath as they swim along. At night, those that live in shallow water will take a deep breath and dive down to wedge themselves among some rocks or coral, surfacing each hour or so for another breath. Those that live in deep water float on the surface with their nostrils above water. That enables them to breathe more regularly.

Other marine reptiles include sea snakes, saltwater crocodiles, and marine iguanas. Each of these organisms has unique physical features to help it live in an ocean environment.

Marine birds live in many more types of ocean environments as compared to marine reptiles. That is because they live above, *not in*, the water. Their bodies are designed to maintain a more constant temperature than those of fishes and reptiles, no matter what the surrounding temperatures are. To help keep in heat, they are covered with feathers that act like a coat. If they need to cool off during warmer times of the year, they will shed some feathers to thin that coat.

A bird is considered a marine bird if it spends most of its life at or near the sea and feeds on marine organisms. The shape of marine birds' beaks plays an important role in their feeding habits. Those with hooked beaks use the hook shape to tear off bits of food and to hang on to prey. Straight beaks are helpful to create a more streamlined shape needed for diving.

FIGURE 12.24
Pelicans' Pointed Beaks for Diving and Their Large Throat Pouch for Manipulating Fish

Most seabirds waterproof their feathers by covering them with a coating of oil they get from a special gland found near the base of the tail. You probably have seen ducks preening their feathers with their beak, but what they are really doing is getting some oil from their oil glands with their beaks. Then they move their beaks along the length of their feathers to spread it out.

Many marine birds have webbed feet to aid in swimming. Some, like penguins, do not fly at all; others, like the albatross, can glide hundreds of miles without flapping and will travel more than 10,000 mi just to bring food to their chick. Of course, they rest from time to time by floating on the ocean surface during that long trek.

Regardless of their flying ability, all marine birds move to land to build nests and lay eggs.

EXPLORE MORE

You can explore how penguins use special camouflage coloration by doing this simple activity. You need a mason jar, water, scraps of black and white craft foam, glue, scissors, a flashlight, and black paper. Cut a small square out of both foam colors and glue them together. Use the scissors to cut out a simple penguin shape about 1½" long. Fill the mason jar about halfway with water and carefully place your penguin with the white side down on the top of the water. Now, shine the flashlight into the top of the jar and observe the penguin from the bottom of the jar. It should be difficult to see. This is the way that penguins swim, making it more difficult for predators to see them from below when the sun shines from above. Now without using the flashlight, set the jar on top of the black paper and look down at the penguin from above. Notice how it is also hard to see. When viewed from above, the penguin blends in with the dark depths below it. This is called **countershading**, and it is a wonderful camouflage design!

Marine Mammals

The final group of marine organisms I want to discuss is class **Mammalia.** This includes whales, dolphins, and porpoises; seals and sea lions; and manatees.

Whales, dolphins, and porpoises are in the order **Cetacea** (see tay' shuh). All these animals are often referred to as whales. These air breathers spend their entire lives in the water. Their streamlined bodies are perfectly designed for swimming. Their flippers, fins, and tail **flukes** help them steer and maneuver in the water. Why do you think they are classified as mammals when they look so much like fishes? Well, even though they are mostly torpedo-shaped and have swimming fins, they have all the features of mammals. They breathe air through a blowhole on their head, which is actually a nostril. They even have hair on a few areas of their skin. And like other mammals, they produce milk for their young.

FIGURE 12.25
Dolphins' Streamlined Bodies Moving Easily Through the Water

They also swim differently than a fish. Fishes swim with a side-to-side motion because their tails are flattened from side to side and the backbone vertebrae are designed to move that way. However, whales swim with an up-and-down movement because their tail flukes are flattened from top to bottom, and the backbone vertebrae are designed to move up and down.

FIGURE 12.26
Orientation of Whale Fluke Compared to Fish Tail

Whales are able to communicate using **echolocation.** They have a unique set of organs that work together to create, send out, and receive sounds that tell them what objects are nearby and what they are made of. Humans can do a form of this by identifying the different sounds when various materials are tapped with a spoon. Try tapping a spoon on your kitchen counter, a metal pot, a wooden cutting board, or other objects to hear the difference.

think about this

Research has shown that bottlenose dolphins use echolocation to communicate. They can be trained to identify what objects are made of by sending out sounds and hearing the returning echoes. In studies, a dolphin can be trained to identify which of 2 identical balls is wood. It will then tell a dolphin in the next pen (who cannot see or send out sounds to the balls) which ball is wood, either the one on the left or the right. Over 80% of the time, the other dolphin will *correctly point* to a picture of the ball on the correct side!

There are 2 major types of whales: **toothed whales** that hunt animals for food, and **baleen whales** that filter tiny plankton out of the water. Toothed whales, such as dolphins, porpoises, and orcas, have cone-shaped teeth to capture fish they hunt. These comparatively smaller whales often hunt in large groups, called **pods**. They will work together to herd schools of fish and then take turns swimming into the school to feed. The largest of the toothed whales is the sperm whale. These animals have a large nose and a long, thin jaw. They feed on giant squid and other marine animals.

FIGURE 12.27
Baleen of a Humpback Whale

The toothless whales are also called the **baleen** whales because of the presence of hundreds of rows of horny plates called baleen hanging down into their mouths. They take in a large mouthful of plankton-filled water and then use their tongue to push against the strands of baleen that behave like a sieve, straining out the food. The largest known animal, living or extinct, is a baleen whale called a blue whale. Blue whales can grow to up to 100 ft (30 m) and weigh 200 tons.

EXPLORE MORE

Examine how baleen works by sprinkling dried herbs into a bowl of water. Parsley, oregano, or basil works well. Now use a fine-toothed hair comb and drag it across the water to strain out the herbs. The herbs represent small plankton that the baleen whales will strain out of the water. The comb acts like baleen, allowing water to pass through, but not the food.

Seals and sea lions are in the order **Pinnipedia** (pin ih pee' dee uh). This word literally means "flipper feet." These animals spend most of their time resting on rocky ocean shores or swimming and feeding in the ocean. All pinnipeds (pin ih' peds) hunt for their food, eating fish and squid. Their streamlined bodies are perfectly designed for moving through water, and their paddle-shaped flippers help them easily move. Both cetaceans

FIGURE 12.28
Seals (top) and Sea Lions

and pinnipeds have a thick layer of blubber to provide buoyancy, store energy, and keep them warm.

There is a noticeable difference between seals and sea lions. Seals cannot move their rear flippers forward to walk on land, but sea lions can. Seals instead have to slink along the ground to move. Additionally, sea lions have noticeable external ears and seals do not. Now that doesn't mean that seals do not have ears—it just means that their ears are tiny holes that let sound travel inside.

Finally, let's talk a bit about manatees. Manatees are in the order **Sirenia** (sy ree' nee uh). They are slow-moving, plant-eating animals. Their paddle-shaped tail helps them to slowly move along shallow marine and freshwater habitats. These animals live in warm water. So though they look quite large, they actually have no blubber—they do not need it. But why are they so big? It has to do with their diet. Because they feed on plants, they need to have a long digestive tract to process all that vegetation. Thus, they are filled with intestine, not blubber!

ON YOUR OWN

12.8 Explain the difference between whale flukes and fish tails and how they cause marine animals to swim differently.

12.9 Explain one difference between toothed and baleen whales.

12.10 Explain one difference between seals and sea lions.

MARINE ENVIRONMENTS

It is easy to think that marine environments are the same all over the world. After all, the entire ocean is made of saltwater, the water moves in currents and waves, and all of the ocean surface is exposed to sunlight. But in reality, there are several ocean environments, each with unique physical features, providing specific living conditions for organisms.

One of the most well-known ocean environments is the **coral reef**. Coral reefs are home to an amazing assortment of organisms and are truly the underwater

FIGURE 12.29
The Great Barrier Reef—The World's Largest Coral Reef Environment

equivalent of a tropical rainforest. This environment consists of reef structures made from living corals and encrusting algae growing over lots of dead material. This 3-dimensional framework provides homes for hundreds of species of organisms. They are mostly located in warmer waters where corals grow well. From tiny bacteria to large sharks and dolphins, reefs provide rich places to live.

Another interesting marine environment is the **deep ocean.** As you learned earlier, sunlight can penetrate seawater only to about 200 m, but the ocean is on average much deeper than that. Therefore, much of the ocean is not able to receive light. That means no photosynthesis can occur in the deep ocean. That affects what types of organisms can live here, too.

EXPLORE MORE

The deeper in the ocean, the greater the pressure. A good way to visualize that is to get an empty 2-liter soda bottle, a small knife, and some electrical tape. Have a parent use the knife to carefully poke 3 small holes into the bottle, evenly spaced down one side of it, from top to bottom. When you puncture the bottle, slowly spin the tip of the knife around to make the hole as round as possible and about the width of a pencil. The smoother the holes are, the better your results will be. Cover the holes with a long strip of electrical tape, smoothing it down to prevent water from escaping. In a sink, fill the bottle with water. With the bottle down in the sink, quickly uncover all the holes at the same time and watch what happens. The water will flow out of the holes at different distances because of different water pressure. The pressure is greatest at the bottom of the bottle and least at the top, so water from the hole at the top will travel the shortest distance, and water from the bottom hole will travel the farthest.

Most creatures in the deep ocean have watery bodies. That's because to conserve energy, they don't move around much. They have large jaws and long, pointy teeth to capture almost whatever food they find. Additionally, many organisms living in the deep ocean have ways to create their own light. This is called **bioluminescence.**

Bioluminescence—The production of visible light by living organisms

Some organisms have bioluminescent organs on the end of a spine and use it like a fishing lure. When a curious fish comes close, the predator quickly gulps him down. Other organisms have several spots all over their bodies that glow in bright flashes. They do this either to attract potential mates or when they are being attacked. You see, flashing light is not common in the deep ocean and it behaves kind of like a car alarm, causing any creatures in the area to take interest.

Bioluminescence is a pretty amazing ability. It is light that is created without much heat. What do I mean by that? Well, think of an incandescent light bulb. Most light bulbs get pretty hot when they are turned on. (Don't touch them to see what I

FIGURE 12.30
Bioluminescent Organisms

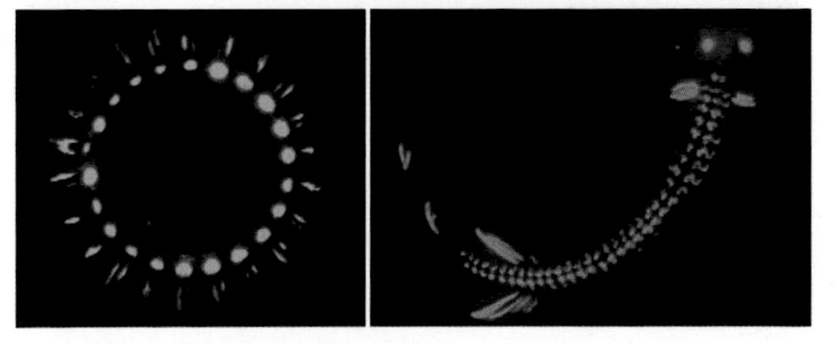

mean—you can burn yourself!) But if a living organism made light the same way, its tissue would burn. Bioluminescence is unique in that it is a *cool* light.

EXPLORE MORE

Bioluminescent organisms mix chemicals together in their bodies to create a glow. This is similar to the way a glow stick works. Take a glow stick and observe it. (Don't bend it yet!) Notice how it has a small glass vial floating around inside some liquid. When you bend the glow stick, you break the glass, allowing the fluids to mix. This causes a chemical reaction that makes a cool light. Go ahead and bend the stick now, but don't shake it. You will notice how the liquids start to mix, but don't completely do that until you shake the stick. Now shake it and notice how the entire mixture glows. To make the glowing last, you can slow the chemical reaction down by storing your stick in a freezer.

The **intertidal zone** is an ecosystem that you are likely very familiar with. It is a narrow strip of land beginning from the lowest point of low tide and extending toward shore up to the highest point where the waves splash. These are the beaches, and more is known about this coastal zone than any other ocean environment. That should make sense to you. After all, the intertidal zone is perhaps the easiest ocean area to visit and study.

One interesting fact about this relatively small environment is that it has the greatest environmental changes of all ecosystems. Think about that. Sometimes the intertidal is covered by water at high tide. Other times it is not. During rainy weather, organisms living here might experience a large amount of freshwater washing into the ocean. Because the water is shallow, extreme heat can warm it up, and cold temperatures can make the water much cooler. And many intertidal areas have to endure times of strong wave action.

FIGURE 12.31
Rocky Intertidal Shore

Because of this, organisms living in the intertidal have to either be able to hang onto something or dig down into the sand to survive. They need to be able to hold in water during dry times or move to somewhere that stays wet. Their bodies need to be strong enough to endure the temperature and salinity changes, too. Many mollusks and arthropods (particularly crabs and barnacles) thrive here because their hard shells are sturdy and protective. Large macroalgae do well, too, because of the constant sunlight and lots of available oxygen for photosynthesis. The wave action also is helpful because it brings in nutrients and removes wastes.

OCEAN CONSERVATION

Because the oceans cover so much of the planet and affect living creatures in so many ways, it is important to make sure we do what we can to protect them. Next module, you will learn about environmental science and how there is a delicate balance between different types of organisms as well as between the organisms and the places they live.

SUMMING UP

Marine science is truly an ocean-sized subject, isn't it? From the unique environments with their physical features to the variety of organisms living there, you can understand why so much of the ocean has not been explored. In fact, we know more about the surface of our Moon than we do about what is on the bottom of the ocean!

ANSWERS TO THE "ON YOUR OWN" QUESTIONS

12.1 Most organisms do not move from one ocean basin to another **because they are not able to handle the differences in temperature, pressure, and even salinity from different parts of the world.**

12.2 **Cyanobacteria take nitrogen gas from the atmosphere and change it into a molecule (nitrate) that other organisms are able to utilize to make proteins.**

12.3 **a-2 Holdfasts attach to hard surfaces. b-1 Blades provide more surface area to collect sunlight. c-4 Pneumatocysts provide flotation to hold the algae upright in the water. d-3 Stipes connect other parts of the seaweed together.**

12.4 Your drawing should look something like this:

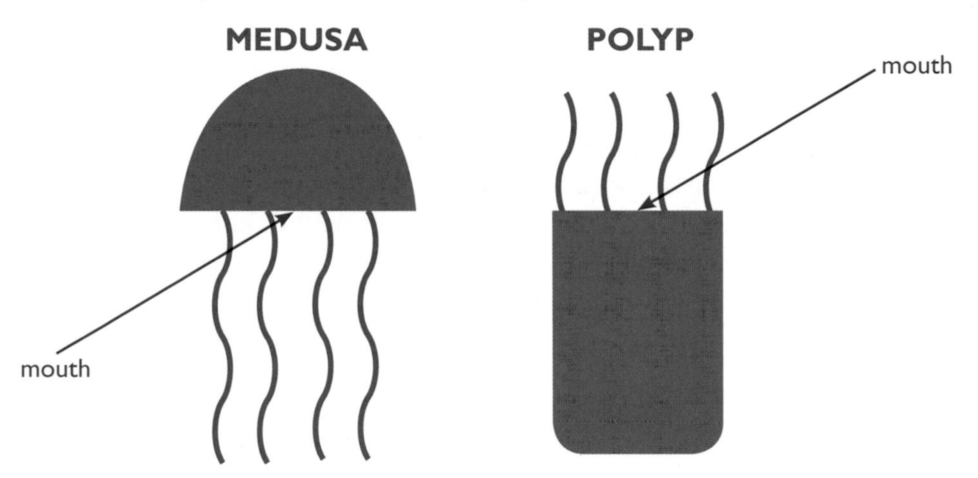

12.5 *Answers will vary.*

12.6 Echinoderms' bodies are designed with a base of **5** radiating parts.

12.7 Sharks benefit from having lots of rows of teeth **because as an old tooth becomes dull, a new one can easily move forward to replace it.** That way they will always have a sharp set of teeth to be able to capture their food.

12.8 **Whale flukes are flattened from top to bottom, and thus they swim with an up-and-down motion. Fish tails are flattened from side to side and they swim with a side-to-side motion. Additionally, the joints of their vertebrae are able to move best in those respective directions.**

12.9 (The student needs mention only one.) **Toothed whales have teeth for feeding while baleen whales have horny baleen to filter plankton out of the water. Toothed whales hunt prey and often do that in pods while baleen whales feed on plankton.**

12.10 (The student needs mention only one.) **Seals are unable to turn their rear flippers forward for walking on land whereas sea lions can. Also seals do not have external ear flaps and sea lions do.**

STUDY GUIDE FOR MODULE 12

1. Match the following words with their definitions.

a. Ecosystem	Organs for taking oxygen from water
b. Symbiosis	The production of visible light by living organisms
c. Gills	A community of organisms that interact with each other and their physical environment
d. Bioluminescence	A close living situation between 2 species where at least one of the species benefits

2. Which of the following oceans is not an ocean basin?
   a. Atlantic Ocean b. Pacific Ocean c. Indian Ocean d. Southern Ocean

3. Which is the more accurate term to describe the tiny organisms that convert atmospheric nitrogen gas into molecules that other living things can use: blue-green algae or cyanobacteria?

4. Although large multicellular algae are not true plants, they do have similarly shaped structures. Which plant structure is an algae's blade similar to?
   a. stem b. root c. leaf

5–6. Choose the correct word.

5. A jellyfish has a (polyp, medusa) body shape.

6. The side of a cnidarian that has a mouth is the (aboral, oral) side.

7. One major physical feature that all mollusks have is ___________.
   a. an outer shell b. tentacles c. claws d. a mantle

8. Echinoderms are known for their ability to regenerate lost body parts. If a person were to cut a sea star in half, each half with a portion of its central disc, under the best conditions, what can happen?
   a. The sea star will die.
   b. One-half will regrow lost parts to form a new sea star.
   c. Both halves will regrow lost parts to form 2 new sea stars.

9–10. Fill in the blank.

9. Fill in the blank: Class Chondrichthyes consists of fishes with body support composed of cartilage, not __________.

10. Bony fishes are able to remain at a specific depth in the water because they have a gas-filled sac called a (an) ____________________.

11. An organism swims with an up-and-down tail motion. Is it a fish or a whale?

12. A person sees an ocean animal on the beach and cannot figure out if it is a seal or a sea lion. What should she look for?

    a. its coloration b. its fur thickness c. its external ears d. its whiskers

13. Which of the ecosystems covered in this module would have organisms that exhibit bioluminescence?

    a. coral reef b. deep ocean c. intertidal zone

ENVIRONMENTAL SCIENCE

It is fitting that one of the last modules we cover in this course is **environmental science**. Why? Well, environmental science is a combination of many elements of Earth and life science. You've already had a good introduction to these branches of science. Environmental science includes a science called **ecology**. Ecology is the study of how living things interact with each other and with their physical environment. Practically speaking, ecology is the study of why and how organisms live where they do. Often these 2 terms are used interchangeably. Just know that environmental science includes even more of the physical features of an organism's surroundings. So with a good understanding of many *-ologies* under your belt, we can now study life at another level—one beyond the individual organism or even group of organisms. We can take a look at bigger systems that are incredibly complex. And that makes this branch of science quite interesting!

Quaestio

By now, you should have a good understanding of the order and design in creation. From chemistry to astronomy and from physics to biology, there is a noticeable complexity and order, isn't there? This module takes us one step further in complexity, combining how living organisms survive and interact *with their environments*. It includes the properties of water and the intensity of solar energy. It involves the location on the planet as well as weather patterns. Indeed, these branches of science give testimony to the One who created them and keeps them in motion! Let's take a deeper look at this fascinating subject!

FIGURE 13.1
Complex, Designed Ecosystems

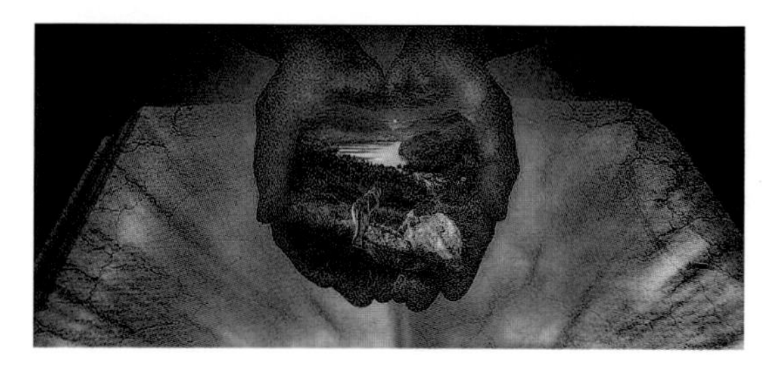

ECOSYSTEM INFLUENCES

There is no situation in the world where an organism lives disconnected from its surroundings. Every living thing lives in a **habitat**. A habitat is the natural home of a living thing, including where it finds its food and shelter. An example of a habitat can be a desert, a forest, or a lake. Now, each organism within a habitat has a **niche** (nich'), too.

Niche—An organism's function in its habitat, including its relationship with other organisms

For example, a lion lives in a grassland habitat. Its niche (function in its habitat) is to hunt zebras and other plant-eaters. That keeps their populations from getting too large. Often, scavengers such as jackals will finish eating what the lion doesn't. When the lion eventually dies, all the materials bound up in its body are broken down into nutrients that enrich the soil, enabling plants to better grow.

The lion example is only one of hundreds within a grassland habitat. All organisms living there, from the tiniest bacterium to the largest elephant, affect and influence one another, forming an **ecosystem**.

Ecosystem—A system made up of all living organisms interacting with one another and their environment

There are 2 major influences within an ecosystem that affect the organisms living there. **Biotic factors** are living organisms and their interaction with each other. The prefix *bio-* means "life," so that should help you remember what these factors are. In our lion example, biotic factors are the zebra it feeds on, the jackals that scavenge for leftovers, the grasses the zebra eats, and even the bacteria that break down the lion's body after it dies. If a bacterial infection spreads through the zebra population, causing many of them to die, that would affect the numbers of lions that could survive, too, because there would be less food for them. Fewer zebras might mean that the grasses overgrow, perhaps affecting other organisms living in the grassland ecosystem.

FIGURE 13.2
A Lion in the African Grasslands

Abiotic factors are all nonliving components of an ecosystem. The prefix *a-* in this case means "not," so *abiotic* refers to not living. These components include amount of sunlight, soil type, weather patterns, and amount of water. Many organisms can survive in a wide range of temperatures but live best within a narrow range. In our lion example, the dry weather systems, dusty flatlands, soil, rocks, and minerals all are abiotic factors that affect how the lion lives in this ecosystem. If several years passed with fewer-than-normal rains, this abiotic change would cause an unusually dry environment affecting how well the grasses grow. That can reduce the zebra population, which can reduce the number of lions that could survive.

All organisms interact with the abiotic and biotic factors of their environment. In fact, you are interacting with your environment right now! Abiotic factors of temperature might make you need to put on a jacket if it is cold or might make your body produce sweat if it is hot. A lack of moisture in the air might mean you need to put lotion on your skin or drink extra water. Biotic factors of bacteria on and in your body can help you to live better or cause you harm. If there is a plant in the room, it is producing oxygen that you are breathing, and you're exhaling carbon dioxide that the plant will use for photosynthesis.

FIGURE 13.3
A Deer in a Forest Environment

ON YOUR OWN

13.1 In the picture of a deer in a forest environment (Figure 13.3), name one biotic factor and one abiotic factor that can affect it.

FOOD RELATIONSHIPS

We can break down biotic factors into the nutritional relationship between organisms. This has to do with what eats what! You see, all living organisms need energy to continue to live. And the energy bound up in the molecules of their bodies is transferred from one organism to the next through food.

You already know that some organisms can make their own food. Plants and algae are able to photosynthesize, using energy from the sun, carbon dioxide, and water to produce sugars that they utilize and store for later use. That means they *produce* their own food. So environmental scientists call them **producers**. On the other hand, those organisms that cannot produce their food—instead feeding on producers—*consume* their food and therefore are called **consumers**.

Producer—An organism that makes its own food using energy from the sun or other sources

Consumer—An organism that obtains its food by feeding on other organisms or organic matter

Think of a deer feeding on a plant, for example. The plant is able to make its own food, so it is a producer. The deer cannot make its own food, so it is a consumer of the plant. Now suppose the deer is hunted by a wolf. The wolf eats the deer. Well, the wolf is a consumer, too. It feeds on another consumer (the deer) instead of eating a producer.

think about this

Some bacteria producers are able to make their own food without using sunlight. They use chemicals that include sulfur and nitrogen to make their energy. We call this process *chemo*synthesis instead of *photo*synthesis because it utilizes chemicals instead of light as its initial energy source. Scientists were fascinated when they first found these bacteria living in the deep ocean where no sunlight could penetrate. They were baffled to see them as the foundation of an entire deep ocean ecosystem—taking energy from chemicals vented from Earth's crust, transforming it into molecules of food, and then passing on that energy to consumers that feed on the chemosynthetic bacteria!

Consumers have to eat others to get energy. And there are lots of types of consumers. In fact, we can go one step further to classify consumers by the *type* of food they eat. **Herbivores** are plant-eaters, **carnivores** are meat-eaters, and **omnivores** eat both. In our deer example, the deer is the herbivore and the wolf is the carnivore. A good way to remember these 3 terms is to think of the root word *vore*. It literally means "one that eats." A person who has a *vor*acious appetite is one who eats a lot! Therefore, herbivores eat herbs and plants. *Carni-* means "meat," so carnivores eat meat. *Omni-* means "many," and indeed omnivores eat many different things. Chimpanzees are a good example of omnivores. They feed on fruit and leaves, but also eat insects and even will hunt small animals.

FIGURE 13.4
Carnivores (Herons) Feeding on Herbivores (Small Fish) That Feed on Producers (Duck Weed)

Let's get back to consumers and producers. There is one more category of organisms based on where they get their food. They are the **decomposers**. I already talked about decomposing bacteria and fungi before. Decomposers break down the wastes or dead material from both producers and consumers. This is a very important role in the ecosystem that helps to make the materials bound up in dead bodies available to the ecosystem again.

FIGURE 13.5
Shelf Fungi and Other Decomposers Breaking Down a Dead Tree

Have you ever heard of composting? It is a natural process of recycling once-living material, such as leaves and vegetable scraps, into rich fertilizer for plants. Many gardeners keep a compost pile near their garden. They will use plant material, such as mowed grass and raked leaves, adding kitchen scraps like apple cores and vegetable peels. Then the decomposers take over. Bacteria and fungi will feed on the dead material as it starts to decay. Earthworms mechanically break up the bits as they chew their way through the pile, creating smaller and smaller pieces for the decomposers to utilize. When they are done, the remaining material is rich, nutrient-filled, carbon-based soil that garden plants can use. Explore this incredible process in Experiment 13.1.

EXPERIMENT 13.1
COMPOSTING

PURPOSE: To better understand the process of composting and how decomposers work

MATERIALS:

- 5 zipper-seal plastic sandwich bags
- 5 plastic straws
- Masking tape
- A marker
- Tape
- Scissors
- 5 oz. of fresh spinach (Most groceries sell 10-oz. bags of spinach.)
- Newspaper (Actual newspaper material works best.)
- A kitchen scale
- Water
- A tablespoon

QUESTION: In composting, organic materials are transformed into rich soil. Carbon and nitrogen are critical ingredients for compost. This experiment uses newspaper (made from trees) as a carbon source and spinach as a nitrogen source. Which combination of these ingredients will be best for composting?

HYPOTHESIS: Write which combination of newspaper and spinach you think will work best for composting.

PROCEDURE:

1. Place a piece of masking tape on each of your 5 bags. Number them from 1 to 5.
2. Tear the spinach leaves in half. This experiment works best if you try to make sure all the pieces are similar in size.
3. With scissors, cut the newspaper into pieces the same size as the spinach pieces.
4. Now it is time to set up your bags. Measure 2 oz. of spinach and place it in bag 1.
5. Measure ½ oz. of newspaper and 1½ oz. of spinach for bag 2.
6. Measure 1 oz. of newspaper and 1 oz. of spinach for bag 3.
7. Measure 1½ oz. of newspaper and ½ oz. of spinach for bag 4.
8. Measure 2 oz. of newspaper and place it in bag 5.

9. Add 1 tablespoon of water into each bag.
10. Place a straw into each bag so that one end is sticking out. Carefully seal the bags on each side of the straw. Use pieces of tape to help the bags stay closed. The straw allows air to flow in and out of the bags without letting any decomposing bits escape.
11. Set the bags in a location away from direct sunlight and in a ventilated area. A laundry room or garage works well if it is not too cold.
12. Check the bags each day and write in your notebook what each looks like. After a few days, gently touch the bags to see if any feel warmer than the others. Write what you discover in your notebook.

CONCLUSION: Write which combination of carbon and nitrogen sources composted the fastest.

What did you notice in the experiment? First, the speed of your results will have to do with the location in which you kept your bags. Colder temperatures slow the decomposition process because the decomposing organisms will not break down the materials as quickly.

If everything worked out well, you should have seen that bag 3 produced compost the fastest. The spinach should have been very wilted and even black in appearance, and the newspaper shreds should be wet and maybe a bit smaller in size. An equal amount of nitrogen and carbon materials provide the best food source for the decomposers. But did you add any decomposers to your bags? You only put newspaper, spinach, and water in them. What was decomposing the organic material?

Well, decomposers are all around you. Many of them are bacteria that float around in the air, just like dust. Spores of molds and other fungi also are in the air. It is likely that many of them were already on the surface of the spinach and the newspaper, too. So once conditions were good for them to grow and reproduce, they did. They had ample food (spinach and newspaper), water, and a good temperature. If you felt any increase in temperature, you should have noticed it in bag 3 because that had the best food combination for decomposers to grow. You see, when they break down organic material and use it for their food, the process releases heat.

FIGURE 13.6
Compost Bins

This experiment is a good one to expand for a science fair. You can alter the types of green material you use. You can add mowed grass or dead leaves instead of newspaper. You also can use a thermometer to measure and record the temperatures during the process. Adding physical decomposers like earthworms can also give you more data. It is a great way to better understand how this process works in an ecosystem.

Food Chains and Food Webs

With a good understanding of what organisms use for food, we can arrange them by their feeding relationships into something called a **food chain.** A food chain is a list of organisms, beginning with a producer, and arranged in order of what feeds on it. Figure 13.7 illustrates 3 food chain examples from 3 ecosystems. In each chain, you can follow the flow of energy. The savanna ecosystem food chain starts with grass, and a zebra that eats the grass, then a lion that eats the zebra. Each step in the chain represents an organism getting energy from the step before it. Now, notice the coral reef food chain in the diagram. It has 4 "links," doesn't it? That is because some food chains are very short while others are quite long. It can get extremely complicated. Of course, there are hundreds (perhaps thousands) of other food chains in each ecosystem, too. For example, other creatures besides zebras feed on grass in the savanna. And other predators hunt zebras besides lions. Can you see how each organism in creation is dependent on other organisms for food?

FIGURE 13.7
Examples of 3 Food Chains

Notice the direction of the arrows in each of the food chains. They are showing the flow of energy as it is transferred from one organism to another. So, when the zebra feeds on the grass, for example, the energy within the grass is transferred *to* the zebra.

Each organism in a food chain represents a **trophic level.** *Troph* means "food," so it is a *feeding* level. The term *trophic level* is how ecologists better describe feeding relationships between organisms. So in our savanna ecosystem example, the grass represents the first trophic level; those are the photosynthesizers. Herbivores like zebras are in the second trophic level, feeding on first-trophic-level organisms. Lions are in the third trophic level.

If we really want to get technical, these chains should be looped, looking more like Figure 13.8. Why is that? Well, it is because of those amazing decomposers. They feed on once-living material so that producers are able

FIGURE 13.8
A More Accurate Food "Chain"

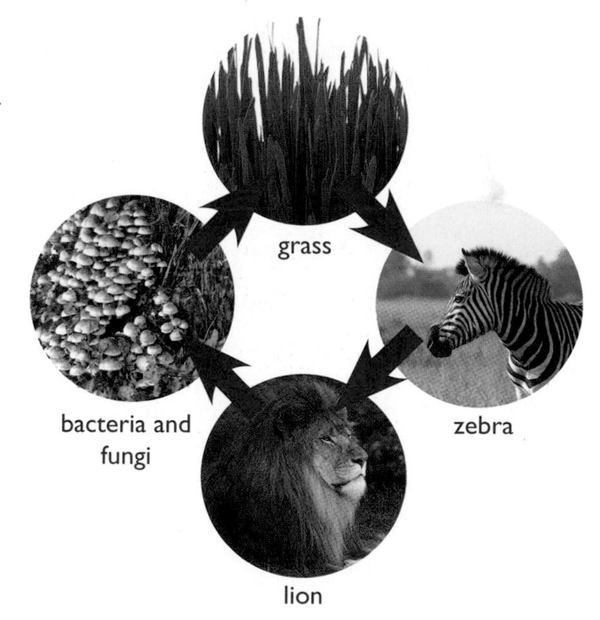

to utilize energy from it. Thus, you see the arrow going from the decomposers back to the grass.

Now I don't want to confuse you, but this is not a complete picture, either. You see, as I mentioned earlier, there are many more organisms that feed on grasses. There are also other organisms that feed on zebras. When we consider that ecosystems can have more than one herbivore species and each herbivore has more than one carnivore species that might eat it, we can see that the food chain should look more like a **food web.**

Food web—A model that shows feeding relationships in an ecosystem

Food webs can include hundreds of species. Figure 13.9 shows one part of a food web of an ocean ecosystem. Let's look at just one food chain within that web. Starting with macroalgae as photosynthesizers in the first trophic level, notice how angelfish are herbivores in the second trophic level. Then small sharks are the carnivores in the third trophic level. Now consider phytoplankton as photosynthesizers in the first trophic level. Corals are herbivores that eat them, so they are in the second trophic level. Parrotfish are carnivores in the third trophic level because they feed on corals. Finally, small sharks are carnivores in the fourth trophic level when they eat parrotfish.

In the first food chain example, I said that sharks are considered to be in the third trophic level. But in the second chain, they are in the fourth level. It all depends on what is eating what. That is why these food webs can be so complicated.

FIGURE 13.9

A Portion of a Food Web in a Coral Reef Ecosystem

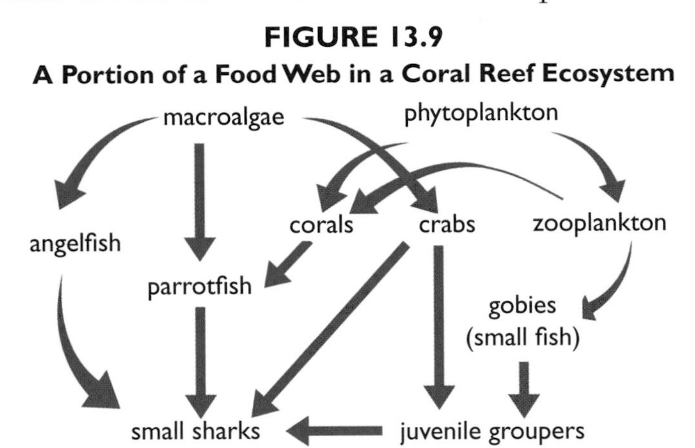

Notice the direction of the arrows in this diagram. Just like the arrows in Figure 13.7, they show the direction of where energy is being transferred. For example, energy goes from the macroalgae to the angelfish when the angelfish feed on the macroalgae.

ON YOUR OWN

Using this food chain, **grass → grasshopper → frog → snake → eagle**, answer the following questions:

13.2 Which organism is the producer and which are the consumers?

13.3 How many trophic levels are there?

13.4 Which organism is the herbivore?

SYMBIOSIS

I've already talked about symbiosis in an earlier module; but because we are discussing how organisms interact with one another in this module, it is worth a deeper discussion. Remember that symbiosis is when 2 species have a living relationship where at least one species benefits. Well, that is a very broad definition. We can actually define 3 different types of symbioses (sim bye oh' seez).

When 2 or more organisms live together, and both get a benefit out of the living situation, that is called **mutualism.** They mutually benefit from being together. The symbiosis examples in Module 12 were examples of mutualism. Both the clownfish and the anemone get a good deal out of living together. Both the cleaner shrimp and the fishes being cleaned also get a benefit from their living relationship, too.

A second type of symbiosis is called **commensalism.** That is when 2 organisms live in a relationship where one benefits while the other is neither harmed nor helped. An example of this relationship is between the cattle egret and cows or other large herbivores. The cattle egret is a type of heron that follows herds around as they move. When the herds move through the grass, they stir up insects that the egret eats. The egret certainly benefits; the herds get no benefit but they aren't harmed, either.

FIGURE 13.10
An Egret Waiting for Insects

The third type of symbiosis is **parasitism.** That is when 2 organisms live in a relationship where one benefits and the other is *harmed*. We call the organism that benefits a **parasite** and the organism that is harmed a **host.** There are thousands of parasitic situations in creation. A common example of this relationship is between fleas and a dog. The fleas are the parasite living off the blood from the host dog. Sometimes a parasitic relationship eventually can kill the host, and other times—as in the case of fleas and a dog—it just makes the host uncomfortable…and itchy!

creation connection

Obligate symbiosis is an extreme type of mutualism where 2 organisms live together and cannot survive without each other. They are so dependent on one another that they not only live better (like a sea anemone and clownfish) but they would die without the other. One example of this is a termite and the bacteria living in its gut. You see, termites feed on wood, but they cannot digest the complex sugar called cellulose that is found in wood. However, many species of microbes live in a termite's gut to help break cellulose down. All of them are necessary to break down this food. These helpful gut species belong to 3 classification groups: bacteria, archaea, and eukarya. So, the gut microbes get protection from the environment as well as a constant supply of food, while the termite gets its food digested. The termites would die without all of these species of organisms. With the proposed slow process of evolution, this living situation is not only difficult to explain, but I would suggest that it is next to impossible. And we see obligate symbioses throughout creation!

ON YOUR OWN

13.5 In your notebook, list the 3 types of symbioses and give an example of each from the information in this section.

ECOLOGICAL CYCLES

Let's shift our discussion from living organisms back to their environments for a bit. Our world is filled with cycles. You already learned about the cyclic nature of organisms and how a food chain actually is more of a cycle when we consider the decomposers. This is a necessary part of life in order to recycle all of Earth's materials. That is a *biotic* cycle. Well, ecologists also study abiotic cycles. In Module 7, you learned that the hydrologic cycle is a constant recycling of water between the Earth and the atmosphere. Actually, to best understand the hydrologic cycle, you must have a basic understanding of geology (groundwater), meteorology (weather), oceanography (ocean currents and temperatures), and even astronomy (solar energy). Atmospheric water condenses into clouds; precipitates onto Earth; collects into lakes, rivers, and oceans; and then evaporates into the atmosphere to start all over again. Depending on the location on Earth, whether it is dry or moist environments, mountainous or flat land, and more, organisms will experience different water conditions that affect how they live in their respective ecosystems.

FIGURE 13.11
Part of the Hydrologic Cycle with Evaporation from the Lake, Condensation as Clouds, and Precipitation on the Mountaintop

Gases that are important to living things are also recycled around the globe as a result of weather and climate. This includes the **carbon cycle** (involving carbon dioxide gas) and the **nitrogen cycle** (involving nitrogen gas) as these elements move around the atmosphere. These materials are continually cycling into organisms' bodies and then back to the environment.

Can you see how abiotic factors play a critical role in what types of biotic factors will be present? A desert, for example, has sand, rocks, little rainfall, and in most cases high temperatures (see the Think About This in this section). These factors determine what kinds of organisms can live in a desert environment. Animals and plants living there need to have physical features that conserve water and withstand high temperatures.

think about this

What is the largest desert on Earth? Most people would say the Sahara in North Africa. But, technically, they would be wrong. That's because the designation of a desert has to do with the amount of precipitation, not temperature. Generally, a desert is defined as an area that receives less than 25 cm (10 in) of precipitation a year. Most of Antarctica receives less than 5 cm (2 in) each year in the form of snow. The existing snow you see on the continent is just blown around during storms; most of it doesn't fall from the sky! Thus, the Antarctic desert is the largest desert on Earth, at about 5.5 million square miles. Therefore, when you think of a common desert animal, you might want to start thinking of a penguin instead of a camel!

ORGANIZATION IN ECOLOGY

In Module 11, I mentioned how there is an organization of living parts within an organism, beginning with a cell, then tissue, then organs, and finally organ systems. Well, Earth is filled with individual organisms that interact with each other and their environment in an organized way.

Ecologists consider the layer of Earth where life exists as the **biosphere.** This region can be divided into the gas-filled atmosphere, the earthen lithosphere, and the liquid hydrosphere. We've already studied several of these *-spheres* in the Earth science modules.

FIGURE 13.12
Ecological Levels

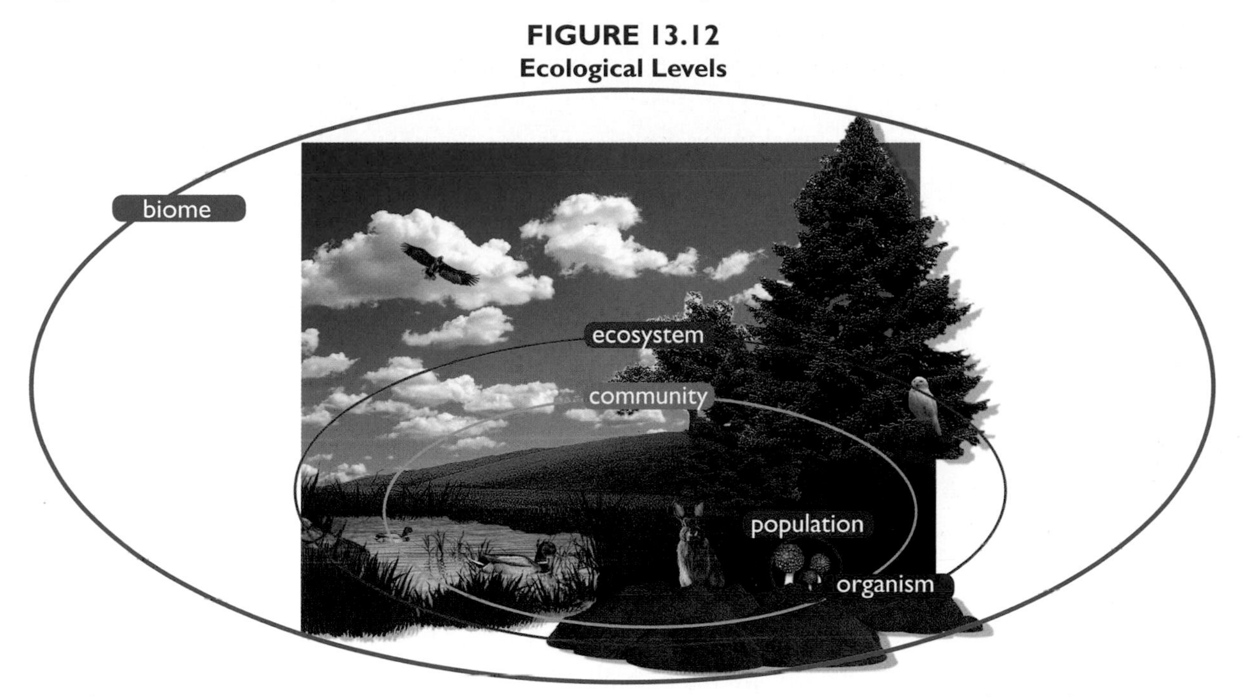

There is another way to divide the biosphere, though. This has to do with categories that consider the major plants and animals that live in an area. Ecologists call these areas **biomes.** Biomes are areas of the world with similar climate, animals and plants. There are terrestrial biomes (land) and aquatic biomes (freshwater and marine).

Each biome has a dominant plant species. Specific **ecosystems** are smaller sections within a biome. Some ecosystems include a forest, a desert, or a lake. Now, within an ecosystem, there will be **communities** made up of all the living organisms that are there. So a lake community, for example, can include reeds, algae, fishes, turtles, mushrooms, and ducks.

We can divide communities into smaller **populations.** A population is all the organisms of one species living within an ecosystem. In our lake community, we could consider all the painted turtles or all the mallard ducks as a population living there. Each population is dependent on other populations for food, oxygen, or even homes.

Within a population, we can go one step further in our organization by identifying a single plant or animal within it. This is an **organism.**

We can sum up these levels of organization with a simple diagram (see Figure 13.12). We begin with a single *organism*—such as a mushroom—living within a *population* of the same species of mushrooms. Many populations live within that *community* (including all life there—the reeds, ducks, rabbits, insects, and bacteria). When we consider all the living things in that community as well as all the nonliving abiotic factors (like the rocks, the air, the water, and the weather), we have an *ecosystem*. There are several ecosystems within a *biome,* which has a major plant species. These biomes make up the entire *biosphere* or the whole area of Earth that contains all its living organisms. The biosphere is, for the most part, self-contained and not really affected by things outside the planet (with the exception of the sun's energy and the sun and Moon's gravitational effects).

EXPLORE MORE

Go to a nearby natural area, like a park or a field. Bring your notebook with you. Grab a seat and observe the area around you for about 15 minutes. Write down the abiotic conditions, such as temperature and amount of water. What is the most common plant life? Do you see any animals? Make a list of all the types of plants and animals you can see. Make an illustration of your view. When you get back home, try to identify the type of ecosystem you were in (forest, lake, mountain, beach, etc.). Then make a circle around the entire list of living organisms you made and mark that as a community. Make a box around one population of organisms you saw (like pine trees or black ants). Finally, make an illustration of a single creature within that population and identify it as an organism.

Ecologists place organisms into these ordered groupings so they can better understand how they live and interact. But the complexity of all these systems is massive. For example, an area on an organism can be an ecosystem. What do I mean? Well, the palm of your hand can be considered an ecosystem because it houses a whole host of bacterial species that interact with each other and with the abiotic features of your skin, its moisture, and even the dirt you might pick up as you touch objects around you.

And think about the abiotic changes these organisms have to endure while living there. When you wash your hands, swim in a chlorinated pool, or even spill salsa while eating a taco, these bacteria have to be tough, don't they?

Well, let's get back to a discussion of biomes. As you can imagine, there are a whole host of biomes on Earth, each identified by its major plant life. Plants are considered instead of animals because animals move around, migrate, and therefore might not live there year-round.

FIGURE 13.13
Ecosystem on a Hand

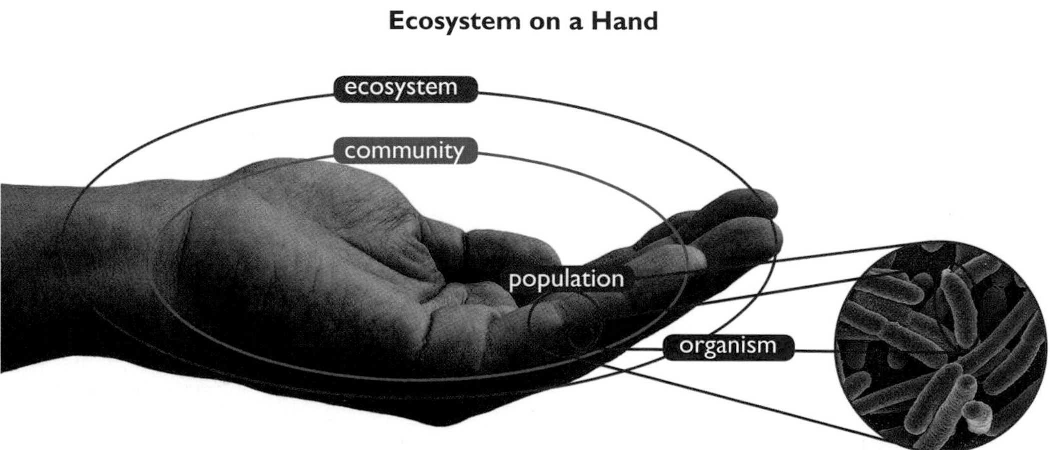

Tundra

The **tundra** biome is one of the coldest and driest biomes on Earth. It is also the largest, covering almost 1/5 of the land on Earth, particularly in the northernmost areas of Europe, Asia and North America. This biome experiences long winters and short summers (often only about 6–8 weeks!).

FIGURE 13.14
A Reindeer on the Tundra in Summer

Tundra literally means "treeless plain," which is a good description. As the name suggests, there are no trees that grow here because the growing season is so short. However, you will find lichens, mosses, grasses, and even small shrubs. In the tundra it is so cold that most of the ground remains frozen year-round. Only about the upper 1–2 ft will thaw during the summer. Because it is permanently frozen, the solid area of soil is called **permafrost**. Large roots and even moisture cannot penetrate into the permafrost, further hindering any chance of large plant growth.

Tundra animals include lemmings, caribou, reindeer, polar bears, seals, and foxes. A large population of insects can survive here as well, particularly in the warmer months. Animals living in the tundra have special adaptations to survive. During the coldest part of winter, some tundra animals will hibernate. That helps them to minimize energy loss by keeping their body processes at a low level. Other animals will migrate, moving away during the harshest season of the year. Many breed and raise their young in the summer.

The tundra can behave as a source of historical information for ecologists. That's because the permafrost can preserve plants and animals in the ice for long amounts of time. This record of the past gives clues to the historical climate in that area. Scientists can compare past climates with the current climate in these areas to see if there have been any major changes.

Tropical Rainforest

Tropical rainforest biomes are generally located near Earth's equator and extend to between the 30°N and 30°S latitudes. They are found in Central and South America, in the western parts of Africa, India, Southeast Asia, and Northeast Australia. Rainforests are...well...rainy. Water that evaporates from the plentiful trees eventually falls as rain. And it often creates rain in other biomes of the world, making rainforests important contributors to our planet's overall weather patterns.

FIGURE 13.15
A Rainforest

The rainforest canopy is so dense that very little sunlight reaches the ground below.

Tropical rainforests are warm and

humid all year long. Some areas can receive up to 1,000 cm (400 in) of rain or more each year.

Plant life in the tropical rainforest includes a large variety of trees. These trees have supportive **buttresses**, which are large branching ridges near their base for support. That is because their roots are often shallow, but the tree needs to grow tall to reach sunlight. Because there is so much water in the air, **epiphytes** are common plants living there. These are plants that live on the surface of other plants, particularly on the trunks and branches so they can gain sun exposure. Orchids and bromeliads are common epiphytes. A notable rainforest feature is the **canopy.** It contains tall trees that spread their branches and leaves out like a large umbrella, shading the forest floor.

Animals of the tropical rainforest represent some of the greatest diversity on the planet. They are uniquely adapted to live in this environment, many living their entire lives in the trees. Mammals, reptiles, birds, insects, and amphibians live in abundance here.

Temperate Grassland

The **temperate grassland** biome gets its name from the major plant life that grows here: grass. Temperate means that these are biomes that do not get *extreme* cold or *extreme* heat, but they will get hot and cold as the seasons change. They contain some of the richest soils in the world, filled with nutrients, so many of these biomes are used for farming. Called the **prairie** in North America, temperate grasslands can be found in the Midwest and Southwest. In Europe and Asia, they are called **steppes** (steps') and are found between Ukraine and Russia. In South America, they are referred to as **pampas** (pahm' pahs) and are primarily located in Argentina and Uruguay. South African temperate grasslands are called **veldts** (velts').

FIGURE 13.16
Bison on the American Prairie

As I just mentioned, the major plants of this biome are grasses. There are very few trees and shrubs. Many animals feed on the grasses, including horses, deer, and bison. These grazers are the dominant vertebrates in the grassland biome. Of course, mice, birds, gophers, and other animals thrive here as well.

Other major biomes of the world include the savanna (tropical grasslands), taiga (tye' guh), which are cold-climate forests; deserts; freshwater ecosystems; and saltwater ecosystems.

ON YOUR OWN

13.6 Figure 13.16 shows a temperate grassland in North America. The group of bison in the photo represents which ecological level: organism, population, community, ecosystem, or biome?

ECOLOGICAL SUCCESSION

Take a look at the landscape in Figure 13.17. It is filled with a complex community of plants and animals living together and interacting with one another. But was it always that way? It takes time for a forest—or any ecosystem—to

FIGURE 13.17
A Forest Ecosystem

grow. Ecologists often study how ecosystems form and develop over time, some beginning from bare rock! By looking at barren locations formed after volcanic eruptions or wildfires, they can see how these sites gradually change as time passes.

When new land forms or when an area is disturbed, a community goes through a period called **ecological succession.** Ecological succession is a series of changes in the species that make up a community as time goes by. Sometimes it happens as a result of volcanic eruption creating lava flow that hardens into new land. Other times a tree will die and fall over, opening up new space for other organisms. Even an overturned rock can create uninhabited space onto which organisms can move in.

A common place where ecological succession happens is on the Big Island of Hawaii. During a volcanic eruption, lava flows into the ocean, forming new rock. Each year, about 32 acres of land are formed this way. What scientists have observed is that first, the mineral-rich lava rock starts to break down and erode a bit due to weather changes, water, and wind. Eventually, there is enough soil for some lichens and plants to take hold. These first organisms are called **pioneer species.** They are the *pioneers* to first establish homes there, and they can do it because they are hardy, able to endure rough abiotic conditions.

FIGURE 13.18
Ferns Growing in a Crevice between Lava Rocks

Pioneer organisms further break down the rock into soil. As they die, their bodies decompose to produce even richer material on which less robust species can colonize. New colonists will grow over and take the place of many of the pioneer organisms. As time goes on, insects, birds, and other organisms will move in. Some come from neighboring environments, and others are brought in via storms, wind, or other forces.

Sometimes, a community is growing well, but there is a disturbance that creates empty space. In a rainforest, for example, an old tree might fall over. The umbrella-like canopy shading the forest floor has an opening now, allowing sunlight to reach it. This new space is not bare rock, so it is a form of ecological succession where the ground has a "head start" in preparation for organisms that move in. Any nearby small trees might experience extra growth as they receive more sunlight than they did before. The race to reach the upper canopy will eventually be won by the tree that has access to the most nutrients and water. If there are no nearby trees, bushes and other smaller plants will grow rapidly. Often-

FIGURE 13.19
A Rare Area Where Sunlight Penetrates the Rainforest

times, the trees already at canopy height will extend their branches wider to capture more sunlight, covering over the newly formed space.

As the plant life regrows in that area, more and more shelter and food become available there. That means animal life will move back in.

It turns out that new land and spaces caused by disturbances are both colonized pretty quickly in nature. Plants and animals are always moving and growing as they attempt to find a good place to settle. But it is not a completely predictable process. It really depends on which organisms arrive first to the scene and are able to establish themselves.

This means that ecological succession is not a predictable path, but is subject to the vast diversity of organisms living in an area. Their complex design often enables them to quickly adapt to new environments so they can adjust and grow well.

think about this

One of the more famous examples of ecological succession involves the relatively new Surtsey Island off the coast of Iceland. On November 14, 1963, explosive volcanic eruptions started emerging from the sea surface. After continued eruptions over 3 years a new island measuring over 500 m long and 45 m high was formed. Soon after the island emerged, insects, seeds, and some plant parts were found washed up on shore, and within 2 years small flowering plants were observed. Eventually, birds, seals, and other animals began to inhabit the island. Ecologists have studied the ecological succession of Surtsey since then and better understand how plants and animals establish themselves in new territory.

FIGURE 13.20
Surtsey Island

MAN AND THE ENVIRONMENT

We cannot study environmental science without discussing the role of man and the environment. You have probably heard people talk about "being green" or "making a small carbon footprint." What do those phrases mean and, indeed, what are our responsibilities regarding the care of the environments around us?

Well, we know that after creation, God gave man dominion over the Earth and every organism in it. Genesis 1:26–28 says,

Then God said, "Let us make man in our image, after our likeness. And let them have dominion over the fish of the sea and over the birds of the heavens and over the livestock and over all the earth and over every creeping thing that creeps on the earth."

So God created man in his own image, in the image of God he created him; male and female he created them.

And God blessed them. And God said to them, "Be fruitful and multiply and fill the earth and subdue it, and have dominion over the fish of the sea and over the birds of the heavens and over every living thing that moves on the earth."

God gave man dominion over all creation and authority to use it. You can see how God created and placed organisms in their proper locations, too—birds in the heavens, fish in the sea, and more. They were designed *for* man.

FIGURE 13.21
Using Trees for Lumber

But does that give us the right to, for example, mow over an entire forest whenever we want? Of course not. That's because we have a responsibility to be good caretakers of what we've been given. It is important that we care for the living organisms of the world along with their environments so that people in the future can use and enjoy them. That is truly the meaning of "being green"—being good stewards of the Earth.

After learning what you have about the organisms of the world, you also should have a greater appreciation of how living creatures can affect one another as well as their environments. So when a population changes, that change affects more than the organisms *within* the population. Understanding how to minimize those effects when we change the environment is critical.

How do scientists know how populations of organisms change? It certainly is difficult to know exactly how many of one species of deer are living in a forest, isn't it? That's because they hide and move around. Without capturing all the deer and counting them, how can ecologists know what is happening to their populations? Well, they do something called mark-and-recapture to get a good estimate. This method involves capturing a sample of individuals from a population, marking them, and then releasing them back into the wild. By doing a second capture, scientists can use those numbers to make a good estimate of the total population in a given area. Perform Experiment 13.2 to understand what I am talking about.

EXPERIMENT 13.2
ESTIMATING POPULATION SIZE

PURPOSE: To better understand how scientists estimate the size of animal populations

MATERIALS:
- A small bag of dry white navy beans (You will need about 1 cup of beans)
- A paper lunch bag
- A dark permanent marker
- A calculator
- Your notebook

QUESTION: How is it possible to get a good estimate of a population in an ecosystem?

HYPOTHESIS: Write how accurate you think your estimate will be when you take 2 sample handfuls of a navy bean population living in a paper bag ecosystem.

PROCEDURE:
1. Without counting the number of beans, dump about 1 cup of them into the paper lunch bag.
2. Reach into the paper bag and pull out a handful of beans. Count them and write that number in your notebook. Designate this number as M for the number you collected on your first "capture."
3. With the permanent marker, place a large dot on each of the beans from your first handful.
4. Return the beans to the bag and shake it up a bit.
5. Now reach into the bag and pull out a second handful of beans. Count them and write that number in your notebook. Designate this number as S for size of the sample of the second capture.
6. In your second capture, you likely collected at least a few beans that were marked from the first capture. They have been caught twice. Count how many were recaptured and designate that number as R for recapture. Place all the beans back in the bag.
7. You can use the 3 numbers you collected to calculate a good population estimate. Using the mathematical formula $N = \frac{M \times S}{R}$

   where M is the total number of beans from the first capture that were marked and released back into the bag; S is the total number of beans in the second capture; and R is the number of sample beans that were recollected in the second capture (the ones that had marks), N will give you an estimated number of the total population. Write your calculated estimate of the total bean population in your notebook.
8. Count the total number of beans in the bag and compare it to your calculated estimate.
9. When you clean up after your experiment, throw away your beans since you have marked them with permanent marker.

CONCLUSION: Write if this method is a fairly accurate way of estimating a population.

Let's go over what happened in the experiment. The white beans represent a population of animals that live within an ecosystem. Because animals move around, fly, or hide, it is often difficult to count all the organisms of a specific species in an area. So you simulated a sampling of a population, the same way that one might use mousetraps in a forest or drop a net to collect fish in a lake. You are collecting only a small part of the total when you grab a handful of beans.

In the first capture, you marked all the individuals you collected, returning them to the environment once you marked and counted them. If the population was not very large, then you would have collected most of the population in that first capture. Thus, you should expect many of the individuals in the second capture to be marked, too. That's because there are not many others around. But if the population was very large, you would have collected only a small part of the total population in that first capture. And it would be likely that very few marked individuals would be recaptured a second time. That is the logic behind the mathematical formula. The larger the recapture number, the smaller the total population is.

In real life, animals are marked in several ways that will not harm them. Birds can have lightweight bands affixed around one leg. Snails might get a spot of waterproof paint on their shells. Butterflies can have labels taped to their wings. After tagging the animals, giving them time to recover and randomly mix with the whole population, the ecologist goes out on a second collecting trip and gathers a second sample of individuals. The size of the entire population can then be estimated from the number of marked individuals recaptured on that second day.

If you want to expand this experiment, try it again with ¾ cup of white beans to see if you get a more accurate result.

FIGURE 13.22
Ibis with an Ankle Tag

Your Worldview

It is clear that we need to be responsible about how we use the Earth. In order to do that, we need to study it and better understand how organisms live and interact with their environment. Why? Let's say a company wanting to start a shrimp business has the right to fish for shrimp along a 10-mi stretch of a certain shoreline, extending out to sea for several hundred miles. Because food shrimp live on the ocean floor, one of the best ways to collect them is to send down a large net that drags across the bottom. As the net is dragged along, the shrimp are collected in it. Now, if the company wanted to maximize how many shrimp it collected, using hundreds of boats to scrape along the ocean floor, can you imagine how that might be difficult for other organisms living there?

First, the ocean floor would be disturbed, churning up the sand into the water. That can clog the filtering organs of creatures that strain plankton out of the water for food. Of course, there is no way to collect only shrimp in those nets. So anything in the path of the nets will also get caught. If too many nets are dragged over too much area, there might not be any shrimp left to reproduce in order to replace the shrimp population for the future. And if the population of shrimp decreases too much, there might not be enough shrimp for the animals that feed on them. That means *their* populations might decrease, too.

FIGURE 13.23
A Shrimp Boat

On the other hand, shrimp are a healthful source of protein for people, playing a large role in the nutrition of many cultures. Additionally, many jobs are made available by this endeavor, from shipmakers and fishermen to food distributors and grocery store owners. How do we make sure we are not creating permanent damage to our world while still providing needed resources and jobs for people?

Well, that is a difficult subject. Discussions about the impact of humans on the environment can often be challenging. In our shrimp example, the impact on the environment can be minimized by fishing in certain areas at a time. Some fisheries rotate where they fish so the population in an area has time to recover. Some nets have escape hatches to allow larger organisms to escape. This way, industries can continue to operate and collect food sources while minimizing their impact on the environment.

Most people have very strong opinions regarding things like overfishing, conservation, pollution, and the health of our planet. But what often happens is that these discussions do not get to the core reasons people feel the way they do. You see, everyone has a **worldview**. A worldview is the perspective from which you live and see the world around you. It is what you believe about God and people as well as what is truth, what is right, and what is wrong. This affects how you live, what you believe, and the choices you make. In discussions about environments, you need to understand the worldview from which a person is speaking or writing.

A biblical worldview starts with the beginning of creation, when God made the creatures of the Earth and gave man dominion over them (Genesis 1:28). They were created for us and our use. But that doesn't mean people should totally destroy any and every creature in their path. Indeed, *because* of this authority over the creatures of the Earth, we have a responsibility to be good stewards of that which is given to us and future generations. God wants us to take care of His creation. The difficulty comes when some people want to give animals a higher status than that of people. They are more concerned with the welfare of certain creatures than that of the people around them. But this type of thinking can lead to situations where some groups of people go hungry because they are not allowed to hunt the animals they have used as a food supply for generations, simply because someone in another part of the world is concerned that the population of animals might be decreasing.

What do we do then? Well, this is why it is important to try to understand how our world works. The more we learn about how living organisms interact with their environment, the better we can make smart decisions. When we see areas of the world experiencing distress due to man's activities, we need to look for ways to prevent or lessen it. That way we can wisely use the gifts given to us at the beginning of time. However, we know that people are the focal point of God's creation and are very important in God's eyes. Thus, we must not make environmental decisions at the expense of the needs of people.

This means, for example, that we need to be alert to minimize non-natural materials that make their way into the environments of the world. Garbage, plastics, motor oils, engine exhaust, and pesticides can cause lots of problems if too much enters natural environments. Reducing excessive exhausts and pollutants is a form of reducing our carbon footprint. That's because many of these gases and airborne materials include extra carbon that could harm living things. However, many of these products help to keep people alive. Think about a hospital. Many of the life-saving devices there are made of plastics and other materials that don't easily decompose. Yet without them, people could suffer and die. Therefore, it is crucial for scientists to work to find ways to minimize pollution while finding ways to allow man to continue the activities of life.

FIGURE 13.24
Non-natural Materials in an Environment

We must conserve the resources of our planet, given to us at the beginning of creation. **Conservation** is the preservation, care and management of natural resources. It requires that we carefully balance the needs of humans while preserving the environment. And that is being good stewards of what we are given!

ON YOUR OWN

13.7 Reread the information about the island of Surtsey in the Think About This in this section. The island is about 55 years old and has a large number of ecosystems, filled with organisms. How do you think this relatively rapid rate of populations establishing themselves (as well as the rapid rate of land formation!) can support your worldview about how the Earth was established?

13.8 Why is it difficult to make an estimate of a population of animals in an ecosystem?

SUMMING UP

The subject of environmental science and ecology is truly a fascinating one. It is an area of study that considers how organisms interact with each other and their environments, helping us to see yet again how organisms are dependent on each other and have a greater complexity of systems that extends beyond their cells, their bodies, and even their species.

The requirements for each of many ecosystems as well as their dependence on each other helps us to see that they could not have developed independently of one another. And that points us to an omniscient Creator who spoke them into being and set them up in their motions.

ANSWERS TO THE "ON YOUR OWN" QUESTIONS

13.1 Abiotic factors can include the cold temperature, the amount of snowfall, or even the lack of sunlight. Biotic factors can include a lack of leaves for food or less foliage to hide behind. Of course, you could come up with something else, too.

13.2 Grass is the producer and the consumers are the grasshopper, frog, snake, and eagle. Remember, producers make their own food, and grass is the only photosynthesizer in this chain.

13.3 Because each organism in a food chain represents a trophic level, there are 5 trophic levels in this chain.

13.4 The herbivore is the organism that feeds on the photosynthesizer. So the grasshopper is the herbivore.

13.5 Mutualism is when 2 or more organisms live in a relationship and both benefit. An example is a clownfish and a sea anemone. Commensalism is when 2 organisms live in a relationship and one benefits while the other is neither harmed nor helped. An example is a cattle egret and livestock. Parasitism is when 2 organisms live in a relationship and one benefits while the other is harmed. An example is a dog and fleas.

13.6 A group of organisms of the same species is a population, so the group of bison in the photo represents a population of bison.

13.7 The island of Surtsey is a visible example that it does not take millions of years for land to form. If it only took 3 years to form Surtsey, larger land formations could possibly form quickly, too. Additionally, scientists have observed the rapid speed at which organisms can inhabit a bare rock location, turning it into a new ecosystem. That means that established environments we see today may not be as old as some might suggest. Of course, only God was present at the beginning of time. So, we can only use our observations in science to form our theories, and that is the beauty of science. Scientists from around the world gather to discuss all possibilities.

13.8 Because animals move around, fly, or hide, it is often difficult to count all the organisms of a specific species in an area.

STUDY GUIDE FOR MODULE 13

1. Match the following words with their definitions.

a. Niche	A system made up of all living organisms interacting with one another and their environment
b. Ecosystem	
c. Producer	An organism that obtains its food by feeding on other organisms or organic matter
d. Consumer	
e. Food web	A model that shows feeding relationships in an ecosystem
	An organism's function in its habitat, including its relationship with other organisms
	An organism that makes its own food using energy from the sun or other sources

2. Which of the following is a biotic factor in an ecosystem?
   a. rainfall b. soil type c. bright sunlight d. bacteria

3. Which of the following is NOT a type of consumer?
   a. herbivore b. calcivore c. carnivore d. omnivore

4–6. Answer the following questions using this food chain:
algae → krill → cod → leopard seal → orca

4. Which organism is the producer and which are the consumers?

5. How many trophic levels are there?

6. Which organism is the herbivore?

7. Butterflies and flowering plants exist in a type of symbiosis where adult butterflies feed on the nectar provided by the flowers. While they get their food, the flower's pollen clings to their body and is transferred to other flowers as the butterflies move around. What type of symbiosis is this?
   a. mutualism b. commensalism c. parasitism

8. Using Figure 13.12, name at least 2 other possible populations living within this lake community.

9. Match the following biomes with their description:

Tundra	warm, rainy forests
Tropical rainforest	grassy land with no extreme heat or cold
Temperate grassland	treeless plain with cold and dry climate

10. Which of the following is not a situation where ecological succession might take place?
    a. a tree falls in a rainforest
    b. a wildfire spreads through a grassland
    c. a monkey turns over a rock
    d. a tree drops pinecones

11. Why is the mark-and-recapture technique used to get an estimate of an animal population—in other words, why can't environmental scientists just count all the animals there?

SCIENCE AND CREATION

In Module 1, we took a tour through the history of science and looked at the accomplishments of many scientists. You might remember that many of them pursued science because they desired to better know God and His attributes. What do I mean by that? Well, let's talk about the famous painter Pablo Picasso.

Why would we look at a painter? Well, he is an artist who has a unique style in his creations. Take a look at Figure 14.1, for example. Notice how this painting by Picasso is of people playing musical instruments. You might be able to discern a guitar and a clarinet, along with some sheet music, too. But do these items look realistic? No. That's because Picasso is known for using **cubism** as a style of painting. It is one of his major signature styles. So when we see a famous painting that looks like it is in the cubism style, Picasso's name should come to mind as the likely creator. That's because we see his style—his handprint—on the creation.

FIGURE 14.1
Painting on Display at the Pablo Picasso Museum

Well, it is the same thing with the creation of the universe and everything in it. By studying the world around us, we are able to see the creative handprints of God.

Quaestio

I am so excited to share this final module with you! After a thorough exploration of general science, you should have a greater appreciation for the ways we can study the world around us. You also have a better understanding about *why* we should do that. This module is one of 2 "bookends." The first module introduced many scientists in history who studied the world around them in order to learn more about the God who created it. This module will expose you to present-day scientists from many scientific fields who are doing the same!

Throughout this course, you have been exposed to many branches of science, and in each module I have endeavored to show you how we can see God's handiwork in each branch. To conclude this course, we get the special treat of hearing from modern scientists who are working in various scientific fields. Indeed, there are many Christians in these fields who believe that their career in science helps them better understand creation. They will share with you from their unique scientific perspectives how they agree with the Psalmist who wrote "The heavens declare the glory of God, and the sky above proclaims his handiwork" (Psalm 19:1).

There will be no exam for this module. Instead, we will do a fun, step-by-step science activity. For the grand finale of the course, you will be creating a **Rube Goldberg machine.** A Rube Goldberg machine is an apparatus or series of devices that use a chain reaction to accomplish a very simple task in a complicated way. Named for Reuben Lucius Goldberg, these inventions were Rube's way of seeing the fun side of everyday situations. He created cartoon illustrations of complex machines that used maximum effort to accomplish minimal results.

FIGURE 14.2
A Rube Goldberg Machine Designed to Turn on a Light Bulb for a NASA Challenge

Now, that might seem a little ridiculous, but from a scientific viewpoint, creating a Rube Goldberg machine helps you to better understand the process of cause and effect, to think in a 3D environment, and to understand how to use simple machines and other basic scientific principles to coordinate together in order to accomplish a task. Plus, it will be fun! The simple task you will complete in our Rube Goldberg machine is the addition of sprinkles to a cupcake.

NOTE TO PARENTS: One section of the setup involves placing a blow dryer on its side next to a shallow dish of water (see Setup 5). Please observe your student carefully to make sure these 2 items do not touch. If you would rather they not use the blow dryer near the tray, you can start the Rube Goldberg machine with the boat in the tray and blow on the sail or manually push the boat to the other end.

RUBE GOLDBERG MACHINE EXPERIMENT SETUP 1

MATERIALS:

- An iced cupcake on a small plate
- Sprinkles
- A large trifold cardboard presentation display board measuring 36" × 48" when open
- A funnel
- Strong packing tape or masking tape
- A 12" × 2" strip of stiff cardboard
- A small paper or plastic cup
- Cellophane tape
- A hole punch (You can use an X-ACTO knife, but be VERY careful!)
- An 18" length of string
- A pencil
- An X-ACTO craft knife

FIGURE 14.3
Rube Goldberg Experiment Setup 1

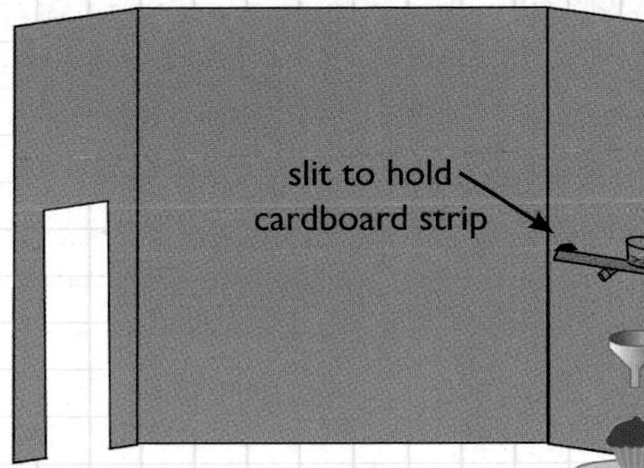

PROCEDURE: (Please refer to the diagram to help you with setup.)

1. You will begin the process of building your machine by working backward from the end task toward the beginning. Stand the cardboard presentation board so that it will not tip over. You might want to set it up against a door or wall and secure it with masking tape. (Check with your parents first so that you do not damage the finish on the wall or door). You could also tape a yardstick across the top so that the flaps don't move. Make sure you have lots of space available to the left of the board because you will be setting up a table and other materials in future construction of your machine.
2. WITH YOUR PARENTS' HELP, use the X-ACTO knife to carefully cut a window out of the left flap of the presentation board like you see in Figure 14.3. The window height needs to be approximately half the height of the board.
3. Place the cupcake on the floor below the lower, right corner of the board.
4. Orient the funnel so that it is directly above the cupcake and the lower end of the funnel is about 6 inches above the top of the frosting. If your funnel has a handle, carefully punch a slit in the cardboard so that the handle can stick through it. Then secure it with tape. If it has no handle, use lots of tape to hold it in place. Refer to Figure 14.3 for reference.
5. Now securely tape the small cup to one side of the cardboard strip. Set it aside for a moment.
6. You will be making a lever with the cardboard strip, cup, and a pencil. The pencil will be the fulcrum, so you first need to hold the strip against the display board so that the cup end is a few inches above the opening of the funnel. Using the pencil, make a mark on the display board where the center of the strip is.
7. With the knife, carefully poke a hole through the display board on the pencil mark so that the pencil will just barely fit through it. Stick the pencil through the hole so that it is poking about 3 inches out of the front side of the board and secure it with tape.

8. Now holding the lever so that it is horizontal, make a mark on the board just above the left side and use the knife to cut a small slit about a half inch wide into the board (see diagram).
9. Cut a small piece of cardboard that is a half inch wide by an inch long. This will be stuck in the slit on the board to hold the lever level.

Between each section of your Rube Goldberg setup, you have the opportunity to read the personal stories of modern scientists who are working in many of the scientific fields you studied this year. Each one sees God's creative fingerprints in Creation!

MODULES 1–4: The History of Science—Search for the Truth; Scientific Inquiry and The Scientific Method; Documenting and Interpreting Experimental Results; and Scientific Analysis and History

Rachael Yunis, MS, MA, Director of Apologia Science

When I was a little girl, I would pull a stepstool up to our kitchen sink and imagine that I was a scientist. My mom would set aside resources that she thought I would enjoy. One of my favorites was the egg. Did you know that there is a thin, skin-like membrane that you can detach from the inner eggshell? It's true, and I was completely consumed by what most parents would have written off as silly childhood play.

Fast-forward a decade and a half, and I became a graduate student studying eggshell membranes. I even went on to have a successful 10-year career in a molecular genetic research lab working with human placenta—a product of the fertilized human egg. And guess what I did! I patiently separated the thin, distinct layers of the placenta so that I could isolate the proteins in each layer.

As a student, it's easy to believe that science is only a compilation of rigid facts whose details we memorize. But you need to remember is that a heartfelt curiosity feels really good. That curiosity is what makes scientists good at what they do. Curiosity, observation, and questioning are not only enjoyable, but also really important in science. Curiosity that makes you look closely at something that has piqued your interest. That interest and time spent observing something leads you to ask questions, and questions lead to learning and gathering information about your world.

FIGURE 14.4
Student Graphing Data

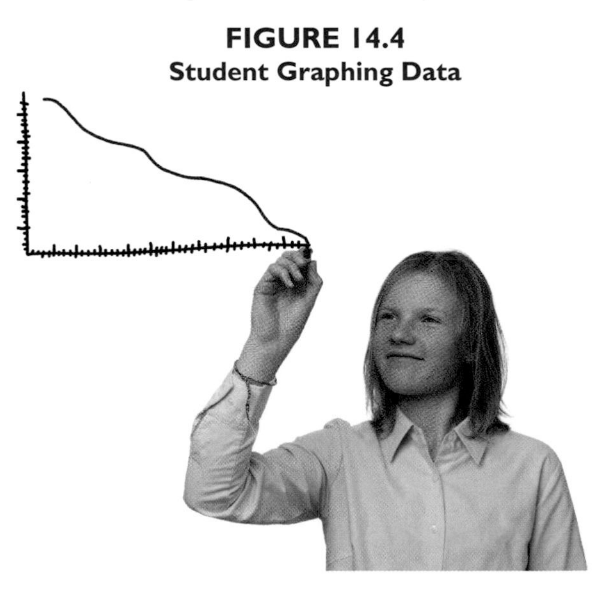

A secular science textbook would have you stop there. However, as a Christian I believe that the scientific method is a process that helps us discover what we, as humans, do not yet know about the structure of life and a universe that already exists. As we develop scientific knowledge, we grow in our knowledge of God.

"For since the creation of the world, God's invisible qualities, his eternal power and divine nature, have been clearly seen, being understood from what has been made, so that people are without excuse" (Romans 1:20).

As the science director for Apologia, I was once asked what I thought every student should be required to know. After contemplating the deepest aspects of the question, I responded that, "Students should intimately know their Creator, be able to recognize their Creator's signature throughout all creation, and earnestly seek to comprehend the mysteries of the created." As you continue your scientific studies, you will be in my prayers. Never forget that science is a process of discovery and even creation, but it is not Creation itself. Do not be afraid to hold strong to the Truth as you further your studies. The Truth will give meaning to your discoveries and help you recognize your unique place in our understandable universe.

MODULE 5: Earth Science—Astronomy

Damian Ludwiczak, Chief—Mechanisms and Tribology Branch at NASA Glenn Research Center

Hi! My name is Damian Ludwiczak and I am an aerospace engineer who has worked for the National Aeronautics and Space Administration (NASA) for 31 years. Throughout my professional career, as well as my school years, I have been fascinated by the higher intelligence that has created our world as well as the elegant universe we live in. Because of my Christian belief, I firmly believe that God is this higher intelligence.

I am disappointed that God is often left out of scientific discussions when we are trying to understand the workings of our world. I am constantly reminded that when scientists and engineers try to solve a problem or develop a new technology, we just need to look around to see how God has already solved it to get our answers. For example, humans wanted to fly above the Earth for thousands of years. The solution to designing a flying vehicle was solved by the Wright brothers when they realized that God had already solved that problem, as was evident by birds. They studied birds and learned how their wings created lift and how they were able to control their flight through the skies. By copying what God had already solved, they were able to develop the airplane.

FIGURE 14.5
Oceanside Observatory

I am also amazed by the intelligence of living creatures. Where did this come from? Our Creator, of course! Today we have created incredible machines and computers, and we are trying to develop artificial intelligence to control them, but we are still not there. We think we are so smart, but we are struggling to create autonomous vehicles that can think and make decisions on their own. Now, think of the ability and intelligence of something "as simple" as a housefly or honey bee. Do you ever think of the incredible intelligence given to these creatures as well as larger animals and mammals? There are no computer programs given to these creatures, yet they think and know how to function. It is just proof that we, at best, can only try to copy what God has already created. And we are not even close.

FIGURE 14.6
Complexity in a Honey Bee

A final example that God is the ultimate scientist comes from the subject of genetics. All living creatures have an embedded intelligence that controls not only how they are created, but how this design is passed down from generation to generation. Two of my favorite and convincing proofs of an intelligent and loving God come from simple examples. The first one I always think about is that if you were to put all the chemicals and equipment in a room and let it sit there for millions of years, something as simple as a blade of grass will not result from this, let alone an animal or human. The second example is that, given the same chemicals and equipment in a room if we put all of our most intelligent scientists in that same room, they would not be able to create a simple blade of grass starting from just these basic chemicals. That, to me, is proof that God has created all of what we know. We need to embrace what God has done when we try to understand subjects such as science, biology, engineering, and astronomy.

So, this textbook has gifted you with scientific knowledge. But remember, this knowledge is based upon how current scientists and engineers understand how things work. This knowledge is our way, as humans, of understanding what God has already accomplished. But your job is now just beginning. What are you going to do with this knowledge? Can you improve upon it? How will you use what you already know and observe to honor God and His wonderful creations?

My advice and wisdom to pass along to you is that as you get older, never separate God from your understanding of life and science. The solutions to your problems have already been solved.

RUBE GOLDBERG MACHINE EXPERIMENT SETUP 2

MATERIALS:

- Setup from Experiment Setup 1
- A stack of books about 8" high
- A few pencils
- Kite string
- A roll of masking tape (NOTE: You will be needing a second roll for the rest of the setup in this module.)
- A second roll of masking tape
- 5–6 dominoes

FIGURE 14.7
Rube Goldberg Experiment Setup 2

PROCEDURE: (Please refer to Figure 14.7 to help you with setup.)

1. Set an 8-inch-high stack of books near the right side of the presentation board. Make sure the top book is a hardcover book and orient it so that the spine is on the right. Place a few pencils under the top book cover so that it is tilted slightly.
2. Cut a length of kite string that is a few inches longer than the distance from the top of your book stack to the slit in the presentation board.
3. Tie the string around a domino and use a piece of masking tape to secure it. Tie the other end of the string around the small piece of cardboard from Experiment Setup 1 and secure it with tape. For now, lay the domino down on top of the books. You will stand it up later.
4. Cut a length of kite string that is a few inches longer than the distance from the bottom of the book stack to the top, left side. Wrap some masking tape around one end of this string and tie the other end to a domino, securing it with tape.
5. Stand the domino next to the book stack on the left side.
6. Take a roll of masking tape and set it on the left side of the book stack. Hold it there with one hand while you place the tape-wrapped end of the string on the top of the book stack so that it keeps the masking tape roll from rolling down the book cover.
7. Carefully stand the domino from step 3 on top of the book stack on the right side, orienting it so that the tape roll will bump into it once it is in motion. Stick the small cardboard piece from the other end of the string into the slit in the presentation board so that it keeps the lever from tilting. Set up the lever by placing the cardboard strip on the pencil fulcrum and secure it by placing a piece of tape on the pencil and the strip.
8. Fill the cup on the right side of the lever with sprinkles.
9. Set up 3–5 more dominoes to the left of the string-wrapped domino on the left of the book stack as in Figure 14.7.

MODULE 6: Earth Science—Geology and Paleontology
Dr. Tom Burbey, Professor of Hydrogeology in the Department of Geosciences, Virginia Tech

As a professor of hydrogeology in the Department of Geosciences at Virginia Tech for the past 22 years, I perform research in the area of groundwater hydrology and aquifer mechanics and teach various undergraduate and graduate courses. Prior to Virginia Tech, I was a hydrologist with the U.S. Geological Survey for 12 years. I have also been a program director for the Hydrology Program at the National Science Foundation.

I became a Christian as a teenager but for many years didn't hold a strong viewpoint regarding the age of the Earth as I was working my way through graduate school. Not really pondering how my scientific worldview fit into God's Word, which I knew to be true, I was challenged when teaching oceanography as a young faculty member as I became aware of many disturbing unanswered questions that the textbooks ignored or dismissed. Also, I became increasingly skeptical about the highly debatable and simplified concepts surrounding plate tectonics that could not explain many of the observations we see on Earth today. As I prayed for answers, God first showed me some scriptures that convinced me that the Earth had to be very young. Then God sovereignly led me to other creation scientists who have spent their lives developing alternative theories that are scientifically sound and that more readily explain many of the challenging questions regarding Earth's history that secular geologists cannot adequately answer.

I believe it is imperative that students today are taught critical thinking as well as the value of genuine hypothesis testing. Realizing that many of today's beliefs about geologic history stem more from a secular worldview than from sound scientific testing, I have witnessed many young Christian students come into the university only to be worn down by old-Earth evolutionary rhetoric they get bombarded with every day in the classroom. Over the course of their academic careers, many of these students ultimately abandon their faith before they graduate from college as the ongoing pressures of an opposing worldview leave many questioning both the Bible and their faith in God. It's my passion to teach and challenge young students desiring to pursue the Earth and biological sciences to become well prepared and equipped with the truth of God's Word with what they can expect as they further their education. They need to know that many of the ideas being taught are not facts as they are often presented, but rather are often tenuous theories based on few observations—and that alternative explanations for the observations can be found in young-Earth, biblically based ideas such as those presented in this book.

FIGURE 14.8
Eroded Sandstone Canyon

MODULE 7: Earth Science—Meteorology and Oceanography
Dr. Robert Carter, Staff Scientist and Researcher, Creation Ministries International

I have always loved science, but for many years there was a contradiction between what I thought about science and what I thought about the Bible. I did not know anyone who actually believed the Bible, and everybody I knew accepted evolution. This was especially true once I got to college. Those professors hit hard with their questions! But I eventually met some people who did not accept evolution. I was stunned. I thought they were crazy. But they encouraged me to rethink what I believed was true. Slowly, with lots of heart-wrenching struggle, I eventually bowed to my Creator and started to believe in His Word, the Bible. I know that many Christians are comfortable believing in evolution and Jesus at the same time, but I could not do that. I wanted a belief that was self-consistent and that did not have a giant contradiction right in the middle of it. The Bible clearly teaches that the Earth is young and that we did not evolve from apes.

Years later, I am amazed that I get to work for Creation Ministries International. It is a major Christian apologetics ministry, and the people who started it had a profound influence on my heart and mind in my early Christian walk. I now get to do for others what they did for me. The significance of how important this subject was to me helps me to relate to others who may be struggling themselves. I also love to study God's world and His Word. These are a never-ending source of wonder and enjoyment.

RUBE GOLDBERG MACHINE EXPERIMENT SETUP 3

MATERIALS:

- Setup from Experiment Setup 1–2
- 1 large hardcover book that is not very thick
- 1 small book
- A toy car (For best results, use a car that is somewhat heavy and a bit larger than a Matchbox-sized car.)
- Kite string
- A tennis ball
- Masking tape
- An empty paper towel roll
- Books
- An empty 2-liter bottle
- A 9″-diameter balloon
- Baking soda
- A liquid measuring cup
- Vinegar
- A butter knife
- A stiff ruler

FIGURE 14.9
Rube Goldberg Experiment Setup 3

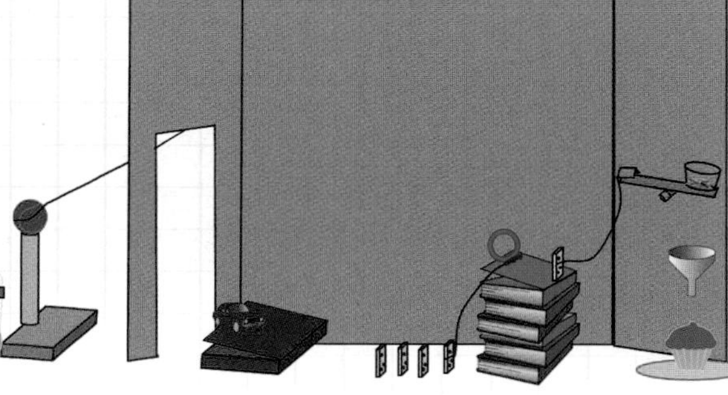

PROCEDURE: (Please refer to Figure 14.9 to help you with setup.)

1. Place the large book so that its spine is on the right side (facing the cupcake) just to the left of the domino run from Experiment Setup 2. [NOTE: You might want to move these dominoes away from the setup for a bit until you have all the other pieces of your machine in place. That way, if you accidentally bump into anything during setup, you won't set off the whole machine!] Place the small book under the large book's cover so that it tilts upward a bit. (See orange book in the diagram.)
2. Place the toy car on the left side of the book cover so that its rear wheels are off the edge.
3. Cut a long piece of kite string. Tie one end around the tennis ball and secure it well with masking tape.
4. Holding the other end of the kite string, use masking tape to hang the ball from the top of the opening you cut on the left side of the presentation board. Make sure that the ball will hit the back of the toy car when it swings in the window.
5. Fill the 2-liter bottle with 2 cups of vinegar. Using the butter knife, fill the balloon with as much baking soda as you can. Do this over a sink or bowl because it can be a bit messy. Carefully place the balloon over the opening of the bottle, but DO NOT lift up the balloon! You want the baking soda to remain in the balloon.
6. Using masking tape, affix the ruler to the left side of the 2-liter bottle so that much of the ruler is sticking up above the top of the bottle. This is so that once the balloon fills with gas, it will bump away from the ruler and move toward the tennis ball to knock it off its stand.
7. Now carefully place 1 or 2 books to the right of the 2-liter bottle as in the diagram, and stand the paper towel roll on the very edge of the books. Set the tennis ball on top of the paper towel roll. You want the ball to be as close as possible to where the balloon will be once it fills with gas. You also want to make sure the string tied to the tennis ball is straight so when the ball falls, it will swing properly.

MODULE 8: General Chemistry

Dr. Chad Snyder, Department of Science and Mathematics Chair/Associate Professor of Chemistry, Grace College and Theological Seminary

I often get the question, "How can you reconcile your Christian faith and science?" Since becoming a Christian I've seen no real struggle with reconciling our God and His Word (the Bible) with what I've learned from science. If anything, my continued study and education of science has only made me more convinced and appreciative of the realty of our Creator God.

Secular science often reminds us this universe is incredibly chaotic and that randomness plays a central role of where we're at today in terms of life and what knowledge we can gather from it. From my Christian worldview, I can affirm why a secular scientist believes this universe is so chaotic. For instance, the secular scientist and I will support the second law of thermodynamics. This law states that the entropy (i.e., chaos, if you will) of an isolated system will not decrease. In other words, the entropy of the universe is increasing, becoming more chaotic. Scientific evidence supports this but also my faith does as well. The apostle Paul wrote the following to the Romans: "We know that the whole creation has been groaning as in the pains of childbirth right up to the present time" (Romans 8:22).

FIGURE 14.10
Chemical Reactions in a Lab

As a Christian I believe the introduction of sin heralded the increase of entropy on the universe, which will continue until the day our Lord makes creation anew. As a result, the second law of thermodynamics actually supports my faith.

There are many other examples in chemistry and physics that point to a Creator. Several examples even seem to support Scripture, which is amazing each time I make those connections to my pre-professional (pre-med, pre-dental, pre-vet, etc.) students in college. However, there's just not enough space allotted to go into each one. The point is this: science and our faith are not exclusive entities. Science's jurisdiction is over the physical portion of God's good creation. As scientists, we give glory to God when we make those discoveries. For those scientists like Isaac Newton, Robert Boyle, Blaise Pascal, and others, even more glory is given to God as they recognized God's unchanging nature within the discoveries each of them made.

MODULE 9: General Physics

Dr. Bob Davis, Professor of Physics, Taylor University

To me, being a Christian and a scientist have developed "hand in hand." I've never tried to separate those aspects of my life. Some of my earliest memories in grade school involve going to Sunday school and church with my family, being water baptized at a young age, learning as many constellations as I could, and wanting a telescope for a Christmas present. I didn't see those 2 features of my life as contradictory, and I still don't. I have greatly enjoyed my life as a Christian, including being a worship leader for many years, being an elder in a vibrant church, and even being a lay pastor in a house church that included many college students from the university where I teach. And I have greatly enjoyed my life as a science teacher, studying physics all the way through a Ph.D. degree (in acoustical physics, not astronomy as I had originally hoped), teaching high school mathematics and science, and now teaching physics at the university level. Every

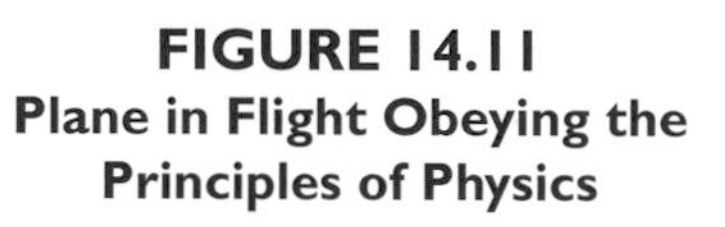

FIGURE 14.11
Plane in Flight Obeying the Principles of Physics

year with a new group of physics students, I try to encourage them to think about the orderliness of the universe, and the beauty of the mathematics that describe it. And then I encourage them to think about how such an orderly universe came to be, and how we have come to be able to study it. My favorite parts of physics are acoustics and electromagnetism. In particular, I continue to be amazed at how our ear physiology and brain can take a complicated sound wave pattern and pick it apart into the many instruments that we might hear playing some orchestral piece, and that we can do the same thing with mathematics. And I am fascinated by the elegance and almost universal applicability of Maxwell's equations, describing light (and many other kinds of electromagnetic waves) in such detail.

RUBE GOLDBERG MACHINE EXPERIMENT SETUP 4

MATERIALS:

- Setup from Experiment Setup 1–3
- A long table
- A stiff ruler
- Dominoes
- Masking tape
- A thin, hardcover book
- A metal or glass 9″ x 13″ baking dish
- Water
- Aluminum foil
- 2 short wood skewers
- Cellophane tape
- A scrap of cardboard
- 2 long strips of cardboard that are the length of the baking dish
- A sheet of paper
- Scissors

FIGURE 14.12
Rube Goldberg Experiment Setup 4

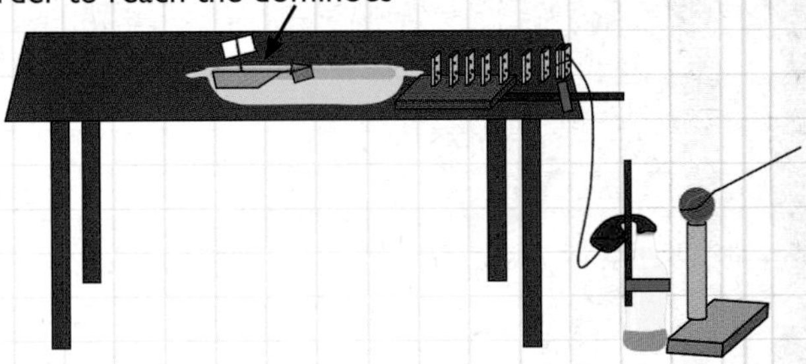

PROCEDURE: (Please refer to the Figure 14.12 to help you with setup.)

1. Orient the table so that the short end is right over the 2-liter bottle from Experiment Setup 3.
2. Take 2 dominoes and tape them together with masking tape. Tie a long piece of string to the dominoes and secure it with more tape. The string should be a bit shorter than the distance from the table top to the floor.
3. VERY CAREFULLY, securely tape the other end of the string to the tip of the balloon that is on the 2-liter bottle, making sure to keep the baking soda from spilling into the bottle. Set the double domino on the floor for now.
4. Set up the ruler so that at least 6 inches is sticking off the end of the table over the balloon and bottle. Secure it with tape and place a book on top of the other end of the ruler.
5. Place the short end of the baking dish snugly to left of the book on the table. Fill the dish with water to a depth of about 1 inch.

6. Use the aluminum foil to fashion a boat. Take a long sheet of foil and fold it in half to make it thicker. Now fold up the 4 sides. Pinch 2 of the corners so that they make a pointy bow of the boat. Cut the paper into a rectangle-shaped sail. Use cellophane tape to tape a skewer to the center of the paper sail. Now use masking tape to affix your sail to the center of your boat. You can pinch the aluminum on the boat's bottom inward to help hold the sail in place.
7. Affix the other skewer to the pointed end (the front) of the boat so that it sticks out like a lance. You can pinch the foil around it to hold it in place, or you can use masking tape.
8. Take the cardboard scrap and cut it into a rectangle, about 1"x 4." Fold it in half and tape it to the lance of your boat so it will behave like a battering ram.
9. Orient the boat facing to your right, and place it on the left side of the pan, floating in the water.
10. Place the 2 long strips of cardboard in the water along both sides of the boat so that it creates a narrow channel for the boat to travel the length of the pan.
11. Line up dominoes starting from the right of the baking pan and continue them to the right side of the table. The last domino should be the double domino that is attached to the balloon. Make sure the string is oriented so that when the double domino falls off the table, the string has to travel over the extended part of the ruler. That will make the other end of the string pull upward on the balloon to allow the baking soda to fall into the bottle. [NOTE: You might want to remove some of the middle dominoes for now until the setup is complete. That way if you accidentally bump anything, the whole setup does not go off! You also might want to lay the double domino down so it doesn't accidentally fall.]

MODULE 10: Life Science
Dr. Marci-Anne Hanks, EdD, MS, BS

When I attended public universities to earn my bachelor's degree in Biological Sciences and my master's degree in Biochemistry, I learned all about evolution. I was never comfortable with evolution and did not enjoy learning about it. Many of my professors taught evolution as fact, even though evolution has no observational evidence. There are no transitional forms in the fossil record and we do not see organisms change into different kinds. Evolutionists claim that fossils and rocks are millions of years old, but their dating systems are inaccurate. I've read so many articles that stated different radiometric dating methods gave very different ages for the same rock! Many of the given ages differed by hundreds of millions of years! Evolutionists want us to believe that it takes millions of years for canyons to form, for sediments to be deposited, and for fossils to form, yet we do not observe millions of years happening. Instead, what we have seen are canyons that formed in a day and layers and layers of rock that were deposited very quickly

FIGURE 14.13
A Single-celled *Paramecium*

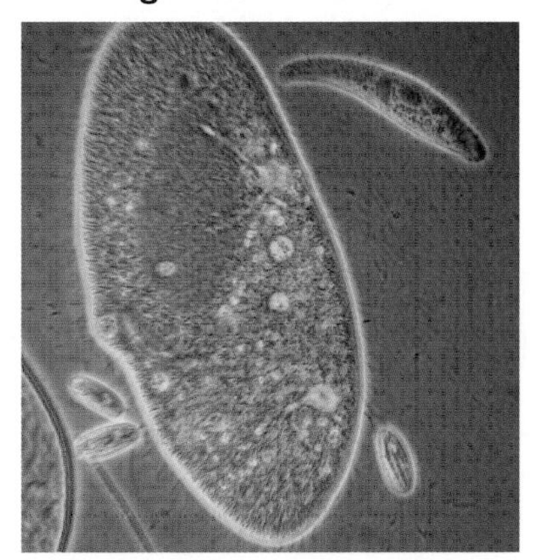

because of catastrophes like Mount St. Helens. We've observed fossils form in a year, in months, even in a week! We have found shark teeth and fossils of marine organisms on the tops of mountains and even in deserts. How did they get there? The best explanation is a worldwide Flood of course!

When I realized that I was a sinner in need of God's grace, I asked Jesus to forgive me of my sins and trusted Him as my Lord and Savior. I asked Jesus to direct my life. I asked Him to help me be the wife and mom He wanted me to be. I asked Him for the friends, opportunities, and experiences He wanted for me. I joined a Bible-believing church where the Word of God was preached. It was at this church that I first learned about Creation science! I read nearly every book and watched every video about Creation science from our church library. I began to research Creation science more and more. I am so thankful for the good work that Creation scientists have done.

Everywhere I look, I see God's design in His Creation, from His beautiful sunsets, to His powerful oceans, to His microscopic cells that work like miniature factories, to the orderliness of His solar system and His enormous universe! God is such an amazing Creator. Studying science helps us to learn more about God, who created the heavens and the Earth and everything that is in them. I know that everything I have belongs to God. I want to use my talents to serve God as He wants me to serve Him for His glory. I have learned so much about Creation science and I enjoy sharing that knowledge with my students and helping them to know that the Bible is true and can be trusted, and that we serve an awesome God. "Oh, magnify the LORD with me, and let us exalt His name together" (Psalm 34:3).

Module 11: General Biology

Dr. Paul Madtes Jr., Professor of Biology, Mount Vernon Nazarene University

Much of my life has been linked to scientific investigation, especially focusing on life. I studied topics about living organisms as a student from grade school through high school. In college and graduate school, I learned more about how to study life, both animals and plants. My doctoral research project involved how plants work with microbes to convert nitrogen in the air into a usable form for living organisms. My post-doctoral training and career projects involved learning about how animals developed from a single-cell into the complex adult forms. What became increasingly clear was the high degree of complexity found in all forms of life.

As my time as a college professor has progressed, my interest in philosophy of science took me into exploring how science works, especially as it relates to living organisms. I continued to learn about various living organ-

FIGURE 14.14
Puppies, Formed From Fertilized Cells

isms, leading me to realize that naturalistic explanations of how these forms arose lacked the ability to be reconciled with the latest scientific evidence since the level of complexity far exceeds the assumptions associated with these theories. As I study cells, tissues, organs, systems, and complete organisms, and I describe these to my students, I am realizing that there must be a Designer/Creator who is responsible for the complexity and design that we find. In addition, when we include the relationship between organisms and their environment, we find that life, and the world in which life is found, are finely tuned for each other. All of this indicates that each part has a purpose. This has confirmed my understanding that the Designer/Creator intends to have people who have purpose, which includes a personal relationship with Him. As I continue to grow in that relationship and learn how to serve His purpose, I find that learning about the living world becomes a way to experience Him each and every day.

RUBE GOLDBERG MACHINE EXPERIMENT SETUP 5

MATERIALS:

- Setup from Experiment Setup 1–4
- A blow dryer
- Masking tape
- Books of various sizes
- An electrical power strip with a switch
- An empty 16- or 20-oz. plastic water bottle with lid
- Sand
- A funnel
- Kite string
- Scissors
- Empty 1-gallon milk jug
- A short candle on a stand

FIGURE 14.15
Rube Goldberg Experiment Setup 5

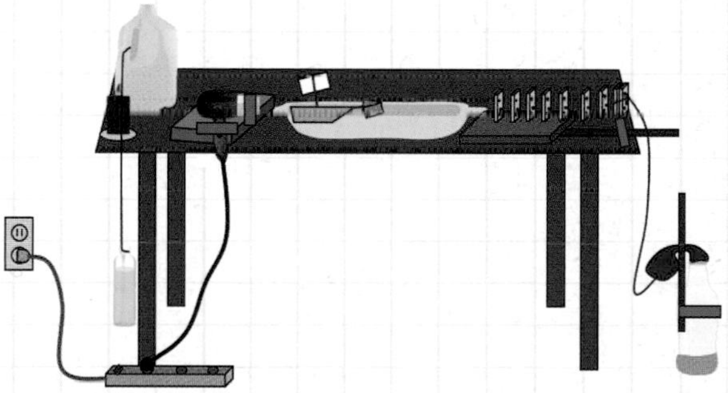

PROCEDURE: (Please refer to Figure 14.15 to help you with setup.)

BEFORE YOU BEGIN THIS SETUP, MAKE SURE YOUR PARENTS READ THE RED-LETTERED STATEMENT LOCATED ABOVE THE FIRST SETUP SECTION.

1. Working on the left side of the baking tray from Setup 4, lay the blow dryer so the nozzle points toward the boat's sail. Use books to stack the dryer so it is at the correct level. Secure the dryer in place with masking tape.
2. Hang the dryer's cord off the table onto the floor below. Plug the power strip into the wall. **Make sure the power strip switch is in the off position.** Using masking tape, secure

the power strip in place on the floor just below the table so that the switch is lined up directly below the table's edge (see diagram).

3. Turn the blow dryer's switch to the on position and plug the dryer into the power strip. The dryer should not turn on because the power strip switch is off.
4. Fill the milk jug at least 2/3 with water. Set it on the table to the left of the blow dryer setup. Orient the jug so that its handle is pointing toward the side of the table where the power strip is. Tie a long piece of kite string to the jug's handle.
5. Using the funnel, fill the empty water bottle about halfway with sand and close the lid tightly.
6. Hold the water bottle a few inches above the power strip's switch. This is the position you want it to be in when you tie the string to the water bottles' neck. Mark where on the string that spot is, and then tie the string to the water bottle, cutting off any extra string. The water bottle should be suspended from the gallon jug, hanging off the edge of the table so that it is a few inches above the power switch.
7. Lastly, place the candle under the string near the gallon jug so that when you light the candle, the string will eventually burn and break. You might need to place the gallon jug on a few books in order for the string to be high enough for the candle to be under it. **Don't light the candle yet!**

MODULE 12: Marine Science
Sherri Seligson, BA in Marine Biology, Curriculum and Film Author for Apologia Educational Ministries

As you have gone through this book, you have read much of my own testimony and thoughts as the author of this course. Yet my career experience is in the field of marine biology. I became a Christian while I was in college and found myself reading the Bible for the first time while I was assigned to read Charles Darwin's book, *The Origin of Species*, for a required course on evolution. Thus, I was reading God's revelation regarding how all of Creation came to be at the same time I was reading one man's ideas about how he thought all living things came to be without a God. I knew God's Word was true, and yet I had to understand why so many people tried to explain how everything was made without an all-powerful God. However, I began to see the precise order in our universe with the perfect physical laws of how things behave. Then I studied the elegant organization of the chemical building blocks of all matter. I realized that these had to point to a Creator God. This complexity could not have occurred on its own! You see,

FIGURE 14.16
Coral Reef Ecosystem Displaying Complexity in Each Organism and in Their Interactions

we see His hand in all of creation. The complexity of the smallest living organisms is testimony enough that they could not have organized themselves into being without the hand of a Designer.

Working as a marine biologist with Walt Disney World, I studied and worked with ocean predators and published shark research. Let me tell you—the more I learned, the more things I saw that continued to point to a Creator. Like so many scientists throughout history, I now love to study our world because it reveals to us the character of the One who made it. He continues to hold it in place so that not a single molecule moves without His hand. Indeed, it is true that "He is before all things and in Him all things hold together" (Colossians 1:17).

MODULE 13: Environmental Science

Lucee Price, BA Limnology, Apologia Online Academy Instructor

I grew up in a small town in Florida. My family attended church every Sunday, but we weren't raised to think about God the rest of the week. In fact, our home life was marked by alcoholism and strife, and my parents divorced when I was 10. Perhaps because of this, I saw God as a far-off entity who had little interest in my personal problems. To me, Christianity was all about rules and never about relationship.

When I was baptized at 13, I began to recognize in my heart that I belonged to God. Yet I still didn't really understand what a relationship with Jesus was all about. Eventually, I began to drift away until church attendance was no longer a part of my life.

In college, as a 29-year-old sophomore, I took a general biology course. This was an essay course, which at first seemed daunting, but it gave me a place to put words to what I actually thought about the subject matter. I was pretty certain that God had created everything, but I believed then that He had done it through the process of macroevolution, or Darwinian evolution. After all, I had been taught in school that evolution was a fact. During this college biology course, however, I kept coming back to questions I had regarding the lack of transitional forms in the fossil record. And as we delved deeper into genetics, it became almost laughable to me that anyone studying cell meiosis could believe that mankind happened merely by chance without forethought and design.

Around that same time, there was a man on campus who called himself "Preacher Paul." He would publicly preach to anyone walking by or stopping to listen, but I felt his teaching was harsh, that he hurled the words of the Bible at his listeners like daggers. I remember asking God one day why He would allow this man to continue in this manner? Didn't He know that Preacher Paul was actually turning people away from the Lord? I was angry, so I sat down and opened up a Bible just to see if what this so-called preacher was teaching was true. That day, the words in the book of John leaped off the pages at me! Suddenly, I couldn't get enough. For the very first time, these words actually meant something to me. Soon after, I began attending a local church.

I graduated 2 years later with a degree in limnology, the study of freshwater and wetland ecosystems. Today, my concern for the environment and how it's impacted by people, nature, topography, and climate is an important part of why I teach. I love helping others to understand what it looks like to be good stewards of God's gift of creation. It's my personal desire to help everyone recognize the beautiful complexity in even the smallest part of creation and to give our Lord the glory for it!

FIGURE 14.17
A Complex Lake Ecosystem Filled with Living Organisms

RUBE GOLDBERG MACHINE EXPERIMENT FINALE

MATERIALS:

- Setup from Experiment Setup 1–5
- A match

PROCEDURE:

The challenge with a Rube Goldberg machine is that it requires precision in your setup. If one item is out of line, the chain reaction will stop. And that means you have to reset everything from the beginning to start the machine again.

To begin your chain reaction, you will light the candle, causing the string to break. Once the string breaks, things will move quickly, so BEFORE you start the process, you need to make sure everything is set up as perfectly as you can.

I will walk you through the entire setup one more time, so you can check each step. You may have noticed that there are several scientific processes that are being exhibited in this machine, too. I will cover them in blue lettering, as we go through our final check.

FINAL CHECK 1: Beginning at the far left of your setup where the candle is, make sure the water bottle is hanging directly above the power strip's switch. When it falls, it should flip the switch. When the candle is lit, it is exhibiting **combustion**, which means burning, or a chemical change that makes heat and light. The heat from the candle's flame causes the string to burn and the water bottle will then respond to the force of **gravity**, falling to Earth.

FINAL CHECK 2: Make sure the switch to the blow dryer is in the ON position. It should not blow air yet because it is plugged into the power strip with the switch in the OFF position. Once the water bottle lands on the power strip, it should move the switch to the ON position.

Before that happens, you have an **open electrical circuit**. The switch is in the OFF position and will not allow electrons to flow through the cords. Once the bottle hits the switch, you form a **closed electrical circuit**, so electricity can now reach the blow dryer.

FINAL CHECK 3: Make sure the blow dryer's nozzle is aimed at the boat's sail. It doesn't have to be exact because it won't take a lot of force to move the boat, but be sure the line-up is somewhat close. Also, check the cardboard strips to make sure they are standing up, creating a narrow channel for the boat to travel. Depending on the size of your boat, you may only need to use 1 cardboard strip. The channel helps direct the boat so the cardboard piece on its front will hit the domino on the other end of the baking tray. The boat is exhibiting **buoyancy**. The boat floats because the gravitational force pulling downward is less than the buoyancy force. That means the boat weighs less than the amount of water it is displacing.

FINAL CHECK 4: Carefully add any missing dominoes from the ones that the boat will bump into on the table. Stand up the double domino on the edge of the table so that when it falls, it will fall off, pulling the string over the ruler and pulling the balloon up. The string going over the ruler behaves as a **simple pulley,** which is a **simple machine.**. The double domino moves downward, and the balloon moves upward. Thus, the direction of the force is changed.

FINAL CHECK 5: Make sure the ruler that is taped to the 2-liter bottle is oriented on the opposite side of where the tennis ball is. That way as the balloon fills up with gas, it will push away from the ruler and move toward the tennis ball. When the baking soda mixes with the vinegar in the bottle, a **chemical reaction** results, creating carbon dioxide gas as one of the products of the reaction. This gas causes the balloon to expand as more is created.

FINAL CHECK 6: The paper towel roll holding the tennis ball needs to be barely on the edge of the book. That way, it only requires a small force to get the tennis ball to fall off. Be very careful when you check it to make sure it doesn't fall! The ball tied to the string behaves like a pendulum. A pendulum is an example of the **conservation of mechanical energy**. As the ball moves in a periodic motion, back-and-forth, the force of gravity and the tension of the string affect its movement.

FINAL CHECK 7: The car should already be placed with its rear wheels hanging off the book's edge and in a location where the tennis ball will hit it. If you haven't placed all the dominoes in position where the car will hit them, do it now. Again, be very careful! The book that the car is resting on behaves as a **wedge**, which is a **simple machine**.

FINAL CHECK 8: Double check the placement of the roll of tape and the domino on top of the stack of books. The domino will pull out the scrap of cardboard holding the lever in a horizontal position. Like the wedge, the **lever** is also a **simple machine**. In this case, the lever has a fulcrum between the force and the resistance. Thus, when the resistance is removed (the cardboard scrap), the mass of the cup and sprinkles will cause the right side of the lever to move downward.

FINAL CHECK 9: Make sure the cupcake is directly beneath the funnel. Now you are ready to go! You might want to take some photos of your setup. You might also want to make a video of yourself explaining each step of the machine and what scientific concept is being represented (The blue sentences will help).

GRAND FINALE: To begin your chain reaction, move the candle away from the string that is tied to the gallon jug before you light it. Then carefully slide the lit candle back under the string so that the flame is below it. You might want to have a helper film your machine running! Because many of the steps happen very quickly, your helper should stand far enough back to get most of the setup in view at the same time.

FIGURE 14.18
A Sample Rube Goldberg Setup

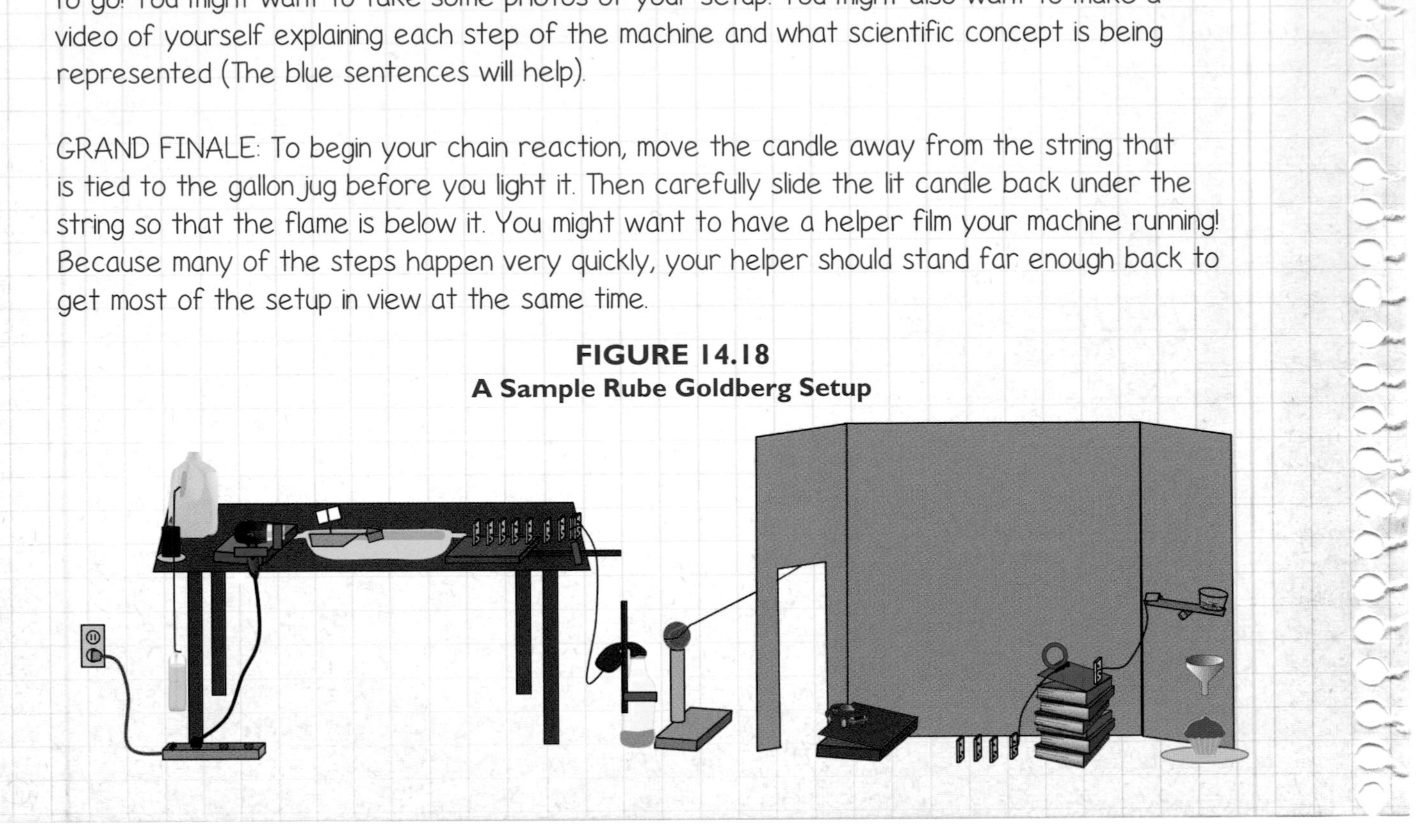

What happened when you started your machine? Did everything work? If the machine stopped partway, is there a better way you can set up that step so it works better? Often, with a Rube Goldberg setup, you have to tweak some portions of the machine a few times to get the entire thing to work.

Visit the Book Extra site for this title to see clips of Sherri Seligson's Rube Goldberg Machine in action.

SUMMING UP

I hope you enjoyed this introduction to science. Science is truly an exploration that involves the "search" in research. It includes asking questions and then looking for ways to answer them. In your quest to discover the world around you, I pray that you will never lose your excitement of discovery. Using your increasing scientific knowledge as a tool to help you study things in a systematic way, the world waits for you to discover its mysteries. Then you will be able to marvel with me how

> The heavens declare the glory of God; the skies proclaim the work of his hands.
> —Psalm 19:1

Dear Precious Student,

Hooray! You have completed this General Science course! I am proud of you for your hard work. As you wrap up this year, I want you to reflect on the things you learned. Was there anything that surprised you? Did one area of science capture your attention more than another area?

This course is designed for students in the midst of their K–12 education. But remember that those years are just a small part of your life. Your "work" right now is to learn and grow. You are filling your mind with information, building skills and abilities, and maturing both physically and spiritually, too. All this is to prepare you for your future. I want you to know how much God is with you right now. He desires a growing relationship with you, and He is always pursuing you because He loves you.

As you learned from me and other scientists from the past and present, a scientific study of the world helps to reveal God's creative hand. He created you, too. In fact, out of the millions and millions of people who have lived up to this day, *you* are uniquely created. There is no one else and there has been no one else like you because God perfectly formed you the way you are.

That is the best message I can give you. We all struggle to see what God has for us in our lives, but *He* knows the path He has laid out for each one of us. So He will be with you for comfort and strength as you go through difficulties, and He will be with you to bring about your successes.

Because I am grown and am able to look back on where God has brought me, I can see how His perfect hand was in everything. He has comforted me during the deaths of family members, He has protected me from making wrong choices when I was younger, and I am confident He still is working in my life to direct me to continue to bring Him glory as I minister to my husband, my children's families, and even to you.

James 4:8 says, "Draw near to God, and He will draw near to you." If you see even the tiniest evidence that God is present in your life, if you recognize that there is no way that the universe and everything in it could have come about on its own, then draw near to God. Call out to Him and He will answer you!

Praising God with all creation,

Sherri Seligson

LAB SUPPLY LIST

MODULE 1

Experiment 1.1
A tall, clear canister or jar with a lid
A ping-pong ball
A 3 oz. lead sinker (the kind used for fishing)
A bag of unpopped popcorn (small dried beans will also work)

Experiment 1.2
A fresh lemon
A small knife
3 tarnished pennies (between 1962 and 1982)
A paper towel
A paper plate
A teaspoon of salt
An eyedropper
Water

Explore More, page 10
2 glasses
Hot and cold water
Food coloring

Explore More, page 15
24 dimes
Kitchen scale

Explore More, page 19
Drinking glass
Water
A piece of card stock

Explore More, page 22
4 drinking straws
Scissors
A stapler
A ruler
Masking or cellophane tape
5 feet of string

MODULE 2

Experiment 2.1
A reasonably heavy book
A sheet of cardboard about the same size as the book
A sheet of heavy paper (like construction paper or card stock) about the same size as the book
A sheet of regular paper about the same size as the book

Experiment 2.2
All the materials from Experiment 2.1
A metal paper clip

Experiment 2.3
A drinking glass
A small glass
Water
An eyedropper
Some paper towels
A penny
Liquid soap

Explore More, page 38
A basketful of small items (like a pencil, bottle cap, stuffed animal, hairbrush, socks, toy, ball)
A helium balloon

Explore More, page 47
A desk lamp
Red construction paper
A marker
Scissors
Tape
2 magnifying glasses

Explore More, page 50
A balloon
A hole punch
A piece of paper

MODULE 3

Experiment 3.1
A tall, clear glass
Measuring cups to measure 1½ cups of water
A fresh raw egg
A teaspoon
A spoon for stirring
Water
Salt

Experiment 3.2
3 glass containers of different sizes
A tea light candle
Matches
A ceramic, glass, or metal pie plate
A stopwatch (or smart phone with a stopwatch feature)
A water-filled glass

Experiment 3.3
A medium glass container (NOTE: This experiment works better if the glass container is tall and thin.)
A tea light candle
Matches
A ceramic, glass, or metal pie plate
Food coloring
A measuring cup of water (It is helpful if it has a pour spout.)
A stirring spoon
A paper towel
A small lump of clay
A medium-height candle that can fit in the medium glass container with room for a flame

Explore More, page 68
Friends and family to poll
Materials to create a bar graph of results (either on paper or computer)

Explore More, page 73
Friends and family to participate in taste-testing
Ingredients to make chocolate chip cookies using two different brands of chocolate chips
Notebook to record results

MODULE 4

Experiment 4.1
Student Notebook
Tree slice image (Figure 4.15) on page 103

Explore More, page 89
A desk drawer to explore

Explore More, page 104
Trees recently cut down or slices of tree trunks from a nursery or craft store
Camera

MODULE 5

Experiment 5.1
A dark marker
A paper plate (A thick paper plate works best.)
A sharpened pencil
A ruler
A plastic straw
Cellophane or masking tape
Paper clips

Experiment 5.2
A piece of chalk
A sheet of corrugated cardboard
Masking tape
A piece of sandpaper about half the size of the cardboard

Explore More, page 115
Materials to create a bar graph of results (either on paper or computer)

Explore More, page 121
A friend or family member

Explore More, page 127
A sheet of corrugated cardboard or a corkboard
A sheet of white paper
2 thumbtacks
A pencil
Some string

Explore More, page 130
Styrofoam ball
A straw or a pencil
A push pin or a bent paper clip
A lamp

Explore More, page 137
A dark room
A flashlight

MODULE 6

Experiment 6.1

Alum (sold as Aluminum Alum in large supermarket spice sections, pharmacies, or hardware stores)
A small glass (like a juice glass)
A liquid measuring cup
A small spoon for dispensing the alum
A large spoon for stirring
Some thin, rough string (Thread will work, but the rougher the string, the better the results.)
2 weights (washers, nuts, fishing sinkers, etc.)
A large plate
A few rocks from outside (Small pebbles work best.)
A sheet of dark-colored paper
A magnifying glass
A stove
A pot to heat water
Oven mitt
Eye protection such as goggles or safety glasses

Experiment 6.2

A large glass jar with a lid
Some dirt of outside (Dig straight down into the ground to get dirt from many depths.)
Some sand
Some gravel composed of various sizes of rocks
Water

Explore More, page 150

16 oz. container of dry cornstarch
A large bowl
Water
A spoon

Explore More, page 163

2 cups of water
2½ cups Epsom salt
A saucepan
A spoon
2-foot length of twine
4 washers
2 juice glasses
A small plate
An airtight container to store extra solution

Explore More, page 170

A shell or other similar item
Petroleum jelly
Clay
A paper plate
Plaster of Paris
A disposable cup
A spoon

MODULE 7

Experiment 7.1

A large mason jar or other clear sturdy jar
A saucepan or kettle to boil water
2 hot pads
A 1-quart zippered plastic bag
Ice
A match and matchbox
A dark sheet of construction paper

Experiment 7.2

A large mason jar or other clear sturdy jar
A balloon
Scissors
A rubber band
A drinking straw
Cellophane tape
A sheet of cardboard
A fine-tipped marker

Explore More, page 193

¾ cup of white vinegar
Empty 2-liter bottle
A balloon
2 tablespoons of baking soda
A butter knife

Explore More, page 200

A lightning storm

Explore More, page 207

A cereal bowl
Plastic wrap
A sunny window
A thermometer
A piece of tape

MODULE 8

Experiment 8.1

A candle
A match
Cotton swabs
2 juice glasses
Water
3 small plates
1 tablespoon of table salt
1 tablespoon of salt substitute (It should have potassium chloride as an ingredient.)
Safety goggles
OPTIONAL: A container of Damp Rid that you will carefully open to use 1 tablespoon

Experiment 8.2
2 beakers - 100 mL and 250 mL (or 2 glasses - one large and one small)
Sand
Table salt
A funnel
Water
A measuring cup
Filter paper (You can cut a circle out of the bottom of a coffee-maker filter.)
Stirring rod (or small spoon)
Measuring teaspoon
Measuring tablespoon
A stove
A saucepan

Explore More, page 216
A balloon
String
A helper
A ruler

Explore More, page 217
A bar of Ivory soap
A bowl of water
A knife
Microwave-safe plate
A microwave

Explore More, page 218
A balloon
Empty soda can

Explore More, page 232
A skillet
A raw egg
A bowl
A stove
A plate

Explore More, page 234
Common crystals (like salt, sugar, finely crushed ice, play sand, and possibly a diamond)
Notebook for illustrations and descriptions
Magnifying glass or microscope (optional)

Explore More, page 236
Clean, clear, plastic food container with recycle logo 6
Scissors
Some permanent markers
A hole punch
Aluminum foil
An oven

Explore More, page 238
A few purple cabbage leaves
Distilled water
A saucepan
Tongs
A stove
A few clear juice glasses
Household liquids (like lemon juice, milk, vinegar, water, dish soap, and -using gloves-some household cleaning supplies)
A plastic spoon or wooden chopstick for stirring

MODULE 9

Experiment 9.1
A large book (The book does not have to be thick, but the larger the surface area of its cover, the better.)
A paper clip
A small pencil-topper eraser
2 lumps of clay each about the same size as the eraser
A ruler

Experiment 9.2
2 D batteries
Electrical tape
Insulated number 22 copper wire (about 18 inches)
Scissors
2 large metal paper clips
A spring-tension wood or plastic clothespin
A cork message board or a sheet of very thick cardboard, about 8" × 11"
Masking tape
3 metal thumbtacks
A non-LED, 3-volt flashlight bulb (You can also use a small car tail-light bulb)

Experiment 9.3
3 tall drinking glasses, all the same size and shape
Water
A metal spoon
A rubber band (Use a thicker one for better results.)
Scissors
A large metal binder clip
A block of wood thin enough for the binder clip to clamp onto (Several layers of cardboard will also work.)

Explore More, page 250
A friend or family member
A swing

Explore More, page 257
A sheet of white paper
A tray or paper plate
A bar magnet
Iron shavings

Explore More, page 258
A strong magnet
A steel nail
A pile of steel paper clips

Explore More, page 262
A stiff bowl
Some plastic wrap
Tape
Table salt
A large metal pot
A metal spoon

Explore More, page 269
A sunny day
A white piece of fabric
A black piece of fabric

MODULE 10

Experiment 10.1
2 strands of black licorice that have hollow centers (Twizzlers brand works best for this.)
2 strands of red licorice that have hollow centers (Again, Twizzlers work well.)
4 different colors of gummy bears - several of each color (Colored marshmallows also work.)
2 long, stiff pipe cleaners (The ones with glitter cellophane fuzz work best.)
6 toothpicks (and a few to spare in case some break.)
Scissors

Experiment 10.2
Eye protection such as goggles or safety glasses
One slice of raw potato
A pale green leaf (The paler the green, the better this experiment will work.)
Rubbing alcohol
Iodine
A jar with a lid
2 shallow dishes
A cookie sheet lined with parchment paper or waxed paper for protection (Don't use a cookie sheet you wouldn't want to risk getting stained by iodine.)
Tweezers
A small non-metallic bowl

Explore More, page 286
A small potted plant
A jar with a lid (with enough extra room for the plant to grow)
Water
A marker

Explore More, page 286
A small potted plant (A small basil plant works well.)
A sunny window

Explore More, page 297
A banana
A knife
Water
Yeast granules
2 zippered plastic bags
A marker
2 paper plates

Explore More, page 297
A clear plastic cup
2 paper towels
Water
4 beans
Plastic wrap

MODULE 11

Experiment 11.1
Warm and cold tap water
A liquid measuring cup
A drinking glass
A permanent marker
2 empty 20-oz. soda bottles (Most water bottles are too flimsy for this experiment.)
A packet of activated baker's yeast
A teaspoon
Sugar
2 balloons

Experiment 11.2
Leaf press or old books and waxed paper
Lab notebook
Tree identification book (from the library or online sources)

Explore More, page 314
A piece of bread (NOTE: the fewer preservatives, the faster this activity will work.)
Tap water
A small paper plate
Some dust from a windowsill
Plastic wrap
A warm, dark area

Explore More, page 321
A few purple cabbage leaves
A saucepan
Distilled water
Tongs
A container with a lid

Explore More, page 326
Purple water from previous Explore More
OR A few purple cabbage leaves
A saucepan
Distilled water
Tongs
A clean, small, clear glass
A straw

Explore More, page 329
Friends and family to poll
Materials to create a table with your results
(either on paper or computer)

MODULE 12

Experiment 12.1
8 Oreo cookies
A butter knife
2 zippered storage bags
Chocolate pudding (Milk chocolate looks better than dark chocolate.)
4 graham crackers
Vanilla, banana, or butterscotch pudding
Whipped cream
A tall, transparent glass
A serving spoon

Experiment 12.2
2 empty toilet paper rolls
3 balloons
Water
A large mixing bowl
Vegetable oil
A funnel
Markers (optional)

Explore More, page 343
A ping-pong ball
A 12" piece of string
A balloon
Cellophane tape
Electrical tape
OPTIONAL: A helper

Explore More, page 355
A mason jar
Water
Scraps of black and white craft foam
Glue
Scissors
A flashlight
A black piece of paper

Explore More, page 357
Dried herbs (Parsley, oregano, or basil work well.)
A bowl
Water
A fine-toothed hair comb

Explore More, page 359
Empty 2-liter bottle
A small knife
Electrical tape

Explore More, page 360
A glow stick
A freezer

MODULE 13

Experiment 13.1
5 zipper-seal plastic sandwich bags
5 plastic straws
Masking tape
A marker
Tape
Scissors
5 ounces of fresh spinach
Newspaper
A kitchen scale
Water
A tablespoon

Experiment 13.2
A small bag of dry white navy beans (about 1 cup)
A paper lunch bag
A dark permanent marker
A calculator
Your notebook

Explore More, page 376
A nearby natural area (like a park or a field)
Your notebook

MODULE 14

Rube Goldberg Machine Experiment Setup 1

An iced cupcake on a small plate
Sprinkles
A large trifold cardboard presentation display board measuring 36" × 48" when open
A funnel
Strong packing tape or masking tape
A 12" × 2" strip of stiff cardboard
A small paper or plastic cup
Cellophane tape
A hole punch
An 18" length of string
A pencil
An X-ACTO craft knife

Rube Goldberg Machine Experiment Setup 2

Setup from Experiment Setup 1
A stack of books about 8-inches high
A few pencils
Kite string
2 rolls of masking tape
5–6 dominoes

Rube Goldberg Machine Experiment Setup 3

Setup from Experiment Setup 1–2
1 large hardcover book that is not very thick
1 small book
A toy car (For best results, use a car somewhat heavier and larger than a Matchbox-sized car.)
Kite string
A tennis ball
Masking tape
An empty paper towel roll
Books
An empty 2-liter bottle
A 9" diameter balloon
Baking soda
A liquid measuring cup
Vinegar
A butter knife
A stiff ruler

Rube Goldberg Machine Experiment Setup 4

Setup from Experiment Setup 1–3
A long table
A stiff ruler
Dominoes
Masking tape
A thin, hardcover book
A metal or glass 9" × 13" baking dish
Water
Aluminum foil
2 short wood skewers
Cellophane tape
A scrap of cardboard
2 long strips of cardboard that are the length of the baking dish
A sheet of paper
Scissors

Rube Goldberg Machine Experiment Setup 5

Setup from Experiment Setup 1–4
A blow dryer
Masking tape
Various sized books
An electrical power strip with an on and off switch
An empty 16- or 20-oz. plastic water bottle with lid
Sand
A funnel
Kite string
Scissors
Empty 1-gallon milk jug
A short candle on a stand

Rube Goldberg Machine Experiment Finale

Setup from Experiment Setup 1–5
A match

INDEX

C

P

T

IMAGE SOURCES

COVER & REPEATING IMAGES
Lab image, cover © Cakeio | Getty Images
Earth, cover and title pages © FrankRamspott | Getty Images
what to do clipboard icon © LisLud | Getty Images

INSTRUCTIONAL SUPPORT PAGE

icons	© iStockphoto.com, modified

MODULE 1

Figure 1.1	Helium balloons © Ankush Minda | Unsplash.com
Figure 1.3	Moldy bread © Martina_I | Crestock.com
Figure 1.4	Papyrus © imagexphoto | Crestock.com
Figure 1.5	Pyramids © pius99 | Crestock.com
Figure 1.7	Sand with hand © Elijah Hiett | Unsplash.com
Figure 1.12	Geocentric system © Bartolomeu Velho | Public Domain | via Wikimedia Commons
Figure 1.14	Crab Nebula © NASA | Public Domain
Figure 1.15	Transportation Map © bubaone | Getty Images
Figure 1.16	Vesalius and Copernicus Books, books © Solobird | Getty Images, engraving book pages | Public Domain
Figure 1.18	Leeuwenhoek Microscope © Jeroen Rouwkema | CC BY-SA 3.0 (http://creativecommons.org/licenses/by-sa/3.0), via Wikimedia Commons
Figure 1.20	Giraffe © jenta | Crestock.com
Figure 1.21	Dogs © Lifeonwhite.com, isselee | Crestock.com

MODULE 2

Figure 2.1	Scientist © kzenon | Getty Images
Figure 2.3	Archer © iofoto | Crestock.com
Figure 2.6	Student Experiment © MonkeyBusinessImages | Crestock.com
Figure 2.7	Icons © Vecteezy.com
Figure 2.9	Surgeon © 4774344sean | Crestock.com
Figure 2.10	Mars © NASA | Public Domain
Figure 2.12	Rover © NASA | Public Domain
Figure 2.13	Telescope © NASA/Desiree Stover | Public Domain
Figure 2.15	graph © tonefotografia | Getty Images

MODULE 3

Figure 3.7	candle © malerapaso | Getty Images
Figue 3.9	Couple eating © AntonioGuillem | Crestock.com
Figure 3.10	Woman baking © 4774344sean | Crestock.com
Figure 3.11	Taste test © tomazl | Getty Images
Think About This	Pie © Alex Loup | Unsplash.com

MODULE 4

Figure 4.12	Dead Sea Scrolls © Ken and Nyetta | Flickr.com | CC BY-2.0 GEN (https://creativecommons.org/licenses/by/2.0/)
Figure 4.16	Tree Rings © Sherri Seligson
Figure 4.18	Layers © vectortatu | Getty Images, modified
Figure 4.18	pottery, tools, logs | Vecteezy.com

Module 5

Figure 5.8	Color wavelengths © Miquel Perelló Nieto (Own work) [CC BY 4.0 (http://creativecommons.org/licenses/by/4.0)], via Wikimedia Commons
Figure 5.9	Radio telescope © CSIRO [CC BY 3.0 (http://creativecommons.org/licenses/by/3.0)], via Wikimedia Commons
Figure 5.12B	Aurora Borealis © Paul Morris I Unsplash.com
Figure 5.14	Sun's Interior © NASA I Public Domain
Figure 5.15	Eclipse © adventtr I iStockphoto.com
Figure 5.19	Moon Rotation earth © loops7 I Getty Images
Figure 5.21	Lunar Eclipse © adventtr I iStockphoto.com, modified
Figure 5.23	Ceres © NASA ESA-ATG Medialab I Public Domain
Figure 5.24	Comet Hale Bopp © E. Kolmhofer, H. Raab; Johannes-Kepler-Observatory, Linz, Austria (http://www.sternwarte.at) - Own work I I CC BY-SA 3.0 (http://creativecommons.org/licenses/by-sa/3.0), via Wikimedia Commons
Figure 5.24	Sun © adventtr I iStockphoto.com, modified
Figure 5.25	Jupiter © H. Hammel, NASA, ESA
Figure 5.27	Hoba Meteorite © Sergio Conti from Montevecchia (LC), Italia (P1000077) [CC BY-SA 2.0 (http://creativecommons.org/licenses/by-sa/2.0)], via Wikimedia Commons
Figure 5.29	Binary Star System © NASA, Cheongho Han, Chungbuk National University, Republic of Korea
Figure 5.30	Hertszprunt-Russell Diagram © ESO
Figure 5.32	Galaxies © NASA, ESA, M. Postman (STScI), and the CLASH team
Figure 5.34	Exoplanet illustration © NASA Credit ESA; Hubble, M. Kornmesser; and ESO, L. Calçada and L. L. Christensen

Module 6

Figure 6.1	Earth © NASA I Public Domain
Figure 6.2	A Cross Section of Earth © Dorling Kindersley I Getty Images, modified
Figure 6.4	Materials in the Earth © Illustration by Dorling Kindersley I Getty Images, modified
Figure 6.6	Afar Region of Ethiopia I Closeup image by NASA I Public Domain Globe image by Przemek Pietrak I https://globalquiz.org/en/quiz-image/ethiopia-from-space/ I CC-BY 3.0 I https://creativecommons.org/licenses/by/3.0/
OYO 6.1	A Cross Section of Earth © Dorling Kindersley I Getty Images, modified Earth's Sea Floor © NASA I Public Domain Kola Borehole I Photograph by Andre Belozeroff I CC-BY 3.0 I https://creativecommons.org/licenses/by/3.0/
Experiment 6.1	Illustration by Andrea Kiser Martin using glass image by Sezeryadigar, plate image by Suradech14 I Getty Images, table image by Adam Smigielski I Unsplash
Figure 6.13	Mesas Buttes © Ganapathy Kumar I Unsplash
Explore More	Illustration by Andrea Kiser Martin using glass image by Sezeryadigar, plate image by Suradech14 I Getty Images, table image by Adam Smigielski I Unsplash
Figure 6.17	Grand Canyon Layers © Andrea Kiser Martin
Figure 6.19	Mount St. Helens © Jaser Cervantes I Unsplash
Figure 6.23	Fossil coelacanth © Haplochromis I CC BY-SA 3.0 (http://creativecommons.org/licenses/by-sa/3.0), via Wikimedia Commons Modern coelacanth (right) by Alberto Fernandez Fernandez (Own work) [GFDL (http://www.gnu.org/copyleft/fdl.html), CC-BY-SA-3.0 (http://creativecommons.org/licenses/by-sa/3.0/) or CC BY-SA 2.5 (http://creativecommons.org/licenses/by-sa/2.5), via Wikimedia Commons
Figure 6.24	Sediments © Dr. Steven A. Austin I Institute for Creation Research
Figure 6.27	Table by Andrea Kiser Martin using animals © Alinabel, MarinaMarinya, and illonetta I Getty Images, modified
Figure 6.28	Strata in Argentina © Dhzanette I Public Domain
Figure 6.29	Erosion Mountt St. Helens © Dr. Steven A. Austin I Institute for Creation Research
Figure 6.30	Fossil Record Groups I Illustration by Andrea Kiser Martin using images by Ambassador806, ilonetta, and Alinabel I Getty Images
Figure 6.31	Fish Photograph by Ken Lucas I Visuals Unlimited Hat Photograph by Dr. Don R Patton I www.Bible.ca
OYO Answer 6.1	A Cross Section of Earth © Dorling Kindersley I Getty Images, modified

Module 7

OYO 7.5	Map © Ranier Lesniewski I Getty Images, modified
Figure 7.11	The Hydrologic Cycle © Danylyukk I Getty Images, modified
Figure 7.21	Pollen Grain © Sophie Warney and Kate Griener I Louisiana State University, Baton Rouge and NASA
Figure 7.25	Waves Forming I Colin Gunn
Figure 7.26	Ocean Tides © Andrea Kiser Martin using images from NASA
Figure 7.27	Ocean Bottom © Colin Gunn, modified
Figure 7.28	Bioluminescent Fish © NOAA
Figure 7.29	NOAA Ocean Research Ship the Ronald H. Brown © NOAA Okeanos Explorer Program
OYO Answer 7.5	Map © Ranier Lesniewski I Getty Images, modified

Module 8

Figure 8.1	Earth, Sun, and Universe © Casey Horner I Unsplash.com
Figure 8.2	Balls with Different Masses Bowling ball © Battle Creek CVB, modified I CC by 2.0 I creativecommons.org/licenses/by/2.0/
Figure 8.3	States of Matter: Ice cube © sbayram, raindrop © BlackJack3D I Getty Images
Figure 8.15	salt, sugar, gold, carbon, water © Vecteezy.com
Figure 8.22	Lemon and Stomach © Vecteezy.com
Figure 8.23	Soap and Cleaner © Vecteezy.com
Figure 8.24	pH Scale © ttsz I GettyImages.com, modified

Module 9

Figure 9.1	A Rocket Operating Under the Laws of Physics © Bill Ingalls I NASA
Figure 9.5	Negative and Positive Acceleration Taxi © Nerthuz I GettyImages
Figure 9.11	Soccer © Ljupco I Getty Images
Figure 9.12	Skater images © asmakar I Getty Images, modified
Figure 9.13	Atom © Eisenatom.svg: FornaxStylised_Lithium_Atom.png: Halfdanderivative work: Groogokk (Eisenatom.svgStylised_Lithium_Atom.png) [CC BY-SA 3.0 (https://creativecommons.org/licenses/by-sa/3.0)], via Wikimedia Commons
Figure 9.16	Created using red and blue atoms © istockphoto.com
Figure 9.19	Magnet © Windell Oskay I CC by 2.0 I https://creativecommons.org/licenses/by/2.0/
Figure 9.23	seesaw © 4x6, wheelbarrow © DonNichols, fisherman © Ljupco I Getty Images
Figure 9.24	Block & Tackle © Themightyquill I CC BY-SA 4.0 I https://creativecommons.org/licenses/by-sa/4.0 I Wikimedia Commons
Figure 9.27	Screw © kckate16 I Getty Images
Figure 9.28	Woman at beach © zooooma I Getty Images
Figure 9.29	Phases of Matter © ttsz I Getty Images
Figure 9.36	Prism I Florenco~commonswiki I https://creativecommons.org/licenses/sa/1.0/ I Wikimedia Commons

Module 10

Figure 10.5	DNA Model © okamigo I Getty Images
Figure 10.6	DNA Andrea Kiser Martin using illustrations by okamigo I Getty Images
Figure 10.12	Cell © TefiM I Getty Images
Figure 10.13	Bacterial cells © Dharmanoid I Crestock.com
Figure 10.15	Onion Cells © staticd I CC BY-SA 3.0 I http://creativecommons.org/licenses/by-sa/3.0, via Wikimedia Commons
Figure 10.17	Prokaryotic/Eukaryotic © blueringmedia, left and TefiM, right I Getty Images
Figure 10.18	Kingdom Systems © Andrea Kiser Martin using bacteria and fungi images from © Vecteezy.com
Figure 10.22	Sulfur bacteria © Lawrence Berkeley National Laboratory I Public Domain
Figure 10.22	Ocean Vent © NOAA
Figure 10.24	Paramecium © Picturepest [CC BY 2.0 (http://creativecommons.org/licenses/by/2.0)], via Wikimedia Commons
Figure 10.25	Left Image credit: By fjouenne (http://planktonnet.awi.de/) [CC BY-SA 3.0 nl (http://creativecommons.org/licenses/by-sa/3.0/nl/deed.en)], via Wikimedia Commons>
Figure 10.25	Kelp Algae © burnsboxco I Getty Images

Explore More	Bean Sprout Illustration by Andrea Kiser Martin using sprout image © Magda Wojtyra	CC by 2.0 Generic	https://creativecommons.org/licenses/by-nc-sa/2.0/ cup image © akinshin	Getty Images paper towels © natthapenpis	Getty Images
Figure 10.26	Plant Cell and Animal Cell © TefiM	Getty Images

<u>Module 11</u>

Figure 11.2	infographic shapes © theseamuss	Getty Images
Figure 11.4	Semipermeable Membrane © Freemesm (Own work) [CC BY-SA 3.0 (http://creativecommons.org/licenses/by-sa/3.0)], via Wikimedia Commons
Figure 11.8	Bacteriophage © Dr Graham Beards at en.wikipedia [CC BY-SA 4.0 (http://creativecommons.org/licenses/by-sa/4.0) or GFDL (http://www.gnu.org/copyleft/fdl.html)], via Wikimedia Commons
Figure 11.10	Bread Mold © Dr. Sahay (Own work) [CC BY-SA 3.0 (http://creativecommons.org/licenses/by-sa/3.0)], via Wikimedia Commons
FIgure 11.16	Leaf shape: needle © scisettialfio	Getty Images
Figure 11.18	Entire © Iarm Rmah	Unsplash, Serrate © Jose Alonso	Unsplash, Crenate © Scott Webb	Unsplash, Undulate © Sarah Sosiak	Unsplash
Figure 11.23	Vascular tree © Brandon Green	Unsplash
Figure 11.24	Muscle cells © Rollroboter [CC BY-SA 3.0 (https://creativecommons.org/licenses/by-sa/3.0)], from Wikimedia Commons liver and intestine © Nephron [CC BY-SA 3.0 (https://creativecommons.org/licenses/by-sa/3.0) or GFDL (http://www.gnu.org/copyleft/fdl.html)], from Wikimedia Commons
Figure 11.24	stem cell © luismmolina	Getty Images
Figure 11.25	Digestive System © ChrisGorgio	Getty Images
Figure 11.26	Spine © XXzoexx	dreamstime.com
Figure 11.28	SkinColors © skodonnell	Getty Images

<u>Module 12</u>

Figure 12.2	Ocean Basins © Colin Gunn
Figure 12.3	Ocean Depths © Colin Gunn
Figure 12.4	Cyanobacteria © Matthewjparker (Own work) [CC BY-SA 3.0 (https://creativecommons.org/licenses/by-sa/3.0)], via Wikimedia Commons
Explore More	balloon © Nathanx1	Getty Imagesean organisms move around the Earth?
Figure 12.10	Portuguese Man-o-war © NOAA
Figure 12.15	Sand dollar © Chan Siuman at English Wikipedia [CC BY-SA 3.0 (https://creativecommons.org/licenses/by-sa/3.0) or GFDL (http://www.gnu.org/copyleft/fdl.html)], via Wikimedia Commons
Figure 12.16	Sea Star © Dean Franklin	CC BY-SA 3.0 (https://creativecommons.org/licenses/by-sa/3.0	Flickr.com
Figure 12.17	Stingray © Becky A. Dayhuff	NOAA
Figure 12.19	Whale Shark © NOAA
Figure 12.27	Baleen © NOAA
Figure 12.30	Bioluminescent © NOAA, both

<u>Module 13</u>

Figure 13.7	Parrotfish © LASZLO ILYES	Flickr.com	CC BY 2.0 Generic	https://creativecommons.org/licenses/by/2.0/
Figure 13.7	Plankton © NOAA
Figure 13.20	Surtsey Island © CanonS2	CC BY 2.0 Generic	https://creativecommons.org/licenses/by/2.0/

<u>Module 14</u>

Figure 14.2	Rube Goldberg Challenge © NASA
Figure 14.5	Girl Writing © pahham	Crestock.com
Figure 14.13	Paramecium © Picturepest (Paramecium & Litonotus - 250x - Phako) [CC BY 2.0 (http://creativecommons.org/licenses/by/2.0)], via Wikimedia Commons